Also by
William G. McLoughlin, Jr.

MODERN REVIVALISM—
CHARLES GRANDISON FINNEY TO BILLY GRAHAM

BILLY GRAHAM

Revivalist in a Secular Age

By

WILLIAM G. MCLOUGHLIN, JR.

THE RONALD PRESS COMPANY • NEW YORK

LIBRARY OF CONGRESS CATALOG CARD NUMBER: 59-12122

To my brothers,

Quin and Frank

Preface .

This book is an attempt to place Billy Graham's revivals in their historical perspective. Millions of words and thousands of pages have been written about Billy Graham in the past ten years but few of them have got to the heart of the matter. The books, articles, and interviews concerning Graham and his work have been written primarily by journalists eager to satisfy the superficial curiosity of Graham's contemporaries. They have explored the man and his revival crusades from the outside, but they have tended to treat him only in terms of here and now.

The revival tradition in America is almost three centuries old. Yet, except for occasional references to Jonathan Edwards, Aimee Semple McPherson, or Billy Sunday, few accounts of Graham have tried to relate him to this tradition. The erroneous impression still prevails that revivals are eccentric phenomena led by eccentric prophets which have little relation to the mainstream of American life. The sophisticated still patronizingly discuss mass evangelism in terms of the "superstitious rituals" of the uneducated and the clever utilization of "crowd psychology." But revivals are not so simple or so crude. They may be called phenomena, but like wars and depressions, they are phenomena which have a direct relationship to their times.

In the first place, there are many kinds of revivals: There are the highly emotional worship services of small sects in the backwoods areas or in the city slums which produce a

revival every Sunday; there are the annual tent-meeting revivals which are still a prominent feature in country towns
across America; there are city-wide church membership
drives organized by the local churches every five or ten
years; there are highly elaborate metropolitan revival crusades like those of Billy Graham and Billy Sunday which
flourish about once every generation; and then, at certain
intervals in history, there are "great awakenings" in which
the whole nation seems to be suddenly concerned with
religion and churchgoing.

In the second place, there are all kinds of revivalists: the
"spirit-inspired" exhorter who roams the rural areas or downtown city streets holding meetings wherever he can draw a
crowd; the small cult leader who gathers his own believers
into a separate revivalistic denomination and rents an old
barn or store for a church; the free-lance itinerant evangelist
who drives around the countryside in a battered car with a
canvas tent which he pitches in a vacant lot on the edge of
town for a two-week stand; the professional evangelist who
comes to a city only at the invitation of the local pastors
and who conducts his meetings in the regular churches or
in a rented auditorium; and the religious prophet who captures the attention of the whole nation and seems to speak
for a whole generation of churchgoers.

In order to see how and where Billy Graham fits into this
religious panoply it is necessary to consider his career in a
much broader context than has hitherto been attempted.
This book, therefore, deals with his place in the venerable
revival tradition, his role in the contemporary great awakening as compared to the role of revival leaders in past
awakenings, his relationship to the institutional development
of the churches, past, present, and future, and his place in
the shifting climate of theological and ecclesiastical thought
over the last fifty years. Above all, this book tries to relate
the man, his message, and his career to the changing pattern
of American social and intellectual life. For it is obvious
to everyone by now that Billy Graham is far more than a

professional revivalist. He is a representative figure of his age. This book attempts to discover, from the viewpoint of the social historian, precisely what Billy Graham and his revivals represent, and what they signify about the temper of American civilization in the middle of the twentieth century.

I am conscious of the difficulties involved in attempting to analyze contemporary events, particularly where these events are so open to subjective interpretation. But there are also some advantages in recording the immediate responses of the contemporary observer and participant. What the future historian will gain in perspective, he may lose in freshness. What this book loses from want of hindsight, it may gain as a document of history itself. I make no pretense at absolute objectivity, but I have striven for accuracy wherever facts are concerned. The page proofs of this book were examined by Dr. Graham and several of his associates who made extensive comments. Where these comments pointed out errors of fact, I have made corrections. Where they questioned matters of interpretation, I have reserved the right to express my own judgment.

WILLIAM G. McLOUGHLIN, JR.

Providence, Rhode Island
March, 1960

Acknowledgments

First I wish to thank the many persons connected with the Billy Graham Evangelistic Association who have kindly talked to me about their work and who have freely furnished me with materials upon which to base this study. In this regard I am particularly indebted to Mr. George M. Wilson, Mr. Paul J. Maddox, Mrs. Betty Lowry, Mr. George Edstrom, and Mr. Willis G. Haymaker. I also wish to thank the many ministers and laymen who have worked with Billy Graham in his crusades who shared with me their views on revivals and revivalists. Several scholars in the field of religious history have gone out of their way to assist me in my research; I am particularly indebted to Professor James L. McAllister of Mary Baldwin College, Staunton, Virginia, Professor Warren Ashby of the Woman's College of North Carolina, and Professor Kenneth S. Inglis of the University of Adelaide, Adelaide, Australia. Mr. Joseph F. Quick, Executive Secretary of the Department of Evangelism of the Protestant Council of the City of New York, has been especially helpful in connection with the New York crusade, and Mr. Denis Duncan, editor of the *British Weekly,* has given valuable assistance in connection with the London and Glasgow crusades.

I also want to acknowledge with thanks a grant-in-aid from the American Philosophical Society which made it possible for me to gather material in various parts of the country for use in this book.

Many friends have assisted me by collecting impressions and clippings for my files. My mother, Florence M. McLoughlin, has been particularly persevering and helpful in aiding my research in this and other ways. Throughout the process of research, writing, and correcting, my wife, Virginia Ward McLoughlin, has given unstintingly of her warm encouragement and her judicious critical counsel.

Contents

BILLY GRAHAM

CHAPTER 1

Billy Graham
and the Revival Tradition

*I have the greatest respect for Billy Sunday
though our methods are different and some
of our emphases are different because we
are living in two different periods. . . . I
would say that our meetings are more along
the lines of the Moody meetings of about 75
years ago. . . .*

BILLY GRAHAM [1]

No one expected a revival of religion to follow World
War II. None had followed World War I, and when the
great depression of the 1930's failed to produce one, the
best-informed sociologists and historians had agreed that the
old revival tradition in America was dead. Even church
leaders and theologians had written off revivals as a primitive and outmoded form of religious expression no longer
suited to the advanced stage of Western civilization. In
1946 the Rev. Willard L. Sperry, Dean of the Harvard
Divinity School, stated in a book designed to explain religion in the United States to the British public, "We are
tired of religious revivals as we have known them in the last
half century. . . . Among all but the most backward

churches it is now agreed that education ought to be, and probably is, the best way of interesting our people in religion and of identifying them with one or another of our many denominations." [2] And at the other end of the theological spectrum, the dean of a small Bible college in New York noted some time later that during the early 1940's "even the most ardent evangelical was convinced that mass evangelism was outmoded. . . ." [3]

Yet within a few months after the war had ended, and before Sperry's remarks on "the passing of the religious revival from the American scene" were yet published, the newest in America's long history of "great awakenings" was already under way. In October, 1945, a periodical which spoke for the resurgent fundamentalist wing of Protestantism reported, "For the first time since the days of Chapman and Alexander, Billy Sunday, and other great evangelists of the early twentieth century, we are faced with the challenging situation of having many more calls for evangelistic campaigns than there are competent evangelists to go around." [4] Four years later a handsome young graduate of Wheaton College strode onto a rough wooden platform under a huge tent pitched on the outskirts of Los Angeles. Five thousand hushed spectators leaned forward, watching intently as he began to speak. In his left hand he clutched an open Bible. With his right hand he jabbed a rigid index finger at heaven. His wavy blond hair tossed loosely over his fervent blue eyes as he shouted into the microphone, "We need a revival. . . . I think we are living at a time in world history when God is going to give us a desperate choice, a choice of either revival or judgment. . . . God can still use America to evangelize the world. . . . In this moment I can see the judgment hand of God . . . about to fall. . . . This may be God's last great call. . . . We need a revival. . . . I believe that we can have [a] revival any time we meet God's conditions. I believe that God is true to His Word and that He must rain righteousness upon us if we meet His conditions." [5]

By the time Billy Graham concluded his eight-week tent

meeting in Los Angeles the readers of *Life, Time, News-week, Quick,* the Hearst press, and the newspapers carrying the Associated Press dispatches across the country knew that America's fourth great awakening had begun. Billy Graham's name was added to the list of revivalists that began with Jonathan Edwards and George Whitefield in the 1740's and continued through Lyman Beecher, Charles Grandison Finney, and Dwight L. Moody in the nineteenth century, down to Reuben A. Torrey, J. Wilbur Chapman, and Billy Sunday in the twentieth.

In 1949 Billy Graham spoke principally to and for the fundamentalists of America. But within five years his revival crusades were being backed by the churchgoers and church leaders of virtually all the nation's Protestant churches. By 1954 *Time* was convinced that Billy Graham was not only the true "successor to Billy Sunday" but that his position in contemporary Christendom rivalled that of Pope Pius XII: "Billy Graham is the best-known, most talked about Christian leader in the world today, barring the Pope." [6] By 1958 Graham had enjoyed the hospitality and the admiration not only of the President and Vice-President of the United States, but of the Queen and Prime Minister of England, the Prime Minister of India, and of numerous other heads of state and influential political, business, social, and religious leaders around the globe. The Gallup Poll's annual survey to discover "the most admired man in the world" disclosed in 1958 that Americans rated only President Eisenhower, Winston Churchill, and Albert Schweitzer ahead of Billy Graham.

But for all the publicity Graham received and all the honors showered upon him in his rapid rise to fame, few Americans and even fewer foreigners understood the purpose and significance of his revivals. His name was a household word, but his career, his methods, and the reasons for his phenomenal evangelistic success were an enigma. To many devout Protestants he was, humanly speaking, inexplicable—he was a man "sent of God" whose work was supernaturally ordained and sustained. To superficial and skeptical observers he was mistaken for another hell-fire and damnation exhorter to be lumped indiscriminately with Billy Sunday, Aimee Semple McPherson, Father Divine, Jonathan Edwards, and Oral Roberts. Many who never witnessed his respectable, well-ordered meetings imagined them to be emotional orgies of hallelujah-shouting, hand-clapping, and hysteria. Others considered Graham an egotistical mountebank out to win fame, fortune, or power by playing upon the credulity of the unsophisticated. And certain sociologists spoke of him as a skilled manipulator of crowd psychology and the mass media; it was inferred that he wanted to create a new denomination of Grahamites, to capitalize upon contemporary social maladjustments by denouncing the shortcomings of the regular churches, and to rally the simple-minded around him by prophesying the imminent second coming of Christ. But neither his detractors nor his admirers caught the true dimension of the man and his work.

The most common question asked about Graham was, "Is he sincere?" But while everyone from the Archbishop of Canterbury to the professional newspaper reporters agreed that he was, this explained nothing. As Graham himself was fond of saying in another context, one of the most sincere men he ever saw was the football player in a bowl game who ran sixty yards with the ball in the wrong direction. Sincerity ruled out charlatanism, but it did not reveal the nature of the rejuvenation of American Protestantism of which Graham's revivals were the symbol. Billy Graham, like all previous revivalists, insists that his success is the work of God. "It is not publicity," he says, which draws the crowds and fills his inquiry rooms with anxious inquirers. "It is not showmanship, it is not personality, it is not organization." But it is the hand of God. "It is God's doing and it is marvelous in our eyes." Yet even those who accept this view of the supernatural origin of revivals might legitimately ask why God has chosen this particular time and this particular nation for the commencement of a revival.

The key to Billy Graham's revivals, like the key to all of

America's previous revivals, lies not in the sincerity or the personal talent of the revivalist, but in the social and theological milieu in which he works. If sincerity or charismatic power were the key to revivalism, then the United States would never have been without a revival. For the active careers of the leading revivalists from Solomon Stoddard in the 1680's to Billy Sunday, who died in 1935, were sufficiently long to have maintained a constant state of religious fervor for 250 years. Nor is the clue to revivalism to be found in such obvious social crises as wars or depressions. There has been no significant correlation between America's periods of revival and her periods of armed conflict and economic distress. (In fact, a more significant correlation might be found between America's periods of prosperity and her periods of revival, were it not for the fact that so much of America's history has been characterized by prosperity.)

Historically speaking there seem to be several conditions which must combine in order to produce the climate in which revivalism can flourish. The most important of these conditions is a basic shift in the emphasis of theological thought within Protestantism (a shift which is invariably connected with a general reorientation in American society at large and which inevitably produces important alterations in the organizational structure and leadership of the Protestant churches). There have been four such basic shifts in Protestant thought since the Puritans first settled in Massachusetts Bay, and each of them has produced a period of revivalism so profound and far-reaching as properly to be called a "great awakening."

It is true, of course, that the English Puritan movement in the first half of the seventeenth century was clearly such an awakening, but since the settling of Massachusetts Bay was only a peripheral aspect of this movement, it is fair to say that the first great awakening in America was the one which took place in the years 1725 to 1750. This was the awakening which is associated with such names as Jonathan Edwards, George Whitefield, Theodore J. Frelinghuysen, and Gilbert Tennent. Theologically it marked the end of the old seventeenth-century form of Calvinism which the Puritans (and Presbyterians) had brought from the British Isles and the beginning of a new kind of Calvinism. This new Calvinism, which might be called evangelistic or evangelical Calvinism, de-emphasized the doctrine of predestination and played up instead the need of the sinner to demonstrate forcefully his faith. George Whitefield so stirred up his audiences (and so, on occasion, did Jonathan Edwards) that hundreds of people who had formerly believed that they were too wicked ever to merit salvation felt as if a great burden had been lifted from their souls; they felt freed from sin and bound for heaven. Whitefield did not deny that God predestined some to hell-fire and some to glory, but he made so many persons feel as if they were among the saved that he took the curse of fatalism off the old Calvinistic dogma. And it was a good thing for Protestantism that he and his fellow revival preachers did so, for Calvinism had grown so formal, legalistic, and dry that many churchgoers in England and America were toying with the free-thinking rationalism or deism which gave the eighteenth century its nickname as "the Age of Reason." The Anglican churches, as well as the Presbyterian and Congregational, adopted a more fervent pietistic or evangelical outlook during this first awakening, and the preaching of Whitefield in America and John Wesley in England translated the growing faith in the individual dignity and rights of man into religious terms.

The second great shift in American Protestant thought occurred in the opening years of the nineteenth century. The leading figures associated with this second great awakening were Timothy Dwight, Lyman Beecher, Nathaniel W. Taylor, Charles Grandison Finney, and a host of camp meeting revivalists who brought a new religious fervor to the expanding frontier regions. In this awakening the concept of free will and free grace (the belief that God offered salvation freely to all who believed in Christ on faith) which had been only implicit in the preaching of the first great awakening became perfectly explicit. In theological terms,

Arminianism (or the belief in free will) replaced Calvinism (or the belief in predestination) between the years 1800 and 1835. Thus the intellectual currents which had brought the separation of church and state in America after 1776 produced not only the self-reliant individualism of the frontier, but also produced an individualistic Protestantism which completely reversed the old Calvinistic principles. The revivalists of this second awakening laid the foundations upon which Billy Graham's revivals are based both in theology and technique. But in making theology compatible with the nation's self-reliant individualism, the leaders of the second great awakening seriously undermined the importance of the church as a social institution and the pastor as a community leader. As a result of this new theological and ecclesiastical emphasis, the pastor became little more than a revivalist himself—a man whose primary, if not sole, duty was to save individual souls by persuading men to make a decision to accept Christ on faith.

The departure from this individualistic gospel, with its emphasis upon crisis conversion, constituted the third basic shift in American Protestant thought. This departure took place between the years 1875 and 1915, and it produced what may be called America's third great awakening, though it is usually referred to as the Social Gospel movement. As its name implies, the Social Gospel movement placed its theological emphasis upon the social teachings of Jesus rather than upon personal salvation. The social gospel preachers, among whom Washington Gladden and Walter Rauschenbusch were the most prominent, were not revivalists in the usual sense of the term. They believed that it was less important to convert individual souls by means of revival services than it was to promote the Kingdom of God "on earth as it is in heaven" by means of social, economic, and political reforms. The social gospelers were also influenced by new trends in Biblical scholarship and in science and came to place less emphasis upon the letter of Christianity than upon its spirit. The essence of the third great awakening lay in its attempt to interpret Protestantism in terms which were more meaningful to the progressive and pragmatic temper of the times. This new shift in theological emphasis, like those in the past, met with serious resistance among many church leaders, some of whom disliked its social reform aspect and some of whom disliked its abandonment of the literal interpretation of the Bible. The result of the latter quarrel was the famous fundamentalist-modernist schism which reached its climax in the Scopes trial in 1925. Billy Graham tends to share the opinions of those who were the opponents of the Social Gospel movement and to find more in common with the fundamentalists than with the modernists. Since one consequence of the third great awakening was a thirty-year decline in the popularity of mass revival campaigns, Billy Graham is understandably pessimistic about the value of that awakening. To him the heroes of the era were not the social gospelers but men like D. L. Moody, Reuben A. Torrey, and Billy Sunday. These men were professional evangelists who, in their revival campaigns, led the unsuccessful fight to save the individualistic evangelicalism embodied in the famous "five points of fundamentalism"* from what they considered (and Graham considers) the rationalistic and socialistic theology of Gladden and Rauschenbusch.

The fourth great awakening in America, which began shortly after World War II and which is still in progress, is pre-eminently a shift away from the social gospel philosophy and the modernist (or liberal Protestant) theology. It is also closely related to the shift away from the economic and political liberalism of the first half of the century. Both the social theology of modernism and the political liberalism of progressivism and the New Deal maintained that to save the individual it was first necessary to save or reform society. The current awakening is dominated by such terms as neo-conservatism, neo-orthodoxy, and neo-evangelicalism because it represents in part a return to the older philosophical

---

* The "five points of fundamentalism" are the literal infallibility of Scriptures, the virgin birth, the substitutionary atonement, the bodily resurrection, and the imminent, bodily second coming of Christ.

and theological emphasis upon the individual as the focus of thought and action. There is little or no attempt to return to the Calvinistic dogma of predestination and its corollaries, but there is a tendency to emphasize the limitations of the optimistic faith in self-reliance and free will which began with the breakdown of Calvinism and reached its culmination in the 1930's. It is important to keep this point in mind. For the three great shifts in American theological and social thought which have preceded the current awakening have not been pendulumlike swings back and forth cancelling each other out. They have each been successive adaptations of traditional religious values and beliefs to an increasingly secularistic, man-centered view of life. The hope of the various revival leaders, of course, was always to stem this secularistic tide, but their methods of doing so have amounted in reality to a series of capitulations to it. In each awakening prior to 1945, Protestantism has taken further steps away from the God-centered universe of the Middle Ages and the Reformation.

While it is fair to say, therefore, that throughout American history revivalism has been primarily a means of reconciling the Christian tradition to changing times, it is essential to recognize that the revivalism of Billy Graham is very different both in theory and in practice from the revivalism of Jonathan Edwards and George Whitefield. As far as revival procedures are concerned, the real break between the theocentric outlook of the Reformation and the anthropocentric outlook of the modern world came in the second great awakening, not in the first. It was in the second great awakening that revivalism first explicitly came to terms with the scientific method—the inductive method of mechanical and psychological experiment. Billy Graham's revivals derive from the theory and practice of Lyman Beecher, Nathaniel W. Taylor, and Charles Grandison Finney. Although he spurns any compromise between religion and science, Graham ultimately bases his revivals upon the same reconciliation between them which Finney utilized to explain and defend his revivals in the 1820's and 1830's.

"A revival is not a miracle or dependent on a miracle," said Finney. "It consists entirely in the right exercise of the powers of nature." Jonathan Edwards and his followers in the eighteenth century had declared that a revival was "a miraculous work of God," a "shower of Divine blessing" which, like a shower of rain, was sent from heaven according to God's will and was not controllable by any device of man. Finney believed that if a preacher utilized "the laws of mind" (i.e., psychology) and the laws of nature and played upon the animal and religious affections or instincts of his hearers, he would be able to promote a revival whenever and wherever he chose. In his famous *Lectures on Revivals,* published in 1835, Finney set forth in clear and unequivocal terms the psychological and mechanical technique which revivalists have employed ever since. Finney was no rationalist, and he was as devoted to the fundamentals of evangelical theology as Graham (which is why Graham admires him), but he was imbued with the belief that God had ordained the laws of nature for the working out of His plans, and it was consequently incumbent upon men to use these laws in order to aid God—to work for God and with God. "The connection between the right use of means for a revival and a revival," said Finney, "is as philosophically sure as between the right use of means to raise grain and a crop of wheat" (and by "philosophical" Finney meant "scientific"). When Billy Graham said in Los Angeles in 1949 that "we can have a revival any time we meet God's conditions" he was simply rephrasing what Finney had said.

Finney had to overcome considerable opposition from ministers who believed, like Edwards, that true revivals were "Prayed down, not worked up." [7] But the success Finney had in saving souls, and the success of those who followed his techniques, put an end to all argument, and today few ministers challenge Graham's right to utilize all the agencies of mass communication and all the methods of psychological persuasion in the effort "to lead men to Christ." It is important to remember, however, that Finney did not say, any more than Billy Graham does, that a revivalist can save souls, or that a man can save his own soul, without God's help. Finney, like Graham, was nevertheless certain that God is ready and willing to offer salvation to anyone who asks for it in the proper spirit. This doctrine of free salvation, of divine grace and pardon freely offered to all men, is the Arminian interpretation of Christian theology which finally overthrew the Calvinistic interpretation that had prevailed in America from its founding until the end of the eighteenth century. Jonathan Edwards, like all true Calvinists, believed in predestination. And the doctrine of predestination taught that God had foreordained those who were to be saved long before they were born; hence Calvinists taught that there was little or nothing anyone could do to effect his own salvation. To Edwards a revival was simply God's way of sealing the predestined salvation of the elect by "implanting" or "infusing" grace into them and regenerating their wicked hearts.

The reasons behind the downfall of Calvinism are exceedingly complex, but the essential characteristic of the second great awakening was the repudiation of the concept of predestination and the alternative assertion of man's free will. Americans, filled with the spirit of liberty and self-reliance after 1776, were convinced by Finney's day that God was benevolent and that man was inherently capable of perfecting himself and society. The Calvinistic concept of an angry God who arbitrarily predestined some to eternal bliss and most to eternal hell-fire made little sense to a people who had wrested their independence from the most powerful empire in the world and who were busily wresting a virgin continent from the forces of nature. The belief that Americans were God's chosen people, and that the manifest destiny of the United States was the manifest destiny of God's plan for the human race, became part and parcel of the Arminian, evangelical, individualistic gospel which pervaded American Protestantism throughout the nineteenth century and which is still deeply imbedded in the thought of Billy Graham and his supporters.

The second great awakening also produced other important shifts in American religious thought which have had a profound influence upon the revival tradition to which Graham belongs. The abandonment of Calvinism led to the loss of interest in all doctrinal or creedal tests of orthodoxy. Preachers emphasized instead "the fundamentals" or "the essentials" of the gospel, and conversion became an experience rather than an affirmation of doctrine. "Experience religion" or "heart religion," as the evangelical churches called it in the nineteenth century, reduced conversion to the verbal acceptance of the fundamentals on faith. In theory such an acceptance was simultaneous with the reception of grace from the Holy Spirit which transformed or regenerated the soul. And under the spirited exhortation of some revivalists, especially on the frontier, the conversion process became a highly emotional and nerve-shattering experience.

Not only were denominational differences blurred in doctrine and practice as revivalists and ministers began preaching experience religion in all denominations, but, more important for revivalism, the practice of itinerant evangelism became institutionalized. (It was no accident that the growing acceptance of the theory of "worked up" revivals coincided wth the final separation of church and state in America. Even the most conservative Congregationalists in New England recognized that with the loss of their favored, tax-supported status it would be necessary to find some means of maintaining voluntary support which would provide both new members and new sources of funds from year to year.) During the first great awakening itinerant revivalists had been generally frowned upon by the regular pastors who considered themselves perfectly capable of handling such showers of blessing as the Lord deigned to send to their communities. But once the theory of worked up revivals became acceptable, it was apparent that certain men were more gifted at utilizing "the laws of the mind" than others. Such specially talented men were ordained as evangelists rather than as pastors and soon made a profession of itinerating in order to bring revivals to communities which needed and wanted them. Largely through Finney's example, many evangelists left the sparsely settled frontier areas after 1835 and began to conduct revival meetings in towns and cities at the specific request of pastors who wished to increase their church membership or whose parishioners were too backslidden to fulfil properly their religious obligations. By the end of the nineteenth century, every town and city in the nation was the scene of annual revival meetings at which the Presbyterian, Congregational, Methodist, Disciples, and other Protestant churches of all hues joined together to pay the expenses for and lend their support to a professional evangelist for a city-wide "union" meeting. It was precisely in such annual revival meetings that Billy Graham began his career in the 1940's.

But Graham owes more to the second great awakening than the institutionalization of itinerancy, the Arminianization of theology, and the definitive scientific defense of worked up revivals. More particularly he owes to Finney a large part of his specific revival techniques. For example, it was Finney who first used "the anxious seat" in respectable urban revivals and thus forced sinners to make a clear-cut public declaration of faith. By accepting the revivalist's invitation to walk forward and take his place before the altar after the sermon, the awakened sinner in Finney's revivals acknowledged his desire to accept the terms of salvation described in the sermon. The fact that the anxious seat had previously been used primarily by uneducated Methodist circuit riders at frontier camp meetings at first brought down upon Finney the angry denunciations of the conservative Presbyterians and Congregationalists among whom he worked. Since Finney's day, however, the invitation to come forward (or to "hit the sawdust trail" as Billy Sunday later called it in his sawdust-strewn wooden tabernacles) has become so central a part of mass revivalism, urban and rural, that it is worth quoting the objections to it which the Rev. Albert B. Dod of Princeton University first raised. Princeton was, in Finney's day, the stronghold of conservative Calvinism; and, Dod, writing in the *Biblical Repertory and Theological Review* in October, 1835, was arguing against the new revival tradition being promoted by Finney. Dod pointed out that when a sinner heard the preacher give the invitation to come forward to the altar after a revival sermon, no matter how good the sermon might be "The divine truth which was but now occupying his mind is forced away, while he revolves the questions, shall I go, or not? Who else will go? What will they say of me?" Moreover, Dod added, the use of the invitation "involves the capital error that no sinner who is truly awakened can refrain from obeying the call to the anxious seat. It assumes that to go to the anxious seat is 'to do something for Christ' and that it is impossible for him who refuses to go to be a Christian." To these objections raised by Dod, other "Old School" Calvinists added warnings that the high pressure techniques which endeavored to produce mass conversions would lead to hypocritical or overly hasty decisions for Christ, and in the long run the mere process of walking forward to give proof of a desire to be saved might deteriorate into a kind of ritual which would be mistaken by many for the conversion process itself.

But the Old School Calvinists, whether Presbyterian, Congregationalist, or Baptist, lost their fight against the "New School" Arminians and their "man-made" revival measures. In 1875, when D. L. Moody was adapting Finney's simple techniques to the more complicated process of large-scale evangelistic crusades in the teeming metropolitan centers of the post-Civil War era, the professors and theologians of Princeton welcomed his revivals, just as in the 1950's they welcomed Billy Graham's. Moody substituted the inquiry room for the anxious bench in order to save those who were aroused by his preaching from the embarrassment of being prayed for in public, but the process was the same in either case. Graham today follows Moody's refinement on the anxious seat, but he still gives an "altar call" prior to sending the anxious to his inquiry rooms.

Among other "new measures" advocated by Finney in his *Lectures on Revivals* and followed by mass evangelists ever since were the necessity for concerted prayer effort by bands of Christians, the use of vigorous advertising methods, the adoption of a dramatic preaching style, and the employment of "protracted meetings" of continuous revival effort stretching over much longer periods than the four-day meetings which previously constituted the accepted duration of frontier camp meetings. But compared to the elaborate procedures developed by Moody, Finney's revival techniques seem crude and feeble.

It was Moody who actually worked out the organizational methods which Billy Graham and his team still use in the 1950's. And Moody's campaigns in London, Edinburgh, New York, Boston, Philadelphia, and Chicago far outshone any of Finney's urban revivals (though Finney too held revivals in Edinburgh, London, Boston, Philadelphia, and New York). Moody was the first revivalist to advertise his campaigns in newspapers, on billboards, posters, handbills, and placards; he was the first to make detailed advance preparations for publicity, church organization, training of ushers, choir, counselors, and prayer meeting leaders; he was the first to publish audited accounts of the expenses, collections, and donations for his multi-thousand dollar crusades which lasted anywhere from six weeks to six months in one city. Like all later evangelists Moody went out of his way to cooperate with the newspaper reporters in order to provide the fullest possible coverage for his meetings. Moody was also the first evangelist to employ a solo singer and choir leader to assist him, and many people said that it was the gospel hymns of Ira D. Sankey rather than the preaching of Moody that attracted the crowds. If Finney made revivalism a respectable profession, Moody made it a big business. The leading captains of industry and finance, men like J. P. Morgan, Jay Cooke, and Cyrus McCormick, served on Moody's committees and donated their time and money for the sake of bringing religion to "the urban masses."

Many people have said that Billy Graham owes more to Billy Sunday's methods than to Moody's, but Graham himself denies this: "I have the greatest respect for Billy Sunday though our methods are different and some of our emphases are different because we are living in two different periods. . . . I would say that our meetings are more along the lines of the Moody meetings of about 75 years ago." It is not surprising that Graham prefers to associate himself with Moody rather than with the more sensational and theatrical Billy Sunday, whose official biographer referred to him as "a gymnast for Jesus." Though Sunday was as sincere and honest as Moody and Graham, he gave revivalism a bad name by his use of slang, humor, and acrobatics in the pulpit and because he was known to have received over one million dollars in freewill offerings from his admirers in the opening decades of the twentieth century. Graham has pretty well avoided these pitfalls, yet his debt to Sunday is deeper than he admits. For Sunday perfected Moody's system of urban mass evangelism to an even more highly organized form of corporate enterprise. To Sunday, for example, Graham owes the idea of a team of associate experts to manage the details of every phase of a campaign. To Sunday he owes the practice of reserving large blocks of seats at every meeting for delegations whose attendance has been arranged in advance. To Sunday he owes the use of massive choirs and elaborate entertainment features as part of his revivals. There is more than a little of Sunday's tendency to inject social and political comment into his sermons in order to produce attention-catching headlines in the next morning's newspapers. And like Sunday, Graham equates conservative evangelical Christianity with patriotic Americanism. But in the last analysis, Graham's revival system is actually indebted to no one revivalist. It is the ultimate product of a long tradition.

The career of Billy Graham becomes comprehensible only when it is placed against this broad background of American revivalism—especially when it is recognized that professional mass revivalism has, since the early part of the nineteenth century, been an essential and closely integrated function of organized Protestantism. It is true that there have always been eccentric revivalists like Aimee Semple

McPherson, Father Divine, Elijah P. Dowie, and James
Davenport, who were more interested in denouncing the
regular churches than in assisting them. But these "come-
outers" and prophets of schism have operated as individuals; they were outside the main line of the revival tradition.
Generally speaking, their sincerity and piety has not been
questioned but their mental stability often has. What puts
these eccentric revivalists beyond the pale in the profession
is their insistence upon separatism and their refusal to adapt
their views and methods to the traditions of respectability,
toleration, and conservatism which are the hallmarks of the
professional evangelists. The essence of revivalism in America has been its note of cooperative enterprise for the good
of religion in general. Within the professional tradition, eccentricity and controversy are taboo. The only things the
professional evangelist can openly attack are those spiritual
and moral evils which the vast majority of American churchgoers agree on defining as sins. The only things he can
espouse are the generally acknowledged moral and religious
virtues. To go beyond the lowest common denominator of
the prevailing religious and democratic dogma is to jeopard-
ize the united support of the leading clergy and laity whose
cooperation is essential to the complex and expensive undertaking which an urban revival crusade entails. For this reason professional revivalists like Moody, Sunday, and Graham
have never been leaders of public or religious opinion.
Rather the significance of the great revival leaders has been
their ability to embody in their colorful and eloquent sermons neither more nor less than the spirit of their times. In
critical periods of religious and social reorientation they have
given new expression to the old religious and secular ideals
which have been the basis of the American dream. But
when the period of readjustment has passed the reassuring
voice of the evangelist is no longer needed. Often the evangelist himself fails to move with the times. It is at this point
that great awakenings come to an end.

It was because the professional evangelists lost touch
with the prevailing trend of American religious and social

thought after World War I (and not because of the vulgarity, sensationalism, or commercialism of Billy Sunday and his imitators) that the revival tradition went into its thirty-year eclipse. Professional evangelists had nothing meaningful to say to the generation which came of age during and after the First World War. By rejecting the scientific and scholarly theories of the twentieth century and by insisting upon the small-town moral code of nineteenth-century America, the evangelists doomed themselves to obscurity along with the fundamentalism to which they clung. And in the 1930's the political and economic conservatism of the revivalists (a conservatism which is indissolubly linked to the individualistic gospel they preach) produced an even greater abyss between them and the average American. When Billy Sunday began to compare Franklin Roosevelt to Hitler, Mussolini, and the anti-Christ, and to predict that the New Deal was the work of the devil, he demonstrated how far out of touch an Iowa farm boy born in 1862 could get with the realities of 1935.

The revival tradition still continued to some extent among the unsophisticated rural folk and among the country-bred evangelical urban dwellers of the 1930's; yet so complete was the collapse of fundamentalism that even in "the Bible belt" city-wide revival crusades were few and far between. The major denominations, having gone modernist in theology and New Dealist in social thought, depended for membership growth upon home visitation campaigns and upon their Sunday school scholars, who were accepted into the churches as a kind of graduation ceremony following their desultory religious education. Dean Sperry of Harvard was right in stating that revivalism had given way to religious education in most American churches after World War I.

Fundamentalism did not die, however, as Billy Graham's revivals were to indicate. And it would also be incorrect to say that fundamentalism went underground between the two world wars. In fact, fundamentalism remained very much alive and growing during this period. But it separated itself so drastically from the mainstream of American religious life that most Protestant church leaders wrongly assumed with Sperry that it was obsolescent if not extinct. Such statistics as are available on the various fundamentalist, holiness, pentecostal, and "independent" churches in this period indicate that, proportionately, they grew far more rapidly in membership than the regular denominations. Between 1926 and 1936, for exmple, while the major denominations in the South (the heart of the Bible belt) increased by an average of about 10 per cent in membership, the General Council of Assemblies of God increased 270 per cent.[8] Sociologists and church historians ignored such statistics in part because the membership in such fundamentalist groups was comparatively small (the Assemblies of God had only 59,343 members in 1936); but the proliferation of such holiness sects put their cumulative total in the millions. The fundamentalists were also ignored because they were considered the vestigial remnants of rural pietism or transitional steps on the road from primitivism to modernism. Certainly the continuous quarreling, schisms, and heresy-hunting among these ardent keepers of the faith seemed to indicate that their movement was disorganized to the point of chaos.

Yet this hectic chaos was a sign of vitality rather than decay. Apathy, not argument, is the symptom of religious decline. After an initial period of disorder in the 1920's the fundamentalists regrouped their forces, reorganized their social and ecclesiastical structure, and consolidated their theological position. Bible schools and colleges like the Moody Bible Institute in Chicago, Wheaton College in Wheaton, Illinois, Fuller Theological Seminary in Los Angeles, and Bob Jones College in Cleveland, Tennessee, became the centers of this reorganization. The unreconstructed fundamentalists, finding themselves completely out of sympathy with the world of the twenties and thirties, withdrew to establish their own "Bible-centered" culture within a culture. They built their own storefront churches, cinderblock tabernacles, and basement gospel halls. They founded hundreds of new Sunday schools, Christian day schools, Christian high schools, Bible institutes, and "Bible-honoring" colleges and seminaries. They gathered each summer at religious camp meetings, Bible conferences, prophetic conventions, and sent their children to Christian boys' and girls' camps. Although most of the people who belonged to this subculture were members of the marginal middle class, they were able and anxious to tithe or donate large portions of their incomes for "the Lord's work." Their money and enthusiasm helped to support hundreds of small fundamentalist periodicals; fundamentalist publishing houses found as eager an audience for their books as fundamentalist radio programs found eager listeners and contributors for their broadcasts. In addition, considerable time and effort went into organizing and building up Christian youth movements, Christian boy scouts, Christian veterans' groups, Christian businessmen's societies, and Christian missionary organizations. Within this "God-centered" and "Christ-honoring" environment the fundamentalists found a satisfactory way of life, insulated from the corrupt and corrupting world around them. They were in the world but not of the world. And their pietistic fervor, an inherent quality of Christianity from its beginning and a particularly vital element in American religious experience, kept alive a spiritual faith which was bound to break forth once the climate was right.

Billy Graham was a product of this pietistic or fundamentalist culture which flourished between the wars. But the reasons underlying the outbreak of America's fourth great awakening after World War II are not to be found simply in terms of the upward thrust of a resurgent fundamentalism, powerful though it was. Fundamentalists were by no means the only religious group to experience a renascence in the 1940's. Roman Catholicism, Judaism, and even liberal Protestantism experienced a similar rebirth as American religious and social thought began a new period of reorientation. One level of this religious reorientation could be seen in the immense vogue of Monsignor Fulton J. Sheen's *Peace of Soul*, Rabbi Joshua L. Liebman's *Peace of Mind*, and the Rev. Norman Vincent Peale's *Power of Positive Thinking*. On a more profound level, the awakening could be seen in the neo-Thomist writings of Jacques Maritain, the Hebraic existentialism of Martin Buber, and the neo-orthodoxy of Karl Barth. The fourth great awakening was, like past awakenings, by no means an isolated American phenomenon. It represented a new era of intellectual ferment throughout Western civilization.

And also, as in past awakenings, its stirrings could be seen long before the outburst of mass evangelistic campaigns which dramatized the readjustment as it reached its climactic phase. Liberal Protestantism, for example, had begun to re-examine its theological position in the 1920's, when the seminal works of Barth, Emil Brunner, and Paul Tillich first appeared. Reinhold Niebuhr and Harry Emerson Fosdick were among the first to urge American theologians to go "beyond modernism" to a more realistic and hardheaded appraisal of Christian thought. By the mid-1930's Fosdick, who was to many the arch-symbol of modernism, was ready to disavow the facile optimism and scientific pragmatism which characterized it: "The modernistic movement," he said in 1935, "adjusting itself to a man-centered culture, has . . . watered down the thought of the Divine and . . . left souls standing like the ancient Athenians before an altar to an Unknown God! On that point the church must go beyond modernism. We have been all things to all men long enough. . . . We have at times gotten so low down that we talked as though the highest compliment that could be paid to Almighty God was that a few scientists believed in him." [9] Fifteen years later Billy Graham made headlines by such statements, but Fosdick's address was noted only by theologians in 1935.

But while this theological reorientation, which had been brewing among religious intellectuals for several decades, provided a receptive mood for Billy Graham's revivals among the college-educated church leaders, the impact of Graham's sermons upon the public at large can be traced more immediately to the sobering effect which fifteen years of world turmoil had had upon the traditional optimism of the American popular philosophy. Between 1930 and 1945,

Fascism, Stalinism, the great depression, the global conflict, atomic bombs, and the postwar "cold war" made a mockery of the liberal faith in such ideas as progress, the innate goodness and perfectibility of man, and the manifest destiny of Anglo-Saxon democracy to triumph peacefully and easily throughout the world. As Americans began once again to re-examine their ideals and beliefs in order to adjust them to a new set of circumstances, Billy Graham struck a responsive chord in their minds and hearts. Amidst the wreckage of so many hopes, Graham reassembled some of the old and cherished symbols of faith and gave new assurance to those who still held to the time-honored tenets of the American and the Christian way of life. American churchgoers were heartened by Graham's words quoted in *Time* in November, 1949: "We are standing on the verge of a great national revival, an old-fashioned, heaven-sent, Holy Ghost revival that will sweep the nation." [10] So many efforts of man had failed, so much of the world lay in chaos and ruin, that the average churchgoer was ready to believe that perhaps a supernatural infusion of grace was needed to redeem civilization. Certainly a new infusion of assurance was needed. A year later, after the Korean War had brought the last faint hopes crashing, Graham's prediction of a revival seemed substantiated. *Time* now announced that "Old-fashioned 'evangelistic crusades' which used to be known as revivals, have been staging an impressive comeback." [11] It was at this point that Billy Graham became for many Protestants the same kind of symbol of faith and hope in a chaotic world that Pope Pius XII was for Roman Catholics.

CHAPTER 2

Who Is Billy Graham?

"Why did God choose you?" asked the reporter.

"When I get to Heaven that's the first question I'm going to ask Him," Graham replied.[1]

William Franklin Graham, Jr., was born in Charlotte, North Carolina, on November 7, 1918, one year after Billy Sunday had reached the climax of his career by winning 98,264 decisions for Christ during a ten-week crusade in New York City. Graham's father owned a prosperous two-hundred-acre dairy farm which he had inherited from his father. The farm was the remnant of a family estate ruined by the Civil War. Both of Graham's grandfathers fought with the Confederacy, but he makes no claims to aristocratic lineage. "I am," he says, just "a farm boy from the sand hills of Carolina." [2]

The Grahams belonged to the Associate Reformed Presbyterian Church (General Synod) which held strictly to a belief in the literal infallibility of the Bible and to the dogma of the seventeenth-century Westminster Confession of Faith (evangelically interpreted). The Associate Reformed denomination was even more conservative than the Southern branch of the Presbyterian Church of the United States.

Not even the Moody and Sankey hymns were sung in its services; only the Psalms of David were thought fit for God. Graham's parents were devout in their religion and his father was an elder of the church in Charlotte. The family seldom missed a service or a prayer meeting and the children attended Sunday school without fail. Like his rigid Scotch-Irish ancestors, the elder Graham was the patriarch in his family. He reared his children "in the fear of the Lord," and exerted a stern moral influence over Graham, his younger brother, and two sisters. As Graham later put it, his father led the children to live pious and upright lives "with prayer and a hickory stick." [2a] Before they were ten, each of the children was well along in the memorization of the entire Shorter Catechism (which is not very short) in preparation for the day when they would formally enter the church. In keeping with the old Scottish tradition, both Graham's parents hoped and prayed that their first-born son would receive a call from God to enter the ministry.

But young Billy wanted to be a baseball player. He was not a disobedient son, yet he displayed the normal reaction against an overdose of religion by finding it uninteresting. "When my father and mother made me go to Sunday school," he said in later years, "and on Sunday afternoon my mother would read to us Bible stories, I sometimes rebelled and thought she was too rigid and sometimes thought she was trying to cram religion down my throat." [3] Consequently he took his religion somewhat less seriously than his parents desired and devoted most of his spare time to perfecting his skill at throwing, batting, and fielding a baseball. His parents might have taken some consolation from the fact that Billy Sunday had himself entered the ministry after a career as a professional baseball star. But young Graham's idol was not Billy Sunday. It was Babe Ruth.

At the age of twelve, Graham, having duly memorized the Shorter Catechism and expressed his belief in its tenets, was admitted to the church. A conversion experience was not required for membership although it was expected to occur at some time during puberty. As a youngster Graham had been bored by the long, arid sermons of the minister, and his father had once strapped him with a leather belt for fidgeting during a service. But he attended church regularly, eventually becoming the president of the young people's society. And he obeyed all the pietistic injunctions against swearing, smoking, gambling, and immoral conduct. Prohibition was in force during most of his youth, so he did not have that temptation. Soon after the Eighteenth Amendment was repealed, however, Graham's father bought a couple of bottles of beer and forced Billy and one of his sisters to drink it in order to see how bad it was. This effectively killed any desire they might have had to indulge in that particular sin. Apart from baseball (and in the winter, basketball) Graham's adolescent energy found the usual outlets: speeding around town in the family car ("I remember driving my father's car down the middle of the town on the sidewalk"); attending the various parties and social outings organized by his high school friends; and dating a multitude of girls ("I remember riding in a convertible with my girl-friend standing up in the back of it with a cowbell, in the middle of town, ringing it"). He also assisted his father's seven hired hands in the dairying chores around the farm.

At sixteen Graham had the conversion experience which was expected of all young people in the pietistic tradition of the rural South. It was inescapable. A group of laymen in Charlotte, among whom Graham's father was a leader, formed a committee to invite the popular southern evangelist, Mordecai Fowler Ham, to hold a revival meeting in their town. For various reasons the ministers of the town were not enthusiastic about revival meetings of Ham's sort and did not take much part in the movement, though they knew better than to oppose it. Ham was a rural edition of Billy Sunday, an itinerant revivalist who had won a reputation among pious folk for his fiery denunciations of sin and his success in producing renewed religious enthusiasm among cold church members. Ham was especially noted for his ability to bring recalcitrant young people to the anxious bench and break them of their adolescent rebelliousness. What bothered the local ministers was that Ham had adopted some of the unsavory racial and political attitudes of the more rabid fundamentalists in the 1930's. At various points in his sermons, for example, he would place the blame for the growing evils of American society upon the Satan-inspired schemes of international Jews, uppity Negroes, or communistic New Deal intellectuals. But Ham's four-week revival in Charlotte in the fall of 1934 was primarily a genuine, "old-fashioned" gospel meeting designed to arouse the slumbering churches and whip the town's black sheep into line.

Ham later recalled that Graham's father had particularly asked him to direct his attention to young Billy who, like most unconverted young people in the South, could not resist attending a ceremony which he knew was designed especially for sinners like him.[4] But the real credit for Graham's conversion seems to belong to a local clothing merchant, J. D. Prevatte. Prevatte was a friend of Graham's father and one of the devout laymen who had been on the committee to bring Ham to Charlotte. During the revival he served as a "personal worker" or counselor in the tent, conversing with those who went forward to the mourner's bench. It was his task to elicit the personal confession of faith that would complete the sinner's transition to salvation which Ham's preaching had begun. Graham and one of his school friends, Grady Wilson, who was also still outside the fold, listened to Ham's sermons in the big tent for several days and were becoming visibly agitated by his hammering at the dangers and sinfulness of holding out against God's mercy. Graham felt a sense of guilt at his reckless impiety which made him think, he said later, that the preacher was referring specifically to him.

The scene is easily reconstructed: Prevatte approached Graham and his friend Wilson as they sat nervously in the audience after one of Ham's tempestuous sermons. The choir was singing, "Softly and tenderly Jesus is calling," and awakened sinners were slowly walking up the sawdust covered aisles to take the front benches which had been cleared for penitents. Ham kept urging others to come forward, to confess their sins, to turn to Christ for forgiveness: "God is calling you. This may be your last chance. God will never be so near to you as he is tonight. He is pleading with you. Won't you come forward and find rest and peace and forsake your wicked ways? If you do not heed this call, you will be rejecting God. You will harden your heart. That's right, brother, come on. God bless you. Come along, sister. The Lord is waitin' on you. Aren't there others here tonight who know they have done wrong and want to get right with the Lord?" Prevatte walked up to where Graham and his friend were sitting and with a serious, kindly face asked if they did not want to come forward now. Graham hesitated, looked at his friend, and then got up. With Prevatte beside him he slowly walked to the front of the tent and took his place with the others before the altar. He recited the well-known words of confession, repentance, and faith, and kneeled as the evangelist prayed for the souls of all those who had accepted Jesus by coming forward and who now promised to forsake their sins and walk in His way. There was much prayer and rejoicing in the Graham household that night.

But Graham still had a year to go in high school and his conversion did not shake his ambition to become a ballplayer. He had acknowledged the authority of God, his father, and his church, but he had not undergone any discernible change in his outlook or behavior. The summer after his conversion he and his friend Grady Wilson (who was also converted) took their first jobs on their own. They became traveling salesmen for the Fuller Brush Company. Graham sold more brushes than any other salesman in North Carolina during the three-month vacation. He did so, he said, because "I believed in the product."

He was a lanky, good-looking boy with a frank, open face, a pleasant smile, and an enthusiastic sincerity which made a winning impression upon the housewives whose doorbells he pushed. Had Graham chosen to channel his

intense energy and warm personality into commercial sales-
manship he would have gone far. But this experience was
not wasted. Like the most famous of the post-Civil War
evangelists, Dwight L. Moody, who had also been a highly
successful traveling salesman in his early life, Graham
learned much from the art of projecting his own enthusiasm
into the promotion of his product. As he was later to say,
"Sincerity is the biggest part of selling anything—including
the Christian Plan of Salvation." [5]

But selling brushes was not as exciting as playing baseball, and after completing his senior year at Sharon High
School (and almost failing to graduate because he would
not concentrate on his lessons), Graham spent the summer
of 1936 as a semiprofessional baseball player. He played
with a local baseball team in Charlotte for ten dollars a
game. But skill in sports requires discipline and Graham's
enthusiasm was undisciplined. His inability to bat, like Billy
Sunday's, typified that overly aggressive earnestness which
yearned to blast every pitch into a home run rather than to
concentrate upon directing the ball toward the openings
which would produce a safe but unspectacular one-base hit.

Parental pressure upon him to enter the ministry mounted
steadily after his conversion. His mother set aside a special
time each day to pray for this end. According to the author-
ized biography of Graham written by Stanley High, the
elder Graham's "prayers at the family altar . . . left no doubt
of the hope he held that" his son would become a preacher.
In the old Scotch Presbyterian tradition a would-be
preacher must go to college. But most American colleges
were too godless for Graham's parents. Only a God-
centered Bible school would do. They decided upon Bob
Jones College, in Cleveland, Tennessee. Bob Jones, like
Mordecai Ham, was an itinerant evangelist. But when
mass evangelism went into its decline in the 1920's,
Jones looked for a new outlet for his abilities. Bob
Jones College was one of scores of such nondenominational
Bible institutes founded on a shoestring by pious preachers
in the 1920's and 1930's. They catered to the sons and

daughters of fundamentalists who feared the atheistic state universities and the "highbrow" liberal arts colleges. The facilities of Bob Jones College were too limited to be accredited by the Association of American Universities, but that was not held against it by pious folk. Moreover, Bob Jones College had the endorsement of Billy Sunday, who had frequently spoken there and whose wife served on its board of trustees.

Although his heart was still set on a career in baseball, young Graham was persuaded to try Bob Jones College. He lasted only four months. The college did not encourage baseball players. It sought to train Christian workers— missionaries, ministers, mission hall superintendents, and evangelists. It did not even have any program for intercollegiate athletics. It also forbade its students to dance, to go to the movies, to gamble, or to indulge in smoking, drinking, or card playing. Extracurricular interest was centered upon daily chapel services, frequent prayer meetings, intensive Bible study, and occasional "concerts of sacred song." In the classrooms the Bible was the focal point of all subjects from sociology to literature. Graham was not yet so devoted to piety, and after several brushes with the school authorities over academic regulations, he was encouraged not to return for the spring semester.

His parents were unhappy, but they did not give up hope. A compromise was settled upon. Billy was to make one more try to get a religious education but his parents would allow him to make that try at the Temple Terrace Independent Bible School in Tampa, Florida (later known as the Florida Bible Institute and now as Trinity College). Here he would be near the spring training grounds for the major league baseball teams, and if God wanted him to be a ballplayer, some talent scout would discover him there. Meanwhile he must get some sort of godly education in case God had other plans for him. Graham accepted the compromise even though he was told that he would have to work his way through the school as any self-respecting young man would do.

This Bible school was similar to Bob Jones College in its outlook, but it was not so well organized. It was located in a second-class resort hotel and its seventy-five students worked their way through the school by serving as waiters, waitresses, dishwashers, bellhops, caddies, and errand boys for the hotel and its guests. Graham was a dishwasher and a caddy. The classes were scheduled so as not to conflict with the duties of the students. All the members of the small faculty had other jobs, principally as pastors of nearby churches. The courses consisted of Bible study and sermon writing based upon the usual literal approach and proof-text exegesis. Most of the students hoped to become preachers or missionaries and practice-preaching played a large part in their training. This was done not only in the classrooms but on street corners, in mission halls, in trailer camps, and in local churches—wherever people were willing to listen to earnest young men tell them in halting and repetitious words about what the Bible said. As long as the students stuck close to God's Word in their preaching their audiences were generally satisfied.

It was while at the Florida Bible Institute that Billy Graham finally made his decision to give up baseball and dedicate himself to preaching the gospel. The turning point seems to have come after he recognized that he had more talent for persuasion than for baseball. No baseball scout ever approached him, but the thoughtful help of the Dean of the Bible school taught him to find satisfaction and confidence in expounding the truths of the old-time religion. Careful coaching by the Dean and various practice exercises under the guidance of other students developed that talent he had displayed as a Fuller Brush salesman in the direction of preaching. His friend, Grady Wilson, had taken up preaching back home and he wrote to Graham of his pleasure and success at it. Experience in leading meetings at the nearby trailer court and at a downtown mission hall built up confidence. The incident which Graham remembers as confirming his choice of a career occurred when a girl whom he had been dating at the institute broke off their budding romance one evening with the frank statement that he was too unsettled in his ways and showed no signs of becoming the devout Christian worker whom she had set her heart upon marrying. Graham took the rebuke to heart. After he left the girl, he wandered disconsolately over the local golf course examining his hopes and his past. He made up his mind that the girl was right; he had to buckle down to some career. That night he knelt in prayer and promised to devote himself to "the Lord's work." And there was no doubt what that meant. Soon after he wrote home that he had decided to be a minister. The call had come .

Graham's talents as a preacher were put to the test in the summer of 1939 when Dean John R. Minder asked him to supply his church near Tampa (for six dollars a week) while he went on vacation. Graham succeeded so well that another church nearby asked him to conduct a series of revival meetings for them. When this revival was well under way it was discovered that Graham had never been baptized by immersion. The church was a Baptist church and Graham had to promise to be immersed at the completion of the meetings in order to keep the revival from breaking up in a quarrel. "The boy preacher," as they called him, converted eighty-one persons and when they went to the river to be baptized, he went with them. Shortly after this sign of God's approval of his ministry, Graham applied for, and received, ordination at the hands of the St. John's Baptist Association of northern Florida. The ordination ceremony took place in the Peniel Baptist Church in Palatka, Florida. He was examined by about a dozen local Baptist ministers. Their questions caused Graham some anxiety, but they accepted his revival converts as sufficient proof of his calling. Apparently it did not bother Graham to leave the Presbyterianism of his family. Like all revivalists he has always maintained that doctrine is less important than saving faith. To Graham, any man who believes in and preaches the fundamentals of the gospel is a minister of God regardless of his denominational affiliation.

Graham stayed at the Florida Bible Institute for another

year after his ordination and was awarded a graduation certificate in June, 1940. He now decided that he must get a broader education than the simple Bible study which the Bible institute provided. During the summer of 1940 he conducted revival meetings at small churches in York, Pennsylvania, and Toccoa, Georgia, and then in the fall entered Wheaton College to work for an A.B. degree. Wheaton was also a Bible-centered, fundamentalist college, but its traditions went back to the middle of the nineteenth century, and it had acquired a better reputation than most schools of its kind. Located twenty-five miles west of Chicago, Wheaton had as its president Dr. V. Raymond Edman, a leading figure in the fundamentalist movement. Its buildings and grounds were well endowed, and in its student body were the children of those who formed the upper brackets among the nation's fundamentalists.[6]

Graham was admitted as a sophomore on the basis of the work he had done in Florida. He chose to major in anthropology, but like all Wheaton students he had to take the required courses in Bible study. When Graham received his degree in June, 1943, he was thoroughly convinced that the Bible was the best book on anthropology ever written, that the creation of man as portrayed in Genesis was the only correct one, and that Charles Darwin's theory of evolution was false because it left God out.[7]

Two months after graduation Graham married Ruth McCue Bell who had been a fellow student at Wheaton. She was the daughter of Dr. L. Nelson Bell of Montreat, North Carolina, a Presbyterian medical missionary to China from 1916 to 1941. The United States was deep in World War II when Graham got married, and while he was exempt from military service by virtue of his ministerial status, he applied for a commission in the army chaplain corps. In order to qualify for a commission, he accepted a call as pastor of a small Baptist church in Western Spring, Illinois, near Chicago. The church had about ninety members, and so little money that it could not complete the new building it had commenced. Services were held in the basement of the unfinished church. Graham received a salary of forty-five dollars a week. (He never entered the chaplain corps.)

The dynamic young pastor at once began to expand the activities of his church. He encouraged it to donate more money to mission work; he organized a men's fellowship program, and he arranged for monthly dinners to be held at a local restaurant where as many as two hundred "business and professional men" gathered to hear spiritual talks by guest speakers like President Edman of Wheaton, evangelist Bob Jones, Jr., and the devout evangelical cartoonist of the *Chicago Daily News*, Vaughn Shoemaker. Six months after taking up this pastorate Graham persuaded his parishioners to underwrite a forty-five minute weekly religious broadcast emanating from a local Chicago station. It would cost $150 a week, Graham told them, but if it were a success it would receive enough contributions from listeners to more than pay its way. Not only might the church obtain enough money to complete its building but it would be helping to spread the good news of the gospel among the unregenerate millions in and around Chicago.

Graham got the idea for the broadcast from his friend, the Rev. Torrey M. Johnson, also an alumnus of Wheaton and pastor of the fundamentalist Midwest Bible Church in Chicago. Johnson had started the show but was moving on to more important work and asked Graham to take it over for him. The show was called "Songs in the Night" and featured the solos of George Beverly Shea, hymns by a girls' quartet called "The King's Karrolers," organ music, and short gospel talks of three or four minutes by Graham. It was moderately successful and while it did not produce enough money to complete the church, it never ran into debt.

Then in January, 1945, Graham received a new suggestion from Torrey Johnson and decided to give up his pastorate. Johnson asked him to become a full-time recruiting agent for a new fundamentalist organization called Youth for Christ. It was Graham's work for this movement which gave him the experience, the associates, the contacts, and the reputation upon which he later built his career as an evangelist.

Youth for Christ was not the inspiration of any one man, but Jack Wyrtzen of New York City is usually given credit for being the first to experiment with the idea. Wyrtzen, a former dance band leader and fire insurance salesman, had been converted to fundamentalist Christianity by a member of the Plymouth Brethren in the late 1930's. He began to conduct Saturday night youth rallies in New York in 1941 in connection with his radio program, "Word of Life." They proved so popular that on April 1, 1944, Wyrtzen hired Carnegie Hall and filled it with his hymn-singing, Bible-carrying young people. Meanwhile a young minister in Indianapolis, Roger Malsbary, had begun similar Saturday night rallies in May, 1943. These too proved highly popular. Soon alert young fundamentalist pastors all over the United States and Canada, like George Wilson in Minneapolis, Charles Templeton in Toronto, Edward T. Darling in Detroit, were starting Saturday night youth rallies. Torrey Johnson had started an organization called Chicagoland Youth for Christ in April, 1944, just about the time he turned over his radio program to Graham. By May, 1945, Johnson had such a large following that he was able to fill Soldier's Field in Chicago with thirty thousand teen-agers for a mammoth Youth for Christ rally. A committee made up of various leaders of these independent Christian youth organizations was organized late in 1944 and issued a call for a convention to be held in the summer of 1945 at the Winona Lake Bible Conference. Several hundred persons attended the convention which met in the Billy Sunday Memorial Tabernacle in Winona Lake (Mrs. Sunday was on hand, but her husband had died ten years earlier). The convention voted to merge the various city-wide organizations into an international organization. A constitution was drawn up, a seven-point creed was formulated on fundamentalist principles, and Johnson was elected the first president. By 1947 there were a thousand Youth for Christ organizations in a thousand different cities. The movement was an astounding success.

A variety of reasons was offered for its popularity. According to its proponents, the movement provided the much-needed answer to juvenile delinquency and communism among the young people of America. The dislocations of the war, mothers working in factories, elder brothers in the army, teen-age boys waiting to be drafted, country folk moving en masse into big cities to take jobs in war plants, a general atmosphere of excitement and "eat-drink-and-be-merry," it was said, prevailed among American youth. Christian leaders were worried. The churches and the traditional young-people's groups seemed unable to appeal to the younger generation. The YMCA was too riddled with liberalism to be an effective Christian counterforce. Teen-agers were roaming the city streets, getting into trouble, becoming undisciplined, taking to drinking, smoking, jazz, jitterbugging, and crime. Hard-working, pious parents, fresh from the country, were upset and felt helpless. Christian businessmen, lay leaders in the fundamentalist churches, decided that something must be done to attract these youngsters to the churches before they abandoned the Christian and American way of life for some pagan atheistic ideology. The Saturday night youth rallies started by young fundamentalist pastors seemed the ideal solution.

These young pastors, like Graham and his friends, were convinced that the old-fashioned young people's groups with their dreary, stereotyped procedure and their watered-down "modernist" theology were not appealing to the children of the 1940's. The Youth for Christ rallies were the modern substitute for the youth meetings of the Christian Endeavor and Epworth League societies. Their slogan was "Geared to the times but anchored to the Rock." The Rock was the infallible Bible, and the modern gearing consisted of slangy pep-talks, syncopated hymn singing, jazzy orchestral groups and singing stars (playing what were ostensibly hymns or patriotic songs), glamorous solo singers, and large doses of

patriotic flag-waving. Rally was the right word for these
meetings. They certainly were not prayer meetings. For
two or three hours every Saturday the fundamentalist young
people of the cities found a place where, with full parental
and church approval, they could go wild over religion,
music, and patriotism. And through it all the young pastors
and group leaders maintained a cheerful but sincere piety,
encouraging the young people to bring their Bibles, to feel
that God was with them, and that all their problems could
be solved by prayer. As Graham said of his work with the
movement, "We used every modern means to catch the ear
of the unconverted and then punched them straight between
the eyes with the gospel." [8] Some ministers in the liberal
Protestant churches fumed that the movement was trying to
undermine the faithfulness of their young people, but to the
supporters of Youth for Christ, the denominational young
people's groups were already dead and if contemporary
youngsters preferred the simple old gospel truths to the
vagaries of liberal Protestantism that merely showed their
good sense.

Some accused the Youth for Christ leaders at first of being
fascistic, authoritarian, manipulators of mass hysteria, who
mixed religion and patriotism for the purpose of attaining
political power. These critics considered the warm support
given the movement by the newspapers of William Randolph Hearst a proof of this. Others noted that there were
few Negro leaders active in the movement and picked up
phrases about the Jews as enemies of Jesus which seemed
to indicate racist tendencies in the group. But these critics
mistook a new kind of fundamentalism for the worst excesses
of the 1930's when Gerald P. Winrod and his Bible Defenders were ardent supporters of Hitlerism. There probably were some older men working in the Youth for Christ
organization who were admirers of Winrod. And there was
certainly a tendency among the Christian businessmen's
associations and Christian veterans groups which supported
Youth for Christ to equate liberal Protestantism with liberal
politics and to mix their dislike for communism with their

dislike for Franklin Roosevelt's New Deal. But the real impetus of the new movement did not come from this source.

Youth for Christ was simply one aspect of the larger reorientation in American social and intellectual and religious thought which began in the war years and slowly built up to the awakening of the 1950's. At one extreme this awakening was related to the rise of that political neo-conservatism which led to McCarthyism; at the other it was part of the theological reorientation urged by Reinhold Niebuhr and the neo-orthodox Protestants. Youth for Christ was a manifestation of the resurgent neofundamentalism which challenged a waning liberal Protestantism. The fundamentalists and holiness groups who have been labelled "the Third Force in Christendom" may have gone down to defeat in the 1920's but they had by no means given up the fight. As liberal Protestantism was undermined by the neo-orthodox movement and by the inadequacy of its optimistic message in the midst of the dire calamities of the years from 1930 to 1950, the neofundamentalists began to take the offensive. In a sermon which he delivered in 1952 Billy Graham accurately caught the mood underlying this new fundamentalist crusade: "A great change is taking place in this country," he said. "Torrey Johnson said to me not long ago that in the city of Chicago there is very little real, old-fashioned, dyed-in-the-wool 'Modernism' left. I have found that absolutely true as I've travelled around. There's a reason that the Modernist is almost in a complete retreat. All his ideals and his intellectual props have been knocked out from under him, and he is standing almost in a vacuum now. He's moving toward neo-orthodoxy, but we're praying that he will go beyond neo-orthodoxy to the true orthodox position. . . . It is time for action. We must quit being on the defensive in Evangelical circles, and we must carry the offensive. We have defended ourselves long enough. Great books on Apologetics have been written, and today our position is being accepted more and more by the Church at large. I think now is the hour to take the flag and attack the enemy and move into the camps of the devil. . . . This

is the time for offensive action on the part of Evangelicals
and on the part of the whole Church. It's time for an offensive in Revival." [9]

Youth for Christ was one of the aggressive spearheads of
this religious conflict. And Billy Graham was one of its
young colonels. Late in 1944 he had caught the spirit of
the movement from Torrey Johnson and had taken time
from his parish and radio work to assist the development of
the Chicagoland Youth for Christ. In January, 1945, he decided that the excitement and challenge of evangelism offered by Youth for Christ was closer to his heart than the
difficulties of building up a small village church. As a leader
of Youth for Christ he would be converting young people
all over the nation to Biblical fundamentalism and helping
to turn the tide against the theological liberals who had for
years been sapping the force of Christianity. Graham began
to lift his horizons and to formulate a national and international outlook in terms of his fundamentalist ideology
which, to his great surprise, later turned out to be an outlook which countless Americans found appealing in the years
of postwar anxiety.

In the summer of 1945 Graham took part in the Youth
for Christ convention at Winona Lake and in September of
that year he became the first "official field representative"
of the international body. It was his task to go from city
to city at the request of young pastors who were starting
or wanted to start Youth for Christ organizations. As a
dynamic, handsome, young preacher with an obvious gift
for oratory and a burning conviction of his call to preach
evangelical Christianity, he was looked upon by the supporters of the movement as a natural leader—a man whom
young people would admire and emulate, and a man who
could be trusted to put the fundamentalist cause before all
of his personal desires.

In 1945 alone, Graham spoke in almost every state in the
union at Youth for Christ rallies and ran up the impressive
total of seven thousand conversions. Like the modern evangelist that he was, he traveled everywhere by airplane and

logged a total of 200,000 miles in one year. One of his trips took him to his home state of North Carolina where, at a Youth for Christ rally, he met a dedicated young trombonist and choir leader named Cliff Barrows. Barrows, a graduate of Bob Jones College, proved so adept at inspiring the youngsters of Asheville to sing and enjoy themselves that Graham persuaded him to become his partner in the work. Barrows' wife, also a graduate of Bob Jones College, went along with her husband to play the piano. And later George Beverly Shea joined Graham as soloist. Graham was starting to build his "team" just as Billy Sunday, fifty years before, had started his career by building up a team of experts (he called it the Sunday Party) to assist him in the complex task of mass evangelism.

Youth for Christ International decided to expand beyond the United States and Canada in the spring of 1946 and Graham was dispatched to Great Britain and thence to various countries in Europe. Other members of the movement went to Korea, Japan, Australia, Africa. In all these places fundamentalist ministers and missionaries, many of them trained in the same Bible schools as the Youth for Christ leaders, eagerly welcomed their aid in galvanizing the religious life of their communities. And, as in the United States, liberal ministers were hostile or aloof. Between 1946 and 1949 Graham made six trips to Europe either to organize new Youth for Christ groups or to attend national and international Youth for Christ conventions. He traveled over 750,000 miles on these missions and established friendly contacts among fundamentalist leaders everywhere. They were impressed by his charm, his enthusiasm, and his success as an evangelist to youth.

By 1947 Graham was so well thought of within fundamentalist circles that the Rev. William Bell Riley, the old war horse of the first fundamentalist crusade against modernism in the 1920's, selected Graham as his successor. Riley was the pastor of the First Baptist Church of Minneapolis, Minnesota, and in 1919 he had founded the World Christian Fundamentals Association which was designed to unite

fundamentalists of every denomination to fight off the in-
roads of liberalism. In the 1930's Riley had become extremely reactionary in his political and social outlook and,
like his friends Gerald B. Winrod and Gerald L. K. Smith,
he indulged in anti-Semitic and anti-Catholic bigotry. But
Riley's main interest in 1947 was in the Northwestern
Schools which he had started in Minneapolis in the 1920's.
The schools consisted of a Bible school, a theological seminary, and a liberal arts college. Riley had obtained sufficient money to erect or purchase half a dozen buildings for
these schools and was engaged in an ambitious new building
program for them. Graham, he believed, could help to raise
the money for this.

In the summer of 1947, shortly before his death, Riley
called Graham to Minneapolis and begged him to take over
the presidency of the college. Graham recognized the honor
that Riley was conferring on him but did not want to give
up evangelism. A compromise was worked out whereby
Graham eventually accepted the presidency but left the
running of the college to a group of his trusted friends. He
raised money for the new buildings, but he did not appear
in Minneapolis more than two months out of the year.
When Riley died in December, 1947, Graham appointed
T. W. Wilson (brother of Grady Wilson) assistant president of the schools; he retained George Wilson (one of the
originators of Youth for Christ International) as the business
manager, and appointed Jerry Beavan, a professor of psychology and Hebrew and editor of one of Riley's magazines,
as the registrar. Graham left almost the entire management
of the schools to these men and continued to devote his own
efforts to evangelism.

In 1947 Graham also became the first vice-president of
Youth for Christ. But the movement was now so well organized and well directed that calls for his assistance were
less frequent. Each Youth for Christ unit was locally controlled and virtually autonomous. Once a unit was set up
in a city the local fundamentalists ran it themselves. Graham was welcomed as a speaker whenever they could get

him, but he was not vital to the movement's growth. Although he helped create new units during the next two years, he now found time to branch out in revivalism of a more general sort. He had the nucleus of a revival team, and he found that many ministers who had attended his Youth for Christ rallies wanted him to conduct revival meetings for their churches. These would not be just to reach young people, but, as in the revivalism of Finney, Moody, and Sunday, they would be attempts to arouse the religious fervor of the churches and community as a whole.

At first Graham tried to kill two birds with one stone. He would accept invitations to conduct revival meetings and, at the same time, help local pastors organize or strengthen a Youth for Christ unit. But soon he began to accept invitations which clearly had nothing to do with Youth for Christ and to engage in precisely that type of itinerant mass evan- X gelistic campaign that so many churchmen and sociologists had said was dead and gone by 1945.

Between 1947 and 1949 Graham conducted revivals of two to three weeks duration in Grand Rapids, Michigan; Charlotte, North Carolina; Des Moines, Iowa; Augusta, Georgia; Modesto, California; Miami, Florida; Baltimore, Maryland; Altoona, Pennsylvania; and Los Angeles, California. In the smaller of these places he was usually able to obtain the support of the local ministerial associations which were predominantly fundamentalist. But this was not true in Grand Rapids, Baltimore, and Los Angeles. Here he was invited by the fundamentalist pastors and assisted by the local Youth for Christ unit, the local Christian businessmen's group, and the Christian veterans group. Usually he rented a hall or theater or set up a tent capable of holding two or three thousand. There was little advance preparation besides the announcement in the local pulpits, a few posters, and the rounding up of volunteers to serve as choir, ushers, and personal workers. Graham would speak nightly at seven-thirty following a half-hour "singspirational service" conducted by Cliff Barrows. After his sermon, Graham, like other evangelists, would ask for those who wished to make a profession of their faith to come forward to the front benches or into an inquiry room to sign a decision card. The number of card signers at these revivals ranged from about five hundred for two weeks in Grand Rapids in 1947 to fourteen hundred for sixteen days in Augusta in 1948.

The local pastors who cooperated in Graham's meetings were pleased by his results, but there was little in his meetings to distinguish them from those of twenty or thirty other professional evangelists who, since the end of World War II, had been profiting by the renewed interest in mass revivalism. Among the more successful of this new crop of evangelists, all of whom were friends of Graham and many of whom were associated with Youth for Christ, were Jack Shuler, Chuck Templeton, and Bob Jones, Jr. There was even a new wave of British evangelists who, like Gypsy Smith and George Campbell Morgan of pre-World War I days, regularly toured the United States. Among these were Alan Redpath, Tom Rees, and Bryan Green. The proliferating fundamentalist magazines carried frequent articles about these men and their work, but on the whole the secular press and the general public were as yet unaware of this renascence of the revival tradition.

Then, suddenly, in the fall of 1949, revivalism became front-page news. And Billy Graham became famous.

CHAPTER 3

Billy Graham Becomes Front-Page News

I don't believe there is a more wicked town in all the world than Los Angeles. One of these days the wrath of God is going to be poured out. Some of these people that laugh at prayer and revival meetings will change their minds. Brother, this old tent won't hold the people trying to get in.
BILLY GRAHAM [1]

The executive committee of the "Christ for Greater Los Angeles" committee invited Billy Graham to conduct a three-week revival in their city in the fall of 1949. They were not expecting anything spectacular. The committee consisted primarily of a small group of Christian businessmen headed by Clifford Smith, president of a sportswear manufacturing firm called Hollywood Togs, Inc. Smith and a few of his friends, together with the local fundamentalist pastors, had sponsored an annual tent revival in Los Angeles for many years. But Los Angeles was so full of religious meetings of all kinds that an annual revival of this sort was nothing extraordinary. Less than two hundred of the one thousand Protestant churches in the city agreed to

lend their support to it. However, the local Youth for Christ
unit cooperated and numerous prayer groups were organized
in advance to pray for the success of the meetings. A tent
capable of holding six thousand was erected in a vacant lot,
and loud-speaking equipment was installed (Graham used a
lapel microphone for the first time in this crusade).

Two weeks before the meetings began, Billy Graham's
high school friend, Grady Wilson, who had recently joined
the Graham "team" as associate evangelist, arrived in Los
Angeles. He made certain that the choir, ushers, personal
workers were gathered and trained, and he checked the
various possibilities for obtaining publicity. Among other
organizations, Wilson talked with the Stars Christian Fellowship Group, an organization made up of minor movie,
radio, and television personalities who met regularly for
prayer, Bible-reading, and Christian missionary work. Most
of these stars promised to support the meetings.

Graham came to Los Angeles a week before the revival
was to open, for a conference with the Christ for Greater Los
Angeles committee. He talked also with Stuart Hamblen, a
former rodeo champion from Texas who now conducted a
popular weekly radio program in Los Angeles called "Stuart Hamblen and His Lucky Stars" over the local Warner
Brothers station. Hamblen, the son of a Methodist minister, promised to give Graham's meetings a boost by men-
tioning them on his show. The mayor of Los Angeles agreed
to say a word of welcome in support of the meetings. Posters and billboards were put up at strategic spots, and the
revival tent was decorated with a sign sixty feet long and
four feet high containing a picture of Graham and the
words "Greater Los Angeles Revival, Billy Graham, 6000
free seats, Dynamic Preaching, Glorious Music, every night,
7:30, Sundays 3 and 8:45."

The opening meeting took place on Sunday, September
25. Cliff Barrows directed the choir, played his trombone,
and led the audience in singing, "Send a Great Revival in
My Soul." Bev Shea sang a solo. The chairman of the revival committee welcomed the crowd, praised Graham, and

asked for contributions to meet the expenses. The collection plate was passed. Grady Wilson read from Scripture. Then Graham stepped forward, told the audience to bow their heads in prayer, and after the Amen, launched into his sermon entitled "We Need Revival." The main burden of his message was an attack upon the materialism, immorality, and paganism of contemporary America and a plea for a return to the old-time religion based on the authority of God's word.

"I believe the only reason that America escaped the ravages and destruction of war was because God's people prayed," he began. "Many of these people believe that God can still use America to evangelize the world. I think we are living at a time in world history when God is giving us a desperate choice, a choice of either revival or judgment." To drive this point home Graham reminded his audience that only a few days before, President Truman had announced that "Russia has now exploded an atomic bomb." Graham warned, "Do you know the area that is marked out for the enemy's first atomic bomb? New York! Secondly, Chicago; and thirdly, the city of Los Angeles!" If the enemy chose to do this, Graham indicated, God would not stop him. "This city of wickedness and sin, this city that is known around the world because of its sin, crime, and immorality" deserved destruction as much as Babylon, Sodom, or Gomorrah. In fact, the whole of America was becoming as wicked as the world of Noah's day.

"There was a time a few years ago, which most of you with gray hair can remember, when this country claimed the Ten Commandments as the basis for our moral code. That is no longer true . . . the American way of life is being destroyed at the very heart and core of society." Graham listed some of the prevailing sins of the day: divorce, crime, gambling, "the problem of sex," "false prophets and cults," and the fact that according to a recent Gallup poll only "27 per cent of the people of Los Angeles identify themselves with a church." One other important reason why "God Almighty is going to bring judgment upon this city unless people repent and believe" was communism. "Do you know that the Fifth Columnists, called Communists, are more rampant in Los Angeles than any other city in America? We need a revival." The time was short; the need was desperate. "In this moment I can see the judgment hand of God over Los Angeles. I can see judgment about to fall."

But Graham offered a way out. "If we repent, if we believe, if we turn to Christ in faith and hope, the judgment of God can be stopped. From the depths of my heart I believe that this message is God's word today." [2] Many in the audience were visibly shaken by the end of Graham's sermon, but the local newspapers gave the revival only six inches of space on the back pages the next day and almost ignored it thereafter.

For three weeks Graham preached nightly and the committee filled the papers with advertisements announcing "Billy Graham" in the "Big Tent"; "Visit the Canvas Cathedral with the Steeple of Light" (a Hollywood searchlight), "Dynamic Preaching, Heavenly Music," "Great Chorus Choir," "All Star Supporting Party," "1000 Cooperating Churches," "Tidal Wave Interest." These ads were supplemented by "spot" announcements over the local radio stations. The attendance reached a total of 100,000 by the end of the third week (an average of 4000 nightly) with almost 1500 conversions reported. The executive committee decided to extend the meetings for another week. "Held Over Until October 23rd" read the advertisements in the newspapers: "Fourth Great Week by Popular Demand," "Los Angeles Greatest Revival Since Billy Sunday."

It was during this fourth week that two important events occurred which first put the revival in the news. The first was that William Randolph Hearst sent a telegram to the editors of his newspapers saying, "Puff Graham." [3] This brought a swarm of reporters, photographers, and feature writers to the tent and resulted in front-page stories in this influential chain of newspapers. The second event was Stuart Hamblen's announcement over his radio program that he had been converted by Graham and was going to sell his string of race horses (all but one, which he kept for sentimental reasons). Graham later stated that he had prayed and worked hard for Hamblen's conversion: "If I could have picked two men in Los Angeles whom I would have liked to see converted in the campaign there, one of them would have been Stuart Hamblen." As one of Graham's associates explained, Graham "realized in even the short while he was in Los Angeles that Hamblen was a key man in the area with tremendous influence." [4]

Hamblen was a member of the Stars Christian Fellowship Group and both he and his wife were noted for their piety and good works. But he had never made a clear-cut "decision for Christ" and it was the influence of Graham and the prayers of Hamblen's friends which finally led him to make this decision during the revival. His public profession of faith on the platform of Graham's tent and his later presentation of his parents to the Graham congregation so that the crowd could hear them testify to their gratefulness for this change in his life, was reported in great detail in the Hearst press.

The committee then extended the campaign for a fifth week. During this week another celebrity, Louis Zamperini, professed his conversion in the tent. Zamperini had been an Olympic track star in 1936 and a hero during World War II when he was captured by the Japanese. Following the war he had lost his grip and taken to drink. His wife attended Graham's meetings and was converted. She persuaded Zamperini to attend and several nights later he too professed conversion and promised to give up drinking. This produced more headlines and a decision to extend the campaign another week. "Held Over by Popular Demand," the ads announced: "Sixth Great Sin-Smashing Week."

Now the Associated Press picked up the story and sent news articles across the nation to its numerous affiliates. On November 14, *Time* magazine devoted ten inches to Graham, comparing him to Billy Sunday. *Time* described him as "blond, trumpet-lunged" and quoted him as saying, "I want to do away with everything that is criticized in mass evangelism. We believe it is a spiritual service. We don't believe it is a concert or a show."

The day after the *Time* article appeared, a third headline incident occurred in Los Angeles. J. Arthur Vaus, an associate of the prominent Los Angeles gambler, Mickey Cohen, was converted in Graham's tent. A few years previously Vaus had been a student for the ministry, but he gave it up and turned to wire tapping. After his conversion he went to the Los Angeles police and confessed to having committed perjury in a recent grand jury hearing regarding police protection of vice. Additional headlines occurred when it was learned that Graham had tried to see and convert Mickey Cohen himself. The revival was extended for a seventh and then an eighth week. The students at Northwestern Schools in Minneapolis suspended classes for an all-day prayer meeting to aid their president. The United Press and International News Service gave nationwide coverage to the campaign. *Life, Newsweek,* and *Quick* ran feature stories.

Graham continued to hammer away at the need for revival and the sins of America. "I am persuaded that time is desperately short. . . . I am also convinced that the only hope of preserving our way of life, the only hope of preserving our present culture, is an old-fashioned, heaven-sent revival." In every sermon he stressed the same notes of fear and anxiety. "Tonight this old world is in fear. Tonight this old city is in fear—the whole Nation is fearful. . . . In Europe everyone knows that war is coming—war is inevitable. . . . They know the atomic bombs are going to start dropping. . . ." Far more than Moody or Sunday, Graham assumed the role of a prophet of doom. But he also held out hope and security: "Brother, I tell you, you want to start praying." "You know they can call me a fool if they want to; they can laugh, sneer, and mock all they want to, but I'm glad I'm on the road to heaven." "What can you do? Right now you can turn to Jesus. Let Christ come into your heart and cleanse you from sin and he can give you the assurance that if you died tonight, you would go to heaven." After each sermon scores of people came forward to find the assurance Graham had described.

When the campaign ended on November 20, Graham was a celebrity. The total attendance in "the Canvas Cathedral" was 350,000 (including those who attended more than once). There were 2703 "decisions for Christ" and 1475 "reconsecrations" by persons already converted. By the end of the campaign Clifford Smith reported that 450 of the city's Protestant churches were expressing support for Graham.[5] A freewill offering taken up to remunerate Graham came to $12,000. He gave the money to the local committee to be used for evangelistic work.

Graham had said in Los Angeles that America was "on the verge of a great national revival." The newspaper and magazine reports reiterated the idea. But it was seldom pointed out that Graham's church support in Los Angeles and elsewhere came almost entirely from denominations which belonged to the National Association of Evangelical Churches. He did not at this time seek the support of the churches of the major denominations which belonged to the Federal Council of Churches (later the National Council of Churches). The difference between the National Association and the Federal Council was crucial.

The National Association of Evangelicals (NAE) was a federation of holiness, pentecostal, and other fundamentalist or "independent" groups. It had been created in 1942 for the combined purpose of uniting the fundamentalists and of competing with the Federal Council of Churches (FCC). The FCC, which had been organized in 1908, was from the outset dominated by modernists. Billy Sunday had done his best to oppose it. So had William Bell Riley and the whole host of early fundamentalists. But by 1942 almost all the important denominations in the country were affiliated with it. Officially it represented about 30 million of the nation's 52 million Protestants.

But in 1942 certain fundamentalist leaders, including Harold J. Ockenga, J. Elwin Wright, and Carl F. H. Henry, were convinced that the time was ripe to organize the ten million or more fundamentalists who were not affiliated with the FCC. They also hoped to win away from the FCC some ten to fifteen million members, perhaps whole denominations, who were dissatisfied with modernism but who had not officially broken with the FCC. As J. Elwin Wright stated in 1946, the NAE was founded on "the conviction that the time had come when groups which could not conscientiously accept the leadership of existing interdenominational agencies must find some means of cooperation and expression." [6]   Wright pointed out that out of 260 Protestant denominations in the United States only about twenty-five were members of the FCC. Within ten years after its founding the NAE spoke for a constituency of over ten million fundamentalists; over fifty denominations were affiliated with it.

That this movement, like Youth for Christ, was part of the resurgence of fundamentalism was abundantly evident. The official magazine of the NAE, *United Evangelical Action,* stated editorially in 1955, "We are proud to walk in the steps of that grand company of so-called 'fundamentalists' who two generations ago blazed a trail for loyalty to Christ and the Bible in a forest of doubt and unbelief." [7]   The members of the NAE therefore were the logical supporters of Youth for Christ and of Billy Graham in the postwar years. The important question for the future of American Protestantism was whether Graham and the NAE would declare open war on the liberals and seek to split their churches, or whether they would seek to reform them from within. Since revivalism would obviously be a key factor in the struggle, Graham's position was of great importance. He could lead a religious crusade of righteous indignation and rebuke against the liberals, denouncing the FCC for encouraging heresy. Or he could seek the cooperation of the moderates within the FCC and gradually try to win them back to the old-time religion by proving that God honored fundamentalist preaching by the conversion of souls in revival meetings. Like all professional revivalists Graham's first concern was to win souls, and since mass revivalism thrived better on cooperation than on dissension he chose the latter method. But in his attempt to keep faith with the fundamentalism of his friends in the NAE while at the same trying to ingratiate himself and his revivalism with the liberals, he found his path fraught with difficulty.

Following his campaign in Los Angeles, Graham began to receive invitations from ministerial groups all over the country to conduct meetings in their cities. He accepted first a request from his friend, Harold J. Ockenga, pastor of the Park Street Church in Boston; Ockenga had formerly been president of Fuller Theological Seminary and he was the first president of the NAE. Graham was to speak for nine days at Park Street Church which, over the years, had earned the nickname of "brimstone corner" for the fiery fundamentalism which had been the basis of its popularity. The Boston newspapers gave Graham front page coverage as the Protestants in that predominantly Roman Catholic city turned out in great numbers to hear him. The crusade soon had to move into Mechanics Hall, then to the opera house, and finally to Boston Garden, an arena which held sixteen thousand persons. It was reported that fifteen hundred persons signed decision cards at Graham's one-night stand in the Garden. The revival was extended from nine days to eighteen days. And when Graham left Boston the seventy-five cooperating churches made him promise to return later that spring for a continuation of the movement. The leading layman of the campaign, Allen Emery, Jr., was the son of the man who had been chairman of the committee which invited Billy Sunday to Boston thirty-four years before.

There were no startling conversions among celebrities or criminals reported in Boston, but the statistics were considered news in themselves: 3000 conversions, 105,000 attendance in eighteen days. The newspapers reported with surprise that "Among those many hundreds there was no seeming hysteria." The reporters had forgotten that there had been no hysteria in urban mass evangelism since the days of George Whitefield. Even Billy Sunday had insisted, "What

I want and preach is the fact that a man can be converted without any fuss." If revivalism was to stage a comeback in the 1950's, it would have to be at least as respectable as Sunday's, and Graham kept this fact constantly in mind. One sympathetic eyewitness noted in Boston, "There was little applause at the end of a solo or choir number, for Cliff Barrows requested that if you approve, say 'Amen' in your own heart." [8]

From Boston, Graham and his team went to Columbia, South Carolina. Here his crusade system began to acquire the characteristics which were to typify all his later campaigns: the rounding up of mass support from the evangelical churches; the formation of hundreds of cottage prayer meetings; the long careful preparation in advance; the saturation advertising; the carefully timed publicity releases; the daily radio broadcasts; the seating of important celebrities and prominent political figures on the platform; the special services for children, high school students, college students; the subsidiary meetings in offices, shops, stores, and banks; the piling up of endless statistics; the climactic meeting in a large outdoor stadium; and the expert direction of crowds of Bible-carrying church people and their revival-hungry pastors who, under Barrows' bouncy direction, sang, "To God be the glory great things he has done," and who echoed Graham's constant reminder, "It is God's doing and it is marvelous in our eyes."

Columbia had a population of 100,000 in 1950. The vast majority of its citizens were regular churchgoers and church members, and its churches were overwhelmingly sympathetic to fundamentalism (though their fundamentalism had grown soft and fuzzy since the Scopes trial in 1925). Graham could hardly accuse Columbia, as he had accused Los Angeles, of being "the wickedest city in the world." But he did say during the campaign, "I thought what God has done in the great cities of Los Angeles and Boston will never happen in the small city of Columbia."

The decision to invite Graham to the city had originated with the Layman's Evangelistic Club. These laymen then obtained support from forty-two of the city's white pastors. The Negroes were not included in the campaign except those who sat in the segregated Jim Crow sections.[9] The revival started on February 19 in the 3800-seat Township Auditorium. It ended on Sunday, March 12, with a mammoth rally at the University of South Carolina football stadium. One hundred thousand attended the auditorium meetings and 5050 decisions were recorded. Forty thousand more were at the stadium rally where two thousand raised their hands when Graham asked for those who wished to signalize their acceptance of Christ. Four thousand high school students attended a Saturday afternoon rally and signed 944 decision cards. Forty-five hundred children attended a Saturday morning children's meeting and five hundred of these were counseled about salvation. Nine hundred students from the University of South Carolina attended a service by Graham at their chapel; fifty of them went forward to make decisions for Christ. It was not considered important that 79 per cent of those making decisions were already church members who came forward "because they lacked assurance that their sins were forgiven." Church membership was no sign of salvation. Only a conversion experience such as those which took place in Graham's meetings was considered a "clear-cut decision."

Statistics alone did not constitute the main element of publicity. There was the newsworthy conversion of Kirby Higbe, a native of Columbia, who was a star pitcher for the major league New York Giants. He had a reputation for being a temperamental and unmanageable ballplayer, but on the second night of the crusade he came forward and made a decision for Christ which, he said, changed his whole outlook. When he reported for spring training later that week newspaper accounts told of his reading the Bible regularly and trying to convert his teammates. Then there were the invitations to Graham to address joint sessions of the Georgia state legislature and of the South Carolina state legislature. These attracted considerable attention. Graham told the Georgia legislature, "Unless God sends a great awakening to the world, my two little girls will never see high school." Noteworthy also was the frequent attendance on Graham's platform of the governor of South Carolina, J. Strom Thurmond, and his wife. "I think the hope of the world today is for more people to turn to Christ," said the governor. "Billy Graham is a great evangelist and is conducting a wonderful meeting in Columbia. We are proud that he is winning so many souls to the Lord." United States Senator Olin Johnston also attended the meetings and praised Graham's work. At the climactic rally in the football stadium the feature personality was the Supreme Court Justice James M. Byrnes, who had been a former United States Secretary of State and who was the most prominent citizen of South Carolina. "I've been with statesmen, presidents, and kings," said Byrnes to the revival throng, "but this is the most inspiring moment of my life."

The revival was so impressive that Henry Luce, the publisher of *Time*, *Life*, and *Fortune*, made a trip to Columbia to meet Graham and, according to one of Graham's coworkers, was so impressed that "He pledged the cooperation of his magazines to support all the subsequent Graham campaigns in other cities." [10] Reporters and photographers from the Luce publications were much in evidence at the crusade. The report published in *Time* afterward, however, was not as complimentary as it might have been. It noted that Billy Sunday had obtained 25,000 converts in Columbia 27 years earlier as compared with Graham's 6000. And while the article called Graham "Evangelist Sunday's likeliest successor" it also said, "passionately wrestling with the microphone, he gave his audiences not a moment's emotional letup. But to old-timers who remembered another generation of revivalists—Sam Jones, Gypsy Smith, Sunday himself —Graham and his enthusiasm looked disturbingly like something out of Hollywood. His sharply-cut double-breasted suits and high-decibel ties. . . were a smooth contrast to the rumpled homespun approach of the old school."

Graham did not differ as much from the old-time revivalists as the *Time* reporter thought. And Billy Sunday, who prided himself upon his well-tailored, sharply creased suits and natty white spats, would have been hurt to think that anyone remembered him as "rumpled." Furthermore, Graham was as much addicted to the "homespun approach" as Sunday. In fact, in many instances he borrowed some of Sunday's own sermon material for this purpose. For example, he used Sunday's rejoinder to the criticism that revivals don't last: "Neither does a bath, but it does you good." And he used Sunday's joke about the farmer who said that before he got converted he wanted to know whether he could chew tobacco in heaven: "Sure," said Sunday and Graham, "but you'll have to go to hell to spit."

It was true that Graham had made some advances in the techniques of revivalism. Sunday had never used a loud-speaker system or a lapel microphone; these had not yet been invented. He had never utilized the radio; it arrived after his prime was passed. Sunday had never conducted his meetings in football stadiums or baseball parks, but he had used almost every other feature which Graham adopted. He had used children's meetings, high school students' meetings, and businessmen's luncheons. He had organized cottage prayer meetings. He had been invited to speak in high schools, hospitals, penitentiaries, college chapels, and state legislatures. He had adorned his platform with celebrities and politicians. He had received a freewill offering for his services by taking up collections at the meetings on the last day and by publicizing, through the local committee, as Graham did in Columbia, that contributions to this offering could be mailed or handed to the campaign's treasurer.

Above all, Graham had profited by the "delegation system" which Sunday had developed to perfection. This was a means of ensuring a full house for every night of a campaign by reserving large blocks of seats in advance for groups who either voluntarily wrote or telephoned for them or who were invited to come by some member of the crusade staff. In order to make the most of this system, Graham had added to his team in 1949 Willis G. Haymaker, whom he called his "Crusade Director." Haymaker had had long experience in revivals and not only had served on Billy Sunday's team of experts but also had acted as crusade director for Gypsy Smith and Bob Jones, Sr. With Haymaker's help Graham adopted the delegation system as part of his revival procedure. Haymaker was able to round up so many groups who wanted reserved seats for the Columbia meetings that at one point in the crusade he temporarily had to halt the system because the ordinary citizens of Columbia complained that they were being crowded out of the auditorium. Few, if any, seats were left for the general public after the delegations of church members, business leaders, lodge groups, veterans' organizations, women's auxiliaries, and office clerks had taken their places.*

In one respect, however, Graham was not as modern as Sunday, nor, at this time, so influential. Sunday had always insisted that the local committees build for him a special wooden tabernacle in which to conduct his meetings (Sunday had a special assistant called a tabernacle architect on his team who supervised the construction of these buildings in each city he visited). Such tabernacles were not only acoustically better than the average auditorium but they were larger. Sunday's New York tabernacle, for example, seated 20,000 persons. Moreover, tabernacles added greatly to the news value of a campaign as the special structure was, like a circus tent, a focus of attention whose sole purpose was to promote that particular revival. Early in the Columbia crusade Graham and Haymaker realized that they could more than fill the 3800 seats of the town's municipal auditorium. They approached the local committee and suggested that a wooden tabernacle similar to the one Sunday had erected in Columbia in 1923 be constructed for Graham. In return for this special action Graham stated that he would

---

* In 1954 Graham adopted a new policy in regard to delegations which he called "Operation Andrew." According to this plan, any church group which received a block of tickets for reserved seats was supposed to see to it that half of the tickets were given to non-church members. But there was no attempt to enforce this provision, and there is ample evidence that it did not serve its purpose of making fifty percent of each church delegation consist of persons outside the church.

agree to extend his crusade beyond the scheduled three
weeks. This would have been essential, for a tabernacle
would cost $50,000 to build, and the nightly collections to
defray this expenditure would take a while to accumulate
(even in Sunday's day when a dollar bought a lot more
lumber tabernacles had cost as much as $60,000). The
ministers of Columbia considered the proposal, but balked
at the expense. Some of them also expressed fear that an
extended revival might have too disorganizing an effect upon
the religious life of the community. Graham could point
out that Sunday had often stayed ten weeks in a city and
that Moody had stayed three to six months in some places.
But the old fears of mass evangelism still lingered, and
Graham did not yet have the prestige to enforce his plans.
The committee turned down the suggestion, and as a substitute Graham made arrangements for a two-week tour of one-
night stands in the various cities of South Carolina (it was
the delegations from these neighboring cities which had
squeezed out the local citizens of Columbia).

Graham's tour lasted from March 12 to March 23, and
then he returned to New England for a similar twenty-eight
day tour of the largest cities in that region. By the time this
New England crusade was over in May, 1950, Graham was
well enough established to make his own terms with local
committees. Like Moody and Sunday, Graham informed all
those who wished to engage his services for a revival that
they would have to show that they had the overwhelming
support of the evangelical churches in their cities, and he
made it clear that his staff and not the local committee
would make the plans, employ the techniques, and organize
the whole program from start to finish in the manner which
they thought most effective. As Graham saw it, those engaged in revivalism as a profession knew from experience
all the details and difficulties involved in a crusade and were
the most efficient and skillful in managing them. Local committees were needed to provide the workers, the money,
and the audiences, but the team would direct the campaign.
Neither Graham nor Haymaker ever put it quite so bluntly

as this. They maintained that the team merely provided the suggestions and the guidance and that all ultimate decisions would be taken in prayerful consultation between the local committee and the team members. But there was no doubt that when a city invited Graham they in fact put themselves into his hands and did what he thought best. On the whole it seemed a fair bargain. Graham's campaigns were self-supporting, and all the converts were directed into the churches. It was only sensible that if the churches hired an efficiency expert they should follow his instructions.

If the Los Angeles campaign first got Graham into the national front page, the Portland, Oregon, crusade in July and August, 1950, was the point at which Graham first took the initiative to maintain his nationwide audience. Prior to the Portland crusade Graham's revivalism was not much different from that of the many other professional evangelists who had sprung up to meet the new interest in mass revivalism. But three things happened in Portland that transformed Graham's team from a small-scale traveling revival company to a national big business. The most important of these was his decision to start a nationwide weekly radio broadcast. The second was the formation of the Billy Graham Evangelistic Association, Inc. The third was his venture into the motion picture business. By the end of 1950 Graham was not simply a small part of the neo-fundamentalist resurgence; he was its titular leader, its standard bearer, and its most prominent spokesman. From this time on he became the popular symbol of America's fourth great awakening.

The Portland crusade was instigated by Frank C. Phillips, the local Youth for Christ director, shortly after Graham's success in Los Angeles. Phillips gathered lay and clerical support and went to Graham with the invitation. Graham agreed to come for a six-week crusade in July and August of 1950, but because there was no building large enough for him, he suggested erecting a special tabernacle. The local committee agreed and raised the money to construct it. The tabernacle was modeled exactly upon those used by Billy Sunday. It was built entirely of wood, 300 by 180 feet, and contained a platform 80 feet long (sufficient to hold two pianos, an organ, and seats for the local committee and various dignitaries); a rising tier of seats behind the platform provided for the choir of four hundred; the main body of the tabernacle had 12,000 seats, four aisles covered with sawdust to deaden the sound, a "lounge room" for the evangelist, meeting rooms for the team, prayer rooms, ushers room, offices, a lost-and-found room, and rest rooms. Two rooms were included which Sunday did not have in his tabernacles: a control room to house the electronic equipment for spotlights and thirty loudspeakers, and a press room with typewriters and telephones for the reporters. A tent was erected behind the tabernacle for counseling the inquirers (Moody had called it an "inquiry room"; Sunday had omitted this part of the procedure). The Portland tabernacle was built by volunteer labor in order to save expenses; Sunday had tried this once but the labor unions made him change his mind.

As in Columbia, a great deal of advance preparation took place, but for some reason Haymaker did not participate in this particular crusade. Instead the preparations in Portland were directed by Jerry Beavan, who left his work as Registrar of the Northwestern Schools at this time in order to accept the position of Executive Secretary and Director of Public Relations for Graham. Beavan arrived in Portland well in advance of the meetings to help in the preparation. With the growing importance of public relations in the Graham organization Jerry Beavan's role on the team soon was more important than that of Haymaker, and Beavan quickly became Graham's right-hand man.

It was probably Beavan's idea, as much as anyone's, to have the Portland revival filmed in sound and color not only as a permanent record but to show other cities how a crusade worked. It could also be used to build up enthusiasm for Graham's work by showing it to groups of ministers and laymen around the nation. The man chosen to do the filming was Richard Ross, the president of a recently organized Hollywood company called Great Commission Films which specialized in short religious features. The film was at first called "The Portland Story" but later the title was changed to "Mid-Century Crusade." The expense of making the picture was considered part of the expense of the crusade to be paid out of the collections taken at the meetings. This film proved so successful and so useful that Graham went on to form his own motion picture company a year later (Billy Graham Evangelistic Films, Inc.) which not only made documentary films of all his major crusades but also, under Ross's direction, made fictional movies built around Graham's work in converting lost souls. The films were made available on a rental basis to church and civic groups, or arrangements could be made to have a member of Graham's staff show the film and take up a collection from the audience to cover the costs.

The Portland crusade followed the same pattern as the Columbia crusade, with nightly meetings at seven-thirty, two meetings on Sunday, and extra meetings for children, high school students, and various groups in the local area. Graham tried one other idea along this line, an idea much used by Moody, Sunday, and almost all earlier evangelists, the practice of holding meetings for men only and for women only. In the early days some titillation had accompanied this division by sexes, and evangelists had dealt with certain sins peculiar to men and to women, but Graham gave virtually the same sermon ("The Problem of the American Home") to both groups and simply stressed the duties of fathers, husbands, and young men to one audience and the duties of mothers, wives, and young women in the other.

Though the Portland tabernacle was built to seat only 12,000, 6000 chairs were set up outside the tabernacle, and Beavan reported that the average attendance nightly for the first week was 14,000. A total of 630,000 attended over the six weeks and another 20,000 were added by the final rally in a football stadium on the last day. Seven thousand persons hit the sawdust trail, as Sunday would have said. Graham preferred to say that 7000 persons made "decisions for Christ" or "dedicated themselves to live for Christ."

It had been one of the stock complaints about mass evangelism since the days of George Whitefield that the converts made in such periods of excitement did not last. The evangelists uniformly blamed this on the local pastors for not following up and consolidating the conversions made at the meetings. The local ministers complained that the evangelist's converts were only superficially aroused and had acted on the spur of the moment, or else they would have voluntarily joined a church and become faithful Christians. Graham sought to overcome this perennial complaint by extensive "followup" work. And in Portland, as in later campaigns, he left a member of his staff in the city for several months after the campaign to see that as many of the converts as possible joined a church. Shortly after the Portland crusade Graham associated himself with a group called The Navigators, Inc., led by Dawson Trotman, which made a business of following up revival crusades. The Navigators had worked with Graham before, managing the follow-up work in his Youth for Christ rallies. They were also employed by various church groups, missionary societies and evangelists throughout the country to do this work. The hiring of The Navigators became a fixed part of every Graham crusade and Dawson Trotman was considered a regular member of the Graham team.[11]

The decision made by Graham and his associates to undertake a nationwide weekly radio broadcast was not directly connected with the Portland crusade. It merely came to a head during that period. The idea started in the mind of the Rev. Ted Elsner of Philadelphia who was himself active in radio preaching and who had among the members of his church an advertising man named Fred Dienert. Dienert was an associate of the Walter F. Bennett Advertising Agency in Chicago, which had been the agent for several well-known religious broadcasts. Through Elsner, Dienert and Bennett took up the project of persuading Graham to go on the air. They first approached Graham in

June, 1950, and suggested that he undertake a half-hour Sunday afternoon show to be carried over the 250 affiliated stations of the American Broadcasting Company. This would reach eight or ten million persons every week. But of course it would cost, including Bennett's commission, about $7000 a week, and it would need an initial investment of $25,000 in advance. Graham was interested at first, then eager, but finally had to turn it down on the grounds that he did not know how to raise the initial $25,000. Bennett kept hounding (or tantalizing) him, and finally in Portland, Graham knelt in prayer with Bennett in his hotel room and said that if the Lord would provide him with $25,000 that night he would sign the contract. The test was to be whether the congregation at the Portland tabernacle would donate or pledge the needed money. During the course of the meeting that night Graham told the crowd of his problem and asked those who wished to help in advancing the Lord's work in this way to meet with him after the sermon at the tabernacle office. When the meeting ended a long queue of people was at the office door and, according to the report, $23,500 was donated or pledged that evening. Bennett offered to put up the rest himself. Graham said that the Lord must provide it all or it was not answered prayer. Returning to his hotel he found two checks, one for $500 and one for $1000 awaiting him there. Graham was satisfied. He called it a "miracle" and signed the contract.[12]

The problem of putting the broadcast together in a workable format took two months. Dick Ross, who had had experience with radio and television as well as in making films, was hired to produce the program. Graham's wife suggested the title, "Hour of Decision." Graham's pianist, Tedd Smith, made a stirring arrangement of "The Battle Hymn of the Republic" as the theme. The program itself consisted of choir singing, directed by Cliff Barrows, solos by Bev Shea, "crusade reporting" (news of Graham's latest meetings and other activities) by Jerry Beavan, scripture reading by Grady Wilson, and a ten to fifteen minute sermon by Graham. Cliff Barrows did the announcing. Guest stars were used to add variety, and Graham kept the show up to the minute by injecting comments on national and international news items into his sermons. Graham was always introduced to the radio audience by Barrows with the words, "And now, as always, a man with God's message for these crisis days, Billy Graham." Each sermon ended with a request for the listeners to kneel by their radios (or if in their automobiles, to look straight ahead) and make their decisions for Christ. After a brief word of prayer Graham always signed off by saying, "And now, until next week, good bye and may the Lord bless you, real good." Then, as a postscript, Cliff Barrows reminded the listeners that the program was dependent for its support upon their freewill gifts.

The first broadcast took place on November 5, 1950, and according to Beavan, was so popular that "After just five weeks on the air, the Hour of Decision had earned the highest Nielsen audience rating ever accorded a religious program." [13] Most of the broadcasts were "live," originating from the scene of Graham's current crusade, but occasionally when Graham was taking a rest or en route the broadcast was recorded in advance. As Graham's popularity grew over the years, Bennett persuaded him to add more stations and networks to his contract until, by 1955, he was being heard on almost a thousand stations by twenty million persons weekly in the United States and on over thirty shortwave stations around the world.

The financial problems involved in these movie and radio ventures necessitated some formal arrangement for handling the money. While he was still in Portland, Graham called George Wilson, the business manager of Northwestern Schools, and asked him for advice. Wilson suggested the formation of a nonprofit corporation, and Graham agreed. The Billy Graham Evangelistic Association, Inc. was formed in Minneapolis later that month with Graham as president, Grady Wilson as vice-president, George Wilson as secretary-treasurer, and Cliff Barrows and Graham's wife on the board of directors. Various Christian businessmen also agreed to serve on the board though it was understood that Graham and his team would have the deciding voice in all decisions.[14]

This corporation soon became the central coordinating agency for a vast range of activities. It not only handled all financial arrangements for the "Hour of Decision," which meant processing thousands of weekly donations from radio listeners, but it also had to cope with additional thousands of letters each week seeking Graham's help on personal and religious problems. This led the Bennett advertising agency to the idea for a daily newspaper column written by Graham in which he would deal with some of the more common of these problems. This column was eventually syndicated in 125 newspapers with a total circulation of twenty million readers. In 1952 Graham decided to produce a weekly television program and the Minneapolis headquarters had to expand to meet new demands. Among the seven thousand to eight thousand letters received in Minneapolis each week were many requests for copies of Graham's sermons and books and for recordings and sheet music by Graham's musical associates. So in 1952 Graham and Wilson formed a sister corporation called the Grason Company (with offices around the corner from the evangelistic association) which handled these requests on a mail-order basis. The profits went to support Graham's evangelism. By 1955 the Minneapolis office had a staff of 125 persons and an annual budget of two million dollars and was still growing.

All of these activities helped to keep Graham before the public eye and to capitalize to the utmost upon his name. But they would have amounted to little without his continued success as an urban mass evangelist. And this might have collapsed rapidly if he had not taken some sound advice in regard to his own financial remuneration. One problem which had helped to wreck mass evangelism in Billy Sunday's day was that a great many evangelists came to look upon the profession as primarily a means for making money. Although Graham, like Sunday, never took this view, it was inevitable that as he became more popular the amount of money given to him in freewill offerings after each campaign would increase. By the end of 1950 he was receiving as much as $16,000 for a single six-week revival. Like Sunday, Graham tried to take some of the odium off this high rate of remuneration by donating most of it to various religious causes. Nevertheless he did accept some of it, and whether he did or not, the local committees felt honor bound to see that he received a handsome sum. Newspapers often gave more publicity to the amounts Graham received than to the amounts he gave away.

In 1951 Graham found a solution to this problem which put an end to all controversy and freed him from the possible taint of commercializing evangelism for personal gain. He made arrangements with the Billy Graham Evangelistic Association to pay him a fixed salary of $15,000 a year beginning January 1, 1952 (and somewhat smaller salaries were voted for several other key members of his team). This was to be his sole remuneration (excepting royalties from his books and the fee for his newspaper column) for each year's work as an evangelist, regardless of how many crusades he conducted. No freewill offering was ever collected for him again. The local committees did, of course, continue to pay for his and his team's expenses in each crusade, and the salaries of some of the minor members of the team were included as part of the regular crusade expenses. But there was no longer any question of using high-pressure methods to raise a large sum of money as a personal gift to the evangelist.

By the time Graham finished his Portland campaign in July, 1950, his revivalistic system was virtually complete. In the years ahead he was to add new refinements and to expand the size of his organization, but the basic pattern of his evangelism was now set. From Portland he went to Minneapolis to conduct a three-week campaign. Then to Atlanta for six weeks. From there to Fort Worth, Shreveport, Memphis, and a score of other cities, until finally, in May, 1957, he rode the crest of the new era of religious awakening into New York City.

That America was in the midst of a nationwide revival of some sort was evident by the end of 1950. In November of that year Reinhold Niebuhr, the leader of Protestant intellectuals, told the readers of the *New York Times'* Sunday magazine that one proof of the fact that there was a revival of religion under way was "the evidence of 'mass' conversions under the ministrations of popular evangelists who arouse the religious emotions and elicit religious commitments with greater success than at any time since the days of Billy Sunday." The managing editors of the Associated Press at their annual convention that same month agreed that "A growing interest in religion is evident all over the United States." As one of them said, "Religion has been doing a good selling job." [15]

Billy Graham did not create this revival, but he was doing a good job of selling it. As he had said about his ability to sell Fuller brushes, he believed in the product. But what exactly did he believe? What was the product he so effectively sold to hundreds of thousands in the 1950's, and why did they buy it?

CHAPTER 4

Theology and Social Philosophy

The Bible embodies all the knowledge man needs to fill the longing in his soul and solve all his problems. It is the blueprint of the Master Architect, and only by following its directions can we build the life we are seeking.

BILLY GRAHAM [1]

One of Billy Graham's most frequently reiterated statements is that America needs to "get back to the old-time religion." But it is not always clear precisely what Graham means by the old-time religion. Sometimes he asserts that it is the religion of Moody, Finney, Whitefield, Jonathan Edwards, and Martin Luther, as though these men all held the same views. Like all professional evangelists Graham feels that doctrinal and denominational differences among Christians are unimportant provided they agree on certain fundamental Christian truths. This is one reason for calling Graham a fundamentalist.

But the term "fundamentalist" has acquired many unpleasant connotations since the days of the Scopes trial. Billy Graham and the leaders of the National Association of Evangelicals often try to show that the neofundamentalism or "evangelical Christianity" which they preach is very different from the old fundamentalism of the 1920's. Graham explains his own position this way: "If by fundamentalist you mean 'narrow,' 'bigoted,' 'prejudiced,' 'extremist,' 'emotional,' 'snakehandler,' 'without social conscience'—then I am definitely not a fundamentalist. However, if by fundamentalist you mean a person who accepts the authority of Scriptures, the virgin birth of Christ, the atoning death of Christ, His bodily resurrection, His second coming, and personal salvation by faith through grace, then I am a fundamentalist." [2] These are, however, the same five points of fundamentalism defined by the Niagara Bible Conference in 1895 and solidified in the books called *The Fundamentals* issued in 1909-1910.[3] They were the nub of the struggle between the fundamentalists and the modernists in the days before the Scopes trial. But Graham purports to treat them in a more broad-minded, unemotional, and socially oriented manner than some fundamentalists do. One of the basic problems, therefore, in defining Graham's theology is to find precisely how he differs from the old, narrow, bigoted, unsocial fundamentalists without becoming too similar to the modernists.

Graham's most clear-cut exposition of his theological position is to be found in his book *Peace with God* which was published in 1953. The fact that it sold 500,000 copies (including the 35c paperback edition) within two years indicates that even in cold print Graham's message appealed to many Americans. The opening chapter of this book is entitled "The Quest," by which Graham means the quest of every man to attain an explanation of the meaning of his life—the quest which can only end when one is at peace with God. Actually the chapter is concerned with four different quests. The first is the quest of the individual to find peace within himself in regard to his internal personal conflicts, peace over pride, selfishness, ambition, and envy— or as Graham puts it, the quest to attain "peace of conscience, peace of mind, and peace of soul." [4] The second is the quest for peace with one's immediate family, friends, and neighbors—the ability to love one's neighbor as oneself. The third is the quest for the means of establishing peace on earth good will toward men, or for creating the Kingdom of God on earth even as it is in heaven. And the fourth is the quest for peace or serenity in the face of all the inexplicable harassments of disease, war, famine, depression, and accidents, and the ability to meet with cheerful resignation the ultimate questions of death and life-after-death. Graham does not specifically spell out these four quests, for to him they are all part of the same quest. But it becomes evident in the course of the book that Graham's explanation of Christianity tends to shift its ground depending upon which particular aspect of the quest he has in mind.

For example, sometimes his emphasis is upon man's search for personal "completeness and fullness" through "fellowship with God," in which case Graham tends to be optimistic about its attainment; salvation and all its earthly and heavenly rewards can be had simply for the asking. At other times, when Graham's emphasis is upon man's search for a "better world" or "the kind of world we long for," he wavers between optimism and pessimism; the world would rapidly become better if all men were converted, but that is a difficult task. And sometimes, when his emphasis is upon the folly of the idea of progress or the futility of science and education to improve man's lot or the ineradicably "depraved and sinful nature" of man, Graham is predominantly pessimistic; the world is lost beyond redemption and only a few are chosen.

Throughout the book Graham borrows the dialectic or paradoxical approach and terminology of neo-orthodoxy. He notes the apparent contradictions in Christian theology and declares that Christianity is a religion of hope and of despair, of triumph and of suffering, the Christian is in the world but not of the world. In the hands of a profound theologian the use of paradox can be enlightening and enriching. In Graham's theology it often seems that he has relied upon it as a means of covering up the inconsistencies in his own thought.

Graham, however, like Sunday and Moody, makes no pretense at being a theologian or an intellectual. His whole message, he frankly admits, rests upon his own interpretation of the literal words of the Bible. He calls the Bible the "codebook" or the "key" to all the perplexing individual and social problems of "our topsy-turvy world." "The Bible," he writes, "embodies all the knowledge man needs to fill the longing of his soul and solve all his problems. It is the blueprint of the Master Architect and only by following its direction can we build the life we are seeking." In his sermons Graham often refers to the Bible as "the greatest how-to-do-it book ever written."

From the first page of *Peace with God* Graham makes it clear that the Biblical blueprint is not only eternally true and unchanging because God inspired and "dictated" every word of it, but it is also based upon historical fact which historical scholarship and archaeological research have verified as fully as they have verified the life and death of Julius Caesar.[5] For those who may deny the historical proof of Biblical revelation, Graham points to the fact that the existence of God can also be proved by the laws of nature ("As a watch must have a designer so our precision-like universe has a Great Designer"[6]), from the existence of conscience ("Conscience tells us in our innermost being of the presence of God"[7]), and from "the ever-present law of cause and effect that operates on every level of the Universe" and which therefore necessitates the existence of a First Cause.[8]

Furthermore, God's Biblical blueprint is available to everyone: "If you do not have a Bible in your home, go out and get one now—get one that suits you best, get the size that is most comfortable for you to handle, get the kind of type that is most pleasant for you to read, and then settle down and find out for yourself . . . why it answers every human need, why it supplies the faith and strength that keeps humanity marching forward."[9] One of the keys to the success of any evangelist is his ability to make the Bible seem clear, reasonable, easily understood, and verifiable to the ordinary

man, woman, and child. Graham has this ability to an emi-
nent degree. "The Bible has no hidden purpose," he says.
"It has no need for special interpretation. It has a single,
clear, bold message for every living being. . . ." In fact,
Graham makes the Christian plan of salvation seem so simple and reasonable that it comes as a shock to some to
discover that the three cardinal points of his theology as he
explains them in *Peace with God* are, in the last analysis,
so "mysterious" and unknowable that they can only be
believed on faith.

What then is the answer offered to all man's problems
and questions in the Bible? And what is the explanation
offered by the Bible for the sorry condition of the world "at
this crucial point in history?" According to Graham it all
began eastward in Eden when Adam disobeyed God. Graham declares that in the beginning God created a "perfect
world," and placed perfect human beings in it. "The first
man was no cave-dweller—no jibbering, grunting, growling
creature of the forest. . . . Adam was created full-grown
with every mental and physical faculty developed." [10] God
created a "perfect man," put him in a "perfect setting"
(because "God could do nothing that was less than perfect"), gave him "total freedom," issued a single injunction
against eating the fruit of two particular trees, and "Then,
like the wise Parent that he was, God waited to see what
choice this child of His would make." When Adam chose
wrongly, God had no alternative but to punish him. "Suppose that God had said, 'Adam, you must have made a mistake, that was a slight error on your part. You are forgiven.
Please don't do it again.' God would have been a liar." [11]
For God had clearly told Adam regarding the tree of knowledge, "In the day that thou eatest thereof thou shalt surely
die." God did not want this to happen. "He wanted to
save man. He wanted to free man from the curse of sin."
But He could not break His word. "His very nature would
not allow Him to lie." He had stated that if Adam disobeyed His injunction he "would die physically and spiritu-

ally" and now that Adam had eaten the apple, God had to go through with his promise or be a liar. So death and sorrow and hell-fire became the lot of all men.

Fortunately God eventually found a way to help his creatures out of this plight. But Graham first endeavors to answer the inevitable question, the basic question in all theology, 'Who is to blame for Adam's fall? How did sin get into the world? Graham answers in the first place, "God is not to blame. . . . The fault lies squarely with Adam . . . who chose to listen to the lies of the Tempter . . ." [12] But how did the Tempter get into the perfect setting in Eden? Graham replies, "We know from the story of Adam and Eve that the Devil was already present on earth before God made the first man. Evil always existed, else God would not have made a tree whose fruit gave the awareness of good and bad." Evil then antedates Adam's fall. But who created the Devil? Was God the creator of evil? "Here," says Graham, "we face the greatest of all mysteries, the most significant of all secrets, the most unanswerable of all questions." On this crucial point the Bible does not have the answer. In fact, the Bible "makes it very clear that man is not supposed to know the full answer until God has allowed the Devil and all his designs to help work out His own great plan." [13] For the Christian it is only important that sin is in the world, that Adam, not the Devil or God, is to blame, and that all men must suffer for Adam's fall.

" 'But this is unfair!' you may say. 'Why should we suffer today because the first man sinned away back in the furthest reaches of time?' " The answer is that "Adam stands as the federal head of the human race. When he failed, when he succumbed to temptation and fell, the generations yet unborn fell with him, for the Bible states very clearly that the results of Adam's sin shall be visited upon everyone of his descendants." Or, using the common analogy, Graham claims that "sin is a disease" and it is transferrable by heredity. "For centuries . . . men have been trying to get back to Eden—but they have never been able to reach their goal." [14] The sin of disobedience is inbred in human nature so that while all men, like Adam, have free will, they always choose evil rather than good. "Every day we have the opportunity to move ourselves and others a little closer to that beautiful living Garden that Adam forfeited," but men continue to exercise their free will by choosing evil over good and thus they disobey God.[15] "We may curse Adam but we still imitate him!"

Men are therefore doubly evil. They are evil because they inherit Adam's sin and because they sin of their own free will. Man's depraved nature is constitutionally incapable of outwitting the Devil. In regard to the Devil, Graham is a true old-time fundamentalist who has no use for those "enlightened" persons who "take issue with the plausibility of a personal, individualized Devil in command of a host of evil spirits."[16] "Don't doubt for a moment the existence of the Devil" for "the Bible describes a personal Devil who controls a host of demon spirits that attempt to dominate and control all human activity." And the only way that man can triumph over the Devil, the world, and the flesh is by accepting the miracle of salvation.

Salvation is God's plan "to free men from the curse of sin." It was achieved by Christ's substitutionary atonement on the Cross. "The only solution" for man's dilemma after the fall, Graham says, "was for an innocent party to volunteer to die physically and spiritually as a substitute before God. The innocent party would have to take man's judgment, penalty and death." And "the only personality in the universe who had the capability to bear in his own body the sins of the world" was "God's own Son."[17] The salvation, or redemption, of man therefore hinges on the belief in the Trinity, for God and the Son are one. But the Bible does not explain how this can be. "This is a mystery that we will never be able to understand," Graham declares. It is the second basic mystery of evangelicalism.

Nevertheless Christ's love for man led Him to become a man in order that He might "meet and overcome Satan" and thereby "appease the wrath of God."[18] By this means God absolves man from his justly merited punishment, death and hell-fire. Ever since Christ's death and resurrection, God "waits to offer individual salvation and peace to the ones who will come to His mercy." [19] Though every man deserves hell for his continuous disobedience to God's laws, God "does not send him willingly." In fact, by man's refusal to accept God's mercy he in effect sends himself to hell. This is the heart and core of the gospel. "God prescribed the remedy for the ills of the human race. That remedy is personal faith and commitment to Jesus Christ. The remedy is to be born again." It is significant for Graham's application of the gospel to social problems that his theology rests firmly and unequivocally on this individual relationship between man and God, for this makes all sin a personal matter.

In the section of *Peace with God* entitled "The Solution" Graham explains what it means to be born again, or converted. While he insists that it is a "crisis" experience, a decisive turning point which occurs in the life of every Christian, he takes care to explain that it does not necessarily require a great emotional or hysterical experience. He opposes the "falsely produced emotionalism in some revival meetings" and the excesses connected with "the old-time mourner's bench." He points out, "My wife, for example, cannot remember the exact day or hour when she became a Christian, but she is certain that there was such a moment in her life. . . ." [20] But Graham categorically denies the theory of Christian nurture which the nineteenth-century New England theologian, Horace Bushnell, expounded; that is the view (paraphrased by Graham) that "every child should grow up to be a Christian without ever knowing that he has not always been one." [21] Bushnell's theory, Graham says (without naming him), produced "a false and improper use of religious training" in liberal churches which became "a substitute for the experience of the new birth." Graham notes that most of the conversions described in the Bible are "the dramatic, crisis type," and the implication is that with rare exceptions, this is the most certain type.

Graham's chapter, "How and Where to Begin" answers the most vital question in all evangelism, "What must I do to be saved?" "Biblical conversion," he begins, "involves three steps—two of them active and one passive. In active conversion repentance and faith are involved. . . . The third [step] which is passive we may call the new birth or regeneration." [22] Now the difference between Calvinism (which was preached by the Puritans and by revivalists like Jonathan Edwards, Gilbert Tennent, and George Whitefield) and Arminianism (as preached by John Wesley, Charles Finney, Moody, Sunday, and Graham) is that in Calvinism the conversion process was at least two-thirds passive, if not wholly so. According to most Calvinists, men not only lacked free will but they were predestined either to be saved or damned by the completely arbitrary and inscrutable sovereignty of God before they were born. To most Americans since 1776 this view reduces man to playing altogether too small a role in a matter of such importance to him; it smacks of fatalism. Modern revivalists, therefore, those who have preached since Finney's day, have usually held the view expressed by Graham that conversion is two-thirds active. This reduces the role played by God or the Holy Spirit accordingly, but it makes more sense to the average man. It also makes more sense out of revivalism. For it was a curious contradiction, as Finney pointed out in 1835, for Calvinists to insist that God required men to be born again before they could be saved from sin and yet that He did not give men the ability to effect their conversion. Predestination may have been good Calvinism, but after 1776 it was not a very effective theory for revival preaching. Graham, like Finney, insists "You can decide right now that you want to be born again," and the sinner is left in no doubt that if he really wants to save himself he can do it quickly and easily.[23] For example, in one of his often repeated revival sermons, based on Matthew 7:13, Graham tells his audiences that conversion can bring "a new world, a brand new dimension, a new area of living that you did not know anything about. And it can be yours tonight!

How? Jesus said, 'Enter in.' He indicated that you must do it yourself. 'Strive to enter in at the straight gate.' " [24]

In *Peace with God* Graham delicately dissects the various parts of the three steps in the conversion process so as to allot the due proportions of effort to man and to God. But while conversion is somewhat complicated to explain, it is perfectly simple to do. And it by no means involves the long, drawn-out process that the Calvinists taught. Graham even maintains that "It may be debatable in which order the three [steps in conversion] should come, but it is generally agreed that they probably happen at the same time." [25]   In fact, "Whether you are conscious or unconscious of it, in that critical moment of conversion, these three take place simultaneously."

This telescoping of the conversion process considerably increases the impression that the individual sinner is the deciding force in effecting his own rebirth. His first action is to repent or "to renounce his sin" or to make a "right-about-face" in his course of conduct. He is to turn *from* sin *toward* God. "When you have determined that you are renouncing sin, forsaking sin, and yielding all to Christ," Graham maintains, you have taken the first step toward peace with God.[26] But "you cannot have genuine repentance without saving faith" and "faith is a confident assurance of that for which we hope." Faith is "utter confidence" that the Bible is true, that Christ's sacrifice was efficacious, and that God will do what he promises to do. The convert should remember that "God does not ask the impossible. He does not ask you to take a leap in the dark concerning conversion. Believing in Christ is based on the best evidence in the world, the Bible." [27]   But the Bible says men are saved by faith. Do not repentance and faith complete the new birth? No. "When you have saving faith in Jesus Christ you have taken an additional step toward having peace with God" but the third step is also necessary.

And this third step must be taken by the Holy Spirit: "Being born again is altogether a work of the Holy Spirit. . . . The new birth cannot be produced by human devices or schemes." [28] What then is the new birth? "It is the infusion of divine life into the human soul," and by it "Christ, through the Holy Spirit takes up residence in our hearts. . . . That means that if you have been born again you will live as long as God lives because you are now sharing his life." This third and last step in conversion is rather complex and not at all easy for the average man to understand. In fact, like the other two vital parts of God's divine blueprint, it is so complex that it is a mystery. Yet, "Even though the new birth seems mysterious, that does not make it untrue." Graham draws an analogy: "We may not understand the how of electricity, but we know that it lights our homes. . . . We do not understand how the sheep grows wool, the cow grows hair, or the fowl grows feathers—but we know they do. We do not understand many mysteries but we accept by faith. . . ." So, in the long run, despite the simplicity and historical validity of the Bible, the process of salvation is a leap in the dark, an act of faith. No matter how clear Graham says the blueprint is, his message in the last analysis is not based on reason or evidence, but on dogma: "You will never know peace with God, peace of conscience, peace of mind, and peace of soul until you stand at the foot of the cross and identify yourself with Christ by faith. There is the secret of peace." [29]

This then is Billy Graham's explanation of the gospel. That it differs little from the stereotype of fundamentalism is apparent. But while critics may call it anti-intellectual, superstitious, primitive, or obscurantist, it has a tremendous appeal for those who, like Graham, are worried and confused by the fact that "the world has changed radically since the beginning of the century." [30] The literal Bible, the blueprint of God's master design, the love of Christ, the certainty of heaven, the reality of a personal Devil—these are the symbols which give meaning to the old-time religion and which make Graham's preaching seem anchored to the Rock. The dogmatic assertion of these old, "eternal," "unchanging," truths gives a sense of meaning and security to those who are perplexed and upset, as Graham is, by "the spirit of revolution that is sweeping away the established landmarks and traditions" of the good old days.

But his reaffirmation of the old-time theology is only one aspect of Graham's appeal. His preaching is directed toward life in the 1950's as well as toward life in eternity. And it is in the application of his theology to the particular stresses and strains of contemporary life that Graham evokes the most popular response to his sermons. It is easy to see how the assurance of salvation and the certainty of knowing he will go to heaven after death may give a kind of peace to the perplexed individual, but a man must also receive some instructions on how to meet the problems of this world if his faith is to have meaning to him. For many Christians the quest for peace is meaningful only in terms of the quest for solutions to their personal problems. Here there is nothing mysterious about Graham's message. He is on much firmer ground, or appears to be, when he brings his blueprint and his fundamentals to bear on the concrete problems of daily life. Graham maintains in *Peace with God* that the Christian life is not "a set of rules, taboos, vetoes, and prohibitions. . . . It is not a series of 'don'ts' but a series of 'do's.' " Yet, like old-time fundamentalists, Graham plainly warns every sinner against worldliness in all its manifold forms: "The world has a tendency to lead us into sin—evil companions, pleasures, fashions, opinions, and aims of the world." [31] True to the pietistic basis of revivalism, Graham preaches *against* sin as much as *for* Christian action.

There is little in Graham's approach to sin to differentiate it from that of Billy Sunday, D. L. Moody, or any of the other rural-born and rural-bred evangelists. Like them he still believes that the small-town moral code of nineteenth-century America is the basic code prescribed by God for all human beings at all times and in all places. To the revivalist and his audiences sin is immorality, and immorality is measurable in specific actions. Like all revivalists, Graham sees sin predominantly in terms of sins. His sermons contain countless warnings against the sins of drinking, smoking, playing cards, going to theaters or movies, dancing, swearing, telling "off-color stories," reading "salacious novels," looking at "filthy magazines," and playing golf on the Sabbath instead of attending church. "I believe that we need to get old-fashioned in keeping the Lord's day." "Watch the books you read. Watch the kind of entertainment you attend. . . . Someone has said, 'You cannot help the first look, but the second is sin.'" "Our newsstands today are so indecent that a Christian cannot look upon them without blushing." Girls who wear tight sweaters or use too much make-up are endangering their souls, and "If you women purposely dress to entice a man to sin, then you are guilty whether the act is committed or not." The sin of dishonesty is pointed out to those who "cheat on their income tax" or "pad their expense accounts." And traveling salesmen are warned that "Off-color jokes and dirty stories have no place in the Christian life." Graham repudiated indignantly an article about him in *McCall's Magazine* in which he was quoted as having said, "I know ministers who smoke, have an occasional drink, dance, and play a mild game of gin rummy. This does not make them any less devout than I am." [32]

About the only difference between Graham and Billy **X** Sunday in this respect is that Graham has to use slightly different terminology in discussing the sins of the 1950's from that used by Billy Sunday a generation ago. Where Sunday attacked saloons, speakeasies, and booze-hoisters, Graham attacks nightclubs, cocktail parties, and alcoholics. Where Sunday denounced "jazz" and "the bunny hug," Graham denounces "rock and roll" and the "mambo." In place of "white-slavers" and "pimps," Graham excoriates "sex maniacs" and "perverts." Graham is somewhat more frank in discussing the "millions spent on contraceptives" and about "sex orgies where married couples exchanged wives and husbands for an evening," but Sunday mentioned abortion and venereal disease more freely. Both evangelists dislike the prevailing fashions of their day in women's clothes: Sunday was shocked in 1910 when women's skirts began to get so short that their ankles were displayed in public. Graham deplores "the Hollywood look" which over-emphasizes "the female bosom." (He consequently wel-comed "the sack" dress because he thought it de-emphasized the female contours.) While Sunday denounced as false prophets those theosophists, Blavatskyites, spiritualists, and "Eddyites" who tried to elevate mind over matter, Graham denounces psychiatrists and psychologists for ignoring the Bible and excusing sin. Sigmund Freud has joined Vol-taire, Charles Darwin, and Karl Marx among the bêtes noires of fundamentalism. "Psychiatrists have invented a new term for sin consciousness, and they call it 'guilt com-plex.'" "The average psychiatrist had little time for reli-gion." "Psychiatrists are saying that the child should be allowed to give free expression and do as he pleases, but the Bible teaches that there should be loving obedience . . . and . . . discipline." [33] And yet Graham sometimes turns Freud-ian himself when he points out that the symptoms of sinful living today can be seen in the "tensions," "frustrations," "anxieties," and "inferiority complexes" that plague Ameri-cans.*

In addition to neuroses and psychoses, there are several other aspects of life in the 1950's which provide Graham with entirely new fields for fulmination. Graham is, for example, the first major evangelist to be able to denounce time wasted listening to radio programs, watching television, and seeing double features at drive-in theatres. He is the first major evangelist to have Hollywood as a synonym for Sodom and Gomorrah. He is the first to devote a whole sermon to the topic of "Highway Safety—A Spiritual Prob-lem" (although Sunday early recognized that automobiles provided "a bedroom on wheels" for evil-minded adoles-cents). While both Graham and Sunday attack "dope ped-dlers" and "dope addicts" in their sermons, Graham is the first evangelist to denounce people who use tranquilizers,

---

* In commenting upon this paragraph in a letter to me, Dr. Graham noted that he was not opposed to all psychiatrists and psychologists and that he was in fact considering adding a psychiatrist to his team in order to assist in counseling inquirers. Dr. Graham is opposed only, he said, to atheistic psychiatrists and psychologists.

phenobarbitol, and vitamin pills. And it is significant of the rising standard of living among the middle class that Graham spends much of his time attacking the "gadget-filled" American home and the curse of "boredom." "We have more boredom per square inch in this country than any country in the world." Graham can apply to almost everyone in his audience the sins which Sunday found only among "the idle rich." He points out that "Americans have the highest standard of living the world has ever known. . . . The poorest person in this audience tonight is rich by the world's standards." And then he makes them feel guilty about it by reminding them that "In India tonight over 100,-000,000 people will go to bed hungry, if they have a bed to go to. And when they drive the trucks down the streets of Calcutta tomorrow morning they will pick up people that died of starvation, as I have seen them in India." The basic trouble with Americans, according to Graham, is that they are too prone to say to themselves, "Soul take thine ease; drink and be merry; you've laid up enough goods. You've got economical security now. You've got money in the bank. You've got good insurance policies. You've got a good job. You've got a good business. Take it easy. Go and get you a little cottage in Florida and take it easy." But remember, he adds, tonight you may hear "a voice from heaven" saying, "Thou fool, this night thy soul is required of thee." [34] Graham is clearly an evangelist to an affluent society, and his success proves that the Protestant ethic, though weakened, is far from dead. For all his attacks on covetousness, Graham is quick to point out that there is nothing inherently wrong with being rich: "There is nothing in the Bible that says it is wrong to be rich if you have gained it honestly." The sin lies in spending it on gadgets and luxuries instead of for the Christian evangelization of the world.

But the most popular feature of revival preaching in all eras has not been the denunciations of the sins of society but the manner in which the evangelist applies the teachings of Christianity to the problems of marriage, child-raising, the family, and the home. These are topics which touch the heart of every auditor. The vast majority of those who attend revival meetings are decent respectable home-bodies. They look upon revival meetings as a family affair and bring their children with them. While they enjoy the evangelist's denunciations of the sins of movie stars, gamblers, the rich, and the social elite, those sermons which elicit the warmest and most deep-seated response are those which deal with the simple problems of everyday life. It is not surprising that Graham's most popular sermons are those bearing such titles as "The Home," "The Responsibilities of Parents," "The Answer to Broken Homes," "The Responsibilities of the Home," "Our Teen-Age Problem," "The Answer to Teen-Age Delinquency," "Juvenile Delinquency and Its Cure," and "The Home God Honors."

The last-named sermon was one of those delivered in Los Angeles in 1949, and it is a model for all his later discourses on this subject. In fact, it is a model for all of Graham's sermons. It demonstrates perfectly his approach to all the sins and problems for which conversion is the solution. Graham begins this sermon on "The Home God Honors" by declaring with Henry Grady that "the foundation of American society and the very heart and core of America is the American home." Like all evangelists he then eulogizes "the old-fashioned home" with its "old-fashioned parents" and delivers a panegyric on his own home: "I'll never forget my father and mother. They raised their children in the fear of the Lord. I never heard my parents argue. I do not even remember their having used a slang word, much less a word of profanity." His home was one of prayer "around the old family Bible," and God honored that home and those faithful parents so that "tonight all of their children know the Lord Jesus Christ as personal Saviour." [35]

The sermon goes on to explain how God established marriage and the home in the Garden of Eden. This calls forth a recital of four verses of "Home, Sweet Home." A brief discussion of Jesus' home is followed by the alarming statement that "the great problem confronting the present world today is not Communism. The greatest problem confronting us tonight is the breakdown of the American home."

But it soon appears that these two problems are intimately connected. "A nation is only as strong as her homes" and therefore "One of the goals of Communism is to destroy the American home. If the Communists can destroy the American home and cause moral deterioration in this country, that group will have done to us what they did to France when the German armies invaded the Maginot line." There is no doubt "of what Satan is doing to destroy the morals of America and to break down our homes." The precise connection between Satan and communism and moral deterioration in the home is not made clear, but the frightful danger and magnitude of the problem is. A few statistics follow on the high divorce rate in America ("one divorce to every 3½ marriages") and then Graham describes the "many major enemies of the home": Among these are selfishness, unfaithfulness, alcohol, "maladjustment," jealousy, and the "spirit of the day" which has made "a laughing stock of marriage."

The spirit of the day is explained as the fact that "we have turned to the psychiatrist and we've turned to the psychologist and we have all sorts of books on the home . . . on how to rear children . . . and now, to top it all, we have the *Kinsey Report*" and "Mr. Anthony." But we have failed "to turn to God's word," and hence "there are more unhappy homes today than ever before in our history." Graham then turns to the Bible in order to show what God's rules for the home are. His first text is, "Wives submit yourselves unto your own husbands, as it is fit in the Lord." One reason why the American home is breaking up is that "the home today . . . is not properly governed." "Some of you wives" may be shocked, he admits, especially those "of you who 'wear the trousers' in your family. . . ." But just as "Christ is the head of the church" so "the husband is the head of the wife." And the reason why women must submit to men is "Because of sin in the Garden of Eden, one of the curses God sent upon the woman was that the man shall rule over her." Of course, "That doesn't mean that the husband is to be a tyrant," but he is to wear the trousers.

Graham then quotes the Biblical explanation of the wife's

role in the home: "to be sober, to love their husbands, to love their children. To be discreet, chaste, keepers of the home, good, obedient. . . ." In simple language, he says, this means when your husband comes home at night, "run out and meet him and give him a kiss. Give him love at any cost. Cultivate modesty and the delicacy of youth. Be attractive. . . . Keep the house clean. . . . Don't be a spendthrift. . . . Don't nag . . . don't gossip" and don't go gadding about to the theater or to card parties or "the corner tavern."

On the other hand, the husband is not to take his wife's love for granted. "Send her a box of candy. . . . Send her an orchid." "Too many men have neglected the home for the club, the lodge, the theater, or the tavern." Also "help bear your wife's burdens. . . . Listen, I'd rather plow in the field all day long than to stay at home and cook three meals and take care of the children one hour. . . . The woman has a harder job." If wives must not be spendthrifts, husbands must not be "tightwads." "Let your wife buy a new hat and dress once in awhile." "Be a gentleman, be courteous, be thoughtful. Do the little things that you know women like."

It is easy to see why this sort of spiritual advice appeals to his listeners, and Graham's sermonizing is spiced with just enough humor and anecdotes from his own experience to keep it from being pontifical. What makes his sermons more pietistic, more fundamentalistic, than those of the average Protestant pastor is first, his strict adherence to Biblical texts, and second, his insistence that the main job of the husband and wife is to rear their children so as to make them born-again Christians. All families should hold daily prayer together and say grace at all meals. "The old-fashioned family altar" is the center of the home. The reading of the Bible is to take the place of movies, the tavern, cards, and the gay social whirl. The trouble with marriage in America is "We've made a big joke out of it."

The sermon next turns to the children. "Now all you boys and girls that have been sitting there and taking it all in, we're coming to you soon." The Biblical text for them is "Children, obey your parents in all things." This brings up the question of juvenile delinquency which, according to Graham, can be traced primarily to the lack of discipline in the home. "Our courts and our jails are filled; juvenile homes are crowded; our Nation is almost 'going to the dogs' because our young people have been undisciplined." Americans have forgotten the Biblical rule, "Chasten thy sons while there is hope, and let not thy soul spare for his crying." Which Graham explains, "In other words, he may cry; he may weep, he may be broken-hearted, but God says, 'Discipline and chasten, and whip if necessary to get the child to learn obedience.'" A child who will not be obedient to parental authority, Graham insists, will not be obedient to the laws of the nation.

Because the newspapers in the 1950's laid heavy stress upon the "crime wave" among juvenile delinquents, Graham made this particular problem a central one in his preaching. He has a ready explanation for the decline of parental authority in the home. "You know what the Devil's philosophy is today? Do as you please. Kick up your heels. Modern psychology is going along with the present program and psychologists are saying, 'Don't spank your children, you'll warp their personalities.'" Graham's attitude strikes a sympathetic chord among the members of the older generation in his audience. The fact that the young are abandoning the old ways has always seemed to their elders to presage trouble. And there is a certain frustrated vindictiveness in the desire of parents and grandparents (particularly fundamentalist parents and grandparents) to lay their hands upon the young and teach them a thing or two. "I stand here before you tonight a warped personality," says Graham ironically, "because I got plenty of spankings. I might not have received much head learning down in the hills of North Carolina, but there's one thing I got. There are plenty of callouses on my backbone that were put there by a razor strap." The proof that he who spareth the rod spoileth the child is all too evident to Graham. He offers an example in a story about a young son of a friend of his who brazenly ignored his father's polite request to close the door after he came into the room.

Having demonstrated the maddening impudence of this young wretch, Graham continues, "Brother, I'd like to have had that boy for five minutes. He'd have gone into the door shutting business for good. He'd shut every door in that community. We need some old-fashioned discipline in the home."

And then to drive home the point that discipline produces good people and lack of it produces bad ones: "I thought my dad was mighty strict, but as I look back I thank God for every time he punished me. I thank God for every time my father got on his knees in prayer for his boy. My father, with prayer and a hickory stick, led his boy into the ministry. . . ." Here is the simple solution to all the perplexing problems of the home, to all the worries over rebellious children and juvenile delinquency—perhaps even the answer to communism: "prayer and a hickory stick." [36] The sermon concludes with the time-honored evangelistic comparison between the God-honoring earthly home and the eternal divine home which Jesus has prepared for us in heaven: "I'm looking forward to getting home. What about you? It's a glorious home in the sky."

Graham has been fortunate as an evangelist in that the authoritarian and patriarchal tone of the Bible fits so neatly the contemporary attitude of many church people toward juvenile delinquency and toward public education. Revivalists thrive in an era of social and intellectual reorientation largely because their dogmatic answers cater to those who find it easier to look backward than forward. For many Americans it seemed easier in the 1950's to turn to the solutions that have worked in the past rather than to make the effort to find new ones.

Graham's treatment of juvenile delinquency and the American school system in other sermons gives ample evidence that there is a direct relationship between the current resurgence of the old-time religion and the current wave of neoconservatism in American political and intellectual life. In his sermon on "The Answer to Broken Homes" in which the Christ-centered home is offered as the "one great insurance policy" against divorce, Graham remarks of the broken home that "Just as Communism, it is another threat to the American way of life." And in his sermon on "America's Immorality" he attributes juvenile delinquency to "the wave of behavioristic philosophy that swept our college campuses and permeated the high school classrooms. . . . Puritanical ideals are scorned . . . God is old-fashioned. The Supreme Court has decided that the Bible shall not be taught in the schools. What else can we expect." Lumping together Friedrich Nietzsche, Sigmund Freud, Friedrich Schleiermacher, and John Dewey as the philosophical progenitors of the twentieth century, Graham denounces "our educational leaders" for undermining American morality: "Moral standards of yesterday to many individuals are no standard for today unless supported by the so-called 'intellectuals.'" [37] And Graham rolls the term "so-called intellectuals" off his tongue with grandiloquent scorn.

One of the most striking aspects of Graham's approach to juvenile delinquency is his apparent willingness to emulate the disciplinary measures and ideological indoctrination methods of the totalitarian systems. For example, when he was holding his crusade in New York City in the summer of 1957, he proposed to Governor Averell Harriman that New York might solve its juvenile delinquency problem by setting up "youth camps . . . on a semi-military basis with educational programs on Americanism and special courses of religious instruction." [38] And a year later he told an audience in Charlotte, North Carolina, "In Russia today young people are disciplined" and hence the Russians have few difficulties with drunkenness, pornography, or idleness. "They have an ideology. They have a control." Juvenile delinquency is no problem, he said, in a nation which is dedicated to a strong ideology: "And ladies and gentlemen, I believe that one of the problems among teen-agers today is that they need something to believe in. They need a cause. They need a challenge, they need a flag to follow. They want a master, they want someone to control them, just as Hitler was able to get the youth of Germany and Mussolini was able to get the youth of Italy and the Communists were able to get the youth of Eastern Europe." [39]   Graham is not, of course, advocating a dictatorship in America. He is urging young people to dedicate themselves to Christ. Yet this authoritarian presentation of Christianity as an ideological alternative to communism is scarcely the appeal to individual freedom which, on other occasions, he portrays as the central theme of Christian teaching. Moreover, this approach leads him into a portrayal of the founder of Christianity which is scarcely recognizable. Christ, he says, was "every inch a 'He-man.'" "Christ was probably the strongest man physically that ever lived. He could have been a star athlete on any team. He was a real man, with His strong shoulders, His squarish jaw. . . ." [40]

Yet at the same time that he advocates more discipline, more leadership and indoctrination, Graham also speaks of the need for more love. Quoting a "prominent sociologist" he says in his sermon "Our Teen-age Problem," "The biggest trouble is that there doesn't seem to be enough love to go around any more." He also mixes psychology with his pietism when he goes on to say, "Unloved, unwanted children become resentful, rebellious children."

At the heart of Graham's approach to the sins of the home, the evils of juvenile delinquency, and the immoralities of society lies his belief that all sin is personal and that it can be cured only by conversion. "That's the reason I concentrate on the individualistic gospel, because I don't think you can clean up a community until you have got men's hearts right." [41]   Conversion makes a man love his neighbors and once a man loves his neighbors all problems will cease. Slum clearance, playgrounds, juvenile courts, and psychological counseling are all mere palliatives. "The best way to combat juvenile delinquency is not by setting up more social agencies to deal with the problem but to restore the old-fashioned home where disobedience and disrespect are frowned upon." [42]   Graham seldom sees beyond personal sins to the social nature of sin. Just as conversions can miraculously transform an evil man into one of God's elect overnight, so, Graham believes, a revival can convert great masses of men and transform a whole social system overnight. "I believe if we can get enough young people to Jesus Christ," he said in Charlotte, North Carolina, "that we can go out and change Mecklenburg County. We can change North Carolina." In fact, he said, "There is enough power among young people in America today to change America and change the world if that power were harnessed and given to Jesus Christ." [43]

Customs, traditions, economic and political systems all can be reformed quickly, easily, and completely by "an old-fashioned, heaven-sent, Holy Ghost revival." "Systems are wrong," he maintains, "only because men are wrong at heart." [44] Or as he put it more explicitly, "No matter how much we tend to think of sin as a social something, it will forever remain true that social groups are groups of individuals. The real problem is always with the individual. . . . Many people are confident that legislation will solve our problems. Our problem is deeper than that. It is the constant problem of the sinner before God." [45] In short, the problem is too deep for legislation and requires supernatural assistance through revivals. On the other hand, it is so simple that everyone can work for it by saving souls.

It is true, no doubt, that deep-rooted problems cannot be solved simply by legislative fiat. But there is something escapist about Graham's view that social justice can only be attained by a miracle which would transform every American. Graham is giving voice to that strong perfectionist streak in American pietism which, by refusing to be satisfied with anything less than a perfect social order, leads to a refusal to make any effort to alter the status quo. It is this type of thinking that brings criticism of Graham's attitude toward the segregation issue.

For the first fifteen years of his ministry Graham not only did not express any sympathy for equal rights for Negroes, he did not even attempt to apply Christianity to their problems. When he became an evangelist he followed the pattern set by Moody, Sunday, Sam Jones, and all previous evangelists who held meetings in the South. Negroes who attended his meetings were directed to sit in "reserved seats" in a special section. He dodged the responsibility for this by stating that the arrangements for seating in his campaigns were left up to the local committee. Even in cities like Greensboro, North Carolina, where Graham held a meeting in the fall of 1951 and where there was no legal restriction against mixed seating at public religious meetings, Graham took no stand and let his committee arrange a Jim Crow section (with the result that the Negro pastors of the city respectfully refused their cooperation).[46] Yet in his book, *Peace with God,* written in 1953, Graham said that "the church has failed" to deal adequately with the race problem; the church "should have been the pace-setter" in granting equal rights to Negroes. But apparently he did not feel that as an evangelist it was his responsibility to help the churches set the pace.

Since the Supreme Court's decision in 1954, Graham has changed his stand and has refused to conduct revivals in Southern cities which will not permit mixed seating. Yet he still maintains that "in the final analysis the only real solution will be found at the foot of the cross where we come together in brotherly love."[47] And he asserts, "The one great answer to our racial problem is for men and women to be converted to Christ."[48] His most forthright statement on civil rights, made in New York City in 1957, was "Certainly we need civil rights legislation. We should do all we can to make sure that no man's rights are limited because of his race or creed or color. But in order to establish race relations that conform to the Christian principles on which our country was founded, we need love."[49]

Because he has failed to clarify his position on segregation Graham has been attacked by both sides in the controversy. Governor George Bell Timmerman of South Carolina asserted in October, 1958, that Graham was "a widely known advocate of desegregation" and Timmerman protested against Graham's proposal to hold a mixed religious service on the lawn of the state capitol. Although the governor could not have legally prevented this meeting and said that he would not try to do so, Graham preferred to avoid controversy and moved the service to a nearby army camp. The meeting at the army camp was not segregated, but Graham took particular pains to provide a special seat on his platform for former South Carolina Governor James Byrnes, who is a leader of the opposition to integration in the South. Graham made no mention of segregation in his address and in a statement to newsmen merely remarked, "God pity us [Christians] if we let our differences [on segregation] prevent us from presenting Christ and his message to a lost world." [50]

It seems evident that a great deal of Graham's popularity in the 1950's stems from the fact that he purposely avoids controversy on divisive issues and generally stresses the old folkways and values on which most churchgoers agree.[51] It is not hard to see why the bulk of his revival sermons deal with problems of the home and of individual morality. In this area his effort to make the nation re-examine its past as it faces new social and moral problems may have certain virtues. If human nature is always the same, then perhaps some problems of personal morality are subject to unequivocal definition.

But a moralistic, legalistic traditionalism is hardly a constructive approach in the area of contemporary politics and economics. The changing relations of groups of men, the advances of technology, and the shifting national and international alignments do not follow such simple and familiar patterns as marriage and the family. Nevertheless Graham continually tries to evaluate the complex problems of national and international affairs as though they were reducible to simple moral terms of right and wrong. And frequently, in dealing with national policies, this moralistic approach, imbued as it is with the spirit of individualistic evangelicalism, has given his sermons a politically partisan tone. D. L. Moody and Billy Sunday frankly admitted their dedication to the Republican party. Graham's partisanship has been camouflaged by a professed apoliticalism.

CHAPTER 5

Politics and World Affairs

I am completely neutral in politics.
BILLY GRAHAM [1]

Billy Graham once explained the great upsurge in interest in religion in the 1950's by saying: "The human mind cannot cope with the problems that we are wrestling with today. And when our intellectual leaders begin to admit that they don't know the answer, and that fact reaches the masses in the street, then they are going to turn somewhere. They will turn to all sorts of escapisms. Some will turn to alcohol. Others will turn to religion in the want of security and peace—something to hold onto." [2] Insofar as he spoke for those who wanted a simple and easy answer to the world's problems, his analysis was not far wrong.

In the aftermath of World War II the American people faced a series of unprecedented challenges which left them baffled, frustrated, and increasingly irritated. The imminent economic and political collapse of western Europe necessitated a program of foreign aid which not only stretched the financial resources of the United States but also necessitated greater involvement in European affairs than ever before. The collapse of the grand alliance of World War II and the recognition that Britain was now a second-rate power pushed the United States into a role of world leadership for which it had no experience and little taste. The failure of the peace conferences and the inability of the United Nations to function effectively within the limits of the veto power produced a sense of frustration surpassing that which followed the Versailles Treaty and the failures of the League of Nations. When Soviet communism began to press forward in one area of the globe after another, a hastily worked out plan of "containment" produced a host of entangling alliances which the average man distrusted and feared. In many parts of the globe American policy seemed to necessitate the support of reactionary and dictatorial regimes. This in turn involved the United States in the nationalistic upsurge in those underdeveloped areas of the world which were ripe for rebellion against the decadent colonialism of Europe. Economic and military assistance to these areas led to further international commitments. The average American picked up his morning paper with increasing apprehension. The United States was now mixed up in everything, everywhere. The tensions between "the West" and "the Communist bloc" produced what was rightly called a "war of nerves" or "the cold war." The traditionally pacifist and isolationist Americans were once again caught in an international maelstrom. Then the policy of containing communism reached a breaking point. In the summer of 1950 the Communist-directed invasion of South Korea compelled the United States and its allies to prove the seriousness of their purpose. The advent of a new war only five years after the cessation of the old one produced a psychological explosion which shook America to its roots.

Billy Graham's popularity was part of the grass-roots reaction to the whole traumatic postwar experience. In some respects it might be said that Graham's revivals represented a positive aspect of this reaction while the Congressional investigations of un-Americanism, subversion, and corruption represented a negative aspect. Congressmen like Nixon, Jenner, Velde, and McCarthy fulfilled the impulsive urge to find likely scapegoats who could be blamed for leading the United States into its frightening predicament, while Billy Graham fulfilled an equally strong impulse to reaffirm the old ideals and values which had given meaning and order to American life in the past. The political processes of democracy helped absorb some of the shock of this postwar readjustment. With unerring skill the political leaders of the Republican party (the "loyal" opposition) seized upon the issues of communism, Korea, and corruption in the 1952 presidential campaign. They pinned upon the Age of Roosevelt the title "Twenty Years of Treason" and returned to power with the slogan, "It's time for a change."

But there was more than a coincidental connection between Billy Graham's religious crusade and General Eisenhower's political crusade. It was inevitable that Graham, in his effort to awaken the nation to its old spiritual traditions, would lend something more than tacit support to Eisenhower's effort to "clean up the mess in Washington," to root out subversives in government, and to provide a new moral leadership which would be incorruptible. As Graham informed his followers immediately after the election, "It has been my privilege during the past year to talk with Mr. Eisenhower on two occasions. I have been deeply impressed by his sincerity, humility, and tremendous grasp of world affairs. I also sense a dependence upon God. He told me on both occasions that the hope of building a better America lay in a spiritual revival." And Graham added reassuringly, "Another thing that encourages me about Mr. Eisenhower is that he is taking advice from some genuine, born-again Christians." The title of the sermon in which he made these statements early in 1953 was "Peace in Our Time."

Officially Billy Graham is registered as a Democrat, but so is almost everyone in North Carolina. It is an amusing coincidence that he is registered as a voter in the county of Buncombe, for Graham is certainly far from being a supporter of the New Deal–Fair Deal philosophy which has been associated with the Democratic party since 1932. As an evangelist, of course, Graham persistently says that he is neither a Democrat nor a Republican and that he does not bring politics into his revival preaching. But even if it were true that he left all partisan issues out of his sermons, which it is not, it would still be a foregone conclusion that Graham, like every other major evangelist since the anti-slavery crusade began, had far more in common with the political, economic, and social philosophy of the Republican party than with that of the Democratic party.

The connecting link between professional evangelists and the Republican party has been a mutual belief in rugged individualism. The affinity between capitalism and the Protestant ethic has been amply demonstrated by sociologists and economists like Max Weber, Ernst Troeltsch, and Richard H. Tawney. Calvinism in particular emphasized the virtues of hard work, thrift, sobriety, and honesty, and it implicitly assured its followers that a man who was diligent in his business and in his piety would prosper by the grace of God. Contrarily, the lazy, thriftless, impious man received his just deserts in poverty and hell-fire. The Puritans and other Calvinists carried this doctrine to America, where it flourished so vigorously in the free atmosphere of the New World that, by the end of the nineteenth century, Protestant ministers like Henry Ward Beecher and evangelists like D. L. Moody confidently asserted that Christianity and economic individualism were two sides of the same coin. "It is a wonderful fact," said Moody, "that men and women saved by the blood of Jesus rarely remain subjects of charity, but rise at once to comfort and respectability." [3] And Billy Sunday similarly asserted in 1915, "I never saw a Christian hitting the ties and panhandling; I never saw a Christian that was a hobo. . . . They that trust in the Lord do not want for anything." [4]

Billy Graham is equally committed to the belief that Christianity and capitalism, like conversion and success, are inseparably linked and that one cannot exist without the other. When Graham speaks of "the American way of life" he has in mind the same combination of political and economic freedom that the National Association of Manufacturers, the United States Chamber of Commerce, and the *Wall Street Journal* do when they use the phrase. And because the Democratic party has, since the 1890's, attacked Big Business and Wall Street and called for government regulation of the economic system in the interests of the general welfare, Graham, like the majority of American Protestant ministers, has cast his influence upon the side of the Republicans (or, in the South, the conservative Democrats). Evangelical Christianity emphasizes not only the necessity for each individual's making his own way into heaven but also the necessity for his making his own way on earth. Like the economist Adam Smith, who defined laissez-faire capitalism in terms of the divine hand of Providence guiding the self-interest of each toward the best interests of all, the professional evangelist has always maintained that if each man would reform himself and run his own business honestly, the economic and social problems of the world would solve themselves.

Without realizing it, Graham endorses the Protestant ethic in its entirety. He denounces laziness or sloth as one of the seven deadly sins and claims "It has kept the hobo from a life of respectability." [5] Frugality is as much a virtue to Graham as it was to Cotton Mather or Benjamin Franklin: "The Bible teaches and encourages a normal degree of thrift." [6] And Graham is as certain as Henry Ward Beecher and the Rev. Horatio Alger that hard work and push will raise any enterprising young man from office boy to corporation president. In 1953 he noted as one of the signs of American decadence that "the youth of this country has lost its drive, its push, its willingness to work and get ahead." Young people today "aren't filled with the spirit that makes work a joy" or "with the determination that makes pushing ahead a pleasure." [7]

One of the first motion pictures which Graham produced for his "film ministry" dealt with the story of Houston, Texas. Graham called the movie "Oiltown, U.S.A." and advertised it as "the story of the free enterprise of America —the story of the development and use of God-given nat-

ural resources by men who have built a great new empire."
His sermons are filled with direful references to "the dangers
that face capitalistic America" and with eulogistic references to the free enterprise system brought over by the
Puritans and "the rugged individualism that Christ brought."
It is essential, he believes, that Americans continue to be
"devoted to the individualism that made America great." [8]
The American way of life, he has said over and over again,
"is in growing danger." And he urges his listeners to "come
back to Christ who gave us these freedoms which are
threatened."

There are three particular dangers which Graham feels
threaten the economic freedom of the American way of life.
The first is corrupt or power-hungry labor leaders, the second is unnecessary strikes which might hurt the economy,
and the third is socialistic legislation or "government restric-
tions" which would destroy the God-given "freedom of opportunity." Because Graham hopes to "reach the masses"
with his message, he is very circumspect in his treatment of
the problems of capital and labor. But it is not difficult to
see the bias implicit in his description of the Garden of
Eden as that happy place where there are "no union dues, no
labor leaders, no snakes, no disease." [9] Nor is it particularly complimentary of Graham to link "labor unrest" with
the hydrogen bomb and an "inevitable conflict with Russia"
as a reason for the revival of religious interest in America.[10]
In 1950 Graham complained "the coal strike may paralyze
the nation," and in 1952 he warned that the steel strike
would have an adverse effect on the success of American
forces in Korea. He said in one sermon, "There is a revolution in the industrial world. On one particular day in
New York City there were more than 200 strikes going on
at the same time." [11] And then he added, "This is a time in
the industrial world when capital and labor need to rethink
their positions or we are in serious danger of losing the
freedom for which our forefathers bled and died." He told
a reporter in Pittsburgh that among other things "The type
of revival I'm calling for is the type . . . that calls for an

employee to put in a full eight hours of work." [12] He emphasized that a Christian worker "would not stoop to take unfair advantage" of his employer through the strength of his union.[13] And he indicated his belief that most union men were not Christians when he stated in a Labor Day sermon in 1952, "I believe that organized labor unions are one of the greatest mission fields in America today." Hence "Wouldn't it be great if, as we celebrate Labor Day, our labor leaders would lead the laboring man in America in repentance and faith in Jesus Christ?" [14] In the same message he warned that "certain labor leaders would like to outlaw religion, disregard God, the church, and the Bible. . . ."

In all of these remarks, Graham's carefully chosen words left the impression that labor unions and labor leaders were somehow a force of unrest and danger in America. While he nowhere specifically attacked either unions or their leaders, his innuendos are by no means lost upon his predominantly middle-class white-collar audiences. While Graham asserts that "The church should be impartial toward the labor union as it is to other economic groups" he seemed to welcome the McClellan committee's Congressional investigation of corrupt labor practices in 1957 and injected references to its work in his sermons. In April, 1957, he called upon the unions to "clean house," and a few months later he said that if they did not do so it would be the duty of Congress to provide coercive legislation to curb them.[15] Graham was not leading public opinion in these remarks but he was helping to solidify it.

Two of Graham's favorite texts in reference to labor are "Set your affection on things above, not on things on the earth" and "It is the Lord thy God that giveth thee power to get wealth." His comment upon the latter is, "Irrespective of what the union may gain for you, remember that all you shall ever have comes from the hand of God." [16] But his most typical utterance on "the problem of capital and labor" is that "If Christ reigned in these labor discussions, the industrial strike that has caused so much heartache and even death would soon be at an end in this country and we would enter an industrial utopia." [17]   While Graham claims that the gospel is the ultimate answer to labor unrest, he also finds hope in the growth of what he, and the National Association of Manufacturers, call "People's capitalism." "Most big business today is actually owned by hundreds and thousands of people who invest in stocks. There are many great business corporations in America that are now sharing the profit with their employees. Each employee feels that he is also part of the business. More and more Management and Labor are becoming working partners." [18] If only someone would tell the labor leaders, he says, that they should join hands with management instead of fighting them, this would put an end to many mischievous and unnecessary labor quarrels.

Like Billy Sunday, Graham includes on his team of experts a number of associate evangelists who have the task in each crusade of visiting the local shops, factories, and mills to preach the gospel to the working class. Naturally the businessmen who support his campaigns encourage Graham's associates to preach to their workers. Graham's semiofficial biographer, Stanley High, states, "In scores of industrial plants in the United States and Great Britain employer-employee relations have improved as a result of prayer groups established during the Billy Graham meetings and maintained thereafter." [19]   A conservative British periodical asserted during Graham's revival in London in 1954 that one of the crusade's principal objectives was to "infiltrate key positions . . . in movements like the trade unions. Instead of key jobs going to Communists they should go to Christians." [20]

The connection which Graham and many of his supporters implicitly made between unionism, socialism, and communism involved Graham in two amusing but revealing controversies in Britain in 1954. Graham, like many political conservatives, has always believed that socialism is the first step down the slippery road to communism and that continued interference with free enterprise either by labor unions or government legislation will inevitably lead to communism. This of course was the crux of Herbert Hoover's quarrels with Franklin Roosevelt in the 1930's. The debate over the virtues of the New Deal and the Welfare State resumed with great ferocity in the postwar years. When the British forsook Winston Churchill's Tory government in 1945 for Clement Attlee and the Labour party, it was a great blow to Graham and other American advocates of free enterprise. Early in his career Graham began to lump together "Communism, atheism, and socialism" as enemies of the American way of life. Speaking in front of the capitol building at Austin, Texas, in April, 1952, Graham announced, "We must have a revolt against the tranquil attitude to[ward] communism, socialism, and dictatorship in this country." [21] And in Houston, a month later, he told a group of 850 wealthy businessmen at a hotel luncheon, "Within five years we can say good-by to England when Aneurin Bevan takes over. Japan could go Communist within two years. The United States is being isolated." [22] He told his radio listeners in June, 1952, that he and his team might soon go to Britain in an effort to halt the steady trend toward "Marxian socialism" in that country. He warned that if Americans did not abandon their materialistic outlook "we may soon go the same way." [23] A year later he announced in Dallas that his plans were set for a revival crusade in London. England is a country "more pagan than France" he reportedly told the Texans. "Behind the pageantry of the coronation . . . Britain's moral strength is so low that America could well suffer." [24]

It was therefore perfectly consistent with Graham's attitude toward labor and socialism when the following statement appeared in a 1954 calendar distributed free by the Billy Graham Evangelistic Association to those of his radio audience who wrote in for it: "There will always be an England. But will it always be the England we have known? The England of history has been an England whose life both national and individual was ever centered upon the things of God. But something happened during the war years of '40-'45 and following. Through fear-haunted days and never-ending nights the German bombs turned England's homes and churches into fire-blackened rubble. And when the war ended a sense of frustration and disillusionment gripped England and what Hitler's bombs could not do, socialism with its accompanying evils shortly accomplished. England's historic faith faltered. The churches still standing were gradually emptied."[25]

Graham failed to realize how this would strike the considerable number of very devout (but not exactly fundamentalist) Christians who supported the democratic socialism of the British Labour party. When a copy of the calendar with this squib reached the pro-Labour columnist of the *London Daily Herald*, Hannen Swaffer, three days before Graham was due to arrive in London to start his crusade, Swaffer published a stinging rebuke: "So the Billy Graham mission apparently is leaving a country where, according to Senator Kefauver, 'a national crime syndicate exists . . .' to convert from 'Socialism and its accompanying evils' a London which boasts the cleanest and most efficient municipal government possessed by any big city in the world! . . . Socialism indeed, by ushering in the Welfare State, saved Britain from degradations of poverty and injustice that might have brought about a revolution. More, its way to power was made more easy by the social crusade led by Dr. Temple, the Archbishop of Canterbury. . . . What does Billy Graham mean by the 'evil consequences' of Socialism? The abolition of the Poor Law? The National Health Service of which Pat Hornsby-Smith recently boasted in the States—until the American Medical Association complained—as though it were a Tory measure? Town planning? Family Allowances? Improved educational facilities? I urge the Bishop of Barking [one of Graham's London supporters] to disown this ignorant nonsense before the Big Business evangelist whom he sponsors, opens his crusade. I challenge him to deny that dry-rot in Church attendance began long before we had a Socialist majority. . . . And I urge him to call Billy Graham to repentance before he has the effrontery to start converting us!" [26]

Swaffer's revelation of Graham's reasons for coming to Britain disconcerted and shocked a number of Labour Members of Parliament who belonged to the Socialist Christian Group which had planned a dinner in Graham's honor at the House of Commons. They declared that they would attend no such dinner until Graham explained his position. Graham's supporters in England were equally stunned by the angry protests which followed the Swaffer article. Cablegrams began to reach Graham on board the liner "United States" three days from London. Graham at once cabled an explanation to his committee in London and sent a message to the editor of the *London Daily Herald*: "I have had my attention called to an article in Saturday's *Herald*. I deeply regret the situation which prompted it, one which was without my knowledge or authorization. By now I believe a full explanation is in your hands, but if in addition to the explanation you feel an apology to the Labour Party is needed you certainly have that, Sir. Sincerely, Billy Graham." [27]

Then, feeling that perhaps more was needed, Graham talked with the editor of the *Herald* on a ship-to-shore telephone: "It is all a horrible mistake," he said. "I never attacked Socialism. I can't tell the people of Britain how sorry I am. Secularism, not Socialism, is the word we meant. The calendar was written by an advertising firm in New York and I gather the word socialism was used as meaning secularism." [28] The Bishop of Barking, who like Graham, had little liking for socialism, nevertheless asked the Labour M. P.'s to reconsider their refusal to attend a dinner in Graham's honor. One of the Labour M. P.'s, Mr. Edward Evans, announced to the press that he would not attend such a dinner. He described Graham's explanation as a "fatuous disclaimer." [29] Graham's public relations director did not make matters better by trying to soothe British feelings with the remark that in America socialism and secularism meant the same thing. Members of Graham's executive committee in London refused to believe Graham's explanation. They told the editor of the *Daily Herald,* "The word socialism, when used [in the Graham calendar] was used deliberately." However, they went on, "It was used in the American sense with a small 's.' In that sense it has no political meaning of the kind it has in Britain." When asked why Graham had claimed that socialism was a typographical error for secularism, the spokesman for the London committee answered with a smile, "You caught him on the High Seas without his documents or his adviser." [30]

The frankness of the London committee, the naive dismay expressed by Graham at his error, and the immediate and humble apology mollified all but his bitter opponents. The London crusade, and even the House of Commons dinner, went on as scheduled and apparently the revival did not seriously suffer. But Graham's American supporters, who had raised half of the money to meet the London expenses, must have been somewhat puzzled by his remark a few days after he landed in London: "I am not anti-Socialist, anti-Liberal, or anti-Conservative. I have not even come here to fight Communism. I am completely neutral in politics." [31]

The problem of Graham's political conservatism came up a second time in London after he had left the city and returned to the United States. This second controversy grew out of Graham's connection with Kenneth de Courcy, editor of the extremely conservative *Intelligence Digest* of London. In September, 1954, De Courcy advertised in the *London Times* the inauguration of the *London Free Press,* a new paper which would, he said, have "a strong editorial slant fully supporting the Billy Graham message." The *British Weekly,* an interdenominational religious journal published in London and Edinburgh which had given Graham's revival strong support, expressed dismay that Graham would permit his name to be utilized by this "ultra-right wing" editor who had for years attacked the Labour party. A staff member of the *British Weekly* interviewed De

Courcy and quoted him as saying, "I am convinced it is impossible for a Biblical Christian to be a socialist. If you accept the Biblical view of history you are forced to adopt a position of extreme political conservatism." [32] De Courcy was a supporter of High Church Anglicanism and an admirer of the Bishop of Croydon, but in the conservative climate of the 1950's there was not a great deal of difference between the political views of many high churchmen and many fundamentalists. It was to this clientele that De Courcy's journals catered.

The *Intelligence Digest* had devoted considerable space to exalting Graham as "the most important single figure in the religious world today." The April, 1954, issue of that journal had a long article describing what it called the current "Revolution in America" of which it claimed that Graham was the leader. According to the anonymous writer of this article (presumably De Courcy himself) this revolution, which had been under way for some time, was directed by religious and conservative people against "Washington corruption," formal religion, materialistic education, Communist agencies which "were at work in the very heart of the Administration—directing American policy to suit Russia," and "a powerful propaganda" machine with "left-wing political associations" which "was teaching Americans to distrust and despise the very spirit of enterprise and adventure which made America great and powerful." Because of Graham's religious leadership in this revolution said De Courcy, the *Intelligence Digest* "investigated" his views and found "He is without doubt not very partial to Socialism."

De Courcy invited Graham to lunch with him as soon as he reached London in February, 1954. "Dr. Graham twice lunched at the *Intelligence Digest* offices," De Courcy reported to his readers in April, "and has on both occasions proved of absorbing interest. We have been tempted to ask him to address a meeting of our readers." [33] It was evidently at these luncheon meetings that De Courcy made arrangements with Graham to reprint some of his sermons in the *Intelligence Digest Supplement*. De Courcy hoped, he wrote, that Graham's revival would reach "the vast industrial masses" who are "almost totally materialistic." If Graham could do that he might help to influence the next national election in Britain. "Dr. Graham preaches that it is sinful to covet; yet Socialism is based upon that very thing. The Socialist covets what belongs to others and asks for Parliamentary sanction to take it. The implication of Dr. Graham's preaching is that such a form of Socialism is wrong. Dr. Graham says that to go slow on a job is to steal time for which someone has paid. This has distinct political implications. He preaches supreme parental responsibility whereas the Socialist believes that the State should partly assume that which Dr. Graham preaches is the duty of the parents. There can be little doubt that a major evangelical awakening would detach hundreds of thousands, if not millions from the Socialist concept." [34]

The article in the *British Weekly* in September, 1954, which called attention to De Courcy's use of Graham's name in order to advertise the *London Free Press* aroused anew the cries which Swaffer had raised in February. Graham had announced that he would return to Britain in 1955 to lead a crusade in Glasgow, and many Scottish ministers feared that if the working class were to associate Graham with De Courcy's obviously anti-Labour policies, they would never come to hear Graham. One of Graham's sponsors reportedly flew to America to obtain his explanation of this newest disclosure. The editor of the *British Weekly*, Shaun Herron, said that Graham should publicly announce that he had no connection with politics, with De Courcy's editorial policies, or with the *London Free Press*. Graham wrote a letter to Herron some weeks later stating, "It is difficult to understand why I should keep giving assurances in Britain that I have no political intentions. . . . I do not intend to be taken over by any political slant, nor do I intend to represent any political viewpoint. However, I cannot help the editorial support of any paper, whether it be extreme right or extreme left. I do not intend to repudiate anybody who may or may not support us. . . . I am just not going to get involved with politicians. . . . I have never seen or heard of the *London Free Press* although Jerry Beavan now informs me that he knew of its existence." [35] (Graham had, of course, heard of the *Intelligence Digest,* though he did not say so in this letter, and he had been quoting De Courcy's editorial remarks in his sermons since 1951.)[36] The editor of the *British Weekly* deplored Graham's "remarkable *naivete* in dealing with political matters" and expressed disappointment that Graham had not seen fit to discourage De Courcy from using his name. Nevertheless Graham's Glasgow crusade did not seem to suffer from his *gaffe* any more than the London crusade had suffered from his earlier one —which may have been some indication that very few of the working class attended either campaign.

These tempests over Graham's attitude toward the Labour party in Britain were scarcely noted in America, but no one who listened attentively to Graham's sermons could avoid agreeing with De Courcy that they expressed the sentiments of many of those conservative Americans who considered the New Deal–Fair Deal policies to be socialistic and hence detrimental. Graham was, if anything, less subtle in displaying his animosity toward the Democratic administration of Harry Truman than his animosity toward the labor unions. In a sermon delivered in January, 1951, he said, "The vultures are now encircling our debt-ridden inflationary economy with its fifteen-year record of deficit finance and with its staggering national debt, to close in for the kill." [37] The local newspaper of Columbia, South Carolina, remarked of one of his sermons there, "Mr. Graham tossed in a broadside at the deficit spending of the federal government declaring that if it is not stopped it will drag America into another depression." [38] In the fall of 1951 he predicted "an economic downfall" for America if the "give-away" program of foreign aid to Europe continued much longer. "The whole Western world is begging for more dollars—the barrel is almost empty—when it is empty—what then?" [39] He informed his audiences that "each one of us—adult or child— pays $2.50 a week for the Marshall Plan" but he said that

Marshall aid was not winning friends in Europe, for the Europeans resented handouts. In another sermon he maintained that one CARE package does more good than all the Marshall Plan aid.[40] This "give-away program is breaking our economic back" he declared six weeks before the election of 1952. "Where is it going to end? The American people want to know."[41] Graham's attitude toward Point Four aid to underdeveloped countries was equally disparaging. "Their greatest need is not more money, food, or even medicine; it is Christ. . . . Give them the Gospel of love and grace first and they will clean themselves up, educate themselves, and better their economic conditions."[42]

But his dislike for foreign aid and deficit spending was merely one of his minor complaints against the policies of Roosevelt and Truman. His major complaints were that the Democrats had permitted too much corruption and immorality in government, that they had been soft on communism and allowed subversives to hold key positions, that they had betrayed Chiang Kai-shek and Syngman Rhee by playing into the hands of the Russians at Teheran, Yalta, and Potsdam, that they had led the country into the Korean War without consulting the people, that once in the war they had failed to carry it through to total victory, and that they placed entirely too much faith in the United Nations. Graham did not adopt these views because the Republican party adopted them. His background, education, and theology all helped make them the natural ones for him. But it was probably his close association with some of the conservative Christian businessmen who supported his campaigns which more than anything else crystallized his views on politics and economics.

Graham's comments on partisan issues were sometimes mere hints or innuendos mixed in with general statements about the decadance of American morality or the dangerous era in which we live, but sometimes he allowed himself to be quite pointed in his comments. Many of his most partisan remarks have been made to his radio listeners on the grounds that it is a primary function of the "Hour of Deci-

sion" broadcast to provide a Christian interpretation of
current events. Graham repeatedly told his radio listeners,
"I hope you will make it a regular Sunday afternoon habit
to listen to the 'Hour of Decision' as we shall keep you
abreast of fast-moving world events and try to interpret
them for you in the light of Scripture." [43] Since he is introduced each week as "a man with God's message for these
crisis days" he apparently sees himself as a combination of
Christian news analyst and Biblical prophet.

During the years 1951-1952 Graham's attacks on corruption in government gradually built up to a crescendo that
coincided with the election campaign. Early in 1951 he
merely lumped this charge with other moral iniquities of the
day: "How long is this pure God going to endure our
divorce rate, our teen-age morals, our immorality in government circles, our truce-breaking, our drunkenness, our
swearing?" [44] Then, as Congressional committees began to
expose alleged illegalities in the conduct of government
bureaus like the Reconstruction Finance Corporation and
the Internal Revenue Department, he mentioned these as
specifically shocking examples of the nation's moral decay.
In a Christmas letter sent to his radio listeners in December,
1951, he listed "moral collapse" as one of the "fundamental
dangers of the day" and described it as follows: "A moral
collapse—the recent investigations by Congressional committees only scratch the surface of immorality in high places
—we are breaking apart from inside." Speaking on the
steps of the Capitol in Washington on February 23, 1952,
to a throng of thirty thousand, he warned, "We must continue to expose crimes and irregularities in government
wherever they may be found and enact strong legislation to
deal with them." [45] Throughout the summer of 1952 references to corruption and immorality in high places continued,
and finally by September he was using the current Republican campaign slogan, "We must clean up the mess in Washington." "We all seem to agree," he told a reporter in Pittsburgh at the start of his revival there two months before
the election, "there's a mess in Washington." [46] In his open-

ing sermon in Pittsburgh he remarked coyly, "All the trouble in Russia started in the Garden of Eden. All the mess in—I mustn't be political—I started to say this mess in Washington, but I'll just say the mess in my hometown of Asheville, North Carolina, started with Adam." [47]

Graham's comments on the closely related political issue of Communist infiltration into the government were equally pointed in these years. Sometimes, as in his sermon in Austin, Texas, he merely expressed fear over "the tranquil attitude to[ward] communism" in the country at large, or warned that "Communists and left-wingers" could sabotage the United States, or said there was "a fifth column in our midst." But during the height of the investigations into subversion in government conducted by the Jenner, Velde, and McCarthy committees, Graham said frankly, "While nobody likes a watch dog, and for that reason many investigation committees are unpopular, I thank God for men who, in the face of public denouncement and ridicule, go loyally on in their work of exposing the pinks, the lavenders, and the reds who have sought refuge beneath the wings of the American eagle and from that vantage point, try in every subtle, undercover way to bring comfort, aid, and help to the greatest enemy we have ever known—communism." [48]

For Graham, as for most frightened Americans, the dangers of communism were twofold. There was first the intellectual danger that Communists might somehow undermine Americans' faith in their own ideals by infiltrating into schools, colleges, unions, social organizations, the entertainment field, and the churches. The second was that they might infiltrate the American State Department, the armed services, and the military research projects and there help betray the nation to the Soviet Union through treasonous activity. The latter problem inevitably involved the question of foreign policy, past and present, and provided a simple explanation for America's international difficulties in terms of individual traitors. Graham lent his efforts to both aspects.

In the winter of 1950-1951 when the term McCarthyism

was just being born, Graham was telling his audiences about "over 1100 social sounding organizations that are communist or communist operated in this country. They control the minds of a great segment of our people; the infiltration of the left wing . . . both pink and red into the intellectual strata of America" has gone so far that our "educational [and] religious culture is almost beyond repair. . . ."[49] Communism, he said at a later date, "has attracted some of our famous entertainers, some of our keenest politicians, and some of our outstanding educators."[50] "There is a cancer eating at the heart and core of the American way of life, subversive groups seek to destroy us, Communists are doing their deadly work in government, education, and even in religion."[51]

When Senator McCarthy called for a revision of the Fifth Amendment so that witnesses before his committee could not invoke it, Graham told his radio audience that if it would take a change in the Constitution to ferret out the Communists and fellow travelers, "Then let's do it."[52] When Graham went to London in 1954 he was asked his opinion of McCarthy: "I have never met McCarthy, corresponded with him, exchanged telegrams or telephoned him. I have no comments to make on the senator." Pressed further as to whether a Christian should not have some comment to make on McCarthyism, he replied, "I am not answering that."[53] But when the United States Senate voted to censure McCarthy in December, 1955, Graham compared the action to Nero's fiddling while Rome burned. It looked, he said, as though the Senate was fiddling "over trifles" and "bringing disgrace to the dignity of American statesmanship" while American airmen languished in dirty Chinese prisons.[54]

The brunt of Graham's political interpolations, however, have been concerned with the Democratic appeasement of international communism under both Roosevelt and Truman. "The Korean War is being fought," Graham told his opening night congregation in Houston, in May, 1952, "because the nation's leaders blundered on foreign policy in the Far East. I do not think the men in Washington have any grasp of the Oriental mind; Alger Hiss shaped our foreign policy and some of the men who formulate it [now] have never been to the East." [55] Graham maintains that communism came to China largely because of America's "diplomatic betrayal" of Chiang Kai-shek at Yalta.[56] "We went to great lengths in appeasing them [the Communists] at Yalta," he insists, and Secretary of State Dean Acheson compounded the betrayal by refusing to let Chiang take part in the Japanese Peace Conference. "One of the amazing and humiliating things about the whole treaty was the ignoring and snubbing of Nationalist China." [57] "During the last three years," Graham said in 1953, "we have lost tremendous prestige in the entire Far East. We have shown our moral weaknesses. We have shown that when pressed we could betray our friends and compromise with the enemy. Our morally weak allies are now calling for the admission of Red China into the United Nations and crying for the scalp of Generalissimo Chiang Kai-shek in Formosa." [58]

Time and again Graham has gone out of his way to praise Chiang and Madam Chiang in his sermons. He calls attention not only to their devout, born-again Christianity, but to their staunch anticommunism and their "crack troops" which could be used to attack Mao Tse-tung. When, in 1953, it looked as though Mao might lead an attack on Formosa through Quemoy and Matsu Islands, Graham included in his radio program a personal interview with Chiang and a "special report" from the missionary-evangelist, Robert Pierce (President of World Vision, Inc., a fundamentalist missionary and social welfare enterprise), which emphasized the plight of Christian believers on these islands who were faced with atheistic communistic aggression.[59] In 1956 Graham was spreading rumors that "the Generalissimo may make the decision to invade the mainland this year." Graham was told, he said, that if Chiang "could stay one month on the mainland that whole armies would desert to his cause and that there would be a general uprising." [60]

And once again in the fall of 1958, when Quemoy and Matsu were for the second time under bombardment from the mainland, Graham interrupted a revival sermon in Charlotte, North Carolina, to ask for prayers for the Christians living on these islands; "Some of the finest Christians that I have ever met are on Formosa and on those offshore islands." "Suppose thousands of rounds of ammunition were being fired on Charlotte every day." He urged everyone in his audience to read the editorial in *Life* supporting the United States' policy of defending Chiang Kai-shek. Chiang is disliked by some people, said Graham, for "two basic reasons, apparently. One, he has courage enough to stand up against communism and the second is, he has been a staunch friend of the United States. Some people seem to take exception to those two things, and it is a very strange thing to me that is happening." [61]

Second only to his admiration for Chiang Kai-shek is Graham's admiration for Syngman Rhee, whom he refers to as "that stalwart old Methodist Christian." But there was some contradiction in Graham's mind over the Korean War. On the whole he disapproved of the war and of the way America entered it. In a sermon illustration which he has used repeatedly, Graham asks his audiences, "How many of you voted to go into the Korean War? I never did." He goes on to explain that the United States entered the war because "one man sitting in Washington" made the decision.[62] On the eve of the 1952 election the *Pittsburgh Press* noted that Graham "drew a rather startling parallel between President Truman and Adam" by comparing the start of the Korean War with Adam's original sin in the Garden of Eden. The illustration went as follows: "Adam was the head of the human race, even as in this country our President is the head of our government. . . . When the President makes a decision, that decision stands as the decision of the entire people. When Mr. Truman went to war in Korea, you and I went to war in Korea whether we liked it or not." [63] The implication is clear that all men must suffer for the sins of their federal head in this day and age as in the past.

However, once the United States was in the war, Graham

was appalled that the administration did not follow General Douglas MacArthur's advice and push the war through to a victorious conclusion even if it meant bombing airfields and military bases inside Communist China. He called the Truman administration "cowardly" for not listening to MacArthur and made repeated references to "this twilight war," "this half-forgotten war," "this half-hearted war," "this terrible bloody tragedy." "It is almost beyond belief that the American people will allow such a half-hearted war to drag on with an average now of nearly two thousand casualties every week." [64]

And when MacArthur was relieved of his command in Korea, Graham showed great restraint by saying, "Ladies and gentlemen, I am not a politician; I refrain from making statements on political matters; I am not choosing sides in the dismissal of General MacArthur. However, there are certain factors relative to Christian Missions in the Orient that need to be brought to the attention of the American people at this moment." He then went on to say how much MacArthur had done for missionaries in Japan and concluded by reporting what his colleague in the Youth for Christ movement, David Morken, cabled from Formosa about the MacArthur dismissal. Morken stated that all Christians in the Orient "were deeply grieved and all felt that Christianity had suffered another major blow." [65] When MacArthur returned to the United States, Graham could not refrain from comparing him to George Washington. He called the general "almost regal" in his bearing, and asserted a year or so later that MacArthur had accurately predicted the failure of the whole notion of a limited war.[66] Two days before the 1952 election, Graham stated to his twenty million listeners on the "Hour of Decision," "We need a new foreign policy to end this bloodletting in Korea." [67] And in 1953 when a Congressional committee uncovered some apparent mismanagement in the conduct of the war, during its early phases, Graham deplored the fact that "someone in Washington decided" that American boys had been "expendable," and he denounced the "diplomats who drank cocktails in Washington" while our soldiers were dying in Korea.[68]

Graham was so concerned over the dangers of communism that he even heckled the Republican administration when it sought to come to terms with North Korean leaders. "Watch these peace conferences," Graham told his audience in August, 1953, "study the communiques carefully and demand that there be no secret agreements that will sell us down the river." [69] In the same sermon he said, "Let us pray that we will not lose this peace as we lost the peace after World War II. Let us pray that we will not listen to the Alger Hisses and the other traitors that have betrayed us. . . . Every boy that died in Korea died because of the tragic failures at the post-war peace conferences." When Syngman Rhee protested against the peace treaty and threatened to continue the war even if he had to do so alone, Graham injected this comment into one of his sermons in Dallas: "The Communists have maneuvered us almost into war with Korea and with Chiang Kai-shek. Isn't it strange to you that we had three great and strong men in the Far East—men whose moral stature and integrity were unquestioned—and we pulled MacArthur back to this country; we pulled the rug out from under Chiang Kai-shek, and now we are almost at war with Syngman Rhee. We need to pray for General Eisenhower. . . ." [70]

Graham helped to provide one other scapegoat in these years of hysteria. In addition to the Alger Hisses, bungling leaders, cocktail-drinking diplomats, and Satan-inspired Communists or left-wingers, he pointed his finger at the United Nations. "We have been caught in the web of the United Nations," he said, quoting an editorial in *Life* in reference to the Korean War: "They set the policies, we shed the blood and pay the bills." [71] And during the Hungarian crisis in December, 1956, he again asserted "the United Nations does not dare to stand up to Russia" and assailed it for ineffectiveness. Graham's explanation of why "the United Nations has become almost the laughing stock of the entire world" was simple enough. "At the first meeting of the United Nations in San Francisco there was no prayer made to God for guidance and blessing. We were afraid that the Godless, atheistic Communists would not like it, so we bowed in deference to Russia." [72]

The United Nations was not a significant political issue in the presidential campaigns of 1952 or 1956 except among the most extreme conservatives and isolationists. Where Graham disclosed his partisanship most clearly was in the tone he adopted toward the three leading figures in the Republican administration, Eisenhower, Dulles, and Nixon. He paid them a deference which he seldom accorded Truman, Stevenson, or Acheson. The *Houston Post*, reporting a Graham sermon in that city in May, 1952, said, "Emphasizing that he does not become involved in politics the Rev. Mr. Graham said that the country needs a President who has the fortitude and moral courage to clean out the 'grafters and hangers-on' who come out in every business." A month later, on June 29, he said "The nation desperately needs a strong spiritual leader" who will guarantee a "clean-up" in Washington. On the Sunday after the inaugural in 1953, Graham declared, "President Eisenhower made history yesterday when he led Americans in prayer at the inauguration. . . . The overwhelming majority of the American people felt a little more secure realizing that we have a man who believes in prayer at the helm of our government at this crucial hour." [73] After attending a prayer meeting in Washington with the President in February, 1953, Graham said he sensed a new feeling of unity and hope in the country and that it looked as though "God is giving us a respite, a new chance." There will be a new foreign policy now, he announced; "We are no longer going to be pushed around" by the Communists.[74] A few weeks later he compared the new President's first speech on foreign policy to the Sermon on the Mount.[75]

Typical of the contrast between Graham's attitudes toward the Truman and Eisenhower administrations was his treatment of their Middle East policies. When the Iranian government seized the Anglo-Iranian oil fields in 1952, Graham chose to publicize the fact that "One of President Truman's representatives was confused and bewildered by it all and seemingly had found no real solution." [76] When the Eisenhower administration was confronted with the crisis over Suez five years later, Graham praised the "bold move" embodied in "the Eisenhower doctrine." [77]

Prominent in Graham's crusade publicity after 1952 was a photograph taken of him and President Eisenhower sitting together on a sofa examining an open Bible. Graham took occasion to remind his listeners of his frequent visits to the White House and to the President's Gettysburg farm and informed them of what he and the President had talked about.

Equally frequent and well-publicized have been his meetings with Vice-President Nixon and former Secretary of State John Foster Dulles. When many critics of the Vice-President were calling him hypocritical and insincere for certain inconsistencies in his opinions, Graham made a point of telling his followers, "I disagree with those who say that Mr. Nixon is not sincere. I believe him to be most sincere and like the President, he is a splendid churchman." [78] As a personal friend and golfing partner of the Vice-President, Graham has escorted him to various denominational conventions and summer Bible conferences, introducing him to religious leaders and presenting him from the platform as a speaker to the assembled church delegates. During Graham's crusade in New York City in 1957 Mr. Nixon was the featured guest at Graham's climactic rally in Yankee Stadium.

Despite Graham's occasional qualms about the "new foreign policy" of the administration (particularly in regard to what he calls "unholy alliances with godless nations"— presumably Yugoslavia and the Mohammedan and Buddhist countries of the Middle and Far East) Graham never openly attacked it and frequently went out of his way to defend Secretary Dulles. In 1956, for example, when the Secretary of State was being criticized for stating that the Republican administration had three times rescued the United States from the brink of war, Graham wrote an article for *Christian Life* magazine in which he declared of Dulles, "I believe that in spite of a few mistakes he has made that he has been one of the hardest working and most effective Secretaries of State in American history." [79] And when Dulles was accused of defending colonialism because of his remarks on the rightful ownership of Goa by the Portuguese, Graham had an interview with him and afterwards told reporters that he thought Mr. Dulles had been "misinterpreted." "I don't think Mr. Dulles meant in the slightest to endorse colonialism. I got the impression [from our talk] that the United States' policy is not to support colonialism in any way." [80]

In return, the Secretary of State, like the President and the Vice-President, endorsed Graham's revivals and even put a seal of semiofficial approval on Graham's international tours. "He seemed to feel," Graham wrote of Mr. Dulles's attitude toward the Graham crusade in India in 1956, "that particularly after the visit of Messrs. Khrushchev and Bulganin of Russia to India that America was in need of someone that could appeal to the masses of India." [81] It is doubtful, however, whether Graham did much to win the masses of India by his remark, after his visit, that the United States could better secure the friendly cooperation of Prime Minister Nehru by giving him personal gifts, like a "streamlined, air-conditioned train or a new Cadillac, pure white" than by giving large grants of aid to India. Gifts of this sort, said Graham, "would do more to demonstrate the friendliness of the Americans than all the millions of dollars given in economic aid." [82]

In making any over-all evaluation of Billy Graham's political views it is necessary to keep two things in mind: first, that he is only indirectly concerned with politics and second, that his comments on political matters have, on the whole, become less rather than more pointed as his own popularity has increased. He urges all Christians to vote, but he tells them to vote for Christian men and Christian principles and not for any particular party program or party candidate.

If his comments on political or economic matters are interpreted by his listeners to favor the Republican rather than the Democratic party, Graham would sincerely deny that such was his intention. As a professional evangelist interested in church unity for the sake of saving souls, he recognizes that avowed political partisanship would be disastrous. Yet he cannot, he feels, ignore the critical domestic and foreign issues of his day. They cry out for Christian comment. The fact that his comments are more partisan than he perhaps realizes is due to personal predilections on these matters which he cannot or will not admit.

Moreover, it is probable that his sympathetic attitude toward the Republican administration is largely due to his belief that Dwight D. Eisenhower himself is a man above party, a man who was not and is not motivated by the personal ambitions of the ordinary politician. Since Graham, like most neofundamentalists, believes that all "humanistic" schemes for settling the world's problems are inadequate and futile, politics becomes for him primarily a matter of finding the God-appointed leader who will bring the people out of their trouble by following the dictates of God. "The people are hungry for a moral crusade," Graham said in the spring of 1952, "and they need a Moses or a Daniel to lead them in this hour." [83] For many Americans, and particularly for those who share Graham's religious views, General Eisenhower became the leader they sought.

There is in Graham's preaching, as in that of all pietistic revivalists, an authoritarianism which stems from the belief that the best possible political system is after all a theocracy. As one of the leading figures in the National Association of Evangelicals, Donald Grey Barnhouse, said in 1945, "The best type of government that men could have is not democracy. It is undoubtedly true that the best type of government that could be on earth is an absolute dictatorship but with the proviso that the Lord Jesus Christ be the Dictator." [84] The strong strain of perfectionism which runs through Graham's preaching and which makes him unsatisfied with all man-made systems makes him long for a charismatic leader, a man of God, who will rule as a benevolent dictator because he will rule according to God's laws. As in the election of Saul, however, Graham believes the people should have some part in the choice of their ruler. He is not antidemocratic in that respect. There is always a danger, of course, that a prominent revivalist may someday mistake a demagogue or a tyrant for a God-appointed leader. But Graham has so far seemed content with the normal American electoral process. Nevertheless, during the 1952 election Graham did think it his duty to urge born-again Christians to form a godly "voting bloc" which could use its power against presumably less godly voting blocs. "In the coming election," he said in April, 1952, "there's going to be the Jewish bloc, there's going to be the Roman Catholic bloc, there's going to be the labor bloc, there's going to be the Negro bloc, there's going to be the Polish bloc, there's going to be the Irish bloc. They will put on tremendous pressure. They will vote as blocs. Some of them will almost hold the balance of power. Why should not Evangelicals across America be conditioned and cultured and instructed until we, too, can make our voice known?" [85]

Whether the decreasing number of political comments in Graham's sermons since 1952 has been due to a growing maturity, as some of his friends claim, or whether it is because he finds the policies of the Republican administration more satisfactory is a moot point. The test may come in 1960. It is indicative, perhaps, that when the predominantly Democratic Eighty-sixth Congress opened in January, 1959, Graham warned his radio listeners to beware of high-spending "liberals" and "eggheads" who might vote to give "another billion to Tito" and thus take another twenty-five dollars out of the pockets of every American family. [86] But even if the Democrats win the election of 1960, it is unlikely that Graham will do more than make equivocal remarks on divisive issues. For example, when questioned about his views on birth control after the statement concerning the issue by the Roman Catholic bishops in November, 1959, Graham said that while he could find nothing in the Scriptures condemning the responsible use of birth control, nevertheless he would agree with President Eisenhower and Senator John F. Kennedy that the United States government should not make information on this subject available as part of its technical aid to nations facing a population problem even if they asked for it.[87] Billy Graham is wise enough to see that if he is to continue to lead city-wide crusades in all sections of the country and in all parts of the world his politics will have to be more, not less, otherworldly. Or at least he will have to choose for comment in his sermons only such issues as all men of good will can agree upon. The trouble is that there are few such issues which can long sustain the tremendous cooperative efforts needed for mass revival crusades. And this is where the ultimate test of a revivalist's greatness enters.

CHAPTER 6

Pulpit Techniques

> *Just one wrong move by some of our diplomats could plunge us all into eternity by intercontinental missiles and hydrogen bombs. . . . Come and give your life to Christ while there is time.*
>
> BILLY GRAHAM [1]

Neither Graham's neofundamentalist theology nor his conservative politics adequately accounts for his popularity. It is the combination of his theological and social message with the manner in which he conveys it that makes him a great evangelist. Pulpit technique in revivalism derives first and most directly from the personality and delivery of the evangelist. But equally important are the nature of the appeals and motivations for action which he stresses.

Billy Graham has those rare qualities of personality and rhetorical talent which make him an attractive and compelling figure on the platform—a man with whom the audience immediately feels not only a bond of sympathy and affection, but also a man whom they admire and respect. His message is timely, but it is the way he delivers his message that establishes the rapport which is the *sine qua non* of revival preaching.

Graham is personally a very likeable young man. He was barely thirty-one when he became nationally famous

MF Hom 57 in M34

(Billy Sunday, by comparison, was almost fifty-two). He is handsome, friendly, ingenuous, and open. Success has not marred his charm and it has added greatly to his poise. There is no doubt about his devotion to his calling or the burning conviction behind his preaching. But his relaxed cordiality off the platform disappears as soon as he steps into his spotlighted pulpit. He becomes as taut and alert as a highly trained boxer stepping into the ring against an unknown challenger. Although he has fought hundreds of similar battles and knows all the tricks, each encounter is different and his own inner tension quickly communicates itself to the throng.

At first Graham tried to model his oratory on the highly individualized style of Walter Winchell, but he soon developed a delivery more suited to his own personality. Its dominant characteristic is the rapid, staccato manner in which he ejaculates his short, simple sentences. He speaks with the strident urgency of a messenger of catastrophe. Though he keeps an outline of his sermon on the lectern before him, he seldom needs to refer to it. His Carolina sand-hill accent, though noticeable in pronunciation, does not impede the swift torrent of his words. He does not drawl; he barks commands. Even his doctrinal sermons on love and grace are delivered in a high-pitched, stomach-tightening tone which seems more like a tongue-lashing than a sermon. As Graham once described his own feelings while he preached, "I felt as though I had a rapier in my hand and, through the power of the Bible, was slashing deeply into men's consciences, leading them to surrender to God." [2] It is a slashing which leaves few listeners unscathed.

The strident quality of his voice is matched by the restless, forceful gestures of his hands. He "repeatedly banged his fists on the pulpit, clenched them in symbolic anguish against his temples, and swept the huge stadium with a punctuating forefinger," said a reporter in Houston.[3] Throughout much of his sermon he holds a limp-covered open Bible in one hand, slapping it as he quotes one text after another, lifting it on high as he shouts, "Billy Graham doesn't say it; the Bible says it," brandishing it like a sword as he warns of judgment to come. In Dallas "he paced the boards and beat on his chest" as he exhorted. When he got too hot, he took off his coat without breaking his flow of words and preached the remainder of the sermon in his shirtsleeves.⁴ He strides back and forth across his platform so constantly as he talks that, like Billy Sunday, he walks a mile during the course of each sermon. While he talks, Cliff Barrows sits behind him on the platform carefully, but unostentatiously, playing out and pulling in the cord which runs from Graham's lapel microphone to the amplifying mechanism.

The drama of Graham's delivery is heightened by the way he acts out his words. As he retells the old Biblical stories of heroes, villains, and saints, he imitates their voices, assumes their postures, struts, gesticulates, crouches, and sways to play each part. He even portrays the motions of the animals in his stories. "If he describes a bucking bronco, as he did the night I was there," said one observer in Washington, D. C., "Graham bobs up and down like a man trying desperately to stay in the saddle. . . . He darts from side to side, from back to front [of the platform]." ⁵ He is a master of comedy as well as of drama. "He demonstrated his impression of a pig prancing in the limelight" one night to illustrate the point that even if you gave a pig a bath, "gave it a Toni, and sprinkled it with Chanel number five" it would still, like an unregenerate sinner, revert to the mud puddle as soon as you let it loose.⁶ "Billy Graham had the audience in stitches of laughter last night," according to one report, when he described the foibles of modern marriage and mimicked the tones of the complaining wife and the bored husband.⁷

He frequently interspersed jokes in his sermons to relieve the tension built up by his hammering on fear, guilt, and judgment. "When asked by her minister if she knew what was in the Bible, one little girl proudly replied that she knew everything that was in it, and proceeded to list 'the picture of her sister's boy friend, the recipe for mother's favorite hand lotion, a lock of baby brother's hair, and the ticket for Pa's watch.'"[8] In one of his sermons on the teen-age problem, he says, "The old-fashioned motto of old was: 'What is a home without a mother?' Now a more appropriate one would be: 'What is home without a can-opener?'"[9] He remarks in his sermon on adultery and divorce that "Our young people today know far more about the statistics of Brigitte Bardot than they do about the Seventh Commandment."[10] The women in his audience laugh heartily when he tells the story of a lady who said to her minister, " 'This morning I stood in front of the mirror for half an hour admiring my beauty. Do you think I committed the sin of pride?' The minister replied, 'No, I don't think you committed the sin of pride—it was more the sin of a faulty imagination.'"[11] He is even willing to inject humor into his invitations to sinners to come forward and accept Christ: "Father, Mother, with grey hairs and bifocals and bunions and bulges, have you given yourself to Christ?"[12]

Like Billy Sunday, Graham frequently uses slang expressions to make his sermons more racy and down-to-earth. Such phrases as "Now you're cookin' with gas," "I was gettin' no place fast," "You ain't seen nothin' yet," or "Boy, you couldn't see him for dust" punctuate his stories. Like Sunday he frequently tells Biblical stories in modern vernacular: "In Noah's day people laughed. They said, 'Ha, judgment coming on the world? The old man's gone crazy! Why the long-bearded fool, there's a screw loose somewhere. . . .'"[13] When speaking to predominantly male audiences, as in military camps, Graham's slang is even more pronounced: "Some big guys think they're having themselves a good time, just lying and cheating and stealing and lusting. But believe me, the gang that are having the best time are the gang who know Jesus Christ. It ain't just a thing for sissies. It's for real he-blooded guys. Oh, yes, that's for you, too."[14] Even when speaking to regular revival congregations he tries to convince young people that

Christianity is a manly religion: "Don't you think of our Lord as a weakling or a sissy. He was a strong man. He would have been a real success on the football field." [15] One of his most popular sermons is called "The Greatest Battle Ever Fought" in which, said a reporter, the "evangelist uses ring jargon" to describe "Christ's battle with Satan" in the wilderness. "Coupling reverence with a sports announcer's verve" he told the story with such interpolations as "The Devil lets loose another powerful punch. . . . Jesus picked up the word of God and flung it back at the Devil. . . . Round 3: the Devil's coming out with everything he's got. He hits Jesus with a right uppercut. Then a left uppercut." [16] When Billy Sunday used such language in 1915 many considered it sacrilegious, but no one seemed to mind it in the 1950's.

✓At some meetings the reverence of a religious service is suspended momentarily as Graham introduces various cowboy and cowgirl movie stars like Roy Rogers and Dale Evans. The crowds "whooped and yelled at the Western stars" forgetting that these celebrities were born-again Christians who had appeared at Graham's request to give a word of Christian testimony.[17] At such services Graham usually delivers his sermon called "The Last Round-Up" in which he concludes by asking the people before him whether on Judgment Day they would be wearing "the brand of Jesus."

Graham often captures the attention of his audience by references to contemporary events which he weaves into his sermons as illustrative material. The sudden deaths of King George VI, Senator Robert A. Taft, Senator Pat McCarran, Senator Charles W. Tobey, illustrated the danger of delay in neglecting salvation, for even the greatest men may be called to meet their Maker at a moment's notice. Interest is also aroused by referring to the marriages and divorces of celebrities like Marilyn Monroe, Joe DiMaggio, Ingrid Bergman, Barbara Hutton, Susan Hayward, in illustrating some point on the problem of the home. When he is talking to young people he is apt to compare the football hero, Pete Dawkins of West Point ("He is the next General MacArthur,

so they say") with the rock and roll singer, Elvis Presley
("Elvis said himself he got so bored that he just stared at
the walls").[18] In Toronto in 1955 he injected this comment
into one of his sermons: "I thought about Ernest Hemingway, who has had four wives; Ernest Hemingway, one of
the world's great writers, who has been known for his doubting about God. He got out of one plane that crashed, and
he got into another plane that crashed and burned. Could
it be that God saved Ernest Hemingway so he might know
the mercy of Jesus Christ?" [19]

Quotations from prominent citizens like J. Edgar Hoover,
Winston Churchill, Arnold Toynbee, Nathan M. Pusey, C. S.
Lewis, and William Vogt reinforce Graham's views concerning the desperate moral condition of the world. And Graham is always ready to relate what Churchill, Eisenhower,
or some prominent general or senator said to him "only the
other day" concerning the dangers, corruptions, and military problems of the moment. "When I met Winston
Churchill he said to me, 'Young man, do you see any hope
for the world?'" "President Eisenhower told me, 'Billy, I
believe one reason I was elected President was to lead
America in a religious revival.'" "A Congressman told me
recently that immorality was the curse of Washington."
"Last week I was talking to one of the richest men in the
world. He put his hand on my shoulder and said, 'Billy,
I'm going to lean heavily on you.' I answered, 'Don't lean
on me, sir. I am only a man. Lean on Christ.'" [20]

Graham ensures an attentive audience by giving his sermons provocative and intriguing titles and then advertising
them a week in advance. Some of the more tantalizing titles
include, "Life's Most Embarrassing Moment," "The Greatest
Sin a Man Can Commit," "The Greatest Sin in Dallas" (or
in whatever city he happens to be in at the time), "The
Unpardonable Sin," "America's Greatest Sin," "Living High,
Wide and Handsome," and "The Greatest Cocktail Party in
History."

By and large Graham's sermons are masterpieces of popular rhetoric. In addition to drama, mimicry, slang, and

tension-relieving humor, Graham is a master of invective, pathos, and the purple passage. Stories of faithful mothers, ungrateful children, sickness, parental pride, homecoming, and death fill his sermons on "Heaven," "Mother's Day," "Father's Day," "The Home," and "Hope in Death." Here is an example of the homely touch: "The little group of loved ones gather on the porch in the summer and by the fireside in winter, but how quickly the children grow up and leave the parent nest; how often the silent messenger comes to rob the homes of their brightest and best. Dear as our homes may be, they are not permanent. Sometimes I look at my own children and can hardly believe they are growing up so fast. Soon they will be gone and Mrs. Graham and I will be alone in an empty house that once rang with the laughter of children." [21]

And this is a typical purple passage: "The secret of America is not found in her whirling wheels or streamlined industry, nor in the towering skyscrapers of our teeming cities where clever men of commerce meet. It is not found in the rich, lush prairies laden with golden grain, nor in her broad green meadows where fat cattle graze. The secret of America is not found in her modern scientific laboratories where keen, trained minds seek out the mysteries of the atom, nor in the stately halls of her many universities and colleges where ambitious young men and women pursue their quest for knowledge and skills. The secret of America is found in the faith that abides in the hearts and homes of our fair land." [22]

A deathbed scene: "Some time ago I read the story of a young girl who lay on her bed in the hospital with a fatal illness. She was the only child, and the idol of her parents. Her every whim had been gratified. One day the doctor came to the room and after the examination whispered in the mother's ear. The sick girl heard the message. Calling her mother to the bedside she said, 'Mother, you have taught me how to dance, how to sip cocktails, how to hold my cigarette, and how to dress. But one thing you have failed to teach me, and that is, how to die.'" [23]

This is coupled with the story of the poor old widow who raised chickens, "took in washing, and did other humble work" to save enough money to send her boy to Emory College. "The son worked hard to get himself through college. He graduated with high honors and won a gold medal for special excellence in study. When it came time for him to graduate he went to the mountain home for his mother and said, 'Mother, you must come down and see me graduate.' 'No,' said his mother, 'I have nothing fit to wear and you would be ashamed of your poor old mother before all those grand people.' 'Ashamed of you!' he said, with eyes filled with filial love. 'Ashamed of you, mother, never! I owe everything I am to you. . . .' " [24]

And for vitriolic denunciation that equals anything Billy Sunday ever expressed about Kaiser Wilhelm and the Huns, here is Graham's view of Karl Marx and socialism: "Karl Marx—a subtle, clever, degenerate materialist—authored this philosophy of world socialism. Having filled his intellectual craw with all the filth of Europe's gutters and garbling perverted German philosophies and half-truths, he spewed this filthy, corrupt, ungodly, unholy doctrine of world socialism over the gullible peoples of a degenerate Europe." [25]

Graham is also master of the shock technique in oratory. According to one report, he told an audience in New Orleans that the only cure for swearing was to "Wash your mouth out with the blood of Christ and nail your tongue to the Cross." [26] He warned young people that God knew all about "that sin you committed last night in a parked automobile." [27] With his usual vividness he portrayed in detail the various crimes of juvenile delinquents, "horse-whipping young girls," "pouring gasoline over an old man and setting him on fire just to see him burn," torturing "younger children for hours in a secluded place and then [forcing] them to participate in perversions." [28] He told of wartime atrocities in which "Soldiers are reported to have severed ears from prisoners, tied live grenades to screaming prisoners, poured gasoline over the

bodies of wounded men and ignited the human torches." [29]
During the Hungarian revolt he claimed that rape was so
common in Hungary under Russian rule that no woman
from ten to seventy escaped it.[30]

· ⌊The purpose of these lurid remarks is to point out "the
exceeding sinfulness of sin" and to make people turn from it
in revulsion.⌉ But even an amateur psychologist can see that
this rhetorical device is also instrumental in creating the
emotional tension which seeks the catharsis of confession,
repentance, and forgiveness. The suppressed passions and
hidden urges in all human beings respond to such images
and among the pious folk who make up the bulk of Graham's audience the reaction takes the form not only of revulsion but of intensification of guilt and anxiety. Each individual recognizes his own worst impulses in the sins Graham so graphically portrays and each longs for some release. ⌊Sometimes the conversion experience satisfactorily
provides this. ⸜ Sometimes it does not. In either case this
type of revival preaching can cause serious mental upset to
unstable individuals. As a result of Graham's campaign in
Greensboro, North Carolina, "Sixty-nine doctors in Greensboro reported 58 cases of serious emotional disturbance
which they attributed to the Crusade.⌉ [31]

At this point Graham's delivery merges with the second
aspect of putting across his message—his motivational appeals. Graham does not deny that the process of conversion may, and probably will, involve emotionalism. "I find
it hard to think that the preaching of John the Baptist,
Christ, and the Apostles set no emotion aflame," he says,
and he insists, "Fear is a legitimate motive" in evangelism.
But like all professional revivalists, he deplores any type of
hysteria or any demonstrative exhibitions of feelings at his
meetings. "We never have any shouting or outbursts of any
kind." [32] Like Billy Sunday and D. L. Moody, Graham per- ✗
mits no one to shout "Amen" or "Hallelujah," no clapping
of hands, "no foaming at the mouth" or rolling in the aisles.
He seeks rapt attention at all times, and the ushers and
counselors at his meetings are instructed to quiet down or

remove anyone who in any way distracts attention from the sermon. Mass revivalism seeks a mass response. The audience is to react as a well-disciplined unit, not as a mob of excited individuals. Strangely enough, individualism is, in this respect, out of place in modern revivalism. Graham could arouse emotional hysteria easily enough, but if he did he would soon lose the majority of his church support.

Graham replies to critics of his emotionalism and his "fear technique" by pointing out that he uses many other appeals beside fear. In fact, there is a wide variety of appeals which he utilizes, as did his predecessors. His use of fear and shock is generally coupled with the use of love and reward. Professional revivalists have always denied that they sought irrational, spontaneous, emotional responses. Religion, they insist, is a reasonable proposition. Revival sermons are reasonable appeals to man's better nature based on the assumption that conversion is a reasonable requirement imposed on reasonable men by an essentially benevolent and loving God. It is true that Graham emphasizes God's justice, wrath, and righteousness to a greater extent than either Moody or Sunday, but he by no means excludes mention of God's love, grace, and mercy.

Graham even maintains that "God wants us to have a good time. We're to enjoy life in the right way." He acknowledges that most of his auditors are decent, respectable people. "I believe every person in this building is counting on being in Heaven." "Everybody here I presume believes in God. You believe in the Bible. You believe in the Church. You believe in God." And he even states that for the agnostic getting saved may be viewed simply as a matter of insurance—just in case there is an after-life: "I want to ask you, Mr. Agnostic, suppose, just suppose you wake up and find there was a hell after all. Suppose there were only one chance in a hundred that there is a hell. . . . Then it would be worth giving everything you have got to escape the place that Jesus called hell." [33]

In examining Graham's various appeals or motivations to action, the first fact to strike the observer is that each of

Graham's sermons follows a readily discernible pattern. Each begins with an attempt to create a feeling of uneasiness, guilt, or anxiety. Tension is built up by showing that this anxiety is justifiable, that all men are guilty of sin and deserve the worst kind of punishment. Then the next step is to proclaim that fortunately there is a way out of this human predicament. Here Graham explains God's plan of redemption for sinful men. The final steps in the sermon show how reasonably, simply, and quickly salvation can be obtained. And the sermon closes with the inevitable note of urgency to the effect that if the sinner does not make up his or her mind to obtain salvation at once, tonight, this very moment, by walking up the aisle in the inquiry room, then it may be too late forever: sudden death, the trump of doom, the cooling of ardor, the departure of the Holy Spirit, the hardening of the heart—all these make it probable that this moment is their one moment of decision. As the evangelist gives the invitation to come and accept Christ, he points out that those who do not come forward are virtually rejecting Him forever.

This pattern has been the basic one for revival preaching for 150 years or more. The fear of hell and the joy of heaven have been the basic motives and provided the fundamental appeal of all revivalists. But what differentiates one revivalist from another and one period of awakening from another is not this otherworldly appeal, but the this-worldly statement of its meaning. What does hell mean and what does heaven mean in the language of each generation? And more important, what may the man who obtains salvation expect in this world during the rest of his life? What are the earthly rewards for God's chosen and what earthly punishments lie in store for those who reject him?

In his early days as an evangelist Graham portrayed heaven and hell in the literal terms of the Bible. Hell, he assured his audiences, consisted primarily of a lake of burning brimstone in which all sinners were perpetually boiled.[34] Heaven was "a place as real as Los Angeles, London, or Algiers. . . . It has streets of gold, gates of pearl, and trees which bear twelve different crops a year." Heaven was also described as "a place where there will be no sorrow, no parting, no pain, no sickness, no death, no quarrels, no misunderstandings, no sin, and no cares." [35] He described the marriage feast of the Lamb after the day of Judgment: "I'm going to be there. Boy, what a banquet that is going to be. The angels are going to serve us manna from heaven. Talk about a banquet at Buckingham Palace or a banquet at some ritzy place in Miami. Why those are like pauper meals." [36]

But in later sermons Graham said it did not matter whether heaven literally has streets of gold or not, for it represents reconciliation and fellowship with God and Christ. And similarly, it does not matter whether hell-fire is literal or not. It is a symbol of punishment: "Hell essentially and basically is banishment from the presence of God. . . . Whether there is fire in Hell or not is not the all-important question. . . . Whatever Hell is, it is going to be a terrible and awful place." [37] This willingness to adopt the figurative or symbolic meaning of the after-life has considerably enlarged the appeal of Graham's message to nonfundamentalists. Some of his fundamentalist followers, however, accuse him of having departed from the old-time religion for this equivocation. Yet Graham has not actually repudiated hell-fire, he simply has ceased to insist upon it.[38]

As for his portrayal of the earthly lot of the born-again Christian, Graham is often contradictory and confusing. On the one hand he pietistically asserts that the way of the Christian is difficult and filled with hardship. The Christian can expect only scorn, abuse, ridicule, and persecution in this world, for this world belongs to Satan and is ruled by the ungodly. "God does not promise the Christians an easy pathway to Heaven, nor does God promise flowery beds of ease. . . . We have been called to suffer and follow the footsteps of the Man of Sorrows. This world is not a place of bliss for the Christian." [39] On the other hand, born-again Christians have the peace which passeth understanding. As sons and heirs of God they have conquered the things of this world. They are free in a way which no non-Christian can

ever be. They are happy, secure, contented beyond all
men: "Christ can take discouragement and despondency out
of your life. He can put a spring in your step and give you
a thrill in your heart and a purpose in your mind. Optimism and cheerfulness are products of knowing Christ." [40]

While these two prospects are not necessarily contradictory if the separation of the material from the spiritual world
is kept in mind, Graham does not always do this. He cannot resist offering his audiences very concrete rewards in
this life if they will accept God's offer of pardon. In doing
so, however, he occasionally passes over the line from pietism to Pelagianism and joins hands with the neomodernist,
Norman Vincent Peale. Theologically Peale's religion, based
as it is upon a mixture of popular psychiatry, autosugges-
tion, and mystic faith, is a far cry from the neofundamentalism which Graham professes. And yet Graham has frequently expressed his admiration for Peale and Peale has
actively participated in Graham's revival campaigns. Some
of Graham's sermons sound as if they were inspired by *The
Power of Positive Thinking* rather than by the Bible. They
have such titles as "The Life That Wins," "What God Can
Do for You," "The Cure for Discouragement," "Are You Getting What You Want?" "The Cause and Cure of Uncertainty," "Partners with God," "The Cure for Anxiety," and
"Victorious Christian Living." What is more, the message
of these sermons, like Peale's, is that man can call upon the
power of God, can harness the dynamic forces of the universe to his own personal life, and through Christian faith
attain the solution for all his earthly woes. When preaching
in this vein Graham offers the born-again Christian not only
peace of mind and peace of soul but wealth, success, popularity, and influence. Since Graham cannot help equating
Christianity with the Protestant ethic and the Protestant
ethic with the success myth, he often repudiates the basically otherworldly character of pietism.

For example in his sermon "Partners with God" which
Graham frequently gives when business groups are present
in his audience he remarks: "I know a businessman in De-

troit, Michigan, who made a promise to God that he would
tithe his entire income to the work of the Lord. He said
his business had tripled and that God had more than fulfilled His end of the bargain. I know a man in the South
that started tithing. His salary is now nearly double what
it was before he began tithing. Some time ago I heard from
a laborer in the San Joaquin Valley of California who said
that he and his wife agreed to give one-tenth of their income to the Lord. At the time they made their decision he
was able to get work only about seven months out of the
year. Now he says he has steady work and is earning
nearly twice what he was before. You cannot get around
it, the scripture promises material and spiritual benefits to
the man who gives to God." [41] Sometimes Graham is less
specific about the kind of material success that comes to the
Christian: "As God's grace never fails, the man that receives
it will not fail. Therefore, the weakest and most ignorant
and most inexperienced man in the world can be the greatest success if he receives the grace of God." [42] The auditor
is left to interpret this any way he chooses.

In his Peale-like sermon "What God Can Do for You"
Graham takes a psychological approach to conversion. The
question "I would like to answer for you is this," he says:
"What can God do for your psychological problems?" And
then he offers the following answers: "God can rid you of
boredom. . . . God can rid you of anxiety. . . . God can rid
you of self-perplexity. . . . God can rid you of loneliness. . . .
Christ can rid you of a sense of futility." In "The Cure for
Discouragement" Graham tells those who are discouraged,
"God did not create you to be a defeated, discouraged,
frustrated, wandering soul. . . . He has bigger plans for you.
He has a larger orb and a greater life for you." Of course
this could be interpreted in the spiritual sense, but when
Graham goes on to explain loneliness and discouragement in
worldly terms, his listeners can hardly be blamed for thinking that God is the poor man's psychiatrist and that salvation is a more pious version of Dale Carnegie's courses in
how to win friends and influence people: "The world to you

is shut off and you are shut out. Social barriers have prevented you from doing what you wish to do. Personality
barriers thwart and hinder you." Graham would probably
maintain that the peace of mind and assurance that comes
from accepting Christ might well provide a man with the
personal self-confidence to forge his way to the top in business or enable a woman to become the most self-possessed
hostess in town. On much the same basis Billy Sunday once
told the women in his audience that if they would "spend
less money on dope, pazaza, and cold cream and get down
on your knees and pray, God would make you prettier."

All these appeals, however, are personal. They claim to
help the individual, but the professional evangelist who
wishes to attract people by the millions and to make converts by the thousands must do more than appeal to the
personal fears and anxieties of the insecure members of society. He must offer a positive and constructive appeal
which will attract the stable, the capable, the successful
leaders of the community. To reach them, a higher goal and
a greater challenge is needed. They already have a spring
in their walk and a thrill in their hearts. And they have
only a casual interest in the intangible rewards of an after-
life. Furthermore, a different sort of motivation is needed
to inspire the church members who are already saved to
become more active Christians. In short, to unite the
church members, saved or smug, of a city like Chicago,
Pittsburgh, New York, or San Francisco, an evangelist must
offer more than the hope of converting the discouraged and
unhappy.

Billy Sunday found the perfect solution for this in the
Prohibition movement. Here was a challenge of great magnitude (as he presented it) which rose above any petty political, geographical, or denominational lines and which, in
the era of progressive reform, attracted both liberals and
conservatives. Sunday built his revivalism around the theme
that the saloon was not only a spiritual problem but a social
problem, a national problem—a problem which called for
the leadership, the vigor, the skill, and the courage of the

principal men in every town, city, and state. And by amalgamating his revivalism with Prohibition, Sunday succeeded in uniting the ministers of every denomination, laymen of every political party, and theologians of every hue behind his old-fashioned revivals. It may well be that the dispute between the modernists and the fundamentalists would have been waged much earlier than the 1920's had Sunday not sublimated this vital but divisive theological issue in the interest of saving the nation from the demon rum.

But Prohibition is a dead issue in the 1950's. Graham is in favor of it, but apart from warning people about the increase in alcoholism and the dangers of drunken driving he cannot arouse much concern. Nor can he return to the cause of "saving the masses" which provided the basic stimulus for Moody's revivals in the early days of urbanism and mass immigration. Most of the masses in America are now not only church members but members of the middle class. There are no masses left to save in America, though Graham often uses this appeal when he talks of his reasons for visiting foreign countries. However, Graham has found an issue around which to center his campaigns which is just as effective as "saving the masses" or as Prohibition. And that is anticommunism. Like Prohibition, this issue is above politics, economics, regionalism, or religious doctrine. Moreover, it has the tremendous advantage of being an international issue in a period when foreign policy is of as great concern to Americans as social reform was in Sunday's day or as urbanism was in Moody's. The positive side of this appeal is, of course, patriotism, although Graham maintains that he is no chauvinist and that the fight against communism is simply a fight of Christianity versus the anti-Christ. (Patriotism was also a central theme in Billy Sunday's revivalism, for the liquor traffic was also a threat to all that was good in America. But it was purely an internal threat.)

The manner in which Graham utilizes the fear of communism and the ideals of patriotism to stir his audiences is as transparent as it is omnipresent. Scarcely one of his Sunday afternoon sermons over a nine-year period has failed to touch on communism and in his regular revival sermons he constantly refers to it to illustrate his doctrinal points. For example, when he delivers his sermon on hell, Graham begins by quoting a *Life* magazine editorial to the effect that Joseph Stalin is doubtless there. If he talks on the Second Coming he compares the end of the world to the chaos that would follow an atomic war with Russia. If he talks of Satan he equates communism with Satan's religion. Almost every time he mentions the need or value of a revival he does so in connection with the spread of communism. And several times he has devoted a whole sermon to the death-duel between Christian America and atheistic Russia. It is no exaggeration to say that communism, the atomic bomb, and World War III have replaced the Devil, the battle of Armageddon, and hell in Graham's revivals as the major means of instilling the motive of fear.

This is hardly surprising. Never before in human history has it been so easy to invest a worldly power with so many of the attributes of the Prince of Evil (though the liquor traffic came close). Communists can be portrayed as a fifth column in the United States; they can be shown to control half the world; they possess the bombs which can destroy civilization and even the earth itself; and they are blatantly anti-Christian. In fact, communism, as it is conceived by the popular imagination, is surprisingly comparable in its beliefs and its apparently pervasive, worldly omnipotence to the supernatural force of Satan. Graham makes the most of this popular superstition.

In fact, Graham himself is absolutely convinced that communism is supernaturally directed, that its whole conception and progress has been guided by Satan, that the United States is the last hope of the world and of Christianity against this anti-Christ. "My own theory about Communism," Graham said in September, 1957, "is that it is master-minded by Satan. . . . I think there is no other explanation for the tremendous gains of Communism in which they seem to outwit us at every turn, unless they have supernatural power and wisdom and intelligence given to them." [43] In a sermon on communism entitled "Satan's Religion," Graham declared in 1953 "The Devil is their God; Marx, their prophet; Lenin their saint; and Malenkov their high priest." (Since then he has substituted Khrushchev for Malenkov.) As Graham sees it, the Bible itself indicates that Russian communism is the anti-Christ: "I have been spending much of my time in private study devoted to Bible prophecy," he says in a sermon called "Christianism *vs.* Communism"; "I am finding not only interesting but amazing things that bear tremendous light upon the conditions of this very hour. . . . There are strong indications that the 38th and 39th chapters of Ezekiel are devoted almost entirely to the tremendous rise of Russia in the latter days. There are strong indications in the Bible that in the last days a great sinister anti-Christian movement will arise. At this moment it appears that Communism has all the earmarks of this great anti-Christian movement. . . . Almost all ministers of the gospel and students of the Bible agree that it is master-minded by Satan himself." [44]

Graham is cautious about predicting the exact date for the end of the world and the second coming of Christ. To do that would destroy the air of expectancy upon which revivalism thrives, and if the date came and went with the prediction unfulfilled, Graham would be thoroughly discredited as a revivalist. But Graham has flatly stated in his sermon on the Second Coming, "I sincerely believe, if I can study the Scriptures aright and read current events and keep up with my current reading, that we are living in the latter days. I sincerely believe that the coming of the Lord draweth nigh." [45] And he has made numerous predictions about the coming of World War III which he often compares to and even equates with the battle of Armageddon. For example, in the fall of 1950 he said, "I believe the judgment hand of God is about to fall upon you tonight, but I believe that God is long-suffering. God's mercy is staying and holding His hand back for maybe one more year. We may have another year, maybe two years, to work for Jesus Christ and [then] ladies and gentlemen, I believe it's all going to be over. . . . I said in Los Angeles one year ago that we had five years. People laughed; some sneered. I'd like to revise that statement and say that we may have two years. Two years and it's all going to be over." [46] A year later in Hollywood he reported, "Kenneth DeCorsey [*sic*] cabled from London that all of Russia's planning [for World War III] is toward an Autumn, 1952, deadline. He lamented the fact that British, American, and French planners are gearing toward the Autumn of 1953. He believes we are missing it by a year." [47] In August, 1952, Graham stated, "Unless this nation turns to Christ within the next few months, I despair of its future." [48]

Each new international crisis, from Russia's acquisition of the atomic bomb to the landing of the United States Marines in Lebanon, has been an occasion for Graham to predict that the battle of Armageddon is at hand. He has always been particularly anxious to point out that "The Bible teaches us that history began in the Middle East . . . and the Bible teaches us that it will end in the Middle East." [49] Hence the crises over Iranian oil, Israel's border clashes, the rise of Nasser, the Suez invasion, the revolution in Iraq, have all been grist for his mill of prophecy. In February, 1957, after the debacle over Suez, Graham gave a sermon on "The Signs of the Times" in which he again referred to the important chapters in Ezekiel: "An Arab professor at Cambridge told me that the third world war would start within five years and it would start in the Middle East. In the 37th, 38th, and 39th chapters of Ezekiel we find accurately foretold some of the events of the latter days leading up to the great battle of the Valley of Jehoshaphat, and the last battle of history which has been called the battle of Armageddon. Many interpret these passages to mean that Israel would be a thorn in the side of her neighbors and would be persecuted by many nations to the point of complete despair. The great battle will take place when the armies of the north, which many believe to be Russia, will move into the Middle East." [50]

Graham makes no bones about the fact that World War

III (and presumably Armageddon) will be between Russia and the United States. In all of his sermons the United States represents the forces of good and Russia the forces of evil. "I believe that America is truly the last bulwark of Christian civilization," he said in 1952.[51] Two years later he said again, "I am more impressed than ever with America's responsibility in this complex world. We might as well face it; there is a war on in the world for the minds of the human race." [52] While he continually deplores the moral decay in the United States he nevertheless declares, "In spite of all the corruption, crime, and moral decay this is still the greatest country in the world." And "We are engaged in a death struggle with Communism." [53]

It is obvious therefore that "we were created for a spiritual mission among the nations." [54] "Throughout the entire world at this moment Christianity and communism are battling for the minds of men." [55] And America is the champion of Christianity. "But America cannot survive, she cannot carry out her God-appointed mission, without the spiritual emphasis which was hers from the outset." [56] Here the link between revivalism and patriotism becomes apparent. Here also is an implicit link between Christianity and the American way of life as represented by free enterprise capitalism. "Until this nation humbles itself and prays and . . . receives Christ as Savior, there is no hope for preserving the American way of life." And "Only as millions of Americans turn to Jesus Christ at this hour and accept him as Savior, can this nation possibly be spared the onslaught of a demon-possessed communism." "You say, 'But Billy, I'm only one person.' Ah, yes, but when you make your decision, it is America through you making its decision." [57]

The whole picture falls into focus as Graham insists that personal, national, and international problems all can be solved by a revival in the hearts of individuals. "Dishonesty, private and public immorality, infidelity, Communism, and all the other things that are troubling us today, would never prevail among a people who honor God and whose hearts are full of faith and of the Holy Spirit. The Church is the channel through which God sends the streams of blessing down to the nation, and I urge all of you today that love America and who have an appreciation for the blood that was shed in Korea and have a pride when you hear our National Anthem or see the Stars and Stripes wave, to fall upon your knees as an individual and . . . pray and turn from your wicked ways, that God might send the revival that we so desperately need as a nation." [58]

That Christianity and patriotism are synonymous Graham makes perfectly explicit. "If you would be a true patriot then become a Christian. If you would be a loyal American, then become a loyal Christian." [59] And it is almost equally explicit that a patriot is a man whose economic, religious, and political beliefs are very conservative or right-wing. "Civilization stands at the cross roads. If the world elects to go to the left and embrace this Godless philosophy of deceit, force, and bloodshed, it will plunge into the dark abyss of totalitarian despair and gloom and ultimate annihilation. If it turns to the right and takes the way of the cross, we well might be entering the greatest economic and spiritual renaissance that modern man has known." [60] In his sermon on "Satan's Religion" Graham stated his five-point program by which every American "can most effectively combat communism." "First: By old-fashioned Americanism. . . . Secondly: By conservative and Evangelical Christianity. . . . Thirdly: By prayer. . . . Fourthly: By a genuine spiritual revival. . . . Fifthly: By personal Christian experience."

Since Graham has no faith in any form of humanly organized resistance to communism, he instructs his congregations to have no faith in them. He constantly demonstrates the hopelessness of the world situation and the fact that mankind "has reached the end of its tether." In fact, it seems at times that Graham does not think that even a great spiritual revival in the United States would suffice. The question was once put to him, "Suppose all the 150 million people in the United States were to be converted . . . we are still left facing . . . the aggressive power of Soviet Russia with perhaps 800 million people under its control. Now just how would the conversion of all Americans affect the solution of that concrete problem?" Graham answered, "I sincerely believe if Americans turned to God at this moment, we would have divine intervention on our side. . . . We can never lick communism with flesh and blood and guns and bullets. It's going to take the divine help of Almighty God." [61] Or, as he put it elsewhere, "If this nation would repent of its sins . . . God Himself would intervene and frustrate and blind the Russians as He did the armies of old." [62]

But this does not necessarily mean that after God frustrates Russia the world will go on as before under America's leadership. As far as Graham is concerned the "satanic, supernaturally empowered" force of communism can only be conquered by the return of Christ in person. This is the intervention he has in mind, and this is why the start of World War III will be the end of the world. "God's answer to the challenge of Communism is—Christ. God's method of setting at nought the councils of men is to place the Messiah on the throne of David. God shall deal with the rebellion by sending back the Redeemer. . . . He shall establish His Kingdom. The 'Age of Righteousness' shall be ushered in, the Millennium shall begin, when He returns. It must be this way. The world shall never have peace until the Prince of Peace returns." [63] If Graham were consistent in this, he would have to admit that patriotic individual conversions, no matter how numerous, would be useless. The world is doomed whether there is a revival or not. He would have to agree with Moody's statement, "I look upon this world as a wrecked vessel. God has given me a lifeboat and said to me, 'Moody, save all you can.'"

But Graham is not consistent, and his patriotism and optimism often triumph over his pessimistic premillennialism. "As a minister of the gospel, I am an optimist," he says. "The world's problems are big, but God is bigger." And "with God all things are possible. It is not all hopeless. . . . A spiritual awakening will restore our spiritual heritage, create moral stamina and consciousness, bring back the sanctity of the home . . . strengthen the bulwarks of freedom and bring integrity back to the people of the world." [64]

It is this affirmative note which has given Graham his widest appeal, particularly among nonfundamentalists. In spite of his prophecies of hopelessness, he has always urged strong military defense and the utmost efforts in preparedness: "We must maintain strong military power for defense at any cost," he said on the Capitol steps in 1952. "We must maintain our economic stability for security. We must continue confidence in each other . . . remembering that we are all Americans and that America is the nation that has made every man a king." [65] He has also urged a foreign policy which would take the offensive in combating communism both in Europe and Asia by encouraging armed rebellion among satellite nations behind the Iron Curtain and by aiding Chiang Kai-shek and Syngman Rhee to wage open warfare against Communist China. This activistic element in his preaching appeals to the American faith in human effort. Many persons who do not share Graham's pietism and premillennialism support his revivals because they believe Graham stands for the old Cromwellian motto, "Praise the Lord and keep your powder dry." Graham is trying to have the best of both the pessimistic and the optimistic view of the world situation. He too seems to be saying that God will help those who help themselves. But there is little doubt that the main emphasis of his message and of his personal belief lies on the pessimistic side, just as there is little doubt that the hard core of his audience is made up of premillennialists.

To the extent that Graham places almost his entire reliance for solving world problems upon divine intervention and reduces human effort to the tasks of prayer, soul-winning, and Bible-reading, he is, in fact, preaching a religion of escape. In one of his revival sermons Graham offers an excellent illustration of the head-in-the-sand attitude to which his pessimism often leads him. In discussing the sense of peace and serenity which is available to all Christians, he refers to a painting entitled "Peace" which he once saw: "The storm is raging, the lightning was flashing, the wind was blowing, the sea was crashing against the rocks, and under the ledge of the rocks there was a little bird with its head under its wing asleep. That is peace." [66]

Kenneth de Courcy summed up Graham's message fairly accurately when he said: "It follows [from Graham's preaching] that a confidence is created which before was entirely lacking; and that a mass of people once afraid and divided become united and brave because inherent in Dr. Graham's preaching is the certainty of human failure, upon which is super-imposed the certainty of Divine intervention and thus, the saving of the world situation. . . . If you like, it is escapism in its ultimate form." [67]

The end result of Graham's pulpit technique then is to exacerbate and exalt the fears and doubts, the frustrations and anxieties, both personal and world-wide, of his congregations and radio listeners. Having reduced those who seek peace of soul to a state of panic and hopelessness, he then offers them a quick and simple way out—a mass ritual of atonement which, momentarily at least, assures them that they have done all they could, that they have been forgiven for their mistakes, and that now a higher power will take over and do what they are unable to do. Meanwhile, they have the satisfaction of knowing that they are on the Lord's side, that they are assured of safety and eternal bliss no matter what happens. And, if they are so inclined, they can also play a small but important part in promoting the divine redemption of the world by trying to convert others to the Christian way of life—or by helping Billy Graham to do so. This is the essence of all revival preaching and this Graham does superlatively well.

But there is more to Billy Graham's revivals than preaching.

CHAPTER 7

Revival Mechanics

> *Every organization that has anything worth-*
> *while to offer the public seizes the oppor-*
> *tunity provided by the miracle of mod-*
> *ern communication. We are presenting the*
> *greatest product in the world. So why not*
> *give it at least as much promotion as a bar*
> *of soap?*
>
> BILLY GRAHAM [1]

Billy Graham's career since his Portland, Oregon, crusade in the summer of 1950 has been a steady progression of success although there were indications by 1958 that he had passed the peak of his popularity. Between the 1949 crusade in Los Angeles and the Charlotte, North Carolina, crusade in the fall of 1958, Graham conducted thirty-two revival campaigns in the United States, one in Toronto, Canada, and eight abroad. Several of these were tours covering wide areas, not centered in any one city. Such for example were his tour of New England in 1950 and his tours of Europe, Asia, Australia, and the Caribbean. Of his thirty-two revivals in the United States, nineteen took place in the South or Southwest, six in the Far West, four in the East and three in the Midwest. Graham averaged five crusades a year, speaking face-to-face to a total attendance of about two million people each year. His total conversions, including those made by radio and television listeners who wrote in to tell him about it, averaged over 100,000 a year or close to a million for the decade. Only Billy Sunday surpassed Graham's face-to-face record; Moody and Finney were hopelessly outdistanced. And even Sunday could not come close to matching Graham's radio, television, and newspaper coverage.

Graham has suffered only two setbacks in his career so far. The first occurred in September, 1950, when he tried in vain to fill the Rose Bowl for a mammoth rally. Despite heroic efforts by his team and friends, more than half of the 101,000 seats were empty.[2] The second setback was his miscalculation about coming to New York City. He thought he was ready to tackle it in 1953. Plans were agreed upon, announcements made, and preparation under way in 1952 when the crusade had to be called off because too many of the city's Protestant churches proved unwilling to cooperate with him.[3] He recouped this misstep in 1957 when his sixteen week crusade in New York brought him to the pinnacle of his career.

To recount the endless statistics of each individual crusade would be tedious, but there is some point in demonstrating the size and scope of his work by a chronological list of the places he visited. His itinerary since 1947, when he first began independent revival campaigns, has been as follows:

1947—Grand Rapids, Michigan; Charlotte, North Carolina.

1948—Des Moines, Iowa; Augusta, Georgia; Modesto, California.

1949—Miami, Florida; Baltimore, Maryland; Altoona, Pennsylvania; Los Angeles, California.

1950—Boston, Massachusetts; Columbia, South Carolina; New England tour; Portland, Oregon; Minneapolis, Minnesota; Atlanta, Georgia.

1951—Fort Worth, Texas; Shreveport, Louisiana; Memphis, Tennessee; Seattle, Washington; Hollywood, California; Greensboro, North Carolina.

1952—Washington, D. C.; Houston, Texas; Jackson, Mississippi; Pittsburgh, Pennsylvania; Albuquerque,

New Mexico; Korea (to visit United States armed forces).

1953—Chattanooga, Tennessee; St. Louis, Missouri; Dallas, Texas; Syracuse, New York; Detroit, Michigan; Asheville, North Carolina.

1954—London, England; European tour; Nashville, Tennessee; New Orleans, Louisiana; West Coast tour.

1955—Glasgow, Scotland; London (one week); European tour; Toronto, Canada; Cambridge University, England (one week).

1956—Asian tour; Richmond, Virginia; Oklahoma City, Oklahoma; Louisville, Kentucky.

1957—Yale University (one week); New York, New York.

1958—Caribbean tour; San Francisco, California; California tour; Charlotte, North Carolina.

1959—Australian tour; Indianapolis, Indiana.

1960—African tour; Washington, D.C. (one week); tours of Switzerland and Germany; New York City (one week).

The average city campaign lasted four or five weeks, had a total attendance of 300,000 to 500,000 and a total of 5000 to 7000 trail hitters. Statistically Graham's best crusade occurred in Sydney, Australia, in May, 1959, where he claimed over 56,000 trail hitters in 28 days. Costs varied considerably from city to city but averaged roughly $100,000 for each campaign or about $20,000 to $25,000 per week. These averages do not include the long and elaborate meetings in London, Glasgow, and New York which were considerably above the average in all respects. The statistics for these larger meetings were as follows:

	Length	*Total Attendance*	*Decisions*	*Expenses*
London	12 weeks	1,500,000	38,447	$ 420,000
Glasgow	6 weeks	500,000	19,835	150,000
New York	16 weeks	2,019,100	56,767	2,500,000

(N.B. These figures vary according to whether they include meetings conducted by Graham's associates and relay meetings and whether decisions from radio and television broadcasts are counted. The above statistics do not include these "extras" but they do include the climactic stadium meetings.)

The statistics of Moody's and Sunday's largest meetings reveal that Sunday obtained a higher proportion of decisions at a smaller investment of time and money than Graham, while Moody obtained a lower proportion.

SUNDAY	Length	Total Attendance	Decisions	Expenses	Freewill Offering
New York	10 weeks	1,250,000	98,264	$200,168.87	$120,490.26
Boston	10 weeks	1,500,000	64,484	93,000.00	53,585.00
Chicago	10 weeks	1,000,000	49,165	135,000.00	56,000.00
Philadelphia	11 weeks	2,000,000	41,724	105,889.95	53,246.80
MOODY					
London	22 weeks	2,400,000	3000-7000	$140,000	unknown
Philadelphia	10 weeks	1,050,000	3500-12,000	50,000	unknown
Chicago	16 weeks	1,500,000	2500-10,000	70,000	unknown
New York	10 weeks	1,500,000	3500-8000	30,000	unknown

The ever increasing size and scope of Graham's activities after 1950 necessitated a steady increase in his organization. In addition to increasing the number of assistants who helped him conduct his campaigns, he had continually to increase the staff of his Minneapolis headquarters, expand his motion picture company, hire more publicists to edit his magazines, World Evangelism and Decision, hire a staff of research assistants, and employ legal and secretarial help for his personal affairs. The only work Graham curtailed was his presidency of the Northwestern Schools. He resigned from that position in November, 1951, but continued to serve as president of its board of trustees until February, 1952.

In addition to his headquarters in Minneapolis, Graham also opened offices in Washington, D. C., Winnipeg, Canada, London, England, Sydney, Australia, and for a time in Dallas, Texas. All of these offices were designed to promote his evangelism in one way or another. The organizational pyramiding and interlocking directorates of these corporate enterprises made Billy Sunday's plant look puny by comparison. Professional mass evangelism had first assumed some of the aspects of big business in Moody's day, but Moody would have been appalled at the amount of organization, advertising, promotion, and solicitation which went into soul-winning in the 1950's.

The Minneapolis office still continues to be the coordinating center of Graham's far-flung enterprises. Starting with one secretary in a one-room office in the fall of 1950, it grew so large by 1958 that it needed a staff of two hundred, a four-story office building, and tens of thousands of dollars worth of I.B.M., Remington, and Phillips-Elliott electronic business machines to cope with its tasks. This headquarters receives and answers ten thousand letters each week, collects and disburses over two million dollars a year, and sends out six to eight promotional and solicitation mailings annually to its list of 1,250,000 supporters (at a cost of $20,000 per mailing). It is the largest user of the United States Post Office in the city of Minneapolis.

From its beginning the Minneapolis office has been under the able and efficient direction of Graham's business manager, George M. Wilson, whose official title is still Secretary-Treasurer of the Billy Graham Evangelistic Association, Inc. Wilson's main task is to help raise the funds necessary for Graham's radio and television broadcasts. But the office also continues to spend a great deal of time answering the thousands of letters written to Graham asking for personal and spiritual advice, and it also plays a part in sending instructional literature to Graham's converts. Typical of the mechanization of revivalism is the manner in which the Minneapolis headquarters handles the letters seeking Graham's advice. These plaintive requests arrive at the rate of about five hundred a day from all over the United States and the rest of the world. They are at first screened, as all letters to the office are, for contributions. If they contain money, checks, or pledges a record is made of the donation and a letter of thanks with a receipt goes out immediately. Next the letter passes to a group of seven women who try to pigeonhole the central problem troubling the writer into one of forty prearranged categories. Among these categories are financial worries, marital discord, wayward children, serious illness, bereavement, chronic drinking by spouse, inability to find God, and spiritual doubt. For each of the forty categories a form letter has been devised by Graham's staff and has been recorded on perforated tape for use in the office's tandem automatic typewriters. A secretary types the sender's name at the head of the letter and Billy Graham's signature is mechanically duplicated at the end. Everyone who has indicated that he is having difficulty finding God receives the same form letter; everyone having mental problems receives the same letter; and everyone having child-raising problems receives the same letter. These letters are couched in general terms and refer to Biblical passages which either mention the particular problem or which counsel resignation, faith, and prayer. Graham says that he has talked with Norman Vincent Peale and Bishop Fulton J. Sheen about this method of mass counseling and finds that they used a method very similar to his with the same number and variety of categories.[4]

Those letters which cannot be pigeonholed are passed on to two ministerial members of the staff who dictate personal replies to several dozen a day. Apart from those letters of obvious personal or business importance, less than one hundred letters out of the thousands received each week are sent to Graham's home in Montreat, North Carolina. These are answered by members of his personal secretarial staff after consultation with Graham. About six of them are selected each week for publication and public answer through Graham's daily newspaper column, "My Answer" (later called "Billy Graham Says").

The Minneapolis office also keeps on file a record of all decisions for Christ which are made either at Graham's revivals or through his broadcasts (listeners on radio and television are urged to write to Graham in care of Minneapolis if they have been converted as a result of one of his broadcasts). These names are all entered on filing cards. As Graham told a group of ministers in London in order to impress them with his efficient follow-up, "I can tell you this, that we are keeping statistics and we are now in the process of being able to tell you where every one of these people are. We can pull out a card and give the whole spiritual case history of each convert."[5] The Minneapolis office mails instructional literature, consisting principally of

Bible study courses, to each convert. The convert is asked to write for additional instruction material over a three to six month period as he completes each course. There is no charge made for these lessons in Christian development, but it is assumed that all converts will donate voluntarily to support Graham's work and if they put their names on Graham's mailing list, they are solicited regularly. The solicitation usually consists of a form letter from Graham and a business reply envelope. On the flap of the reply envelope is printed a blank check made out to the Billy Graham Evangelistic Association. On the envelope itself a pledge reads:

With God as my helper, and in dependence upon Him, I make the following PLEDGE:
—prayer support. __financial support. . . . $____weekly. . . . $____monthly. I herewith enclose (circle or write in):
$____ $100 $50 $25 $10 $5 $3 $2 $1 $____
Name_____
Street_____
City_____zone____state_____

All gifts to the Billy Graham Evangelistic Association are deductible for income tax purposes.

The Minneapolis staff are all dedicated, born-again fundamentalists. The office contains a special prayer room which employees are invited to use. Every morning starts with devotional services attended by all of the staff. Staff members must be not only church members but nonsmokers and nondrinkers. The pay is admittedly below standard for office help and the employees often work long hours without overtime pay. But for them it is service for God and not for personal profit. Every typist and file clerk is as dedicated a partner in support of Graham's revivals as are the members of his "team."

The team itself has more than quadrupled in size over the years in order to divide the labor of each phase of the campaigns and to free Graham from all burdens except that of preaching. In 1950 the team consisted of five basic members: Cliff Barrows, choir leader and master of ceremonies;

George Beverly Shea, soloist; Grady Wilson, associate evangelist who conducted outside meetings in churches, offices, and factories and stood in for Graham when he was overtired or ill; Jerry Beavan, executive secretary and public relations director; and Willis G. Haymaker, in charge of advance preparations. By the time Graham began his New York City crusade in May, 1957, the team had twenty-two regular members and a corps of twenty "special assistants" who took part in the large crusades. The more important additions to the team since 1950 have been Charles Riggs, who directs the counseling and follow-up work (in association with the Navigators); Dan Piatt, assistant to Riggs; Tedd Smith, pianist; Paul Mickelson, organist (later replaced by Lorne Whitney); three associate evangelists; Leighton Ford (Graham's brother-in-law), Joseph Blinco (a British Methodist minister), and Paul S. Rees (a former president of the National Association of Evangelicals who worked in the London and Glasgow crusades); Mrs. Elizabeth Lowry, press secretary and assistant to Beavan (she left the team in 1959); Paul J. Maddox, personal secretary to Graham; and Walter F. Bennett who, though not officially on the team, takes charge of the commercial advertising over local radio and television stations.

All of the team members are born-again Christians. Most of them, like Graham, were in their early thirties when the 1950's commenced. Almost all of them have had some training in Bible colleges, and several were active in Youth for Christ. They are hard-working, enthusiastic, pious young men who radiate good will and determination. One New York columnist referred to the team as "a curious mixture of prairie town corn, Rotary Club exuberance, and the hard-boiled approach of a political campaign headquarters."[6]

Special assistants to the Graham team who lent color and performed useful tasks in New York and other campaigns included the Rev. Abdul Haqq, an assistant evangelist from India; Mel Dibble, formerly a radio announcer for the Kate Smith radio show who produced and announced the daily television program for the New York crusade (a local pro-

gram); the Rev. Tom Allen, a dynamic young Scottish evangelist who conducted meetings on evangelistic methods for
New York pastors; Lane Adams, a former night club singer
now studying for the ministry who evangelized among New
York actors and entertainers; Walter H. Smyth, a Maryland
layman who was director of reservations for delegations and
assisted Haymaker in the advance work; Paul E. Little, a
ministerial student who preached on the various college
campuses in the New York area; and Patricia Campion, a
convert of Graham's London crusade who spoke at "drawing
room meetings" to New York's social elite.

In addition to his personal secretary and executive secretary, Graham hired a former newspaperman, Lee Fisher, as
his research assistant in order to help him gather material
for writing his sermons, books, and newspaper articles. He
also had part-time research assistance after 1957 from Robert
O. Ferm, the Dean of Students at a small Bible college in
New York State (in 1959 Ferm became a permanent member
of the Minneapolis headquarters). Graham was sadly in
need of some research assistance in regard to history for in
sermons delivered as late as 1957 he referred to the French
Revolution as though it preceded the Wesleyan Revival, he
called Jonathan Edwards "a nineteenth century evangelical
revivalist," he said the leader of the Scrooby Pilgrims was
John Robertson, and he confused Lyman Beecher with his
son Henry Ward Beecher.

Graham's decision to enter television in the fall of 1951
did not prove satisfactory. Though not exactly a setback to
his career, it was not sufficiently successful to compensate for
the time and expense entailed. The half-hour show ran for
about two and one-half years and was filmed in advance
each week. Graham stated that although it reached an audience of eight to ten million weekly over twenty stations, it
had to be dropped because it was expensive and because it
restricted his revival crusades. Moreover, Graham was not at
his best before a camera in a studio. He needed a revival
audience in order to come to life. During the New York
campaign, arrangements were made to telecast his Satur-

day night meetings direct from Madison Square Garden over a coast-to-coast hookup. It almost doubled the cost of the crusade but it elicited such a wide and enthusiastic response that Graham repeated the practice during his San Francisco and Charlotte crusades in 1958 and his Australian crusades in 1959.

Graham's "film ministry" expanded because each new crusade produced a new documentary film and often a new full-length dramatic feature. By 1959 Graham had seven documentaries and six full-length features available for hire, most of them in color. A staff of twelve, headed by Dick Ross, managed the filming, printing, and distribution. In 1957 the title of the motion picture company was changed from Billy Graham Evangelistic Films, Inc., to World Wide Pictures when it merged with Ross' Great Commission Films Company.

With the exception of movies, television, and radio broadcasts, however, the actual mechanics of Graham's revivalism contained little that had not been foreshadowed by Moody and Sunday. The system Graham evolved after 1950 was simply an elaboration of that used by Sunday and passed on to Graham by Haymaker. The operation of the revivals was distinctly separate from the Minneapolis headquarters. It was controlled by Graham and his team of experts from start to finish. (The offices of the team headquarters were originally in Dallas, Texas; in 1955 they were moved to Washington, D. C., and in 1958 they were moved to Charlotte, North Carolina, where Graham also has his "personal executive office.") The steps of a city-wide crusade are simple enough in outline. They consist first of the formal invitation extended to the evangelist by the local ministers, second, the financial arrangements to underwrite the campaign; third, the advance preparation; fourth, the campaign proper; and fifth, the follow-up to consolidate the effect of the campaign. These were the steps Moody followed and Sunday followed and which every professional evangelist of any importance has followed since the Civil War.

Graham, like Moody and Sunday, made the decision early in his career that he would never try to conduct a revival campaign in a city unless he had the cooperation and support of the ministers of that city. Though he adopted an "all-inclusive policy" in regard to the denominational and theological support he was willing to accept, it was essential that he know in advance that at least a majority of the "evangelical" churches of each would be behind him. Graham told a large group of British churchmen in March, 1952, "We do not go to any city now unless we are invited by the church. We haven't been to a city in eighteen months in which we were not invited by the churches of the city. And in many cases, particularly in the South, it is the Church Federation which invites us." [7] When Moody and Sunday said that they required an invitation from a majority of the evangelical churches before they would hold a crusade in a city, they meant simply that they required the support of a majority of the Baptists, Methodists, Presbyterians, Congregationalists, and Disciples (and, if they could get them, of the Episcopalians and Lutherans). But when Graham uses the term "evangelical" he equates it with those who accept his fundamentalist theology. Since "evangelicals" of this sort are in a minority in most big cities, Graham has had to adopt an "all-inclusive" policy which accepts support from liberals and modernists. For this he has been criticized severely by many fundamentalists, but he has no choice if he wishes to make any impact on the cities. Graham has never set any definite figure or proportion of churches in a city which must support him before he will come. Actually the number or percentage of churches cooperating in a crusade is not so important as the fact that there are enough of them (and of the important ones) to provide the funds, the volunteer workers, and the level of community support needed to make the crusade a success. It is part of the business of the professional evangelist to know when an invitation from any city represents this level of support.

The task of obtaining a clear mandate from urban Protestants for a mass revivalistic campaign is by no means easy. In large cities with three hundred to three thousand Protestant churches and several dozen different denominations, neither the ministers nor the laymen are always eager to lay aside personal or traditional quarrels, even for the sake of saving souls. Graham has not lacked invitations, but he has not been so foolish as to accept them all. Every invitation is carefully examined before he commits himself. Too much is at stake to take a chance with failure. Usually months or years of behind-the-scenes manipulation go on between Graham's team and the ministers and laymen of a city before an open invitation is given and publicly accepted. Neither Graham nor the ministers want the bad publicity of a tentative acceptance and then a withdrawal. Consequently, before any invitation is even considered, certain conditions set by Graham have to be met.

In addition to requiring the promised support of the majority of the "evangelical" churches and a sizable proportion of the other Protestant churches, Graham also requires that the local group agree to furnish a meeting place suitable to him, that they accept the full responsibility for financing the meetings, and that they agree to follow to the letter the prescriptions and commands of the Graham team in preparing for and conducting every phase of the campaign. Graham presumes that the churches need him just as much as he needs them and that as the foremost revivalist of the day he can set the terms for his services. The ministers, meanwhile, recognize that Graham can draw crowds and stir religious interest which they sadly need and cannot arouse. They also presume that he can produce thousands of new church members for their city and reactivate an equal number of lukewarm members or former members. He counts on their full cooperation and they on his experience and ability to stimulate the religious life of the churches. In practical terms this is the meaning and the function of professional evangelism as it has been institutionalized in American Protestantism.

The details of the behind-the-scenes maneuvering which

precedes a commitment by Graham to conduct a crusade consist primarily of obtaining the necessary pledge of ministerial support and of spelling out the mechanical and financial aspects of the transaction in terms suitable to both sides. Evangelism is very much a matter of cool calculation at this stage. The movement to invite Graham to a city usually originates with a few prominent evangelical ministers who know Graham and his work personally through Youth for Christ or the National Association of Evangelicals and who seek to arouse their colleagues to agree that a Graham crusade would be good for their churches. In this the clergymen are usually aided by some of the more prominent laymen. In fact, in some cities the laymen have been the prime movers and not the clergy. Christian businessmen's groups and the International Christian Leadership organization (in Washington, D. C.) were particularly active in promoting Graham's early revivals.[8]

It is interesting to note how many times the leading figures in Graham's campaigns have been men who either were themselves active in the support of former evangelists like Sunday, Gypsy Smith, J. Wilbur Chapman, and Reuben A. Torrey, or who come from families which have long been active in promoting such movements. In New York, for example, the Phelps and Dodges, who supported Graham in 1957, have been promoting mass revivals in that city since the 1820's when Anson G. Phelps and William E. Dodge first invited Charles Grandison Finney to rejuvenate the churches of "Satan's capital." The Vanderbilts, Goulds, and Whitneys have supported Moody, Sunday, and Graham. A number of ministers on Graham's New York committee like John W. Bradbury, Theodore F. Savage, and Jesse M. Bader also supported Billy Sunday's campaign in New York in 1917. Dr. Henry P. Van Dusen, who was also on Graham's New York committee, was converted by Sunday during his New York campaign. In every city he has visited Graham has been welcomed by old-timers who see him as Sunday's legitimate successor.

There are also prominent churches in every city which

have maintained the revival spirit and attracted ministers and laymen of this type for generations, such as Park Street Church in Boston, Moody Church in Chicago, and Calvary Baptist Church in New York. In addition to those ministers who support the Youth for Christ movement and who belong to the National Association of Evangelicals, Graham has generally received the cooperation of a wide range of fundamentalists and neofundamentalists who see him as one of their own and are anxious to have him boost their theological and ecclesiastical cause.[9] There are also the publicity-hungry and self-important city ministers who eagerly push anything new which has the possibility of bringing religion and the clergy into the limelight. And there are local businessmen who, whether they agree with Graham or not, feel that a religious revival would be "a good thing" for their city. As the *Houston Post* reported of Graham's revival there in 1952, "Businessmen . . . became interested because of its importance as a civic function."[10] For the same reason Graham can almost always count on organizations like the local Chamber of Commerce, Rotary, and Lions to lend support.

But all of these elements could not be brought into coordination without some effort and what is more the large body of moderate Protestants, lay and clerical, would not enter a Graham crusade without some goading. In large part this pressure is locally applied by the leaders of the group which is determined to invite Graham. They do it by friendly buttonholing at ministerial and business meetings; they do it by forming self-appointed committees and delegations which visit prominent men and talk them into lending their names to the movement; they do it, on occasion, by coercion, especially when a clergyman is found holding out against his most prominent laymen. The threat of dismissal has more than once been used against a pastor to whip him into line for an evangelistic campaign. The *Christian Century* reported of Graham's first attempt to obtain an invitation to come to New York: "A few years ago when he announced that he was open to the right kind of invitation from the right people in the big city, some of the Graham zealots on the *ad hoc* committee made things so hot for the 'right people' that the evangelist lost part of the sponsorship he required and called the whole thing off." And in Seattle, Washington, in 1951, "Twelve churches reported that considerable pressure had been put on them to secure their cooperation. Some of the pressure came from sister churches in their own communions and some from members of the crusade committee." [11]

It is clear that the members of Graham's team, particularly Beavan and Haymaker, play an active and influential part in helping round up ministerial and lay support in a city for a united evangelical front. They do this by explaining away objections, real and imaginary, which have been raised against various aspects of Graham's work. Speaking informally to local religious and business groups in a city which is considering a Graham crusade, they allay fears about excessive commercialism, excessive emotionalism, excessive fundamentalism, or excessive reliance upon statistics and machinery. They provide testimonials from church and civic leaders in cities which have gone through a Graham crusade. They bring ministers and converts who have taken part in a crusade to give their encomiums in person. They provide all sorts of pamphlets, brochures, and illustrative material to show the efficiency of Graham's work. They claim that Graham's revivals in many cities have been accompanied by decreases in crime, divorce, alcoholism, juvenile delinquency, labor unrest, and corruption and by increases in the sales of Bibles, church attendance, formation of Bible classes, and the payment of old debts. And above all they demonstrate by their own piety, respectability, enthusiasm, and fervent evangelical spirit that the team is a consecrated and "church-centered" group interested in advancing the cause of the Christian religion in general and not of Graham or his organization.

If there is still resistance on the part of influential laymen and pastors whose opposition would be fatal to the crusade, Graham himself is called in and demonstrates his own sincerity and conviction of the value of evangelistic crusades. In some cities Graham not only addressed meetings of ministers and meetings of businessmen in advance of an invitation, but he conducted a one-night public meeting to demonstrate his ability to draw a crowd and to show the hesitant how powerful (without being hysterical) his preaching can be. Shortly after Graham was invited to New York City, for example, he was informed by his friends and his team that the Episcopalian ministers in the city were unwilling to cooperate in a crusade. Since the Episcopalians are highly influential in New York, Graham came to address these ministers personally and, it is said, won over a sufficient number of them to make the opposition or neutrality of the others less dangerous. Graham also conducted a sample meeting at Madison Square Garden on March 3, 1955, under the sponsorship of Youth for Christ: "This is expected to serve as a 'test,' " said the house organ of the NAE, "of New Yorkers' reaction to his appeal for a spiritual revival." [12] While it ostensibly tested Graham's drawing power and his preaching power, the meeting was obviously packed with persons ardently devoted to the Graham crusade and not with average New Yorkers. Yet many New York ministers accepted the enthusiastic crowd as a proof of Graham's ability to "reach the unchurched."

The difficulties of obtaining support from a majority of the Protestant ministers in a large city like New York was demonstrated not only by Graham's failure to do so in 1953 but also by the fact that only 40 per cent of the members of the Protestant Council of New York, which officially sponsored Graham in 1957, were actively in favor of his coming when they extended the invitation to him in 1955. Another 40 per cent were neutral and either voted without enthusiasm or abstained.[13] The 20 per cent who opposed him were thus outvoted and Graham was able to maintain that his support represented a majority of the evangelicals in the city. Moreover, many fundamentalist ministers in New York refused to cooperate with Graham because of their antagonism toward the liberal-dominated Protestant

Council. Actually it was not until the crusade began that Graham's office publicly announced that fifteen hundred of the three thousand Protestant churches in the New York area had signified their willingness to support the movement.

In smaller cities, particularly in the South, there has been much less difficulty in arranging ministerial and lay support. The fundamentalist and revival traditions may have burned low in this region from 1920 to 1950, but they never died out. This is one reason why 60 per cent of Graham's American crusades have been in the South and so few in the East.

While the attempt to round up "majority" support goes on, the details of the site for the meeting are discussed by the self-constituted local committee in consultation with Beavan and Haymaker. Only five cities have agreed to build Graham a special tabernacle. In most places Graham uses either the largest auditorium available or an outdoor stadium. The auditoriums usually have the disadvantage of being too small for the crowds Graham can draw, while the stadiums are usually too big and are inconvenient on rainy nights. It is probable that some cities that could otherwise have met all the requirements for a crusade lost the chance because they lacked the facilities.

Once the site is chosen and the majority of evangelical clergymen and laymen (including the most prominent of both) are lined up, the next problem is to find a suitable date for the revival. Graham holds at most five or six full-scale campaigns a year and this means that many cities have had to wait two years or more for his services. (He has kept some cities dangling for months and then turned them down.) This is discouraging to those who have got all fired up in the preliminary skirmishes over uniting the clergy, but it has been an unavoidable problem in mass revivalism since Finney's day.

The second step of the crusade, after Graham has formally accepted the invitation and a site and date have been chosen, is to make the financial preparations. Here Graham follows Sunday's method of suggesting that a local

committee made up of prominent businessmen and ministers be selected to guide the crusade, and that this committee incorporate itself according to the laws of the state in
which the city is located. Every revival committee is thus
a chartered business corporation and subject to the privi-
leges and requirements of such an organization. One of the
principal values of this is to prevent any individual, church,
or society, from being held financially responsible for any
debts or suits for damages. A second value is that as a non-
profit corporation all donations to it can be used as tax
deductions which helps in raising the funds. The third
value is that it gives a businesslike tone to the meetings and
seems to ensure more efficiency. Graham, like Moody and
Sunday, always insists that careful records of all expenses
and income be kept by the local committee so that the
accounts can be audited by a certified public accountant at
the conclusion of the crusade and a statement published.
This assures the public and the contributors that no individual or church group makes any financial profit from the
large sums invested.

Once the general committee is incorporated an executive committee and a finance committee are selected from
it, the latter consisting predominantly of businessmen.
These committees then begin the task of raising funds. It is
assumed that each crusade will pay for itself out of the
collections taken during the meetings and out of gifts vol-
unteered by those who may benefit spiritually or otherwise.
But cash on hand is needed long before the meetings com-
mence in order to make the necessary preparations. Moody,
who never took collections at his meetings, always raised
the expenses in advance by cash donations from wealthy
individuals. Sunday raised what he called a "guarantee
fund" by means of pledges which were then used as col-
lateral for a bank loan sufficient to get the campaign under
way. Graham's committees usually attempt to raise about
one-third of the estimated expenses by voluntary donations
in advance of the meetings. The donations are solicited
through the churches, through personal appeals to wealthy

laymen, through mail solicitation of Graham's supporters, by fund-raising luncheons and "inspirational breakfasts." Graham himself, like Sunday, often participates in these fund-raising luncheons to which as many as one thousand wealthy businessmen are invited.[13a] The amount of money needed in New York was so great that Graham's committee seriously considered using a professional fund-raising organization. In London the finance committee sent letters not only to individuals but to sixteen hundred business firms which presumably contributed for philanthropic reasons. If these methods are not sufficient it is almost always possible to arrange a loan with a local bank for which members of the committee stand as surety.

Usually these advance solicitations are able to raise from one-third to one-half of the total expenditures and the collections taken at the meetings supply the rest. In New Orleans, for example, $25,000 of the total $75,000 expenses was raised in advance. In Nashville, advance donations totalled $31,268.48 and the collections at the meetings, $57,374.62. In London, local advance donations totalled £48,435, the collections £50,626 (and in addition £40,729 was raised in the United States by the Graham organization). New York was not typical, but the finance committee there raised $2,004,532.17 by outside gifts and only $812,938.87 from collections at the meetings.[14]

The budget for each crusade is made out in advance largely by the Graham team which knows exactly what is needed and what can be expected. Of course the budget must be cleared with the local executive committee, for the committee is responsible for raising the money. But by and large the committee can do little more than rubber stamp the team's plans. The major items in the budget are the expenses for the meeting place, the advertising, the administrative offices and personnel, the salaries and expenses of the Graham team (excluding Graham), the printing and mailing of promotional material, and the cost of counseling and following up converts. A large item called "miscellaneous" takes care of "unforeseen contingencies."

Whether the meeting place is a specially built tabernacle, a stadium, or an auditorium, it is almost without exception the single most expensive item in a Graham crusade. Tabernacles have cost Graham's committees as much as $125,000 (in Detroit); the Armory in Washington, D. C., cost a total of $45,000 for five weeks; the rent of Madison Square Garden and the other meeting places used in New York cost $622,960.83; the rent for Harringay Arena in London and the running expenses and insurance for it came to £46,670. Stadiums, while they are sometimes given for a nominal rent, inevitably involve a great deal of money for night lighting, renovations, building the platform, the public address system, insurance, and decorating.

The advertising is usually the next most expensive item. It includes the money spent for posters, newspaper ads, radio and television commercials, and billboards. The expenses for the administrative offices or crusade headquarters in each city includes rent for a suite of four to twelve rooms (many of which are filled with machines for handling correspondence and accounting), salary for several stenographers and typists, and the cost of telephone and telegraph services. The living expenses of the Graham team are not as high as they might be, for local hotels frequently offer suites free of charge to Graham and the more important members of his staff in return for the publicity and added business which will come their way. The counseling and follow-up costs are high because it is Graham's practice to hire an office in each city for six months or more following the crusade; this becomes the headquarters for follow-up work; one or two members of the team who specialize in this work stay behind after the crusade ends to run the office, and their living and traveling expenses for that time are considered part of the crusade expenses. In many cities Graham has conducted local radio or television broadcasts daily which seek to extend the influence of the crusade and also to provide publicity. These programs are a considerable extra expense. The daily television program in New York costs $1400 a week for air time.

In view of all this it is not surprising that Graham's campaigns have cost anywhere from $20,000 to $150,000 per week. Moody's averaged $3000 to $5000 a week and Sunday's about $10,000. Allowing for the depreciation in the purchasing power of the dollar over the years, critics still question whether Graham's results are in proportion to his increased expenditure.

While the local committee is soliciting advance donations, the preparation for the meetings gets under way. Beavan and Haymaker arrive in the city from six months to a year before the opening date of the crusade to set up the crusade headquarters and direct the organization of local committees. In addition to the general committee, the executive committee, and the finance committee, every crusade has about a dozen smaller committees. These include the pastor's advisory committee to explain evangelistic methods to the local ministers; the cottage meeting committee to organize daily and weekly prayer groups throughout the city; the men's prayer meeting committee; the music committee which obtains volunteers for the choir and has charge of its training and of the sale of hymnbooks; the ushers committee which trains doormen and ushers and has charge of passing the collection plates; the auditorium committee which has charge of decorating and maintaining the auditorium or stadium; the publicity committee which works with Beavan, Mrs. Lowry, and the Walter F. Bennett agency in preparing and carrying out the advertising campaign (usually the volunteers on this committee take care of such tasks as distributing posters and handbills and putting stickers and bumper-cards on automobiles); the children's committee has charge of setting up a nursery at or near the meeting place where mothers deposit their babies while they attend the service (this committee has been dispensed with in recent years); the young people's committee which contacts local youth groups and arranges to have them attend the special young people's meetings; the delegation committee which has charge of reservations for seats at the meetings; and the counseling and follow-up committee which trains the counselors (in six two-hour meetings) in the proper method of dealing with inquirers who come forward after each sermon. All of these committees are staffed by volunteers from the cooperating churches and a local minister or layman is made the chairman of each. Actually, however, they are under the direction of Beavan and Haymaker during the preparatory months. Once the campaign begins the members of Graham's team who are specialists in each of these areas arrive to take over the supervision of their respective committees.

Apart from the actual preparation for the meetings, the advance work of these committees serves three functions. It enlists thousands of church members in the movement, filling them with enthusiasm for the revival and for church work. It provides publicity which can be fed to the newspapers month by month and week by week as the opening approaches. It creates an air of excitement, expectancy, and concern not only among those directly involved but among their friends and neighbors. When a movement enlists the names of the most prominent leaders of a city and then persuades thousands of respectable families to participate, it has gone a long way toward permeating the life of the community. Graham's team considers it one of the prime assets of mass evangelistic crusades that "they start everybody talking about religion." The churches and their ministers suddenly become front page news and not merely routine items on the Saturday religious page. In addition, as Graham's aides admit, it is logical that those who work hardest for the campaign will want to attend the meetings regularly in order to see the results of their handiwork. Thus the crusade is assured of filling thousands of seats at every meeting with this large group of dedicated workers who provide a responsive unit upon which Graham can rely for whole-hearted enthusiasm.

A large part of the preparation consists in building up reservations for blocks of seats for each night of the crusade. Usually one-half or more of the available seats for each meeting are reserved long before the opening night, and the opening night is assured of success by reserving at least two-thirds of the seats for church groups.   Since part of the purpose of the campaign is to revive the churches, Graham does not feel it necessary to defend the fact that cooperating pastors are urged to reserve seats for their church members as often as once a week throughout the campaign.   In New York, for example, Norman Vincent Peale's church members had a special block of seats set aside for them on a set night each week and so did dozens of other ministers.   A small block of seats is also kept permanently reserved for parties of "very important people" who may come without notice but who, for obvious reasons, should be given prominent seats in the front.   Less defensible perhaps is the practice of inviting large delegations of church people from cities where Graham has had revivals in the past to charter a bus, train, or plane and come hundreds of miles to experience again the excitement of taking part in one of Graham's meetings. During the New York campaign in the summer of 1957 Graham urged his "Hour of Decision" radio listeners to take their summer vacations in New York so that they could attend the meetings.   It is hard to see what advantage this provides for the local ministers except in the form of publicity, for the seats might be filled to much better advantage by local people.

It is part of the carefully worked out system of all citywide crusades to organize them into a series of well-spaced, prearranged climaxes.   The decision to invite Graham is the first such climax; his acceptance is the second.   The third is the opening night of the campaign; then there is a buildup to the first announced closing date, followed by a series of extensions, each working toward a new climax, until finally a definite closing date is fixed and a huge outdoor rally is held in the largest stadium or outdoor park in the city.   Minor climaxes in the form of outdoor rallies are scattered through the campaign.

Graham assists his publicity director in preparing for a climactic opening night by making public statements about the vastness of the undertaking he is about to embark upon;

about the particular sins or sinfulness of that city; and about his own fears and trepidations at undertaking this new and difficult task of revivalism. (It is surprising how many cities seem to have the reputation of being "the graveyard of evangelists.") Every city visited is portrayed as exceedingly wicked and yet a key city for that area and perhaps for the world. "The eyes of the world are upon Columbia" or "Albuquerque" or "Charlotte" Graham says as he approaches each campaign. When he came to Washington, D. C., in 1952, Graham spoke of it as the most important city in the nation, where decisions for Christ among federal legislators and executive officers could change the course of world history. He said the same thing about London two years later. Then New York City was described by him as his most important campaign: "Because of its size and its importance in the cultural and communications field, New York has a special influence on the rest of the country and even the whole world. A spiritual awakening in New York could echo all over the world." [15] Each foreign tour, whether in Europe, Asia, the Caribbean, Australia, or Africa is described as a danger spot in the international scene, perhaps the most vital spot for revivalism. And cities like Atlanta, Dallas, and San Francisco are played up as at least the most important in their region even if not in the country. No local newspaper can afford to miss quoting and commenting upon these challenges or salutes to local pride.

Graham's arrival in the city a day or two preceding the opening meeting is cause for a flood of new publicity releases about what the team expects to do, the amount of preparation completed, the new statistical records in prayer meetings or volunteer workers, and the important personalities participating. A large delegation of local ministers and churchgoers greets Graham at the railroad station or airport with cheers and hymns. Graham is interviewed not only by local newsmen but for the fifteenth or twentieth time by the national press services and national magazines and he offers his opinion on all sorts of questions from women's fashions to foreign policy. The opening night is given added luster and news value by the attendance of the city's mayor, the governor of the state, senators, congressmen, important socialites and businessmen, local sports or entertainment celebrities, all of whom pay tribute to Graham and praise the great things he will do for their area. In his opening remarks Graham praises the magnificent work of the local committees, states how happy he is to be in this great city, quiets apprehensions about hysteria or eccentricity by saying that he wants no emotionalism but simply quiet acceptance of the old-fashioned message that the Bible proclaimed to their forefathers. The newsmen are impressed by the respectability and reverence of the meeting, the size and enthusiasm of the choirs, the restrained but forceful preaching, and the solemn appeal for converts which brings hundreds of serious or radiant persons down the aisles without a trace of the old camp meeting fervor.

After a climactic opening night the campaign slowly settles into its regular routine. In addition to the main preaching service at seven-thirty each night (and at three on Sunday afternoons) countless smaller meetings are undertaken by Graham and his team. Graham himself makes news by conducting meetings at the state penitentiary, in the veterans hospitals, or on local college campuses. Saturday afternoon services for children are featured. There is a young people's night once a week with delegations from schools, boys clubs, religious societies, and colleges. The week-end meetings are for out-of-town delegations which are featured in proportion to the distance they have come and the size of their group. Special nights are set aside for men's Bible classes, for businessmen, for businesswomen, for old folks. In Houston, Graham conducted a service at a drive-in theatre for "shut-ins" too old or crippled to attend a meeting at the coliseum but able to come by auto. In Memphis, Graham conducted a revival service in an airplane which was carried on the radio to local listeners; the plane was the first in a new schedule of flights by Chicago and Southern Airlines from Detroit to Memphis. It flew in circles over the city as Graham preached. Another method of maintaining public interest and publicity is the importation of former converts and Christian entertainers who give their testimony at the meetings. The cowboy star Roy Rogers and Dale Evans have appeared at several of Graham's crusades, and at children's meetings Rogers brings his horse, Trigger, to perform. The well-known Broadway singer Ethel Waters has often assisted in this capacity and so have movie starlets Colleen Townsend and Georgia Lee and Metropolitan Opera star Jerome Hines. Donn Moomaw, a former All-American football star, is a favorite celebrity at young people's meetings. And when Graham held a "Teen-age Week" during his New York crusade in an effort to curtail juvenile delinquency, his parade of stars included Carl Erskine, a Dodger pitcher; Ray Robinson, the boxing champion; Red Barber, a sports announcer; the White Sisters, a popular song group; and a trumpet trio.

Spectacular outdoor rallies, however, are the principal means of keeping interest as the campaign proceeds. They not only provide news but stimulate the cooperating churches and their volunteer workers to new activity as attempts are made to fill some vast stadium or park. New York had six such climactic meetings between its opening and closing date: one a meeting at Forest Hills Tennis stadium, the second at Yankee Stadium, another in Harlem, a fourth in Brooklyn, a fifth on Wall Street, and the sixth in Times Square. In Washington the big meeting was held on the Capitol steps. In Boston a meeting was held on Boston Common. In London in Hyde Park and at the Nelson Memorial Monument. While the hope is that these meetings will attract many nonchurchgoers, Graham's team takes no chances and assures a large crowd by urgent pleas to all participating churches and all loyal evangelicals to make "a great Protestant witness" to their faith by coming to each rally. For one of the New York rallies the Minneapolis office sent a mailing to over 100,000 "Prayer Partners" enclosing unsolicited tickets entitling them to reserved seats if they appeared an hour or more before the start of the meeting. Along with the tickets went a form letter signed by Graham which said, "No matter what the cost or sacrifice you must be at Yankee Stadium on July 20. All of us are going to have to work extremely hard if we are going to fill that great stadium for the glory of God." Graham also uses his "Hour of Decision" broadcasts to urge his followers to support these mammoth meetings.

The build-up to a closing date which is then extended "by popular request" also creates new excitement. The New York campaign was extended three times although each time Graham and the committee said that there would be no further extensions. However, to avoid the possibility that any extensions would conflict with other users of Madison Square Garden the committee had signed a lease before the crusade began which gave them a five-month option even though the crusade was originally planned for only six weeks. A closing rally larger than any of those which occur during the crusade creates the ultimate climactic moment.

The day after the concluding meeting Graham and the team leave the city amidst a blizzard of statistics concerning total attendance, total converts, total meetings conducted. An avalanche of praise by local clergymen, editors, businessmen, and city and state officials testifies to the tremendous and beneficial impact which the crusade has had upon the community. Graham himself exudes confidence that the meetings have been more successful than any he has ever conducted. "We are praying," he said at the conclusion of the New York crusade, "that forces will be starting here that in the next five years will make an impact on this country. I believe there is a spirit of revival today in America. I believe that history will say that 1957 was the year of spiritual awakening." [16]

It is another six months before the audited expense account becomes available and a year or more before the results in terms of new church members can be adequately measured.

CHAPTER 8

Converts and Commercialism

All right, we are criticized for spending one million dollars, but how do you evaluate the worth of a soul?

BILLY GRAHAM [1]

The two most frequent complaints made against Billy Graham are the same ones which have been leveled against all professional evangelists: They are that his converts do not stick and that as his organization increases its size and scope it tends to become increasingly commercial in character. Graham denies both criticisms, and so far the critics have not been able to convince the average evangelical minister or layman that these allegations are true. Since Graham has been in the public eye for a decade now, it appears that the critics have had ample opportunity to prove their claims. And yet the nature of revivalism is such that, while the truth or falsity of such claims can probably never be fully demonstrated to the satisfaction of both sides, time is on the side of the critics. For ten years Graham has been saying that America is on the verge of a sweeping, heaven-sent, Holy Ghost revival. For ten years his followers have insisted that Graham is the God-appointed spearhead of such a revival, and Graham has said of himself, "I'm just a Western Union boy delivering God's messages." [2] Yet Gra-

ham is forced to admit with each passing year that the revival he calls for has not yet begun. America has not yet
repented of its sins and turned to God. As time continues
to pass, more and more people will begin to wonder whether
Graham is really the prophet "with God's message for these
crisis days" that his friends claim him to be, or whether he
is not simply an extremely able promoter of Protestant
church rallies.

The central purpose of each campaign, of course, is to
inaugurate a revival of religion. This means first to stimulate new enthusiasm among current or former church members, and second, to awaken nonbelievers or occasional
churchgoers to the need for saving their souls and joining
a church. The high point of each service and of the meetings as a whole is the call for sinners to repent and be saved.
Graham follows the usual procedure of giving an "altar call"
or an "invitation," to accept Christ at the conclusion of every
sermon. Having worked up to his dramatic climax regarding the need for making an immediate choice, he says:
"You can leave here with peace and joy and happiness such
as you've never known. You say, 'Well, Billy, that's all well
and good. I'll think it over and I may come back some night
and I'll——' Wait a minute! You can't come to Christ any
time you want to. You can come only when the Spirit of
God is drawing and wooing you. . . . I beg of you come now
before it is too late. You know you need Christ in your life.
Now while the choir sings a hymn, I'm going to ask you to
leave your seat and come forward. Every head bowed in
prayer and every eye closed. Everyone quietly praying. If
you have friends or relatives here, they'll wait on you.
Whether you're old or young, rich or poor, white or colored,
come quietly up now and say, 'Billy, tonight I accept Christ.'
Come on."

The choir, following the gestures of Cliff Barrows, softly
begins to sing, "Come every soul by sin oppressed there's
mercy with the Lord. . . ." And slowly by ones and twos
and then in groups of six, eight, or ten, the converts walk
down the aisles. Graham stands in the pulpit, a serious,

almost grim look on his face, as he scans the congregation intently. "That's right; come right on down here. We're going to give you a word of instruction and prayer and talk with you for a moment in the inquiry room. We won't keep you long. The spirit of God is moving here tonight. I can feel it. You come right now. Just get up out of your seat, right now, and come quickly. Hundreds of you from way back up there. You folks in the balcony, you in the mezzanine, come right on down, reverently and quietly. You say, it's a long way. Yes, but Christ went a long way to the cross for you. Certainly you can come a few feet to give your life for Him. We'll wait on you. Many people are already on the way."

As each person makes his way forward, one of the trained counselors who have been scattered in seats throughout the audience gets up and walks down beside him. The counselors wear little white or red badges, but to the onlooker it is difficult to tell the counselor from the convert. The fact that 50 per cent of those standing in front of the platform after the invitation are counselors is sometimes lost on the reporters as well.

As the choir pauses between verses, Graham makes another plea. "Come on . . . we're waitin' on you. Don't you want to be born again? You come now." Sometimes he adds a warning. "This may be your last chance. The spirit of God may never be so near to you again. You may be hit by an automobile on your way home tonight. Then it will be too late. You come now." The choir begins again, this time with the song, "Only trust him, only trust him, he will save you now. . . ." A new flood of converts and counselors comes down the aisles. Graham waits, tense but restrained, occasionally biting his thumb or pressing one hand over his eyes to pray. His voice is calm but strong and urgent. He never becomes excited or violent at this juncture. This is the moment in small town revivals when the excitement begins to burst the bounds of normal behavior and people begin to shout or faint. But Graham keeps the meeting firmly in hand and the well-behaved audience knows exactly what is expected of it.

Occasionally Graham's invitation contains an appeal to prestige as well as to eternal life. "I'm going to ask you to do something that I've seen people do all over the world," he began one invitation in New York. "I've seen the Congressman, the governor, the film star. I've seen lords and ladies. I've seen professors. . . ." And then follows the invitation to come forward. It is little wonder that some of the converts describe their feelings at walking forward under the eyes of twenty thousand people by saying, "I felt proud and wonderful as I walked down the aisle." [3] Graham also makes no distinction between inviting persons to come forward who are nonbelievers and those who are already church members in good standing. In fact, he expressly says, "You may be a deacon or an elder. I don't know. You may be a Sunday school teacher. You may be a choir member. You may be an usher, but you need Christ tonight." [4]

After five, ten, or fifteen minutes of urgent pleading, when the flow of converts dwindles to a halt, the choir stops singing. Graham takes a last look around the arena for stragglers, and then leads the audience in prayer for those who "have given their hearts to Christ tonight." The congregation is dismissed as the trail-hitters are led out a door near the platform and into the inquiry room. The counselors, who have been at their sides since they left their seats, usher them to chairs in the inquiry room, introduce themselves, and then sit waiting for Graham or one of his associate evangelists to come and lead them in a word of dedication and instruction in regard to the momentous decision they have made. Then each counselor begins a series of questions with his particular inquirer:

"Now, Mr. Smith, can you tell me just why you came forward tonight?"

"I wanted to make a decision for Christ as Billy Graham said."

"Do you know what it means to make such a decision?"

"Well, I guess it means that I have not lived the way I should and I want to try to do better."

"It means that you must confess your sins, turn from your sins, and follow Christ." The counselor then patiently explains the fundamentalist terminology and interpretation of salvation. He quotes from his Bible to prove that although all men are sinners Christ came to seek and save that which is lost.[5] If the convert is puzzled or is not sure that he is worthy of salvation he is asked to read aloud certain passages from the Bible. "Do you believe what you have just read there? That all men are sinners; all have fallen short of the glory of God and deserve eternal punishment? That Christ died for your sins?"

"Why, yes."

"Do you repent your sins? Are you willing to give up your sins and to accept Jesus Christ as your Lord and Master? Are you ready to serve and obey Him in all things?" Questions may then follow about personal sins which must be confessed and repented. "Nothing must stand between you and God. You must surrender yourself completely." Sometimes there are tears and sobs as an inquirer relieves his pent-up emotion by lamenting past transgressions and expressing gratitude for being able to cast all such burdens upon Christ. The counselor and the convert kneel beside their chairs and pray for forgiveness, assurance, and the strength to continue in the right path.

Meanwhile, all around the large room other pairs engage in the same quiet and serious talk. After the counselor receives the final assent and confession of faith from the convert, he then gives him a packet of Christian literature prepared by the Graham follow-up experts. This contains a copy of the Gospel of John, a form letter from Graham, two Bible memorization lessons, a list of instructions, and a business reply envelope addressed to the crusade headquarters. The form letter from Graham informs the new convert that "in order for you to grow in your Christian life it is necessary for you to . . . 1. Read your Bible daily. . . . 2. Pray every day. . . . 3. Witness for Christ. . . . 4. Attend church regularly. . . ." The instruction sheet explains: "After you have 1. Read the letter from Mr. Graham; 2. Memorized John 3:16; 3. Filled in the answers to the questions in Lesson I in your own words . . . then 1. Mail your completed Lesson I in to the Crusade headquarters in the envelope provided. 2. Write in the answers on Lesson II while you are waiting for the next helpful Bible study from the Crusade headquarters. 3. Keep Lesson II in your possession. Further instructions will follow."

The counselor then fills out a decision card with the convert's name, address, age, occupation, telephone number, church and pastoral preference, and the type of decision. (There are five possible types of decision listed on the card, though the distinctions between them are vague: Acceptance of Christ as Saviour and Lord; Assurance of Salvation; Restoration; Dedication; Reaffirmation of Faith. The first is called a "first decision" which means that the inquirer has never before had a conversion experience. The others are various forms of reconsecration.) The counselor turns this card into the follow-up office where it is kept on file to enable the office to send further instructions to the convert and to send a notice to the proper pastor to visit the convert as soon as possible. A copy of the decision card is also sent to Graham's Minneapolis headquarters.

The last step in the conversion process at the meeting is for the counselor to take the convert to one of the "advisors" who are scattered throughout the inquiry room. The advisors are usually ministers or members of Graham's team who supervise the counseling. If a counselor has difficulty explaining salvation to someone who has come forward, he calls an advisor for assistance. All converts are brought to an advisor to make their first statement of testimony. "This is Mr. Smith," the counselor says, presenting his convert to the advisor. "He has just made his decision for Christ." "How do you do, Mr. Smith," says the advisor. "Can you tell me in your own words what this decision means to you?"

"It means," says Mr. Smith, if he has been properly instructed, "that I have given myself to Christ; that I have repented of my sins and accept Him as Lord and Saviour, and that with His help I will dedicate my life to Him." The advisor may then congratulate him and welcome him into the fellowship of born-again Christians or may quiz him further. He also advises him to join a church as soon as possible in order to obtain the counsel of a pastor and the fellowship of other Christians who will aid him in keeping the faith and give him opportunities to demonstrate his dedication to Christ by working for His church.[6]

Graham, like Sunday and Moody, has reduced revivalism to such a science that there is never a night when scores of converts do not come forward. Usually several hundred persons make decisions each night of the crusade. At the ninety-six meetings in the New York crusades there was an average of 580 decisions each night. In a short crusade, like that in Houston, the average was 207. Total decisions for any crusade have seldom been less than 5000 since 1950 and the largest campaigns have produced 30,000 to 50,000 over a three or four month period. To all outward appearances there is seldom any doubt that a Graham revival has succeeded. He and his team have done what they said they would do. They have taken over a whole city and its surrounding area and saturated it with news about revivalism. They have stirred up thousands of church members to take a new interest in religion. They have made nonbelievers talk about religion. And above all, they have produced concrete evidence in the form of converts and decision cards to show that they have improved the position of evangelical Protestantism in that city. To this extent they have produced what is commonly called a revival. But does it last?

According to the customs and traditions of professional mass evangelism Graham is not personally responsible for seeing that all those who make a decision for Christ in his crusades join a church. That is the job of the local pastors. But Graham tries his best to help. "We are doing all in

our power," he says, "to keep those that fall away at a mini-
mum through an extensive follow-up system." The first step
in the system is to send each convert "a personal-looking
letter" from Billy Graham within thirty-six hours after he
makes his decision in the inquiry room. The convert is
urged to join the church of his choice as soon as possible
and to fill out and return the Bible Lesson I given to him in
the inquiry room. At the same time a copy of the decision
card is sent to the minister designated on the card, or, if
the convert has not listed a preference for a specific church
which he would like to join, his card is sent to the cooperating minister whose church is nearest his home. The minister is asked to visit the new convert at once and to fill out
and return a printed form describing what steps the convert
is taking or intends to take to implement his decision. If the
minister does not return this form within a week, he receives
another letter warning him that if he does not act at once
the new convert's name will be passed on to another nearby
pastor. In addition to these and subsequent letters urging
the converts and pastors to action, the Graham follow-up
process tries to make the counselor who helped the convert
in the inquiry room feel responsible for keeping in touch
with this "Babe in Christ" until he is safely in some church.

Several old-fashioned fundamentalist leaders have criticized Graham on the ground that persons converted at his
meetings often end up joining a modernist or liberal church.[7]
Graham does not deny it, but he tries to discourage it. In
his sermons, many of which are directed to new converts,
Graham urges those who have made the decisions to join "a
Bible-believing, Christ-honoring church" right away. There
is no doubt that by these terms Graham means a church
whose minister preaches the five points of fundamentalism.

Special classes for new converts are conducted each
Monday through Friday evening at the tabernacle or auditorium an hour before the service. At these meetings a
member of the Graham team explains the process of "growing in Christ." All converts are notified of these meetings

and are told, "Be sure to bring your Bible, notebook, and a pencil. Seats in the main auditorium [for Graham's preaching service] will be reserved for all those attending these classes. No one can afford to miss the benefit of this warm-hearted fellowship and instruction."

The Graham team keeps detailed statistics on the new converts and does not hesitate to make these available. Charts have been made for most of Graham's crusades which list night by night the number of men and of women who made decisions, what age groups they fall in, which sex predominates in each age group, the percentage of those who listed a specific church preference, the percentage which listed only a denominational preference, the percentage which had no preference, the percentage of "first decisions" and the percentage of decisions made by persons who were already church members and regular churchgoers. These charts reveal the following facts about Graham's converts: over 60 per cent of them are women; roughly 45 per cent are under eighteen and about 20 per cent are in the age group from nineteen to twenty-nine; almost 90 per cent know what specific church (not just what denomination) they wish to join; 65 to 75 per cent are already church members, and about 65 per cent are already faithful in their church attendance. (In some cities the number of decisions made by children and adolescents under eighteen has been as high as 60 per cent of the total.)[8]

It is surprising that according to these official statistics only 45 per cent of the decisions made in each crusade are "first decisions" (that is conversions or regenerations). If these statistics are correct they signify that 55 per cent of Graham's trail-hitters are not only active, faithful church members, but they are "born-again," "Bible-believing" church members who simply "rededicate" their lives to Christ. This seems to indicate a high proportion of wasted effort. The following statistics obtained from the charts furnished by the Billy Graham Evangelistic Association give the breakdown of decisions for four of Graham's typical crusades:

City	Date	Decisions *	Men	Women	Aged 5-18	Aged 19-29
Detroit . .	1953	4954	38%	62%	45%	20%
Nashville . .	1954	6868	40	60	47	25
New Orleans .	1954	4431	36	64	39	21
Oklahoma City . . .	1956	2204	41	59	61	22

	First Decision	Church Members	Attend Regularly	Gave Specific Church Preference
Detroit . .	58%	—	—	87%
Nashville . .	32	68%	60%	95
New Orleans .	42	68	60	—
Oklahoma City . . .	43	—	80	94

* N.B. These statistics do not include decisions made at special "rededication services" for church members nor those made at "children's services."

Graham has admitted that his statistics show a high percentage of decisions made by persons who are already church members, but he explains this by saying, "Most of these are people who have their names on a church roll but are not faithful and loyal in the church, who probably attend church only rarely and who have lost their interest in spiritual matters. To bring back one of these people is just as important as to get an outsider to Christ." [9] But the statistics are compiled from the decision cards and each decision card has a place on it which reads: "(Attend Regularly) Yes___ No___." [10] The counselors are instructed that to check "Yes" means that the inquirer is a regular and faithful attendant at the local church which he lists as his specific preference. Consequently the statistics compiled from these cards (showing that 65 per cent have indicated that they attend church regularly) seem to refute Graham's assumption that those who make decisions at his crusades are people who "probably attend church only rarely."

The descriptions of Graham's meetings in newspapers and magazines contain much evidence to substantiate the above statistics. Nevertheless many of the ministers who support Graham's revivals do so specifically because they think that he will "reach the masses"—the people in the cities whom the churches are not able to reach. And Graham insists that he does reach them. Of the New York crusade he said, "it took in the whole gamut of social life in New York. We had the extremely wealthy, we had some of New York's top social names there night after night, and we had hundreds and thousands of people from the slum areas." [11] But almost every reporter who has described the crowds which attended the New York crusade, and every other crusade, has described them as being made up primarily of middle-class, neatly dressed, respectable, well-behaved people who sang the hymns as though they were familiar with them and who carried their Bibles. The audience at Madison Square Garden, said one reporter, was made up of "people who would have been just as much at home at a PTA meeting in Scarsdale or Oyster Bay. There was a good, clean, solid look to those in the seats and those who came forward to repent." [12] A Salvation Army captain in the New York inquiry room said that he scarcely ever saw a "Bowery bum" at the meetings: "It's too far to come; besides, they would feel out of place among those nicely dressed people." [13] Graham went to the Bowery to hold a meeting, but the Bowery derelicts did not come to his services.

Even Graham's former associate and constant booster, Carl F. H. Henry, editor of *Christianity Today,* summed up Graham's impact on New York by saying, "Admittedly there are few signs that Graham's meetings significantly affected the worlds of business and labor. . . . The campaign did reach the comfortable middle class, as one could tell from its nightly dress; the extreme poor and the rich were seldom present." [14] The same was true of crusades elsewhere. The crowd in Pittsburgh was described in the *Pittsburgh Press:* "The women dress in current fashion. Most of the men wear business suits. Many display lodge buttons in their lapels and not a few have fraternity pins. The younger set leans toward sport clothes. . . . Many have returned the second, third, and fourth nights to hear him." [15] In Washington, D.C., Graham asked all those who were carrying their Bibles with them to the meetings to raise them in the air. The reporter from the *Washington Post* noted, "nearly the whole congregation responded." [16] Those who came forward in Glasgow, Scotland, at the end of Graham's sermons to accept Christ were described as follows: "They are for the most part women, with mother-and-daughter combinations numerous among them, but there were men too, most of them with their wives. Men unaccompanied by women were fewer. . . . There were no workingmen to be seen among the converts. In Glasgow, a workingman dresses differently from a clerk. These were all white-collar people." [17]

The *Christian Century* described the New York crowds as "a pleasant, earnest group of Bible-and-binocular toting church folk" and ascribed the lack of interest in the meetings by the newspapers to the fact that "The meetings take on largely the character of rallies" and are "much like very, very large Sunday morning services repeated nightly for Christians." [18] This same writer for the *Christian Century* also noted that most of the converts came "from the reserved seats. Many of them carried Bibles. They seemed to be responding unemotionally as if they were proceeding to the Lord's table of a Sunday morning." But while they were obviously churchgoers, the correspondent noted that many of them checked "Acceptance of Christ as Saviour and Lord" on the decision card instead of "Reaffirmation."

Early in the New York crusade Graham reported that "about sixty per cent" of those who had come forward in New York were not church members and were "coming for the first time" to Christ. "This percentage is the highest of any crusade," he said. [19] But the *Christian Century* said of the first night's inquirers, "Of forty queried by our correspondent, only two were not already church members." [20] And *Life* reported after Graham had preached thirty-seven nights in New York: "The great bulk of Billy's hearers have been church members already. Of the New York area's six million non-church-goers, about one in 40 has actually

gone to the Garden. A *Life* spot-check shows that of the
21,000 who have come forward at Billy's invitation to make
'decisions for Christ'—to become wholly and actively Christian—four-fifths belong to a church." [21]

Cooperating ministers try to put a good face on the matter by saying they are gratified to see their old church
members instilled with new fervor. But it must be some
disappointment to them when they receive their share of
the decisions cards each week to find how many of them
are signed by their most faithful church members. A spot-check of 127 Minister's Follow-up Reports from fifty-five
churches received by the Graham headquarters in New York
during the campaign provided the following statistics (these
reports represent the results of a ministerial call upon the
convert shortly after he had made his decision):

Attendance:

Was already attending regularly	104
Has now begun attending	4
Expects to begin attending	4
Does not expect to attend	1
(Not checked)	14
	127

Membership:

Was already a member	88
Has now become a member	1
Intends to become a member	20
Apparently does not expect to become a member	2
(Not checked)	16
	127

In short, only one trail-hitter out of 127 joined a church at
once. Twenty indicated that they intended to join. One
hundred and six out of 127 were either members already or
were uninterested in joining. Assuming that all of those in
this sample who said they intended to join did join eventually, it could be said that 17 per cent of those who came
forward in New York were additions to the churches. That
would mean 6,950 new members out of 56,567 decisions. [22]

That this represents a somewhat optimistic estimate can

be seen by the analysis of the Minister's Follow-up Reports for the Toronto crusade of 1955. These statistics were compiled by the local follow-up committee four months after the close of the crusade and were turned over to the Minneapolis office. A total of 8161 decisions were officially recorded in the Toronto inquiry room (including 531 decisions made at a children's rally and 654 at a dedication service). Sixty-two of these requested that no church follow-up be made. Ministerial reports were made on 4960 of the decisions:

Attendance:	
Already attending	3572
Now begun attending	339
Intend to begin attending	281
Do not intend to attend	178
(Not checked)	590
	4960
Membership:	
Already members	2246
Now have become members	102
Intend to become members	800
Do not intend to join	242
(Not checked)	1570
	4960

Of those checked for church attendance, 82 per cent were regularly attending at the time they made decisions. Of those checked for membership, 66 per cent were already members. The cooperating churches of Toronto received 102 new members and the promise, as yet unfulfilled four months later, of 800 more.

A similar report was made of Graham's Seattle campaign in 1951. Three months after Graham left Seattle, Professor Arthur L. Frederick of the College of Puget Sound interviewed 230 of the 234 pastors in the city who had a telephone. Graham's team had reported 6254 decisions for the six-week crusade. But only 3349 cards were received by the 230 churches in Seattle; the remainder were evidently sent to out-of-town pastors designated by out-of-town trailhitters. Of the 3349 cards, 1155 were signed by children under fourteen and only 1244 were "first decisions." Only 80 out of the 230 Seattle churches received any new members and only 534 new members were reported since the campaign. Because over 100 of these 534 new additions went to a single Presbyterian church, this meant that the average for the other 79 churches was about 5 new members apiece. (Incidentally, only 81 of the 230 churches which Frederick interviewed actively supported the crusade and 36 of these received no new members.)

Frederick also asked the 230 pastors how they felt about the general effect of the campaign upon the city's religious life. Ninety-one of the ministers thought the effects were "negligible, poor, or detrimental;" 45 ministers said the effects were "fair" or "very slight;" and 60 ministers said the effects were "good" or "excellent." While these findings were challenged by Graham's supporters, they correspond to investigations made elsewhere. [23]

The Rev. Charles Farrah, a member of the San Francisco "follow-up" committee, gathered data for six months on the 26,689 decisions registered in Graham's 1958 "Bay Area" crusade. He reported that 60 per cent of the decision cards were signed by "students," 19 per cent by "white collar workers and manual laborers," 15 per cent by housewives, and 4 per cent by business and professional men. According to a report in *United Evangelical Action,* in March, 1959, "Dr. Farrah said his committee concluded that the Cow Palace Crusade had stirred up the faithful and backsliders but had only a negligible impact on those with no prior church affiliation."

Various unofficial polls and surveys concerning the influence of Graham's revivals upon church membership and church attendance have been made in London, Glasgow, and New York. On the whole these bear out the view that Graham has not produced any great upsurge in religious interest among the nonchurchgoing public—certainly not to the extent that could be called a "sweeping" revival. A comparison of these unofficials polls with the highly publicized official statistics indicates the difficulty of making an accurate assessment of Graham's work. For example, ac-

cording to Lorne Sanny, Graham's director of follow-up
work, the official results of the London crusade in 1954 were
as follows: there were 34,661 decisions made during the
twelve-week period; 2500 cooperating ministers turned in
follow-up reports on 23,595 of these; one year after the
campaign 20,350 of those who made decisions were "still
attending church."[24] (At the time the London crusade concluded, the official statistics listed 38,447 "decisions" but
apparently cards were not obtained for all of these.) Although it was officially admitted that 40 per cent of those
who made decisions in London were already church members, the implication left by Sanny's follow-up statistics was
that the 20,350 churchgoers "still attending" were all the
product of the Graham crusade and that they represented a
net gain to the cooperating churches.

In stark contrast to these official statistics was a survey
made by the *London Evening Standard* seven months after
the crusade concluded. A reporter for the *Evening Standard* interviewed the ministers of twenty of the largest par-
ishes of the Church of England in London. These ministers
had received a total of 336 cards from Graham's committee.
They told the *Evening Standard* that 226 of these cards (or
67 per cent) were signed by persons already members or
regular churchgoers of their churches. Of the 110 who were
not members or churchgoers, only 35 were still attending
church seven months after Graham's departure. Applying
this sample to the figure 36,000 (which was another "official" total for the London crusade) the *Evening Standard*
concluded that only 4000 of Graham's decisions represented
a worthwhile gain to the churches.[25]

These figures were challenged by the *British Weekly*, a
nondenominational "Christian" paper which, under the edi-
torship of Shaun Herron, had staunchly supported Graham's
London crusade. Herron sent out 1500 questionnaires concerning Graham's results to 1500 ministers of all denominations in and around London. He received replies from 520
of them. Of these, 144 indicated that they had received
"no converts" and Herron therefore did not include them
in his further calculations. He also discarded 42 replies

which were incomplete or otherwise unusable. The 334
remaining replies came from ministers who had received a
total of 3222 cards representing decisions made at Graham's
meetings. Out of this total, the reports indicated that 1657
(or 51 per cent) were already churchgoers. The remaining
1565 Herron called "outsiders" although he stated that
"more than half of these" were people "who came to church
'spasmodically' or 'irregularly'" or who were members of
Sunday schools and young people's church groups. (Herron's figures showed that 60 per cent of the 3222 cards were
signed by children between ten and nineteen years old.)
In other words, more than half of these "outsiders" had had
"some connexion with churches or church organizations"
prior to Graham's campaign. But the point Herron was
stressing was that 1002 (or 64 per cent) of these so-called
"outsiders" were now attending church regularly nine
months after the crusade ended. This he considered a
significant achievement.

Herron's statistics also provided illuminating information
concerning the proportion of the decisions which were made
by persons sympathetic to the liberal Protestant churches
and the proportion made by persons sympathetic to the fundamentalist (or holiness and pentecostal) churches. The
following preferences were expressed on the 3222 cards
examined by Herron (they do not, however, show which
specific churches within the regular denominations the converts preferred and it is probable that they chose the more
fundamentalistically inclined of these):

Denomination	Number of Churches	Number of Cards
Anglican	110	1198
Baptist	90	902
Methodist	48	486
Evangelical	41	373
Congregational	25	111
Mission halls and unidentified	9	73
Pentecostal	7	55
Presbyterian	4	24

The problem with Herron's poll and with that of the *Evening Standard* was that neither of them indicated how many of the outsiders who were now attending church had actually joined the church they were attending. There are still no figures available on this point and probably never will be. It may be a fair guess, however, that out of the 38,447 trail-hitters in London not more than 2000 were added to the church rolls.

The analysis of the results of Graham's impact on Glasgow in March–April, 1955, was slightly more helpful on this point. This analysis came about as a result of the censuses of the church membership and church attendance in the city made by Dr. John Highet, Lecturer in Sociology at the University of Glasgow. One of these surveys was made the year before Graham came to Glasgow, one was made a month after his crusade concluded, and the third, a year later. Highet had no connection with either Graham or his supporters, nor was his work specifically designed to evaluate Graham's results. It was simply an objective survey or census of the church life of the city.[26]

Highet's statistics dealt with the seven denominations which contained 98 per cent of the Protestant church members of the city. In these denominations the church members in May, 1954, totalled 203,430. A year later (one month after Graham's crusade ended) Highet's second census showed that the membership in these same seven denominations had decreased by 1395 to 202,305. But when he made his third survey, in 1956, the membership in these denominations had risen to 207,232. It seemed fair to say, therefore, that Graham should be given some credit for reversing a downward trend and for the fact that 3802 persons had joined the Glasgow churches between May, 1954 and May, 1956. But it was difficult to assess precisely how much credit should go to Graham.

Highet's surveys on church attendance for these same denominations showed a somewhat different picture. Church attendance in Glasgow increased from 54,503 in May, 1954, to 67,078 in May, 1955, one month after Graham's crusade. (This total represented the average number of persons attending the Sunday morning services on three successive Sundays.) But the third survey showed that church attendance had then declined to 62,224 in the year following Graham's crusade. Although there was a net increase in attendance of 5721 over the two-year period, it might seem that Graham had merely provided a temporary stimulation in attendance which would soon return to its former level. Graham had officially claimed 52,253 decisions from his crusade in Scotland (19,835 of these obtained during his six weeks in Glasgow's Kelvin Hall.) Even if he were given full credit for all the gains noted in Highet's censuses, it would mean that only 7 per cent of this total had joined a church and only 11 per cent had begun attending church regularly. Inasmuch as the Scottish churches had already embarked upon an ambitious evangelistic crusade of their own before Graham came to Glasgow, and inasmuch as they continued it after he left, it would hardly be fair to give him all the credit for the improved condition of the churches, whether it be considered impressive or not.

These statistical analyses of Graham's impact on London and Glasgow can be supplemented by the comments of three well-informed observers of British Protestantism. The Rev. Donald Soper, the foremost spokesman of British Methodism, stated six months after Graham's revival in London, Graham "has caused no religious revival. His audiences have been almost exclusively church people or near-church people. He has not touched the outsider." [27] Cecil Northcott, the London correspondent of the *Christian Century* wrote an article entitled "Four Years After Billy Graham" for the *British Weekly* in which he asked, "Did Graham 'break through' to the unchurched, the nonreligious" in Britain? "The answer," he said, "by and large is 'no.'" [28] And Denis Duncan, who succeeded Shaun Herron as editor of the *British Weekly*, summed up his estimate of Graham in April, 1958, with these words "With regard to the 'lasting effects' of the London Crusade, the position appears to be

this (and it is equally true of the later Glasgow Crusade):
The main impact was among already sympathetic church
members. The effect outside the church, speaking generally, appears to have been very little indeed in terms of
figures." [29]

The first survey of the result of Graham's New York crusade was made five months afterward, in January, 1958, by
George Dugan of the *New York Times*. Dugan sent a ques-
tionnaire to 504 Protestant ministers in the New York area
and received 159 replies. The front-page story on the replies was headlined, "Graham Impact Held Fleeting As
Ministers Appraise Crusade." The 159 ministers had received a total of 3997 decision cards from the Graham
committee. About 64 per cent, or 2552 of these, were already members of their churches. Of the remaining 36 per
cent, most of them failed to join or even to attend regularly
the church they had designated on their decision cards.
Dugan's survey also revealed that Graham "made the least
impact on mission churches in underprivileged areas." In
fact, one minister who works predominantly with juvenile
delinquents in the Greenwich Village area stated that Graham's revivalism had "set back the Christian cause by several years." Dugan's conclusion was that other than giving
a temporary "spiritual lift" to the churches of New York,
the crusade "had little lasting impact on the city." [30]

On the whole the evidence everywhere led to the same
conclusion. Like the urban mass revivals of former days by
Moody and Sunday, by Sam Jones and J. Wilbur Chapman,
by Reuben A. Torrey and Gypsy Smith, Graham's crusades
seemed capable of influencing only those already committed to his religious outlook. They reached a few backsliders, a few occasional churchgoers, a large number of
youngsters in Sunday schools who were already on the way
to church membership, and a few unhappy people who
came in search of an answer to their personal problems.
But their impact upon the community at large was superficial and ephemeral. Graham claims that his revivals make

whole cities "God-conscious" but it seems more accurate to say that they do little more than make people "Graham-conscious."

Many of the critics of Graham's revivalism claim that the reason his impact is so fleeting is that he takes no interest in anything but converting souls. His viewpoint is so other-worldly that it loses contact with the realities of this world. Graham, they say, has an unquestionable talent and sincerity and he has organized a magnificent religious machine, but he has harnessed himself and his machine to the perfectionist view of world evangelism. In the vain hope of converting the whole world to his brand of fundamentalism he is pouring a vast amount of time, energy, and money into a streamlined treadmill. He employs misleading statistics, say these critics, to try to convince people that he is accomplishing the impossible.

But the fault does not lie entirely with Graham. Like all professional revivalists since Moody's day, Graham is a businessman. He frankly compares revivalism to selling. His product is not only personal salvation to individual sinners and redemption to the nation, but it is revitalization to the institutional structure of Protestantism. Like all big businessmen, Graham and his corporation tailor their product, as much as they feel they honestly can, to meet the demands of the market. If this influences his theological and social message in the direction of ambiguity and chauvinism, it influences his revival organization and techniques in the direction of statistics and self-advertising. It almost seems that the more vague his message becomes the more concrete his organization tries to make its results appear. This is not, as the critics maintain, simple proof of the evangelist's egotism or showmanship. In part it is in the very nature of itinerant, urban, mass revivalism. But equally important, and too often forgotten, is the fact that the ministers and laymen who turn to Graham for help are themselves responsible for this emphasis upon statistics and publicity. They want it. In fact, they demand it. Wealthy laymen will not invest their time and money in a selling campaign without

concrete evidence that the enterprise stands a chance of success. Ministers will not commit themselves and their members to a revival unless they feel certain they can reap some
fruits. Trail-hitting totals, decision cards, follow-up letters,
the myriads of charts, forms, and figures played up in ministers' meetings and headlined in the newspapers are the
concrete evidence that Graham has fulfilled his contract. If
ministers find these figures inflated and the results insub-
stantial they might remember that they have themselves
helped design the package they bought.

Graham's revivalism long ago became top-heavy with organization. Now, as his decline begins, the burden of keeping the machine running is putting undue emphasis upon
publicity and fund raising. And yet to retrench or curtail
activities is to yield ground to Satan and his host. In the
near future the strain of keeping the Graham organization
functioning may well cause the same tensions under which
Billy Sunday's revivalism finally collapsed. There is evidence that evangelism for evangelism's sake is leading to
commercialism for evangelism's sake.

The question of a nationwide, commercially sponsored
television program, for example, has long tantalized Graham. He is convinced that he can and must use this new
medium of mass communication. "We have a greater opportunity than Paul ever had. I imagine that if Paul can look
down here he is champing at the bit. How he would like
to be on television!" [31] In March, 1955, the *New York Times*
reported that Graham would probably soon accept an offer
to appear on a sponsored television program similar to those
of Bishop Sheen and Norman Vincent Peale.[32] Nothing
came of this plan and Graham's staff later denied that he
had even for a moment seriously contemplated appearing
on a commercial program. Then in May, 1957, the *New
York Times* printed an interview with Graham indicating
that he was again thinking about a television program of
such lavish proportions that it would require commercial
sponsorship: "I have an idea for a certain program, although
some of my associates disagree with me. It would be a

religious extravaganza. I would have someone like Fred
Waring's orchestra and glee club playing and singing old
religious hymns. Then a five- to eight-minute skit emphasizing a moral or spiritual truth. And then an interview
with a famous person such as Roy Rogers or Vice-President
Nixon who would tell of his spiritual experience. This
would be followed by a five-minute sermon. The program
would be produced on the same scale as a major entertainment show." Graham realized, he said, that "such a program would require the backing of a big company interested
in institutional advertising rather than the 'hard sell' " but he
insisted that "Television is the greatest method the church
has ever known for getting over its message" and should be
used to its fullest extent.[33] So far this program has not gone
beyond Graham's imagination, but it is characteristic of the
evangelistic outlook which one critic of Graham's methods
described as "this strange new junction of Madison Avenue
and the Bible Belt" in which "the Holy Spirit is not over-
worked; he is overlooked." [34]

The charge of commercialism has been so far principally
directed against Graham's employing the Walter F. Bennett
Advertising Agency to assist him in publicizing his crusades
and in directing his television and radio work. No statement
has ever been made of the profits made by the Bennett company from the sizeable commissions it makes from the networks and elsewhere as Graham's official agent. But there
are several other aspects of Graham's multimillion dollar revival business which show signs of adopting a Madison
Avenue approach, albeit on a nonprofit basis.

The "Hour of Decision" radio program, for example, has
become increasingly insistent in its weekly pleas for financial gifts from its twenty million regular listeners. Cliff
Barrows, the master of ceremonies for the program concludes every broadcast with the words: "We invite you to
send your free will gifts and offerings for the support of this
program to Billy Graham, Minneapolis, Minnesota—that's
all the address you need, just Billy Graham, Minneapolis,
Minnesota." Often Graham himself, after concluding his

radio sermon, returns to tell the audience how much "we need to hear from you this week if this program is to continue on the air." From the very outset, Graham made a point of using the traditional solicitation "gimmick" of sending free gifts to all who wrote in after hearing his broadcasts. Free gifts of all sorts are regularly offered to "Hour of Decision" listeners and Graham himself urges them to send for these "unique" mementoes. Among the gifts which have been offered are "a little gold lapel cross," "a square record" (sometimes these records have been called "the picture that plays"), a calendar containing pictures of the team, a clip to put on a telephone dial which says "Pray for the Billy Graham New York Crusade," a gospel song book, sheet music for one of Bev Shea's solos, a wall plaque made of "rustic plastic" which reads "Divine service will be conducted here daily," a packet of Bible verses, reprints of various magazine articles describing Graham's latest crusade, a "Christian Life Guide," and copies of Graham's radio sermons. No donation is required to obtain these free gift offers, but the obligation is implicit and with each gift comes a business reply envelope with a blank check and a pledge. Those who write in are added to the mailing list for future solicitations.

As part of the attempt to publicize Graham's work, Cliff Barrows and Jerry Beavan make a point of informing the radio audience whenever a new interview or feature story concerning Graham appears. The listeners are urged to go to their newsstands and obtain this month's or this week's copy of *Time, Life, Newsweek, American Mercury, Look, U.S. News and World Report, Ladies' Home Journal, Reader's Digest*, or any of a host of other magazines which have written about Graham. (But of course no articles which might be considered uncomplimentary toward Graham, such as Reinhold Niebuhr's articles in the *Christian Century*, are mentioned.)

Graham has been particularly eager to have his readers subscribe to the new magazine *Christianity Today*. This is a neofundamentalist fortnightly edited by Graham's friend

Carl F. H. Henry, formerly of Fuller Theological Seminary. Graham's father-in-law, L. Nelson Bell, serves as Executive Editor and Graham is listed as a Contributing Editor.[35] A copy of the first issue of this magazine was offered free to all "Hour of Decision" listeners in October, 1956, and since that time Graham has sent three letters to those on the mailing list of the Billy Graham Evangelistic Association asking them to subscribe to it. In one of these letters he urged, "Every Christian who wants to be informed on spiritual matters as they relate to this hectic world in which we now live should receive *Christianity Today*. . . . My first article will be 'The Authority of the Bible in Evangelistic Preaching' in the October 5 issue—a message I'd like you to prayerfully read." After describing the magazine in detail, he then added, "I not only ask, but urge you to subscribe to *Christianity Today*," and his last paragraph announced "This 'Special Introductory Offer' is made to the friends of the HOUR OF DECISION Sunday radio broadcasts: 78 issues (3 years) . . . only $10 (save $6.25)." He also added a postscript: "P.S. Place your name on the enclosed postage-paid envelope and you will become a charter subscriber to this MUST in Christian journalism."

Graham has also endorsed *Christian Life* magazine and loaned his mailing list to its advertising agency for solicitation purposes. There is nothing unethical in an evangelist's endorsing magazines and urging his followers to subscribe to them, nor is it unethical for Graham to utilize his mailing list to solicit support of Northwestern Schools, as he did in 1951 while he was their president (he praised the institution because "For two generations it has stood for old-fashioned Americanism—the Word of God—Evangelism—Conservatism . . ."). But in the interest of advancing the neofundamentalist cause and the cause of evangelism in general, Graham inevitably becomes bogged down in what seem to be commercial activities.

Perhaps the most blatant of these is the manner in which he advertises the books written by or about himself and the various publications and recordings of the Grason Corporation. The Grason Corporation is not a non-profit firm, but by an understanding between the interlocking directorates, it arranges to shift its profits to assist the Billy Graham Evangelistic Association. The Grason company is actually a mail-order book and record store. Through it anyone may purchase a large variety of items including all the books written by or about Graham, all the records made by Graham's musical associates, the sheet music for songs and arrangements by Graham's musical associates (including Roy Rogers, Stuart Hamblen, and those in his motion pictures like Redd Harper and Cindy Walker), morocco-bound Bibles in various colors with prefaces by Graham, morocco-bound devotional books, Bible dictionaries, concordances, the complete New Testament on records, and various comic books drawn by Graham's staff artist, Robert Blewett, and featuring Bible stories as told by Graham or Barrows. The Grason company does not publish these books or manufacture the records but presumably it pays a profit to the firms which do. Every December those on Graham's mailing list receive Christmas gift suggestions for items which may be purchased through the Grason company, and announcements are made over the "Hour of Decision" reminding listeners that copies of the latest volumes by or about Graham would make excellent presents to friends and relatives. Graham has admitted using the royalties from his books to help purchase a new house and to establish a trust fund for his children. How much, if anything, his friends and associates make from Grason's sales is not disclosed, but undoubtedly sizeable royalties must result from the Graham-stimulated sales through Grason and other channels.

A similar commercial character is involved in the Billy Graham Evangelistic Films Company, now doing business as World Wide Pictures. The films made by this company rent for a fixed fee. They are advertised over the "Hour of Decision," through materials sent out in the mailings from Minneapolis, and in various religious journals. They are often shown free of charge to promote Graham's crusades and other activities (though a collection is usually taken). To

date this company has made no profits, but presumably
when it does, and when past indebtedness is paid, these
profits like the Grason profits, will be passed on, at least in
part, to the Billy Graham Evangelistic Association.[36]

One of the most confusing aspects of Graham's financial
arrangements is the way in which the Minneapolis office
applies the funds it receives. In 1955 the association reported that its annual budget was $2,000,000 a year. It has
undoubtedly increased considerably since then. There are
four principal sources from which the association draws its
funds. The most important is the freewill gifts and offerings mailed in by radio and television listeners. In 1958
the association was receiving about 7500 letters each week
which contained an average of five dollars apiece. Two-
thirds of these were received in the official business reply
envelopes used by the association, indicating that they came
from regular contributors. This mounted to a total of
$1,960,000 per year. The second source of gifts, but one
which George Wilson says is comparatively small, is the gifts
from religious foundations and private individuals. The
association once received a gift of $50,000 from a religious
foundation but it has not received many such. The third
source of income is the profits of the Grason company which
presumably are substantial but which Wilson has never disclosed. And the fourth important source is the collections
taken "for the 'Hour of Decision'" at all of Graham's crusades.[37]

In the early years of his evangelism Graham asked the
local committees to take one collection during each crusade for his radio ministry. Since the average donation in
the collection plate is thirty-five cents per person and the
average audience about fifteen thousand, this meant $5000
for the association from each crusade. But by 1954 Graham was asking that one day's collection each week throughout the crusade should go to the "Hour of Decision." It
was usually agreed that the collections on Sunday should
meet this purpose. Sunday not only was a day of especially
large audiences, but it was the one day in the week when

two meetings were held. Hence, in recent years, the Minne-apolis office may well have received about $10,000 per week from the local citizens of each city in which Graham held campaigns. In addition, the local committees usually have agreed to donate to the Minneapolis office any surplus which might accrue from the collections. Surpluses have reached as high as $217,618 (in New York City). Some indication of the sizable amounts that came to Minneapolis from the smaller crusades may be seen in examining the audited ac-counts of the Nashville, Tennessee, crusade in 1953. The total expenses of the crusade amounted to $75,234.75. The offerings taken for the "Hour of Decision" plus the surplus received from the collections amounted to $80,497.64. This means that the "Hour of Decision" (or rather the Minne-apolis headquarters) received more money from the people of Nashville than was spent to finance Graham's crusade.[38] The money raised in New York City for the "Hour of Deci-sion" came to $223,283.81.[39]

Under these circumstances, which were repeated else-where, it seemed odd for Graham's team to claim that no money was raised locally to pay the salaries of Graham and his leading team members. These salaries are paid by the Billy Graham Evangelistic Association and whether they take that money from the funds turned over by the local committees or from one of the other three sources of income it is clear that Graham's revival machine is being supported in large part by local contributions which have no connec-tion with the running expenses of the crusades themselves.

The money which goes to Minneapolis is spent in vari-ous ways. Roughly a million and a half dollars per year goes to pay for the "Hour of Decision." Then there are the salaries of Graham, certain key members of the team, and the two hundred employees in Minneapolis. A considerable amount also goes for rent, for printing, for the free gift offers, the overhead, and the six to eight mailings a year at $20,000 each. Some of the money sent to Minneapolis is specifically earmarked for use in other crusades. For ex-ample, the New York crusade committee turned over

$150,000 of its surplus to the association to be used specifically for paying the cost of televising the meetings in San Francisco. Out of the $80,000 sent to Minneapolis from Nashville, $38,000 was set aside to help pay for Graham's 1955 tour of Europe. Large sums raised in Richmond, Virginia, and Louisville, Kentucky, helped to pay for the New York crusade. Eleven thousand dollars raised in the New York crusade went to finance the Charlotte crusade and $11,000 raised in Charlotte was sent to Australia to aid Graham's revival there. One-quarter of the expenses of the London crusade was contributed by the Billy Graham Evangelistic Association from gifts made to it in local crusades.

In short, the Minneapolis headquarters acts as a kind of savings bank or revolving fund for Graham's evangelistic work. Money which comes into it from one undertaking is later withdrawn to finance a new undertaking. In the days when the Graham motion picture company was running at a deficit it was assisted by the association. The association is constantly in the process of building up its funds so as to help Graham promote his crusades in whatever way he and his team think best. The tours of Europe, Asia, the Caribbean, Australia, and Africa would not be possible except by this means. Only a well-organized fund-soliciting and fund-dispensing headquarters can assure Graham the flexibility and support he needs.

Graham's big business corporation is capably and honestly run, but no organization that large can hope to avoid the secularizing tendencies forced upon it by the constant need to publicize its activities and raise money for them. It is the necessity Graham feels to excuse this commercialism which leads him to picture St. Paul as a television preacher, to compare preaching salvation to selling soap, and to "guarantee" to his followers that the more they contribute to evangelistic work the more money they will make and the more successful they will become.

Graham's personal financial honesty is beyond reproach. He does not, as Billy Sunday did, claim that "the laborer is worthy of his hire" and consequently enrich himself. In

1957 he refused to allow his association to raise his salary from $15,000 to $20,000. Although he lives comfortably, he does not live lavishly. He owns a comfortable new home and two hundred acres in Montreat, North Carolina. He has a half-interest in a $25,000 farm given to him and his brother by his father. He carries $40,000 worth of life insurance for his family and the association carries a $50,000 policy on him with his wife as beneficiary. He has few expenses outside of his home and has received many expensive gifts from friends and admirers. But he has not made one-tenth of the money he could have made out of his evangelism and has in fact refused to use for himself much of what he has made.[40]

Although two of his books have made over $100,000 in royalties he spent only $10,000 of this on himself. He has seldom kept the fees he is paid for newspaper and magazine articles, and has more than tithed his income by giving to religious organizations and charity. There have been reports that he is in difficulty with the Internal Revenue Department over his income taxes, but the difficulty is certainly not one of dishonesty. If there is any trouble it is more likely the result of his confusion in handling large sums which he wishes to give away. Speaking for himself and his wife he asserts, "We intend to leave behind nothing that accrued from my ministry." And he means it.[41] If financial entanglements ever taint the Graham organization it will not be because of Graham's personal greed.

In fact, it seems unlikely that either Graham's commercialism or his inability to produce new church members will in the long run be remembered as the principal failing of his evangelism. The most serious criticisms against his work are along other lines.

CHAPTER 9

Billy Graham: An Estimate

> When we come in for the landing in the
> great airport in heaven, I don't want any
> broad-mindedness. I want to come in on
> the beam. . . .
>
> BILLY GRAHAM [1]

In 1917 John D. Rockefeller, Jr., summed up his reasons
for supporting Billy Sunday's forthcoming New York revival
with the statement: "I have felt convinced of Mr. Sunday's
sincerity. . . . I became convinced that in spite of all criticism he was doing a very great work. . . . I think Mr.
Sunday is a great power for good. I don't think it's any one
thing he does or says that counts in particular. It is evident that people are interested and that he gets their attention. And the organization and follow-up work are magnificent. . . . Mr. Sunday is a rallying center around whom all
people interested in good things may gather." [2] John Wanamaker explained his support for Sunday's Philadelphia crusade by saying, "Billy Sunday is no longer an individual
only. He is the center of a great Gospel work." [3]

Much the same things have been said about Billy Graham. E. G. Homrighausen, the Dean of Princeton Theological Seminary, writing in July, 1956, declared, "Graham is a
symbol or rallying center for many Protestant Christians

around the world." [4] And an editorial in the *Christian Century* noted that "many leading American churchmen are willing to let him represent the whole American church." [5]

Any estimate of the value and impact of Graham's revivals must acknowledge that he is something more than a colorful exhorter or a professional evangelist plying his trade. Like the major revivalists of America's past great awakenings, Graham is "a symbol or rallying center" for forces far beyond his own immediate supporters. He may not be the foremost spokesman of his age, but he is certainly one of its spokesmen. Some of those for whom he speaks are easily identifiable; others are not.

In general it may be said that Graham's revivals operate on four different levels. In the first place, Graham was, and still is, a spokesman for the newly consolidated and articulate pietistic movement which is challenging the old Protestant church system. Theologically this movement is an amalgamation of the mellowing fundamentalism of the 1920's and the maturing pentecostalism of a much older date. Whether it is called "the new evangelicalism" or "neofundamentalism," this theology represents a middle ground between the fanatical or ultrafundamentalist fringe groups (the followers of Carl McIntire, the Holy Rollers, the faith healers, the snake handlers) and the liberalism or modernism that is associated with the major denominations. Ecclesiastically it seems to have found a center in the National Association of Evangelicals. Socially the bulk of its followers are among a lower-middle-class group with predominantly a rural background which is trying to break through to suburban respectability without yielding too much of the religious pietism it cherishes.

At the second level, Graham must now be accepted as one of the spokesmen for organized Protestantism in America. Since 1954 he has won the support not only of the rank and file of the laymen and clergy of the major denominations, but also of many of the leading figures of all theological hues. By endorsing his revivals through their official church groups (particularly through the city federations of the National Council of Churches), the major Protestant denominations have acknowledged him as one of their titular leaders. (Graham's endorsement by the Archbishop of Canterbury in England and by the Church of Scotland in Scotland has given him a similar stature among British Protestants.) To what extent the churches have accepted his religious views it is still too early to say. But there is no doubt about how desperately they are searching for something to replace the collapsed theological framework which upheld them for the past generation. "Ministers have been discouraged and frustrated," Graham said in discussing the reasons for his New York campaign. "In talking with many of them we found almost a sense of desperation. Ministers who do not agree with us theologically . . . are willing to cooperate simply because there seems to be nothing else in sight for them to reach the conscience of this city." [6] Graham does not offer the regular churches any radically new theological outlook to fill the vacuum left by the collapse of modernism, but he offers them a new emphasis based upon a few commonly accepted beliefs which are capable of broad interpretations. The whirlwind of organized activity which surrounds his revivalism serves as a temporary substitute for a new theology, and American churchmen have always preferred doing to thinking. No doubt they secretly hope that while they are hard at work evangelizing, the theological crisis will pass and somehow a new theological structure will emerge which will satisfactorily amalgamate Graham's neofundamentalism, Peale's neomodernism, and Niebuhr's neo-orthodoxy. At least something like that has happened in each previous great awakening.

The third level of Graham's revivalism is much broader and less easy to define. It may be summed up by saying that his popularity symbolizes one aspect of the nationwide tension and insecurity which have branded the postwar era as "the Age of Anxiety." This soubriquet does not fit the whole generation by any means; the old optimism and self-confidence are not nearly so shattered as Graham would like to think. Yet there have been sufficiently widespread areas of malaise in American society during the past decade to provide a sympathetic audience for Graham's exhortations which extends far beyond the range of faithful church-goers. The current reorientation in theology has been part of a much wider reorientation in American social and intellectual life. The long-prevailing belief held by most Americans that reason and science were forging the means of perpetual progress and that man was inherently good and society ultimately perfectible have sustained such serious blows that a re-evaluation of some sort was essential. Many people have found a great deal of truth in Graham's wide-ranging arraignment of the prevailing order, particularly in regard to America's preoccupation with materialism and success. The affluent society is not yet so flabby as to have lost its conscience. The fabulous pleasures of a consumption- and leisure-oriented society in the midst of a world of poverty and disaster are too incongruous to be ignored. In this respect Graham's revivals provide a means of massive self-flagellation for a guilt-ridden middle class which believes that in a democracy every citizen is directly responsible for the sins of the nation. Many who disagree with Graham's eschatology accept his views on the need for greater personal morality and asceticism and want to "get right with God." Graham's revivals also elicit a national response because in spite of his arraignment of America's immorality he also provides a comforting reaffirmation of the American way of life and of America's "God-appointed mission" to the world.

The fourth dimension of Graham's revivals is their relationship to the international predicament of Christianity. For four centuries Christianity has been expanding around the globe as a counterpart to the aggressive cultural and economic imperialism of Europe and America. But in the past thirty years or more, Catholicism and Protestantism have suffered grievous setbacks at the hands of concomitant waves of communism, anticolonialism, and nationalism. Not only have foreign missions been wiped out or curtailed and native converts backslidden in Asia, Africa, and the

Middle East, but the whole prestige of Christianity has fallen with the rise of "the backward nations." Not only are these nations rising without the benefit of Christianity but they are directly challenging those nations which are Christian. Protestantism has been particularly hard hit in colonial areas because it was more closely associated with nineteenth century capitalist exploitation than Catholicism and because it was less successful at integrating itself into the life of these alien cultures. Moreover it lacked the organizational unity and hierarchical authority to make terms with the rising nationalists, socialists, and communists. Even in Europe Christianity has suffered serious losses to secularism, communism, and anticlerical socialism. And the same lack of unity (plus an intrinsic aversion to direct political action) has made it more difficult for Protestantism than for Catholicism to enter the arena of politics and labor to combat these trends. As a symbol of embattled Christendom Billy Graham may not be the Protestant counterpart of the Pope that *Time* pictures him to be, but he is one of the few Protestant ministers of international reputation whose primary commitment is not to any denomination or creed but to the whole range of Protestantism. In addition, he is an American and his well-publicized friendship with the President, the Vice-President, and the former Secretary of State tends to associate him with the political leadership which the United States exerts in international affairs. Of course in many parts of the world this is as much a detriment as an asset to his evangelism. Nevertheless in their extremity, Protestant ministers and missionaries at home and abroad have accepted Graham as a symbol of the dynamic, aggressive Christianity which they long to see revived.[7]

As a symbol, spokesman, or rallying center of this quadruple reorientation, Graham has stressed a common core of values and beliefs which are traditional, authoritative, and easily grasped. The intellectual meaning of these beliefs may be vague, but their emotional content is very real. Because Western civilization in general, and Protestant countries in particular, are so thoroughly imbued with the

Judeo-Christian tradition imbedded in the Bible, Graham is on firm ground in using it as the source of his message. The clearest notes in his preaching are his emphasis upon the patriarchal authoritarianism and righteous Jehovah of the Old Testament and his assertion of the individualistic aspects of faith, hope, and love in the New. In appealing to "the doctrines of our forefathers" Graham is looking backward rather than forward. His dominant theme is that the only answer to today's problems lies in a return to the old ways, the old faith, the old values—particularly in the United States where he frankly associates Christianity with the Protestant ethic and the American way of life. But if Graham is trying to turn back the clock, he is at any rate sufficiently perceptive not to formulate any clear-cut prescription for this. His popularity, like Billy Sunday's, is not based on "any one thing he does or says" but simply on the conservative trend he represents.

A large measure of Graham's success is due precisely to the ambiguity of his preaching. If he were to become more concrete he would split the broad base of his support. He can remain a symbol of Protestant Christendom only so long as he is regarded simply as "a rallying center around whom all people interested in good things may gather." But there is danger in being all things to all men. He thereby incurs the charge of preaching "bland pietism," perfectionist escapism, and simple obscurantism. He is accused of being too liberal by the fundamentalists and too fundamentalist by the liberals. Some consider him as literalistic as William Jennings Bryan and others think him as mystic as Norman Vincent Peale. His pietistic friends worry that he is putting the church too much into the world while the social gospelers criticize his failure to relate his theology to social reform. Political liberals say he is too conservative and ultraconservatives say he is as far left of center as President Eisenhower's "modern Republicanism."

The theological and political moderates on both sides who cooperate in his campaigns are ready to defend his position and his work, but they sometimes seem to do so apologetically. They emphasize his youth and his sincerity, for example, and suggest that whatever shortcomings he may have he is showing signs of maturing and rising above his background and early training. They say he certainly is a big improvement over Billy Sunday because he does not use acrobatics in the pulpit or collect large freewill offerings. Though some chastened liberals who support Graham express reservations about his lack of social consciousness, they also point out that an evangelist cannot do everything and that it is sufficient that he preaches an evangelical theology and unites the churches in an effort to win souls for Christ. His revivals, it is now admitted, may not reach as many unchurched people as had been hoped, but they are still of great value in instilling new spirit into old church members. And certainly it is commendable, say these moderates, that so many different denominations and theological views are brought together to cooperate in his campaigns. The campaigns may be expensive and may make excessive use of commercial advertising techniques, but Graham is attracting more attention to Protestantism in the cities than has been seen in decades. Would any Christian deny, his defenders ask, that even if only one soul is saved it is worth all the effort?

Above all, Graham is praised for bringing Protestantism back to some of the old Biblical truths that have been neglected too long. He is emphasizing the doctrines of sin and repentance and redemption which modernism, to its shame, forgot or undervalued. In sum, whatever Graham's faults, and they admittedly exist even for his admirers, he is felt to be doing good; his heart is in the right place and his theology is headed in the right direction. In this time of crisis, his supporters conclude, carping criticism is out of place. Let the churches be thankful that someone is stirring the dry bones and let every servant of the church put his shoulder to the wheel to help Graham's revivals along.

Some Protestant spokesmen whose views are far removed from Graham's, like John C. Bennett of Union Theological

Seminary, John A. MacKay and E. G. Homrighausen of Princeton Theological Seminary, and Ralph Lord Roy, author of *Apostles of Discord,* have publicly expressed a certain respect and sympathy for Graham and his work. And for all his criticism of Graham, Reinhold Niebuhr has declared that "This handsome, youthful, modest, and obviously sincere evangelist is better than any evangelist of his kind in American history." [8]

At heart, however, Graham is still a fundamentalist of the old school. The spirit which animates his preaching and provides the driving force behind his career is that of traditional American pietism. His strength comes from his profound dissatisfaction with the prevailing order and his deep conviction of the imminent personal return of Christ to set it right. But in this strength lie the seeds of his weakness. For it is from his pietistic fervor that Graham's opponents derive the two criticisms which are, in the long run, most likely to undermine the broad support for his revivals. These are, first, that his Biblical literalism leads inevitably to anti-intellectualism and self-righteousness, and second, that his exclusive concentration on soul-winning ignores not only the social aspects of Christianity but the functional role of "the Church."

The charges of anti-intellectualism and self-righteousness stem directly and indirectly from Graham's absolute insistence that the Bible is the revealed and infallible word of God. "I have accepted the Bible as fully inspired of God," he says, even though "I may not have the ability to prove mathematically" that this is true.[9] He is willing to say that "The Bible is of course not a textbook on science" and he even says "I would be the last to say that we have nothing to learn from the devout and scholarly studies of the Bible in recent years." [10] His Calvinist background has inculcated a certain respect for learning and he is not above emphasizing the fact that he was a student of anthropology in college and that he devotes considerable time to reading and study. Yet it is quite clear that Graham's respect for education is limited to those colleges which are Bible-centered and his respect for learning is limited to those men who have not let it dissuade them from the tenets of fundamentalism.[11]

When there is any conflict between the Bible and the findings of science or scholarship, Graham quickly reverts to the view he expounded in 1949: "I don't care what the scientist has to say. I'm not dependent on what the scientist tells me to believe about this Book. Every time some big shot scientist comes along and makes a statement complimentary to the Word of God we rush out and say, 'Boy, look what so and so said—Look what Dr. so and so, a Ph.D. from Oxford, had to say.' I don't care what any scientist says. The Word of God is enough." [12] When *Life* published a series of articles in 1956 describing the history of mankind in evolutionary terms, Graham rebuked its editors for helping encourage the view that man is descended from a monkey.[13] He is not even willing to accept the view of the theistic evolutionists that no matter when life started it still was created originally by God: "I do not believe that God created life and then, over a process of many thousands of years, it evolved into what we call man." [14] Only the Biblical account in Genesis is acceptable to him and apparently he follows Bishop Ussher's chronology which placed the creation of Adam in the year 4004 B.C.[14a]

But what particularly leaves Graham's preaching open to charge of anti-intellectualism is his belief that education is dangerous unless the restraining influence of fundamentalist Christian doctrine is inculcated with it every step of the way. "I sincerely believe that partial education throughout the world is far worse than none at all, if we only educate the mind without the soul. . . . Turn that man loose upon the world [who has] . . . no power higher than his own, he is a monstrosity, he is but half-way educated and is more dangerous than though he were not educated at all." [15] By educating the soul Graham of course means conversion. He is particularly appalled at the thought of foreign students who are being educated in godless American colleges and "are going back to their nation to some day turn upon us with the very tools we have given them because we gave them no moral balance and restraint. To think of civilizing the heathen countries without converting them is about as wise as to think about transforming them into lambs by washing them and putting on them a fleece of wool." [16]

The same holds true for the education of Americans. Unless education leads to a change of heart such as he defines in his sermons, as well as to an increase in knowledge, it is useless. "You can stick a public school and a university in the middle of every block of every city in America and you will never keep America from rotting morally by mere intellectual education." [17] During the Red scare of the early 1950's Graham regularly warned about Communist infiltration into the schools and decried the intellectuals who were soft on communism. "What is the secret of Communism that will make university professors forfeit their reputations, their families, and all they have to follow the ideology of Communism?" [18] And when the scare diminished and Graham felt more certain that a revival was on the way, he said, "During the past few years the intellectual props have been knocked out from under the theories of men. Even the average university professor is willing to listen to the voice of the preacher." [19]

Graham's most concrete complaint about American education is that since the turn of the century the schools have ceased to teach the moral code of the Bible and have instead inculcated a system of moral relativity. In place of the Bible, he wrote, "we substituted reason, rationalism, mind culture, science worship, the working power of government, Freudianism, naturalism, humanism, behaviorism, positivism, materialism, and idealism." [20] This is the fault of the "so-called intellectuals." "Thousands of these 'intellectuals' have publicly stated that morality is relative—that there is no norm or absolute standard. They say, 'As long as you enjoy it and no harmful physical or psychological effects occur, go ahead. It must be all right.'" [21] There has been what he calls "a conspiracy of silence" about Christianity in the classrooms. "Teachers refuse to answer questions or discuss matters pertaining to the Christian Religion. Their silence implies to us unbelief and hatred for Christ. . . . Stand by—listen to the young people today as they turn from their classrooms—have they studied from the best seller of every year and all time? No! They are the victims of a conspiracy of silence. There is no Bible to study from." [22] Graham lays part of the blame for this upon the Supreme Court. "I disagree with the Supreme Court's decision in the McCollum case. Our forefathers gave us freedom *of* religion not freedom *from* religion. Unless we bring God into the classroom and make Him the center of education we are not preparing our young people for their roles in Christian society." [23] And he has frequently said, "The Supreme Court ordered the Bible out of our schools. Many of our educational leaders sneer at the old-fashioned idea of God and a moral code." [24]

Supporters of Graham who disagree with the implications of these remarks look upon them as simply careless or thoughtless asides. What these more moderate friends fail to see in these remarks is how central they are to the total pattern of his thought and the extent to which they appeal to those fundamentalists who are only too ready to believe the worst about intellectuals, Supreme Court judges, university professors, scientists, and higher education in general. Moreover, it is only a short step from this sort of anti-intellectualism to the self-righteousness of bigotry.

Graham has twice delivered over the air and distributed free to his listeners a sermon entitled "The Sin of Tolerance" in which he says, "The word 'tolerant' means 'liberal,' 'broad-minded,' 'willing to put up with beliefs opposed to one's convictions,' and 'the allowance of something not wholly approved of.'" In the most recent version of this sermon, in July, 1958, he began by applying the term to America's appeasement of Russia which, he said, "reflects the easy-going compromise and tolerance that we have been taught by pseudo-liberals in almost every area of our life for years." [25] The central theme of the sermon is that in matters of faith it is wrong to be tolerant for there is only one true path to salvation: "When we come in for the landing in the great airport in heaven I don't want any broadmindedness. I want to come in on the beam and even though I may be considered narrow here, I want to be sure of a safe landing there." But Graham is concerned with more than spiritual narrowness in this sermon. Its basic tone and implication is that there is no room for tolerance in any sphere of thought or action. It is sinful, says Graham, that "We have become tolerant about divorce; we have become tolerant about the use of alcohol; we have become tolerant about delinquency; we have become tolerant about wickedness in high places; we have become tolerant about immorality; we have become tolerant about crime and we have become tolerant about godlessness." In this, as in other sermons, Graham seeks to divide the world into two groups, the born-again Christians and the godless. "Christ said, '. . . no man can serve two masters'" and "If we are not with Him we are against Him." [26] There can be no freedom to differ, for tolerance is a sin. Applied to matters of faith Graham may have grounds for argument, but applied to foreign affairs and social mores his assertion of fundamentalist dogmatism becomes worse than self-righteousness; it becomes fanaticism.

This is particularly evident in Graham's patronizing attitude toward the heathen of Asia and Africa. "What a difference there is between the Christian in India and the average man in the street," he wrote in an article for *Christian Life* during his visit to Asia. "The average man in the street seemingly has a fairly hard and dark morbid look on his face. You know the look of heathenism. Yet the Christian is so completely different." [28] When he returned from Asia he was interviewed by someone on the staff of *U.S. News and World Report,* who framed the questions about India in such a way that, despite his attempt to be diplomatic, Graham clearly gave the impression that the morality of the people of India was inferior to that of Americans because they were not Christians. The interviewer asked:

"You speak of the religious background of these people and their interest in spiritual things. One thing that puzzles many people here is that when an issue of right and wrong arises, India will often take a position between those two positions and say that she's neutral. For example, if there are crimes committed, people enslaved and people sent to prison camps, people maltreated in various ways, deprived of their liberties—as we read from day to day in the press report about what's happening in Russia—how can people with a spiritual background like that take a position of indifference and detachment toward these highly moral questions of right and wrong?"

Graham answered:

"First of all, when I say [that the people of India are] religious, I do not mean necessarily Christian. Therefore the standards of morality [in India] are somewhat different than our Judaistic and Christian standards of morality."

The interviewer pressed him:

"What are the differences between their standards of morality and ours?"

Graham hesitated:

"I'm not sure that I'm qualified to give the differences of the standards of morality. . . ."

The interviewer tried again:

"What about principles of justice? Do they hold that persons who commit wrong should be punished?"

Graham answered:

"I'm not sure that I'm qualified to answer that question. . . ." [29]

This may be more revealing about the attitude of *U.S. News and World Report* than about Graham, nevertheless the reader leaves this interview feeling that Graham doubted whether the people of India do know the difference between right and wrong in any sense recognizable to a Christian. His refusal to answer the question posed by the interviewer was not merely carelessness. In fact, Graham was probably bending over backward to avoid making any statement about India that might give offense to the

Indians. But the truth of the matter may well be that Graham inherently believes that no non-Christian culture would be able to distinguish between crime and justice, maltreatment and kindness, slavery and freedom. In the light of Graham's conviction that the struggle between America and Russia is a struggle between Christ and Satan, neutrality is not a morally defensible position. Evangelism and missionary work in India is therefore a form of Christian imperialism which Graham finds thoroughly justifiable.[30] He has stated elsewhere that the doctrine of the universal brotherhood of man and the universal fatherhood of God is false. "You say, well isn't God the father of us all? No . . . until you come to the Cross of Christ and receive him as your Saviour, you cannot properly say, 'Our Father.' "[31] When he concluded the interview in *U.S. News and World Report* with the statement that "Asia can be won," he meant that it must be won not only from communism but from Buddhism and Hinduism. In his simplistic vision, it is as easy to indict a nation of 500,000,000 as it is to indict a single sinner.

Graham is partially aware of how simplistic his sermons are. According to him, "The average religious intelligence of an American is that of a twelve year old. Therefore the preaching of today must be in utter simplicity almost as if you were talking to children."[32] The end result is, as Reinhold Niebuhr and others have pointed out, that Graham's preaching becomes almost irrelevant to the difficult domestic and international problems of the day. Graham's "pietistic individualism" Niebuhr rightly says, "is in danger of obscuring the highly complex tasks of justice in the community and of making too sharp distinction between the 'saved' and the 'unsaved.' "[33]

There are innumerable examples of the way in which Graham obscures the highly complex task of achieving a just society and at the same time denigrates the functional role of the church. All of them stem from his view that sin is entirely an individual matter which can be settled by making the right answer to his question, "Are you on God's side or the Devil's? Do you accept Christ, or reject Him?" Where the evangelist or Christian soul winner can solve the problem of sin, what is left for the church to do?

Graham's irrelevant approach to the complex question of the causes of war, for example, can be demonstrated by this statement in *Peace with God:* "It is the same sin that causes an African savage to skulk along a jungle trail awaiting his victim with a spear in hand and a well-trained, educated pilot to fly a jet plane over that same jungle ready to bomb an unsuspecting village." [34] His comments upon the Soviet Union's invasion of Hungary in 1956 were equally obtuse: "The same thing that produced juvenile delinquency and crime in America produced the tortuous outburst in Hungary." [35] With no sense of incongruity he lumps together in one paragraph as evidences of the "iniquity and sin abroad in the world today," "Racial tensions . . . rising in North Africa, South Africa . . . the terrible division and tension over Suez . . . our divorce rate the highest in history . . . an American movie . . . filled with rock 'n' roll music . . . a young man [Elvis Presley] whose songs emphasize the sensual. . . ." [36]

Graham argues that summit meetings with godless nations are useless, that no form of international conciliation is possible, that wars—even atomic wars—are inevitable. [36a] Yet at the same time he offers the miraculous fantasy of world leaders converted to Christianity who will bring peace and tranquility to the world overnight. Time and again he raises the hopes of his pious auditors by beginning a sentence, "Wouldn't it be wonderful if. . . ." He realizes that it is not likely that Khrushchev, Nasser, and Mao Tsetung will be converted (though he has long entertained hope of conducting a revival in Russia) but if only they were, then everything would be all right.

On a simpler level, the problems that wrack the home life of the average American are offered an equally magical, irrelevant, and escapist solution. Graham has several times offered to all his "Hour of Decision" listeners "a remembrance of the Billy Graham New York crusade" which he calls a "Biblegraph." This is a cardboard disc about six inches in diameter on either side of which a slightly smaller disc with three small holes in it is superimposed. Around the edges of the larger disc are listed "the 36 most trouble- some questions of modern everyday life," and beneath each question are the days of the week. The smaller discs re- volve so as to point to any of the eighteen questions listed on each side. The instructions on the Biblegraph read as follows: "Select the question that troubles you most *today* and turn the dial-pointer to *that day* [of the week]. Then look in the little windows and you will find Book, Chapter, and Verse of a passage from the Bible. . . . Apply the mes- sage to yourself. If the same question arises the next day, repeat the process and you will find another specific refer- ence. . . . If your problem persists after 7 days, turn to some other related question." Among the questions listed are, "Do you feel inferior?" "Are you harassed by money mat- ters?" "Do you have domestic problems?" "Are you lonely?" "Are you depressed?" "Do your children seem ungrateful?" "Is business bad?" The Biblegraph's answer for Monday to the question "Is business bad?" is Ecclesi- astes 5:12, "The sleep of the labouring man is sweet whether he eat little or much; but the abundance of the rich will not suffer him to sleep." The answer to "Do you feel inferior?" for Friday is Psalms, 138:6, "Though the Lord be high, yet hath he respect unto the lowly; but the proud he knoweth afar off."

This is not too far removed from Norman Vincent Peale's handy little cards (designed to fit easily into a pocketbook or wallet) which list the ten steps to overcome an inferiority complex. The pietistic fundamentalist and the mystical modernist meet in the realm of hope and miracles. It is not altogether surprising therefore that Graham's New York crusade netted more decision cards for Peale's church than for any one of the other fifteen hundred cooperating churches.[37] Nor is it surprising that the university-educated, seminary-trained pastor of the average suburban church around New York often found his members confused by

listening to Graham's sermons: "Following up 'commitments' secured from members of my congregation," wrote
the Rev. George C. Bonnell, pastor of the West Side Presbyterian Church of Englewood, New Jersey, "I was surprised to note how foggy a notion most of them had about
their actions. More than one family of our church is terribly confused and upset because they feel that somehow
their brand of faithful, everyday Christian living does not
possess the emotional fervor and dedication of 'conversions'
at the Garden." [38] In Graham's preaching the fundamental
activities of Christian living are soul-winning, Bible-reading,
and prayer. But this is not the average American's view of
religion.

The average middle-class American still believes in the
brotherhood of man and the Fatherhood of God; he still
thinks of religion as primarily an application of the ethics
of Jesus to the social problems that surround him. To be
told to pray for miracles, or to search for answers to business problems in the Bible, or to confront his friends with
the question, "Have you accepted Jesus Christ as Lord and
Saviour?" seems unthinkable. Naturally it is exciting to
hear Graham preach because he makes religion so dramatic
and faces his auditors with such a heroic challenge in the
name of patriotism and Christianity. Ordinary church services seem dull by comparison. Yet if his converts did what
he wanted them to do or what he implies that they should
do, they would at once leave their jobs and become missionaries to save the heathen from hell and communism.
For the college-educated suburbanite who has gone with
his fellow church members to hear Graham because he feels
that Graham is doing some good, it is a shock to hear that
to believe in evolution is ungodly and that saving souls is a
more effective method of social reform than community
action. This is also a shock to many pastors who have a far
broader conception of their duties and of the role of their
churches.

Occasionally Graham has made some concessions to the
American penchant for do-goodism. In a recent sermon on

juvenile delinquency he offered as one of ten "suggestions that may be helpful in the present situation" that Americans should "clean up the bad slums and housing conditions that breed a great deal of our crime." [39] But this is one of the few statements in all of Graham's sermons in which he shows any awareness that sin may have a social origin. It is also one of his first intimations that collective or governmental action rather than an individual and voluntary approach would be useful in alleviating a social problem.

The week after he gave this sermon in March, 1958, Graham delivered another on the "social application" of the gospel which showed no indication whatever that he thought Christianity stood for any type of social action other than charity and pity. The sermon was called "The Sin of Omission" and Graham began it with the statement that "If the gospel we preach does not have a social application, if it will not work effectively in the work-a-day world, then it is not the gospel of Jesus Christ." He then offered six examples of applied Christianity which it would be sinful to omit: "There is a man in your community who has done you an injustice. . . . You could extend to him the warm hand of forgiveness." "You know a man who had had misfortune and bereavement . . . offer him a helping hand and some financial help." 'You know a young man . . . fighting against temptation. . . . Lay your hand on his shoulder and give him a word of encouragement and cheer." "You know a mother . . . standing over the fevered body of a sick child. . . . Visit her and relieve her for one night." "You know a poor family down the street. . . . The father is out of work and . . . they have scarcely a thing to eat. . . . Visit that family and offer your help." "You know a man in your neighborhood who needs Christ. . . . Bring him to the Saviour." The sermon closed with a reference to "the starving millions of Asia" and the "underprivileged in Africa," but again the suggested remedy was personal philanthropy: God "has given you wealth. Have you divided it? He has given you love. Have you shared it?" Collective effort in the form of Point Four assistance or foreign loans was ap-

parently still a "give-away" program which would weaken
the United States and undermine the individual initiative
and incentive of the Asians. Most American churchgoers
were aware by 1960 that, while Graham's proposals for
Christian living were valid enough in terms of small-town
neighborliness or even within the city block or apartment
house, they were of little help in solving the major dilem-
mas of the day.

In spite of the hopes (expressed ten years ago by many
who wished Graham well) that he would "transcend his pa-
rochial background" and "break his own pattern," there is
little evidence that he has altered his underlying fundamentalist and politically conservative point of view. He has,
however, matured sufficiently to show a vague awareness of
what he is expected to say. Soon after he got to London he
was quoted as remarking, "You can say what you like about
socialism, but it's done a lot of good here." [40] And he told
Stanley Rowland, Jr., in an interview for the *New York
Times* shortly after his New York crusade, "I was critical of
India because I didn't understand India . . . until I went to
India and saw for myself the terrible economic and social
problems [there]. . . . That gave me an understanding." [41]
But he has not yet introduced these attitudes into his sermons. Nor, despite all his statements about the need for
granting equal rights to Negroes, has he yet made it an obligation of all truly converted Christians that they should take
a stand against segregation. He also refuses to see any
moral implication in the testing of atomic bombs and claims
that any comment on this matter is "a little out of my field"
as a minister.[42]

His sermons show no indication of dropping the "scare
technique" that he first used in Los Angeles. When the
Soviet Union launched its first earth satellites in the fall of
1957 and President Eisenhower made a special radio speech
urging Americans to keep calm, Graham told his "Hour of
Decision" listeners that same week, "it is not only possible
but very probable" that the Russians would use the sput-
niks for launching rocket attacks and that someday the

United States' leaders might find it necessary to "capitulate" to communism.[43] A year later when the United States showed eagerness to withdraw its troops from Lebanon soon after it had sent them there, Graham chided the administration for giving "another victory" to communism. "We hesitate, we vacillate, and weakly back down when the going gets rough. Why doesn't our President tell them in no uncertain terms that we will get out of Lebanon if they will get out of Hungary?" [44] In September, 1958, Graham said, "I do not know one great victory we have won in recent years over Communism. It's gaining slowly but surely . . . and coming ever closer to the shores of this country. . . . The church as we know it today may someday have to go underground." [45] In short it seems that Graham, instead of breaking his pattern, has at best merely managed to be somewhat more tactful in displaying it. It remains to be seen whether this will be sufficient to maintain his symbolic leadership of Protestantism much longer. Individualism has never constituted more than a part of the American democratic faith and pessimism is not yet the predominant strain in the American character.

On the whole it now looks as if Billy Graham's revivals have lost their luster. So much has been written about him and his work and each crusade is so similar to all the preceding ones that public curiosity has been satiated. Billy Graham's revivals are no longer news—or at least they are only news when they show signs of not being particularly successful. Furthermore, there are no discernible results of his meetings which seem to merit conspicuous attention. The cooperating ministers in cities where he has preached may note a new interest among their members or a few new faces, men's Bible classes may be slightly enlarged, a greater interest in foreign missions is apparent, but these changes are hardly front-page news.

On the other hand, it is not likely that Graham will soon sink into oblivion. Like other major evangelists of the past he can undoubtedly look forward, health permitting, to a long career of honor and respect. Charles Finney continued to conduct revivals for almost forty years after he passed the peak of his fame. Moody was active for twenty years, Sam P. Jones for twenty, Gypsy Smith for twenty-five, and Billy Sunday for fifteen years after they were no longer front-page news. Those who were most honored in their later years, like Finney and Moody, took up new interests in addition to their revivalism. Finney became a professor and later President of Oberlin College. Moody founded two schools in Northfield which have achieved an enviable academic standing. Graham has hinted that if he ever retires from evangelism he would take a job as a college president. But perhaps, like Finney, he can do both. He has in the past.

Graham's future role in Protestantism will depend primarily upon the course which America's fourth great awakening takes in the next decade. It is one of his major achievements to date that through his revivals he has temporarily succeeded in creating a modus vivendi between the resurgent neofundamentalists represented by the National Association of Evangelicals and the retrenching modernists represented by the National Council of Churches. He would obviously like to see these groups merge in some kind of "spiritual fellowship" so that the NCC would become more "evangelical" and the NAE would gain some of the prestige and power which is attached to the older organization. But it is unlikely that the rank and file of the NAE would take kindly to any such maneuver unless the leaders of the major denominations were willing to accept a more rigid adherence to the fundamentalist creed than they are apt to. The current readjustment in Protestantism is infinitely complex and it involves basic attitudes toward ecclesiastical policy as well as theological doctrine which Graham, despite his best efforts, is not capable of resolving.

The members of the NAE with whom Graham has been associated almost since its start in 1942, have for years denounced ecumenicalism in general and the NCC in particular—calling it "the Super-Church" and "the Coming Great Church." Ever since the great modernist-fundamentalist

schism began in the 1920's the fundamentalists have emphasized the pietistic doctrine of "separatism" and called upon
the faithful to come out from among the apostate denominations affiliated with the Federal Council of Churches and its
successor the NCC. The NAE was formed primarily to fa-
cilitate this withdrawal, and its most active spokesmen today
still hope that it will eventually unite within its "evangelical
fellowship" the thirty million Protestants who, they claim,
are not in harmony with the liberalism of the NCC.

Because of his personal membership in the NAE and
because its members have formed the nucleus of his support in almost all of his revivals, Graham is committed to
defending the organization. Since 1952 he has been a regular speaker at its annual conventions, exhorting it to further
efforts to preserve the faith. Yet while Graham has fully
sympathized with the NAE's attacks on modernism and its
fears of ecumenical unity, he has become increasingly less
sympathetic with the pietistic separatism of some NAE leaders. Consequently, during the past few years Graham has
become more active in his own denomination, the conservative Southern Baptist Convention, than in the NAE. He is
no separatist.

Ever since his failure in 1952 to win sufficient support to
hold a campaign in New York, Graham has recognized the
need for accepting support from nonfundamentalist ministers if his revivals are to have the scope and impact necessary "to reach the cities for Christ." Some of his friends,
particularly those associated with the magazine *Christianity
Today,* consider it a significant triumph for "the new evangelicalism" that Graham has been able to obtain the cooperation of ministerial councils and federations which were
dominated by liberals and modernists. Mass revivalism had
become so closely associated with fundamentalism in the
days of Billy Sunday and the Scopes trial that to many neofundamentalists it seemed like an admission of error on the
part of the liberals when they returned to the support of
revivalism in the 1950's. Since Graham refused to compromise on the doctrines he preached in his revivals, it was

assumed that the liberals had made the concessions by backing him. If the ministers who supported Graham did not succumb to his message, at least it was thought that many of their church members would.

To date the official spokesmen of the NAE have not quarreled with Graham concerning his liberal sponsorship. They have in fact defended his actions as a statesmanlike attempt to "penetrate" or "infiltrate" the regular denominations and thus to sap their strength from within by siphoning their members off into churches more sympathetic with the NAE. Nevertheless, a growing number of prominent fundamentalists within and without the NAE have, since 1954, begun to express serious doubts concerning Graham's policy of cooperation. Led by such old-time fundamentalist stalwarts as Bob Jones, Sr., the founder of Bob Jones University, John R. Rice, editor of the *Sword of the Lord,* and Ernest Pickering, the executive secretary of the Independent Fundamental Churches of America, this group has begun to speak out against him and to discourage other fundamentalists from supporting any Graham crusade in which liberal churches cooperate.

A dozen or more pamphlets and scores of magazine articles in fundamentalist journals and mimeographed broadsides have been printed in the past three or four years denouncing Graham for "selling out" to the modernists. Fundamentalist ministers in New York, San Francisco, and Chicago have actively banded together to repudiate his crusades in these cities. These are not members of the fringe group of ultrafundamentalists led by Carl McIntire, founder of the American Council of Christian Churches. They are former friends and supporters of Graham and the NAE who feel that he has strayed from the "true evangelical" path in order to gain greater worldly success. The four principal accusations they make against Graham are first, that by permitting himself to be sponsored by ministers whom he admits to be liberals and modernists he is associating with known apostates, thereby strengthening their position, weakening his own, and acting contrary to Biblical injunctions on the matter of separatism. The second charge is that by such cooperation Graham is forced to compromise on his message, perhaps unwittingly; at any rate he must refrain from attacking modernists while he is cooperating with them and this confuses many Bible-believing Christians who do not know why Graham is consorting with people like Norman Peale and Ralph Sockman and Henry Van Dusen whom their pastors so vigorously denounce. The third accusation is that Graham frankly admits that all those who make decisions in his revivals are permitted to join the church of their choice even if it is a liberal or modernist church; decision cards are knowingly turned over to liberals by Graham thereby virtually ensuring their loss to fundamentalism even though Graham may have preached it faithfully during his crusade. And the fourth charge is that after Graham's campaign in New York (and presumably the practice was followed elsewhere) the sum of $67,000 (taken from the surplus of contributions) was turned over by the crusade committee to the Protestant Council of New York to be used for evangelistic purposes; this will presumably strengthen that liberal-dominated organization to the detriment of New York's truly fundamentalist churches who are not members of the council. Many of the fundamentalists who make these complaints against Graham remember all too vividly how they smarted in the debacle of the 1920's when liberals took their churches from them and drove them from their denominational posts. Graham, a second generation fundamentalist, did not go through this trial of faith and the old-timers now see him as either naive or self-centered in his willingness to befriend these bitter enemies.[45a]

On the whole Graham has ignored these critics, though his research associate, Robert O. Ferm, and his father-in-law, L. Nelson Bell, have vigorously tried to refute them. They are, say Graham's defenders, fanatical "ultra-fundamentalists" and "narrow separatists" who fail to see that God is blessing Graham's cooperative evangelism which, like Moody's and Sunday's, must accept broad support if it is to succeed. Graham's only comment is that he will preach anywhere, under any sponsorship, so long as he is permitted to preach "the doctrines of historic Christianity" without qualification.

One of the most shrewd and ardent of Graham's supporters, Carl F. H. Henry, has been trying to erect a middle ground for "the new evangelicalism" somewhere between the NAE and the NCC. Using his editorial columns in *Christianity Today*, Henry praises "the gigantic evangelistic impact spearheaded by Billy Graham" on the one hand but condemns the NAE for being too separatist on the other. Henry and those closest to Graham at present have no quarrel with the theological creed of the NAE which they claim is their creed and Graham's creed as well. But they find that the NAE is too limited in its funds, in its theological scholarship, in its social outlook, in the scope of its polity, and by its lack of able leaders to compete successfully with the NCC from outside the regular denominations. These middle-of-the-roaders feel that Graham has broken down the old wall of separation between modernists and fundamentalists. They believe that the NCC is now turning away from modernism and liberalism and that through neo-orthodoxy it is working its way back to the old fundamentalist doctrines. They are opposed to ecumenicalism, but they are in favor of "a true interdenominational, international evangelicalism" based on "the Lord and the Book." Precisely what this middle road of "the new evangelicalism" stands for it is still impossible to discern.[46]

It may be that the present trend in theology among those who are leading the NCC is toward a theological position halfway between twentieth century liberalism and nineteenth century evangelicalism, and if the liberal elements in the NAE continue to push their associates toward a clearer understanding of Biblical scholarship, then Graham may see some sort of merger between the two organizations in his lifetime. His future may be that of an elder statesman mediating between the distrustful factions on both sides.

It is more probable, however, that when the hectic days of revivalism die down in the next decade the two wings of

Protestantism will still be as far apart as they are now. Instead of having broken down the wall of separation between fundamentalism and modernism in the name of greater harmony, Graham may simply have opened the gates for another battle royal. Only this time the battle will be more evenly waged than it was in the 1920's. There is no doubt which side Graham will be on if such a fight does occur. He will never forsake his fundamentalism, and he may well become a kind of party war horse, an exhorter of Gideon's army, who will be called upon to address each new fundamentalist rally and to instill through his oratory the zeal for each new foray. His statesmanship then might consist in his ability to keep together the various factions within and around the NAE. But it is unlikely that he would be one of the inner circle of the neofundamentalist party. He is too ingenuous to be conniving, too unsophisticated to be an ecclesiastical politician. Nor does he have the educational and intellectual attainments to serve as a formulator of party policy or theology. His friendships with many liberals may even become an embarrassment rather than an asset.

Certainly Graham would sincerely deprecate any such internecine warfare among Christians as the future might bring. He has already spoken out against the failure of the fundamentalists to stick together: "These dissensions in the ranks of Evangelical Christians are a stench in the nostrils of God. If ever there was a time for Evangelical Christians to demonstrate unity and love, it is now. Christians, this is an emergency—this is a war to the death with Satan and all his hosts—this is a time for prayer on the part of God's people, not dissension and strife. *Certainly* we are to be separated from the world. The Bible teaches that. But I find nowhere that we are to be separated from Bible-believing Christians." [47]

For the present Graham is still a figure to reckon with on the American scene. He has revival tours and city-wide crusades scheduled well into the 1960's. His next big targets are Chicago and Philadelphia. America's fourth great awak-

ening is by no means ended, though Graham's part in it is
dwindling. If the awakenings of the past are any precedent,
this one, in its broadest sense, may well encompass a whole
generation. On the basis of Graham's part in it so far, the
historian of the future will probably treat him as a catalyst
of theological and ecclesiastical change rather than as a
prime mover.

The essence of the current reorientation of Protestantism
is not to be found in Billy Graham's revivals. The catalyst
is neutral in the reaction. Or, to put it another way, revivals have, at least since Finney's day, been like the smoke
which betokens a theological fire; but the fire is not in them.
They hover around and often simply obscure the real flames
of controversy. It is probable that the theological and
ecclesiastical aspects of this great awakening will take place
wholly within the organized churches and among the leaders of the NCC and the World Council of Churches. The
fundamentalists will remain, as pietistic groups generally
have, outside the mainstream of Christendom. Like the
third parties in American politics, the NAE is a form of
organized protest which will wither away as its major complaints are assimilated into the regular churches. The
pitched battle between neofundamentalism and neoliberal-
ism is not likely to take place, and those pietists, like Graham, who have penetrated temporarily into the stronghold
of the organized churches will either capitulate or withdraw once more to the fringe of protest.

No one can yet tell what form the new theology, which is
to replace liberalism, will take. That it will abandon the
more relativistic and optimistic emphases of modernism is
apparent. But it will never repudiate science and scholarship in such a way as to satisfy the pietists. This is where
Graham's anti-intellectualism weakens him. Nor will the
regular denominations heed the pietists' demand to abandon
their belief in the social function of the churches—their
duty to deal specifically with questions of economic and
political justice in this world. And this is where Graham's
individualistic emphasis weakens him.[48]

But the Christian churches can never forsake their evangelistic function in a pluralistic and unredeemed world. And in this lies Billy Graham's strength. It is unfortunate for the cause of evangelism, however, that it requires a pitch of fervent, cooperative effort which it is impossible to sustain. Ten years of crisis is the limit of human endurance, and Billy Graham has now had his ten years. Perhaps, like Charles Grandison Finney, he will live long enough to see America's next great awakening in forty years or so. Meanwhile he must make the fateful choice between the new school and the old pietism, while skeptics continue to wonder whether his revivals have been any more successful than those of previous professional evangelists in stemming the increasing secularism of American life.

Whatever the outcome of this fourth great awakening, Billy Graham's place in American history is sure. Some religious historians will no doubt look back upon him as a twentieth-century Whitefield or Savonarola calling a wicked nation to repentance for its sins. Other historians may treat him simply as a colorful "Gabriel in gabardine," a "thunderer of God," or a "heavenly huckster." But those who know American history best will probably portray him as the heir of an ancient and honorable revival tradition, a significant symbol of religious and intellectual reorientation, a spokesman of his times, an importunate pietist in a portentous age.

Bibliographical Note

The primary source for a study like this is, of course, to attend Billy Graham's revivals and to interview those who have helped promote them. I have talked with more than a dozen of his close associates and with several scores of persons associated directly in his various crusades over the past eight years. I have met and talked briefly with Mr. Graham, and I have benefited from the painstaking comments which he and other members of his staff made upon this manuscript. Through the courtesy of his personal secretary, Mr. Paul J. Maddox, I was given a press pass for the New York crusade: I sat on the platform at Madison Square Garden; I went with the inquirers into the inquiry room; I talked with counselors, advisors, team members, cooperating ministers, choir members; I attended pastors' meetings and showings of the various films concerning Billy Graham's crusades. I was in London during the crusade at Harringay Arena in 1954 and attended many of the services there as well as preliminary and auxiliary meetings. I have visited the Minneapolis headquarters of the Billy Graham Evangelistic Association and have taken notes on almost two hundred "Hour of Decision" broadcasts since April, 1951. I have watched Billy Graham on television.

In addition to relying upon this accumulation of personal experience and notes, I have been on the mailing list of the Billy Graham Evangelistic Association for eight years and have kept a file of all the mailings. I also received all the mailings sent out by the local committes for the London and New York crusades. Among the most valuable data received from the Billy Graham Evangelistic Association have been the hundred odd printed radio sermons offered free to listeners from time to time, and the various editions of *Decision,* the newsletter of the Billy Graham Evangelistic Association. These contain many statements indicative of Graham's political and economic views as well as his theology.

Some of Graham's early sermons have been published in the following volumes: *Calling Youth to Christ* (Grand Rapids, Michigan, 1947), *Revival in Our Time* (Wheaton, Illinois, 1950), *America's Hour of Decision* (Wheaton, Illinois, 1951). Graham's books, *Peace with God* (New York, 1953), *The Secret of Happiness* (New York, 1955), and *The Seven Deadly Sins* (Minneapolis, 1955) contain material he has used in his sermons. Various accounts of his evangelistic tours abroad have been written by himself and by members of his staff. These have been carefully edited to avoid controversial material but occasionally they provide revealing insights. Two volumes have appeared describing the New York crusade and one on the San Francisco crusade from the point of view of Graham's admirers. Stanley High's biography, *Billy Graham* (New York, 1956), contains most of the relevant data, but it is a highly eulogistic account with several errors of fact. Charles T. Cook's *The Billy Graham Story* (London, 1954) has some useful material not in High's book.

Magazine articles by Graham, his wife, his mother, his father-in-law and multifarious friends and feature-writers provide additional insights into his outlook and personal history. Among the most revealing interviews with Graham have been those published from time to time in *U.S. News and World Report.* The best short account of a Graham revival is by James L. McAllister, "Evangelical Faith and Billy Graham," in *Social Action,* March, 1953. Mr. McAllister also kindly loaned to me his 160-page manuscript study of Billy Graham's Greensboro, North Carolina, crusade of

1951 entitled "Greensboro and Billy Graham: Effects of the Billy Graham Crusade on the Community, Churches, and Individuals of Greensboro, North Carolina." This carefully prepared, scholarly analysis contains a mine of detailed information gleaned from close observation, personal interviews, and questionnaires, as well as many astute observations made by Mr. McAllister and his associates, Esther H. Artman, Paul L. Hammer, and Warren Ashby. A copy of this manuscript, which was written in 1952, is on file in the social ethics library of the Yale Divinity School, Yale University. The best feature story to date about Graham has been Noel Houston's "Billy Graham" in *Holiday,* March, 1958. Several incisive analyses of various aspects of Graham's theology and methods have appeared in the *Christian Century* over the past five years. Sympathetic accounts of Graham's work can be found in *Christianity Today, United Evangelical Action,* the *Moody Monthly, Youth for Christ* magazine, and *Christian Life.* The best source for material on Graham's work in Britain is the *British Weekly,* which has been by turns cool, favorable, and cool toward him. The numerous articles in *Time, Life, Newsweek, Look, Ladies' Home Journal,* the *Reader's Digest,* etc., provide few fresh insights.

The most useful sources for data on Graham's individual revivals are the local newspapers of the cities in which he has campaigned. Unfortunately few libraries keep files of the "yellow" journals and tabloids which often contain the most colorful accounts. Few of the sedate dailies have carried Graham's sermons in full the way those of D. L. Moody and Billy Sunday used to be. But all the relevant facts concerning the mechanics and statistics of the crusades are contained in the local press reports.

I have relied heavily upon the texts of Graham's sermons as published in the *Observer* (Charlotte, North Carolina), September 22–October 26, 1958.

I have utilized such statistics as are available from various independent polls in regard to the conversions and new church members resulting from Graham's revivals, but I cannot vouch for their accuracy. The statistics released by the Graham team and local committees are usually overoptimistic; those dug up by his critics are perhaps overly pessimistic. No thorough analysis has been made by a trained sociologist as yet. It is probable that no statistical study could adequately measure the influence of a revival campaign.

Space does not permit any listing of the many peripheral and secondary sources which were consulted to provide the background for this book, but the most important of them may be found listed in the footnotes to this book and to my earlier work, *Modern Revivalism, Charles Grandison Finney to Billy Graham* (New York, 1959).

Notes

CHAPTER 1: Billy Graham and the Revival Tradition

1. *U.S. News and World Report*, August 27, 1954, p. 70.

2. Willard L. Sperry, *Religion in America* (New York, 1946), pp. 161-162.

3. Robert O. Ferm, *Cooperative Evangelism* (Grand Rapids, Michigan, 1958), p. 12.

4. *United Evangelical Action* (Cincinnati, Ohio), October 15, 1945, p. 12.

5. William F. Graham, "We Need Revival!" in *Revival in Our Time* (Wheaton, Illinois, 1950), pp. 69-77.

6. *Time*, October 25, 1954, p. 54.

7. Consider this attack upon Finney, for instance, which sounds very much like the opposition voiced by certain ministers against Billy Graham today: "Revivals are always spurious when they are *got up* by man's device and not *brought down* by the Spirit of God. . . . What is that piety that courts observation and wishes to be seen, that obtrudes itself on the notice of others, that talks of its own experience and attainments, that is bold and assuming, that wishes to be put forward and that unblushingly exclaims with Jehu, 'Come, see my zeal for the Lord! . . . They [revivalists who "get up" revivals] count their converts and when they survey their work there is a triumph, a self-reliant exultation over it, which looks like the triumph of the Pagan monarch when he exclaimed, 'Is this not the great Babylon which I have built.'" Gardiner Spring, *Personal Reminiscences* (New York, 1866), Vol. I, 217-219. For a detailed study of Finney's contribution to the revival tradition see W. G. McLoughlin, *Modern Revivalism: Charles Grandison Finney to Billy Graham* (N.Y., 1959).

8. Haskell M. Miller, "Religion in the South," *Christendom*, VII (Summer, 1942), pp. 305-318.

9. Quoted in Herbert W. Schneider, *Religion in 20th Century America* (Cambridge, Mass., 1952), pp. 107-108 from the *Christian Century*, December 4, 1935.

10. *Time*, November 14, 1949, p. 63.

11. *Time*, November 13, 1950, p. 61.

CHAPTER 2: Who Is Billy Graham?

1. Stanley High, *Billy Graham* (New York, 1956), p. 16.

2. *Pittsburgh Press*, September 21, 1952, p. 2.

2a. See *Revival in our Time* (Special Edition for Youth for Christ International, Wheaton, Illinois, 1950), pp. 90, 102.

3. William F. Graham, *Mother's Day Message* (a radio message copyright 1953 by the Billy Graham Evangelistic Association, Minneapolis, Minnesota).

4. See Armin Gesswein, "How Billy Graham Was Converted" (an interview with Mordecai Ham) in the Special Reprint of *Christian Life*, September, 1957.

5. High, *op. cit.*, p. 108. In 1958 Graham was awarded the honor of "Salesman of the Year" by the Sales Executive Club of New York for his ability to sell religion.

6. Wheaton College, which calls itself "a Christian liberal arts college," requires all its faculty members and members of the administration to declare their belief annually in a creed which begins: "We believe in the Scriptures of the Old and the New Testaments as verbally inspired by God and inerrant in the original writings, and that they are of supreme and final authority in faith and life." All students at Wheaton are required to sign an agreement that they will "abstain from the use of alcoholic liquors and tobacco, from gambling and the possession and use of playing cards, from dancing and from meetings of secret societies, and from attendance at theaters, including movies." See *Bulletin of Wheaton College 1959-60* (Wheaton College, Illinois) pp. 10-11.

7. See for example, William F. Graham, *Calling Youth to Christ* (Grand Rapids, Michigan, 1947), pp. 21-22.

8. *Revival in Our Time* (Special Edition for Youth for Christ International, Wheaton, Illinois, 1950), p. 3.

9. This sermon entitled "The Holy Spirit and Revival in Our Time" was delivered at the 1952 convention of the National Association of Evangelicals. It is reprinted in Charles T. Cook, *The Billy Graham Story* (London, 1954), pp. 90 ff. While Graham also said in this sermon that he believed that modernists could "be loved back into the fold of orthodoxy" he was in reality sounding a war cry.

CHAPTER 3: Billy Graham Becomes Front-Page News

1. William F. Graham, "The Resurrection of Jesus Christ," printed in *Revival in Our Time* (Wheaton, Illinois, 1950), p. 141.

2. This sermon is reprinted in *Revival in Our Time* (Wheaton, Illinois, 1950), p. 69 ff.

3. See Stanley High, *Billy Graham* (New York, 1956), p. 148. I have been unable to verify whether Hearst sent his "Puff Graham" telegram before or after the Los Angeles Executive Committee decided to extend the revival for a fourth week. I assume that the committee was unaware of the telegram when it made its decision.

4. See *Revival in Our Time, op. cit.*, p. 14. Graham never said who the second person was but a good guess would be Mickey Cohen.

5. Smith was quoted to this effect in the *Columbia State* (Columbia, South Carolina), February 19, 1950, p. 2.

6. *United Evangelical Action* (Cleveland, Ohio), April 15, 1946, p. 5. See also *ibid.*, August 15, 1956, p. 5.

7. *Ibid.*, February 15, 1955, p. 13.

8. For an account of the Boston revival with newspaper quotations see *Revival in Our Time, op. cit.*, pp. 28 ff.

9. For most of the information on the Columbia campaign I have relied upon the files of the local newspaper, the *Columbia State*, and *Revival in Our Time, op. cit.*, pp. 43 ff.

10. *Revival in Our Time, op. cit.*, p. 49. Graham later said that Bernard Baruch, who lived in Kingstree, near Columbia, was the man who persuaded Luce to come and hear him; see *Charlotte Observer*, October 27, 1958, p. 1.

11. For information on Trotman and the Navigators see *Time*, July 2, 1956, p. 59, and *United Evangelical Action*, August 1, 1958, p. 8.

12. For variant versions of this story see *America's Hour of Decision* (Wheaton, Illinois, 1951) pp. 47-48 and Stanley High, *Billy Graham* (New York, 1956) pp. 163-164.

13. *America's Hour of Decision, op. cit.*, pp. 64 ff.

14. The members of the board of the Billy Graham Evangelistic Association, Inc., as of January 1, 1959 were Roger Hull (Executive Vice-President of the Mutual Life Insurance Co., of New York), E. O. Spencer (oilman and hotel owner of Jackson, Mississippi), Charles Pitts (contractor, Toronto), Carloss Morris (attorney of Houston, Texas), Robert Van Kampen (publisher, Wheaton, Illinois) Dr. R. C. Sherer (physician, Bozeman, Montana), V. Raymond Edman (President of Wheaton College, Wheaton, Illinois), William Jones (printer, Los Angeles), Dr. L. Nelson Bell (Graham's father-in-law, a surgeon in Asheville, North Carolina), Harold Ockenga (pastor of Park Street Church, Boston), the Rev. Leighton Ford (Graham's brother-in-law and associate evangelist), Cliff Barrows, Grady Wilson, George M. Wilson, and Billy Graham. *United Evangelical Action*, January, 1959, p. 13.

15. *Time*, November 27, 1950, p. 54.

CHAPTER 4: Theology and Social Philosophy

1. William F. Graham, *Peace with God* (New York, 1953), p. 26.

2. *Look*, February 7, 1956, p. 49.

3. See Stewart G. Cole, *History of Fundamentalism* (New York, 1931), p. 34. See also *Christianity Today* (Washington, D.C.), September 16, 1957, p. 3, in which Carl F. H. Henry, one of Graham's chief promoters, states that Graham is preaching "the 'five-points' of fundamentalism."

4. Graham, *Peace with God*, p. 98.

5. A typical instance of Graham's attempt to use archaeological evidence to bolster his Biblical interpretations occurs in his sermon on Noah's Ark in which he tries to prove that "the world was destroyed before" (by the flood) and God will destroy it again if man persists in his wickedness: "You remember the story of Noah. A lot of people have laughed it out of school and scoffed at it, but archaeologists no longer laugh at the story of Noah. There is plenty of archaeological evidence that a flood did exist at one time over a certain portion of the world—the portion that Noah lived in." *Charlotte Observer,* October 12, 1958, p. 6-A. That this evidence weakens rather than strengthens the validity of the Bible was recognized as long ago as 1851 when the *Princeton Review,* the foremost Presbyterian theological journal in the United States, maintained that unless the flood was universal, the Bible was not the Word of God. See Barbara Cross, *Horace Bushnell* (Chicago, 1958), p. 122.

6. Graham, *Peace with God,* p. 33.

7. *Ibid.,* p. 27.

8. *Ibid.,* p. 49.

9. *Ibid.,* p. 30. One of the distinctions between Graham and the more extreme form of fundamentalists is his willingness to use and recommend to his auditors the Revised Standard Version of the Bible. "I like a Bible that is of modern translation," he says. "I have about five or six translations that I keep on my desk all the time." But he also adds, "Now keep your King James. I preach from the King James. . . ." *Charlotte Observer,* September 26, 1958, p. 4-B.

10. Graham, *Peace with God,* p. 44.

11. *Ibid.,* p. 87.

12. *Ibid.,* p. 45.

13. *Ibid.,* p. 58.

14. *Ibid.,* p. 88.

15. *Ibid.,* p. 48.

16. *Ibid.,* p. 62.

17. *Ibid.,* p. 89.

18. *Ibid.,* p. 90, 93.

19. *Ibid.,* p. 49.

20. *Ibid.,* pp. 106-107. Some think that Graham's de-emphasis of emotional conversion distinguishes his revivalism from that of Billy Sunday and D. L. Moody. But both these evangelists were as insistent as he that conversion need not be an emotional experience.

21. *Ibid.,* p. 143.

22. *Ibid.,* p. 107.

23. *Ibid.,* p. 134.

24. *Charlotte Observer,* October 18, 1958, p. 6-A. At other times Graham says almost the opposite: "I told God 'I don't have the power to

forsake my sins.' . . . There is an evil principle down inside of me which is pulling me and tugging at me—there's nothing I can do. . . . You can't work your way to heaven. . . . Salvation is by the grace and mercy of God." *Ibid.*, September 25, 1958, p. 6-A.

25. *Ibid.*, p. 113.

26. *Ibid.*, p. 119.

27. *Ibid.*, p. 129.

28. *Ibid.*, p. 136.

29. *Ibid.*, p. 98.

30. *Ibid.*, p. 19.

31. *Ibid.*, pp. 155-156.

32. The repudiation of the *McCall's* article is referred to in *United Evangelical Action*, December 1, 1954, p. 11. The other quotations in this paragraph are taken from Graham's radio sermon "America's Immorality" (published by the Billy Graham Evangelistic Association in 1954) and from sermons printed in the *Charlotte Observer* September 22-October 26, 1958.

33. From Graham's radio messages, "What God Can Do for You" (1956), and "The Responsibilities of the Home" (1955), published by the Billy Graham Evangelistic Association (hereinafter referred to as the BGEA).

34. See *Charlotte Observer*, September 25, 1958, p. 6-A.

35. This sermon is reprinted in *Revival in Our Time* (Wheaton, Illinois, 1950), pp. 89 ff.

36. Graham is not so rigorous in disciplining his own children as these quotations might indicate: "I have a teenage daughter," he said in 1958. "Once in a while I have to discipline her. And always I call her in and spend a half an hour loving her, then I explain what I am going to do —going to take away television or something like that for a while. Then I love her for about half an hour afterwards." *Charlotte Observer*, September 24, 1958, p. 8-A. Yet on another occasion in 1958 he seemed ready to advocate the return of the whipping post as a cure for juvenile deliquency: "In some of the West Indies where we visited they still use the whipping post. We heard of a youth who was publicly whipped for the crime of rape. Little wonder that juvenile delinquency is practically unheard of in many of these islands." See Graham's radio sermon "Teenage Vandalism," published in 1958 by the BGEA.

37. See Graham's radio message, "The Bible and Dr. Kinsey" (1953), published by the BGEA.

38. See Curtis Mitchell, *God in the Garden* (New York, 1957), p. 177.

39. *Charlotte Observer*, September 24, 1958, p. 8-A. Graham has also hinted that the child labor laws in the United States ought to be amended so that adolescents can go to work at an earlier age and thus the devil will not find so much mischief for idle hands: "When I was a boy I didn't

have time to be a delinquent. I was too busy. If our young people today were gainfully occupied, delinquency would soon disappear. Our society has produced a generation of young people who are bored. They have too much leisure on their hands. The Bible warns against idle hands." From Graham's radio sermon, "Teen-age Vandalism" (1958), published by the BGEA.

40. *Charlotte Observer,* October 5, 1958, p. 14-A.

41. *Ibid.,* October 25, 1958, p. 11-A.

42. See Graham's radio message, "Juvenile Delinquency and Its Cure (1955), published by the BGEA.

43. *Charlotte Observer,* October 1, 1958, p. 6-A, October 5, 1958, p. 14-A.

44. See Graham's radio message, "Juvenile Delinquency and Its Cure" (1955), published by the BGEA.

45. See Graham, "The Bible and Dr. Kinsey" (1953), published by the BGEA.

46. See James L. McAllister, "Evangelical Faith and Billy Graham" in *Social Action,* XIX (March, 1953), 22.

47. Graham, *Peace with God,* p. 195.

48. *New York Herald Tribune,* May 12, 1957, p. 24.

49. *Ibid.,* July 21, 1957.

50. *Charlotte Observer,* October 27, 1958, p. 1. Graham was similarly ambiguous concerning segregation during his two-day crusade in Little Rock, Arkansas, in September, 1959. Although he was denounced as an integrationist by the city's White Citizens' Council, Governor Orval Faubus sat in a box seat at one of his meetings. The most direct reference Graham made in Little Rock to segregation was, "I have not come to make any inflammatory statements or preach on the subject of race. . . . I don't think we're ever going to solve our basic social problems apart from the Cross of Christ." See *Arkansas Gazette* (Little Rock, Arkansas), September 13, 1959, p. 2a, and September 14, 1959, p. 2a.

51. This aspect of Graham's preaching was explicitly praised by Sherwood E. Wirt who reported after the San Francisco crusade in 1958, "A real secret of Billy Graham's power . . . is his ability to bring believers into touch with each other by omitting things that divide them. Today it can be said that Christian unity in the San Francisco area is very real. . . ." Sherwood E. Wirt, "New Life Surges in 'Graveyard of Evangelism,'" *United Evangelical Action,* August 1, 1958, p. 3. Mr. Wirt is now editor of *World Evangelism,* the magazine published by the Billy Graham Evangelistic Association.

CHAPTER 5: Politics and World Affairs

1. *London Daily Herald,* February 26, 1954, p. 1.

2. *U.S. News and World Report,* August 27, 1954, p. 87.

3. William R. Moody, *D. L. Moody* (New York, 1930), p. 171.

4. *Boston Daily Herald,* January 17, 1917, p. 9.

5. William F. Graham, *The Seven Deadly Sins* (published by the Billy Graham Evangelistic Association, 1955), p. 37.

6. See Graham's radio message, "America's Immorality" (1954), published by the Billy Graham Evangelistic Association (hereinafter referred to as that BGEA).

7. William F. Graham, *Peace with God,* (New York, 1953), p. 17.

8. The description of "Oiltown, U.S.A." is taken from a flyleaf published by the Graham crusade headquarters in London in 1954 in order to advertise showings of the film there. The references to "rugged individualism" are found in James L. McAllister, "Evangelical Faith and Billy Graham," *Social Action,* XIX (March, 1953) p. 23.

9. *Ibid.* Graham has sometimes listed the three internal threats to the American way of life as "Big Labor, Big Government and Big Business," but like previous revivalists he seldom finds occasion to say anything about the latter, except that it should treat its workers fairly.

10. *Columbia State* (North Carolina), February 19, 1950, p. 2.

11. See Graham's radio message, "Revival or the Spirit of the Age" (1952), published by the BGEA.

12. *Pittsburgh Press,* September 7, 1952, p. 25, sec. II.

13. Graham, *Peace with God, op. cit.,* p. 194.

14. See Graham's radio message, "Organized Labor and the Church" (1952), published by the BGEA.

15. These statements were made on the "Hour of Decision" on April 7, 1957 and October 6, 1957.

16. "Organized Labor and the Church," *op. cit.*

17. "Revival or the Spirit of the Age," *op. cit.*

18. See Graham's radio message, "Partners with God" (1957), published by the BGEA.

19. Stanley High, *Billy Graham* (New York, 1956), p. 63.

20. *Intelligence Digest* (London), May, 1954, p. 5.

21. "Revival or the Spirit of the Age," *op. cit.*

22. *Houston Post,* May 28, 1952, sec. I, p. 7.

23. "Hour of Decision," June 8, 1952.

24. *Dallas Morning News,* June 3, 1953, sec. II, p. 1. Dr. Graham tells me that he did not make this statement concerning Britain's moral strength. It was made, he says, by a member of the British Parliament who was visiting Dr. Graham at the time and was asked by Dr. Graham to speak at the businessmen's luncheon in Dallas.

25. Quoted in the *London Daily Herald,* February 20, 1954, p. 3, and the *New York Times,* February 21, 1954.

26. *London Daily Herald*, February 20, 1954, p. 3.

27. *Ibid.*, February 22, 1954, p. 1.

28. *Ibid.*

29. *Ibid.*, February 24, 1954, p. 1.

30. *Ibid.*, February 22, 1954, p. 1.

31. *Ibid.*, February 26, 1954, p. 7.

32. *British Weekly* (London), September 30, 1954, p. 5.

33. *Intelligence Digest*, April, 1954, pp. 2-5.

34. *Ibid.*, June, 1954, p. 5.

35. *British Weekly*, October 21, 1954, p. 6.

36. For an early sermon quoting De Courcy see the radio message, "Grace *vs.* Wrath" (1951), published by the BGEA.

37. *America's Hour of Decision* (Wheaton, Illinois, 1951), p. 144.

38. *Columbia State*, February 23, 1950, p. 1.

39. This is contained in a Christmas letter sent by Graham from Minneapolis in 1951 to all those on the association's mailing list. The letter is not dated.

40. See *Columbia State*, February 22, 1950, p. 1; the statement about CARE packages was made on the "Hour of Decision," August 17, 1952.

41. "Hour of Decision," September 21, 1952.

42. See Graham's radio message, "Three Minutes to Twelve" (1953), published by the BGEA. In recent years Graham has taken a slightly more liberal attitude toward foreign aid and in particular has urged that America's surplus foods should be distributed more freely to underdeveloped countries where there are food shortages.

43. See Graham's radio message, "Hate *vs.* Love" (1951 and 1955), published by the BGEA.

44. See Graham's radio message, "What Is God Like" (1951), published by the BGEA.

45. See Graham's radio message, "Program for Peace" (1952), published by the BGEA.

46. *Pittsburgh Press*, September 7, 1952, sec. II, p. 25.

47. *Ibid.*, September 8, 1952, p. 7. On occasion Graham carried his thinly veiled dislike for the Truman administration to the point of personal ridicule of the President. For example, during his crusade in Greensboro, North Carolina, in October-November, 1951, Graham mentioned in his sermon on the Last Judgment that Hitler, Mussolini, Joe Stalin, and Harry Truman would be there; when the audience laughed at this grouping, he added: "Don't you Democrats laugh. Harry is doing the best that he can. The trouble is that he just can't do any better. After all, when a man's been in the haberdashery shop—but I won't say anything more about that. Except that I have found that after my car has run for a long time it needs

a change of oil. That's the strongest political statement I'm going to make." Quoted from an unpublished article by Professor Warren Ashby of the Woman's College of North Carolina, entitled, "The Message of Billy Graham."

48. See Graham's radio message, "Labor, Christ, and the Cross" (1953), published by the BGEA. Dr. Graham, in commenting upon this reference to McCarthyism, stated to me that while he supported the activities of Senator McCarthy for some time, he ultimately came to realize that the Senator was more interested in advancing his own position than in serving the country. Dr. Graham mentions that he refused on several occasions to participate in meetings at which Senator McCarthy spoke and he states that he privately expressed satisfaction with the rather critical portrait of Senator McCarthy which Edward R. Murrow presented on his television program in 1953. However, I have not been able to discover any public statement by Dr. Graham indicating his loss of confidence in Senator McCarthy either during the Senator's lifetime or since.

49. *America's Hour of Decision, op. cit.*, p. 144.

50. See Graham's radio message, "Satan's Religion" (1953), published by the BGEA.

51. "Hour of Decision," July 5, 1953.

52. "Hour of Decision," June 10, 1951.

53. *London Daily Herald*, February 26, 1954, p. 7.

54. "Hour of Decision," December 5, 1954; see also Graham's radio message, "Christ Is Coming" (1955), published by the BGEA.

55. *Houston Post*, May 4, 1952, sec. II, p. 1.

56. See *America's Hour of Decision*, p. 143.

57. See Graham's radio message, "Christianity *vs.* a Bloodless Religion" (1951), published by the BGEA. Dr. Graham, in commenting on this passage in a letter to me, pointed out that he never once mentioned Dean Acheson by name in this sermon.

58. See Graham's radio message, "America's Decision" (1953), published by the BGEA.

59. "Hour of Decision," January 30, 1955.

60. *U.S. News and World Report*, April 6, 1956, p. 69.

61. *Charlotte Observer*, September 25, 1958, p. 6-A, and October 4, 1958, p. 6-A.

62. "Hour of Decision," July 26, 1953, December 5, 1954.

63. *Pittsburgh Press*, September 8, 1952, p. 7. The sermon is not quoted in the newspaper.

64. "Grace *vs.* Wrath," *op. cit.* Dr. Graham, in commenting on this passage in a letter to me, pointed out that while he considered wrong (and still considers wrong) the decision not to let General MacArthur push the Korean War to ultimate victory even at the risk of starting a general war

with China, he never mentioned the Truman administration by name in this sermon and he considers many Republicans equally to blame for this faulty decision.

65. See Graham's radio message for April, 1951, "Hate *vs.* Love," published by the BGEA.

66. "Hour of Decision," May 25, 1952.

67. "Hour of Decision," November 2, 1952.

68. "Hour of Decision," April 26, 1953.

69. See Graham's radio message, "America's Decision" (1953), published by the BGEA.

70. *Dallas Morning News,* June 20, 1953, sec. II, p. 5.

71. "America's Decision," *op. cit.*

72. See Graham's radio message for March, 1953, "Teach Us to Pray," published by the BGEA. In 1958 Graham was willing to say, "We should back every effort of the UN to bring peace," but he also maintained that all its efforts in this direction would be futile for "you see, at the UN they don't really look to God." *Charlotte Observer,* September 28, 1958, p. 8-A, and October 6, 1958, p. 13-A. Dr. Graham, in commenting on this passage in a letter to me, indicated that despite these criticisms of certain aspects of the United Nations, he is nevertheless a supporter of the United Nations.

73. See Graham's radio message, "Three Minutes to Twelve" (1953), published by the BGEA.

74. "Hour of Decision," February 8, 1953.

75. "Hour of Decision," April 19, 1953.

76. See Graham's radio message, "Position *vs.* Penalty," (1951) published by the BGEA.

77. "Hour of Decision," January 6, 1957.

78. *Newark Sunday News,* September 4, 1955.

79. *Christian Life,* July, 1956, p. 14.

80. *New York Herald Tribune,* January 15, 1956, p. 3.

81. *Christian Life,* July, 1956, p. 14.

82. *Ibid.,* April, 1956, p. 54. Dr. Graham, in commenting on this passage in a letter to me, indicated that Mr. Nehru was not offended by this remark and that Mr. Nehru has, in fact, continued to express sympathetic interest in his work.

83. Quoted in Charles T. Cook, *The Billy Graham Story* (London, 1954), p. 100.

84. *United Evangelical Action,* November 1, 1945, p. 12.

85. Cook, *Billy Graham Story, op. cit.,* p. 100.

86. "Hour of Decision," January 11, 1959.

87. *New York Times,* December 13, 1959, p. 49.

CHAPTER 6: Pulpit Techniques

1. *Charlotte Observer,* October 16, 1958, p. 6-B.

2. *Christianity Today,* October 15, 1956, p. 6.

3. *Houston Post,* June 2, 1952, p. 1. The following remark made by a spectator at a Graham meeting typifies the reaction of many young people to Graham's compelling power in the pulpit: "I get goose pimples when Billy Graham uses his hands." Quoted in James L. McAllister, *et al.,* "Greensboro and Billy Graham" (1952) an unpublished paper in the social ethics library of Yale Divinity School, Yale University, p. V, 6.

4. *Dallas Morning News,* June 3, 1953, sec. III, p. 1.

5. *Washington Post,* February 3, 1952, p. 13-M.

6. *Pittsburgh Press,* September 18, 1952, p. 2.

7. *Columbia State,* February 25, 1950, p. 1.

8. William F. Graham, *Peace with God* (New York, 1953), p. 25.

9. See Graham's radio message, "Our Teen-Age Problem" (1955), published by the Billy Graham Evangelistic Association (hereinafter called the BGEA).

10. *Charlotte Observer,* September 26, 1958, p. 4-B.

11. See Graham's radio message, "The Rivers of Damascus" (1956), published by the BGEA.

12. *Charlotte Observer,* September 24, 1958, p. 8-A.

13. *Revival in Our Time* (Wheaton, Illinois, 1950), p. 159.

14. *Manchester Guardian,* May 12, 1954.

15. *Dallas Morning News,* June 10, 1953, sec. III, p. 1.

16. *Pittsburgh Press,* September 26, 1952, p. 2.

17. *Houston Post,* June 9, 1952, p. 1.

18. *Charlotte Observer,* October 17, 1958, p. 8-B.

19. Quoted in the *London Daily Herald,* February 24, 1954, p. 4.

20. See *New Orleans Times-Picayune,* October 8, 1954, p. 13; radio message "Revival or the Spirit of the Age" (1952), and "Hour of Decision," June 1, 1952.

21. See Graham's radio message, "Heaven" (1955), published by the BGEA.

22. See Graham's radio message, "The Home" (1956), published by the BGEA.

23. See Graham's radio mssage, "Mother's Day Message" (1953), published by the BGEA.

24. *Ibid.*

25. See Graham's radio message, "Satan's Religion" (1953), published by the BGEA.

26. *New Orleans Times-Picayune,* October 9, 1954, p. 5. Dr. Graham

in a letter to me denies that he ever made such a statement and considers this a misquotation by the reporter.

27. "Hour of Decision," July 26, 1953.

28. See Graham's radio message, "Our Teen-age Problem" (1955), published by the BGEA.

29. See Graham's radio message, "Hate *vs.* Love" (1955), published by the BGEA.

30. "Hour of Decision," December 9, 1956.

31. James L. McAllister, "Evangelical Faith and Billy Graham," *Social Action*, XIX (March, 1953), p. 17. Inasmuch as it is a serious (but seldom documented) charge against professional mass revivalism that it tends to increase or exacerbate mental disturbances in a community, it seems advisable (as well as informative) to quote at some length from the unpublished report of James L. McAllister, *et. al.* on the effects of the Billy Graham crusade on Greensboro, North Carolina in October-November, 1951, in this regard: "In the last few hours of our study in Greensboro we uncovered a whole new area of concern: that of possible mental disturbances resulting from the crusade. The information came through two doctors who are leaders in the local medical association, and they suggested that we make a systematic coverage of the Greensboro doctors. It was too late for us to do anything in Greensboro, but on returning to New Haven we prepared a letter and a return postcard and sent them to 113 doctors. The mailing list was secured from a Greensboro telephone directory. The following is the data received:

"No. of doctors contacted	113
No. of doctors responding	69
No. of doctors reporting cases of mental disturbance	20
No. of cases reported	58
No. of referrals reported	19
(We have not included such answers as 'several.')	
No. of children (under 15)	9

Kinds of disturbances reported:

Schizophrenia
Psychotic reactions requiring shock therapy
Mild psychotic reactions needing only reassurance
Psychosis
Severe anxiety state
Aggravation of previous psychoneurosis
Feeling of uselessness and insomnia
Mild depression
Exaggerated guilt complex
Religious hallucinations
Feeling of guilt and worry over sins
Auditory hallucinations
Feeling of not being saved
Crying spells
Restlessness
Severe depression

Severe headaches and abdominal cramps associated with fear of sin
Digestive disturbances and loss of energy
Disruption of normal sex relations
Threatened self-mutilation and removal of genital organs because of
past sins

Quotations [from doctors' replies]:

'I'm sure I saw many who were harmed by the Graham Crusade. I
know also of two cases of marital difficulty and excess drinking in
which both cases were helped by Graham. Personally, I believe his
contribution to religion bears about the same worth as Hadacol to our
medical armament.'

'I question whether the good produced balanced the harm done the
community.'

'Three of these children (9-14) have demanded parents to follow
Graham to Washington and have made the trip from Greensboro.'

'Too much of an appeal through fear and guilt. Exploitation of personalities—big business—not sound, conservative and durable religion.'

'Impressions gained from talking to patients—not many took things too
seriously—"a good show." '

'I advise *my* nervous patients to stay away.'

'I believe this type of revival has many bad effects on a community and
I wonder if the good effects overcome this.'

'Billy Graham's Crusade had no effect whatsoever on our people. Very
few are interested in his type of segregated religion.'

'I firmly oppose such revivals.'

'I did not go to hear Billy Graham. But from my observations and
what I hear I think he did a lot of good here.'

'Personally I am much opposed to this type of religious expression—
religious quackery—although I feel Billy Graham is sincere.'

Two quotations concerning cases:

'I did have one patient who came to me of his own accord, and
threatened self-mutilation and removal of his genital organs on account
of past sins. I would hesitate to say that this was a result of the Billy
Graham Crusade, although this patient had been attending regularly.'

'Mrs. M. K. married fifteen years, two children, had always enjoyed
normal sexual relations. It had been their custom to have a highball
(maybe two) before supper and a "night cap" before retiring. But
during the "Crusade" they decided that this was not quite right, so
they stopped all alcoholic drinks. Now she can't sleep, sexual relations
have been unsatisfactory for two reasons: one, they were not sure this
was the right thing to do, and second, her husband was unable to
sustain an erection and she was frustrated.'

"These are the facts and impressions that we have received from the
doctors. However, in evaluating them we need to keep in mind that in

the case of mental disturbances, generally, no single factor is the cause. Nevertheless, it seems that in a significant number of instances the Crusade was a precipitating factor; at least this is what some of the Greensboro doctors have reported."

The foregoing data was quoted, with permission, from James L. McAllister, Esther Artman, and Paul Hammer, "Greensboro and Billy Graham" (1952), pp. III, 27-III, 30. A copy of this typewritten manuscript is on file in the social ethics library of the Yale Divinity School, Yale University. I have quoted here from Mr. McAllister's personal copy which he was kind enough to lend to me.

32. For Graham's answers to charges that his preaching is too emotional (from which these quotations are taken), see *Look*, February 7, 1956, p. 48.

33. *Charlotte Observer*, September 24, 1958, p. 8-A; October 4, 1958, p. 6-A; October 2, 1958, p. 2-D; October 16, 1958, p. 6-B.

34. See *Time*, October 25, 1954, p. 58.

35. *Ibid.*, and *Picture Post* (London) March 20, 1954, p. 40, and Graham's radio message "Heaven" (1955), published by the BGEA.

36. *Columbia State*, March 10, 1950, p. 7-B.

37. See Stanley High, *Billy Graham* (New York, 1956), p. 63, and Graham's radio message, "Immortality" (1957), published by the BGEA.

38. Graham occasionally seems to be embarrassed by certain aspects of a literal interpretation of the Bible. For example, in the following description of the exploits of Samson he glosses over events which might shock the credulity of his audience by making jokes out of them: "One day he [Samson] was walking down the road and a lion came out and he grabbed this lion with his bare hands and ripped him apart. Now that takes a pretty good man. . . . Why even Tarzan had trouble doing that. Then on another occasion he took the jawbone of a donkey and went out and killed one thousand in a battle. . . . Now Audie Murphy couldn't do that. Samson was a man, a strong giant of a man, with muscles that rippled and rolled. He was a Floyd Patterson, Sugar Ray Robinson, and a Paul Anderson all rolled into one." *Charlotte Observer*, October 8, 1958, p. 4-A.

39. See Graham's radio message, "Why Christians Suffer" (1956), published by the BGEA.

40. See Graham's radio message, "The Cure for Discouragement" (1954), published by the BGEA.

41. See Graham's radio message, "Partners with God" (1957), published by the BGEA.

42. *America's Hour of Decision* (Wheaton, Illinois, 1951), p. 128.

43. *U.S. News and World Report*, September 27, 1957, p. 72.

44. See Graham's radio message, "Satan's Religion" (1953), published by the BGEA.

45. See Graham's radio message, "The Second Coming, A Glorious Truth" (1952), published by the BGEA.

46. *America's Hour of Decision, op. cit.,* p. 119.

47. See Graham's radio message, "Grace *vs.* Wrath" (1951), published by the BGEA.

48. See Graham's radio message, "Revival or the Spirit of the Age" (1952), published by the BGEA.

49. *Newark Evening News,* July 17, 1958, p. 10.

50. See Graham's radio message, "The Signs of the Times" (1957), published by the BGEA.

51. See Graham's form letter from Pusan, Korea, December, 1952, sent to all persons on the association's mailing list.

52. See *Decision* (the newsletter of the BGEA), May, 1954.

53. See Graham's radio message, "Christianity *vs.* a Bloodless Religion" (1951), published by the BGEA.

54. See Graham's radio message, "The Revival We Need" (1956), published by the BGEA.

55. See Graham's radio message, "Christianism *vs.* Communism" (1951), published by the BGEA.

56. See Graham's radio message, "The Revival We Need" (1956), published by the BGEA.

57. See Graham's radio messages, "Revival or the Spirit of the Age" (1952), "America's Decision" (August, 1953), and "Christianism *vs.* Communism" (1951), published by the BGEA.

58. See Graham's radio message, "America's Decision" (1953), published by the BGEA.

59. See Graham's radio message, "Spiritual Inventory" (1955), published by the BGEA.

60. See Graham's radio message, "Satan's Religion" (1953), published by the BGEA.

61. *Town Meeting* (publication of Town Meeting of the Air), January 2, 1951, p. 9.

62. See Graham's radio message, "Christianity *vs.* a Bloodless Religion" (1951), published by the BGEA.

63. See Graham's radio message, "Grace *vs.* Wrath" (1951), published by the BGEA. Dr. Graham in commenting on this passage in a letter to me indicates that he does not hold that World War III will inevitably mean the end of the world but only that it *might* mean this.

64. See Graham's radio messages, "Revival Today" (1955) and "Spiritual Inventory" (1955), published by the BGEA.

65. See Graham's radio message, "Program for Peace" (1952), published by the BGEA.

66. *Charlotte Observer*, October 18, 1958, p. 8-A.

67. *Intelligence Digest* (London) July, 1954, pp. 6-7.

CHAPTER 7: Revival Mechanics

1. *This Week*, April 21, 1957, p. 12.

2. For an account of the Rose Bowl failure see Carl F. H. Henry, "The Marvel of the Rose Bowl" in *America's Hour of Decision* (Wheaton, Illinois, 1951), pp. 97 ff.

3. See the *New York Times*, December 17, 1954, p. 28 and *United Evangelical Action*, February 1, 1955, p. 13. (For opposition to Graham's revival in St. Louis, Missouri in 1953, see *United Evangelical Action*, May 1, 1953, p. 13.) The opposition in New York City in 1952 was partly from fundamentalists who disliked Graham's willingness to cooperate with liberal Protestants. What might be considered a third setback in Graham's career, and a good indication of his waning popularity, was the refusal in 1958 of the Church Federation of Chicago (made up predominantly of liberal Protestant ministers) to give united endorsement to his proposed crusade in Chicago. For details of this see *United Evangelical Action*, August 15, 1958, p. 7.

4. See Noel Houston, "Billy Graham," *Holiday*, March, 1958, p. 107.

5. See *Billy Graham: The Work of an Evangelist* (London, 1952), p. 20.

6. Andrew Tully, quoted in Curtis Mitchell, *God in the Garden* (New York, 1957), pp. 65-66.

7. *Introducing Billy Graham: The Work of an Evangelist* (World's Evangelical Alliance, London, 1952), p. 23. For the implications of Graham's "all-inclusive policy" in regard to the resurgent fundamentalist-modernist quarrel see Chapter 9, *infra*. But it should be noted here that Graham stated in 1952, that while he would "welcome all men of every theological structure to come and join with us" in evangelistic crusades, he also added, "I tell you this, I would never pull a punch from the Word of God in order to compromise with one man. . . . On the Executive Committee of our campaigns we have only men who accept the deity of the Lord Jesus Christ, which includes the Virgin birth, the vicarious atonement and the bodily resurrection." *Ibid.*, p. 23.

8. See for example *United Evangelical Action*, July 1, 1954, p. 7, where the role of the International Christian Leadership group in the Washington, D.C. crusade is discussed.

9. Since 1954 a growing number of fundamentalists has voiced its opposition to Graham for a variety of reasons which are discussed *infra*, Chapter 9.

10. *Houston Post*, June 2, 1952, p. 1.

11. *Christian Century*, September 21, 1955, p. 1076; and April 23, 1952, p. 494.

12. *United Evangelical Action,* February 1, 1955, p. 13.

13. *Christian Life,* February 19, 1956, p. 45.

13a. Jerry Beavan has pointed out to me that no donations or pledges are made at these businessmen's luncheons. They are designed primarily to enlist the support of "the better elements" in a city, and while it is indicated that solicitation will later be made of those businessmen who indicate their interest, no funds are actually raised at these luncheons.

14. See *New Orleans Times-Picayune,* October 2, 1954, p. 8; for the Nashville statistics see Stanley High, *Billy Graham* (New York, 1956), pp. 156 ff; for the London statistics see the *British Weekly,* October 7, 1954, p. 3; for the New York statistics see Noel Houston, "Billy Graham," *Holiday,* March, 1958, p. 98 and the *New York Times,* December 20, 1957, p. 31. It is worth noting here that one of the methods used by the Graham organization in soliciting funds has been to ask the cooperating ministers in a crusade to supply the finance committee with a list of names of the members of their churches who might be persuaded to give. See James L. McAllister, *et al.,* "Greensboro and Billy Graham" (1952), p. IV, 14a. A copy of this manuscript is in the social ethics library of the Yale Divinity School, Yale University.

15. *This Week Magazine,* April 21, 1957, p. 12.

16. Mitchell, *God in the Garden, op. cit.,* p. 11.

CHAPTER 8: Converts and Commercialism

1. *Newsweek,* July 22, 1957, p. 57.

2. *Pittsburgh Press,* September 25, 1952, p. 5.

3. *Newsweek,* May 27, 1957, p. 96.

4. *Time,* May 27, 1957, p. 46.

5. The counselors for Graham's crusades are trained by the Navigators, Inc., weeks ahead of the meetings, in special counseling classes. Some ultrafundamentalists have recently claimed that because Graham is cooperating with liberal Protestants in his crusades, counseling is being done by persons not committed to fundamentalism. Graham and his team vigorously deny this and the Navigators have special tests in choosing those whom they certify for counseling positions so as to weed out all liberals and modernists.

6. Not all counseling done in the inquiry rooms goes so smoothly as this fictitious case. A minister who worked in the Graham crusade in New York told me of a narrow-minded counselor trained in a southern Bible school who completely alienated an inquirer whom he knew to be Jewish. He began his counseling by quoting Biblical texts to prove that the Jews had killed Jesus and then remarked, "That is why the Jews have always had so much trouble in the world. You refused to accept Christ." The inquirer left the room incensed and unconverted.

7. For further discussion of the fundamentalists' criticisms of Graham on this score see *infra,* Chapter 9.

8. See for example *Decision*, the newsletter of the Billy Graham Evangelistic Association for November, 1958, (vol. VI, #2) concerning the crusade in Charlotte, North Carolina. According to this "Nearly 60 per cent of those making decisions were under eighteen years of age."

9. *Look*, February 7, 1956, p. 48.

10. Although the decision cards used by Graham since 1956 omit this feature the pastor who makes the follow up visit to each convert is supposed to ascertain whether or not he has been previously attending church regularly. It might also be noted here that the term "first decision" applied to a convert does not mean that the person was not already a church member. Only a conversion experience is a "first decision" and many church members have not had such experiences.

11. *U.S. News and World Report*, September 27, 1957, p. 74.

12. Bob Considine quoted in George Burnham and Lee Fisher, *Billy Graham and the New York Crusade* (Grand Rapids, Michigan, 1957), pp. 73-74.

13. Interview with the author.

14. *Christianity Today*, September 16, 1957, p. 32.

15. *Pittsburgh Press*, September 11, 1952, p. 2.

16. *Washington Post*, January 15, 1952, p. 2-B.

17. A. J. Liebling in *The New Yorker*, May 28, 1955, p. 105.

18. *Christian Century*, June 12, 1957, pp. 725-726.

19. *New York Times*, May 30, 1957.

20. *Christian Century*, May 29, 1957, p. 677.

21. *Life*, July 1, 1957, quoted in Curtis Mitchell, *God in the Garden* (New York, 1957), p. 104.

22. I made this spot check myself at the New York crusade office on June 18, 1957.

23. See the *Christian Century*, April 23, 1952, pp. 494-496 and *United Evangelical Action*, July 15, 1952, p. 7. In refuting Frederick, the Rev. Albert J. Lindsey of Tacoma, who had served on the Graham committee, stated that 1971 new church members had been reported by Seattle pastors and that 1504 others were "in the process of affiliation."

24. *Evangelical Christian* (Toronto), June, 1955, p. 271.

25. See the *British Weekly*, February 10, 1955, p. 1, which quotes the *Evening Standard's* survey in full.

26. The results of Highet's surveys were printed in the *British Weekly*, August 22, 1957, p. 1, and August 29, 1957, p. 1.

27. *Christian Century*, October 12, 1955, p. 1179.

28. *British Weekly*, May 29, 1958, p. 1.

29. Letter to the author, dated Edinburgh, April 26, 1958. For an equally pessimistic estimate of Billy Graham's impact upon Britain by a

social psychologist see Michael Argyle, *Religious Behavior* (London, 1958) pp. 53-57. Argyle, who is Lecturer in Social Psychology in the University of Oxford, concludes that the percentage of genuine converts made by Billy Graham in his three revival crusades in Britain (1954-1955) "is probably much lower than that for the earlier evangelists" in British history.

It is still too early to make any final judgment of the results of Graham's three-month crusade in Australia in the spring of 1959; however, an official report to the Victorian Methodist churches by the Rev. J. W. R. Westerman, Methodist director of social services, in October, 1959, stated that Graham's impact upon persons outside the regular church members in the circuits of Victoria was "slight," "negligible," and "disappointing." "The report raises the question whether less spectacular but better results could have been achieved if the time, work, prayer, and money that went into the crusade was devoted to evangelism at the local level." From an article in *The Age,* a Melbourne daily newspaper, October 23, 1959, transmitted to me by Professor Kenneth S. Inglis of the University of Adelaide.

30. *New York Times,* January 26, 1958, p. 61. This poor showing in New York also seems to indicate the failure of the home visitation campaign which directly followed the crusade there and which was considered an integral part of it.

One of the greatest difficulties in evaluating the impact of any religious revival is that of defining what a true conversion experience entails. A study made recently by the Harvard Research Center on Creative Altruism under the direction of the well known sociologist, Pitirim A. Sorokin, examined intensively by interviews and questionnaires seventy-three persons who professed conversion during revival meetings conducted either by Billy Graham or by the Rev. Bryan Green, a contemporary British evangelist. The study revealed that although "about half of the converts changed somewhat their speech reactions" and used the verbal formulas of fundamentalism to describe their changed lives and outlooks, "their outward behavior did not change at all." In fact, "Only one" out of the seventy-three converts "has shown a tangible change of his personality and overt behavior" according to Sorokin. Sorokin concludes that modern revivals of the Billy Graham sort are virtually useless as a means of altering either individual or social behavior and values. Although this conclusion is probably too negative, it indicates the difficulty in ascertaining concrete evidence of the impact of mass evangelism on contemporary society. See Pitirim A. Sorokin, "The Power of Creative Unselfish Love" in Abraham H. Maslow, ed., *New Knowledge in Human Values* (N.Y., 1959) pp. 4-5.

31. Stanley High, *Billy Graham* (New York, 1956), p. 152.

32. *New York Times,* March 3, 1955.

33. See Val Adams' column in the *New York Times,* May 26, 1957, sec. X, p. 13.

34. *Christian Century,* May 15, 1957, p. 614.

35. Some of Graham's critics have claimed that Graham himself donated or invested $10,000 toward this magazine. Others have said that its principal backer is J. Howard Pew, wealthy former president of Sun

Oil Company who has for years accused the National Council of Churches of fostering "creeping socialism and pro-Russian radicalism." See Ernest Pickering, *Should Fundamentalists Support the Billy Graham Crusades* (Chicago, 1958), p. 17 and William E. Ashbrook, *Evangelicalism: The New Neutralism* (Columbus, Ohio, 1958), pp. 23-24.

36. Noel Houston, "Billy Graham," *Holiday,* March, 1958, p. 108.

37. See *ibid.,* also *Kansas City Star,* January 1, 1956, feature section, p. 1. I have obtained additional information about the Graham organization by visiting the Minneapolis office and talking with George Wilson and other members of the staff.

38. See High, *Graham, op. cit.,* p. 156.

39. Noel Houston, "Billy Graham," *loc. cit.,* p. 108.

40. *Ibid.,* 109 ff.

41. *Ibid.,* 110. Dr. Graham, in commenting on this passage in a letter to me, states that he is not aware of any difficulty between himself and the Internal Revenue Department. But in the article by Noel Houston cited above (note 36) Dr. Graham is quoted as having said in 1958, "For several years I have given the $7200 a year I am paid for my weekly newspaper column to the [Billy Graham Evangelistic] association. Now the Internal Revenue Department tells me this was personal income and I will have to pay income tax on it all the way back. . . . The revenue men seem like nice people and I hope some kind of settlement can be made" (p. 109 in Houston's article). Jerry Beavan tells me that he carefully checked this article for accuracy before it was printed, and Noel Houston's widow assures me that every quotation in the article was checked with Dr. Graham.

CHAPTER 9: Billy Graham: An Estimate

1. See Graham's radio message, "The Sin of Tolerance" (1957), published by the Billy Graham Evangelistic Association, Minneapolis, Minnesota (hereinafter referred to as the BGEA).

2. *Boston Herald,* January 19, 1917, p. 1.

3. Letter from Wanamaker to Sunday, July 1, 1915, among the Sunday papers, Winona Lake, Indiana.

4. E. G. Homrighausen, "Billy Graham and the Protestant Predicament," *Christian Century,* July 18, 1956, p. 84.

5. *Christian Century,* February 29, 1956, p. 262.

6. *Time,* February 11, 1957, p. 56.

7. The renascence of fundamentalism has given a new thrust to the foreign mission movement in America and Billy Graham is one of the driving forces behind it. In theory Graham's missionary emphasis is put on the basis of competing with communism for the allegiance of the uncommitted countries, and yet to date Graham has given most of his attention to mission work in such staunchly anti-Communist places as South Korea, Formosa, Japan, the Caribbean, and South America. In the middle of

1958 the Billy Graham Evangelistic Association announced that it would send a number of evangelists to Japan, India, and Africa "to aid programs of Christian missions already operating there." In January, 1959, the Association began a weekly evangelistic broadcast in Spanish, called "Decision," which was carried over twenty Latin American radio stations. And in June, 1959, the Association announced that it would soon begin publication of a monthly missionary magazine called *World Evangelism* which was expected to find several hundred thousand subscribers. See *United Evangelical Action*, July 1, 1958, p. 9; January, 1959, p. 12; and *Newsweek*, June 15, 1959, p. 88.

8. *Life*, July 1, 1957, p. 92.

9. *Look*, February 27, 1956, p. 49.

10. *Ibid.*

11. Graham is entitled to be called "Doctor" by virtue of five or six honorary degrees conferred upon him by various Bible schools and colleges, but he has never engaged in any advanced academic or scholarly work. It will be interesting to see whether he will, like D. L. Moody, send his sons to Yale, or, like Billy Sunday, try to persuade his sons to go to Princeton. It seems more likely that he will prefer that they go to a "Bible-believing, Christ-honoring" college like Wheaton in Illinois.

12. *Revival in Our Time*, (Wheaton, Illinois, 1950), p. 144.

13. "Hour of Decision," January 8, 1956.

14. Noel Houston, "Billy Graham," *Holiday*, March, 1958, p. 99.

14a. Dr. Graham, in a letter to me, denies his acceptance of Bishop Ussher's chronology, but insists that the account of creation in Genesis is correct. What date he does hold for the creation of the world and of Adam and Eve he does not say.

15. See Graham's radio message, "Christ's Marching Orders" (1955), published by BGEA.

16. *Ibid.*

17. *Ibid.*

18. See Graham's radio message, "Satan's Religion" (1953), published by the BGEA.

19. See Graham's radio message, "Hate *vs.* Love" (1955), published by the BGEA. The most recent attack by Graham upon American education is contained in his sermon "Christian Philosophy of Education" (published by the BGEA, 1959) in which he joins the current effort to make John Dewey the scapegoat for all America's present educational, religious, moral and political problems: "Since the advent of John Dewey, an insidious movement has been set in motion to undermine our traditional educational system . . . self-styled progressives . . . are to a large degree responsible for the mass departure from American principles, American ideals, and Biblical morals. . . . They contend that the old, the tried and proven, and the heritages of the past must be replaced by new ideas. . . . [They] actually despair of, and make light of, our traditional

political concepts. . . And this is done in the sanctity of the classroom unbeknown to the faithful and loyal American parents who foot the bills for our education." Graham delivered this sermon on the Hour of Decision broadcast, October 4, 1959, and offered to send extra copies for distribution to all who wrote in for them.

20. Quoted by Ralph Lord Roy in "Billy Graham's Crusade," *New Leader*, August 1, 1955, p. 7.

21. See Graham's radio message, "The Bible and Dr. Kinsey" (1953) published by BGEA.

22. See Graham's radio message, "Hate *vs.* Love" (1955), published by the BGEA.

23. *United Evangelical Action,* June 1, 1956, p. 5.

24. See Graham's radio message, "The Responsibilities of Parents" (1955), published by the BGEA. It is indeed careless of Graham to accuse the Supreme Court of doing something it has never done. Graham may be thinking of the decision by the Supreme Court of New Jersey which prohibited the Gideons from distributing the King James version of the Bible in the New Jersey public schools in 1953 because of Roman Catholic objections that it was a sectarian book. The Supreme Court of the United States refused to deal with this case because it has always studiously left the decision of Bible-reading in the public schools up to the states.

25. This sentence, taken from the "Hour of Decision" broadcast of July 27, 1958, was not included in the printed version of "The Sin of Tolerance" (1957), published by the BGEA.

26. The latter quotation is from "The Urgency of Revival," a radio message published in 1954 by the BGEA.

27. This does not mean that Graham indulges in anti-Semitism or anti-Catholicism. He does not. It is interesting to note, however, that whereas Billy Sunday turned decision cards signed by Roman Catholics over to the local bishop or archbishop, Graham instructs his counselors and co-operating ministers that an inquirer can be assumed to be adopting Protestantism if he comes forward in the meetings, and it is therefore right to proselyte any Roman Catholic—or Jew—who does so. Nevertheless Graham has been so friendly toward the Roman Catholic church that some of his original supporters among the fanatical fundamentalists have attacked him for betraying their cause. See for example, *The Converted Catholic* (New York), June, 1956.

28. *Christian Life,* July, 1956, pp. 14 ff.

29. *U.S. News and World Report,* April 6, 1956, p. 65.

30. See for example the comments in George Burnham, *To the Far Corners: With Billy Graham in Asia* (New York, 1956), pp. 34, 42, 80, 83-84, 86, 91. Graham's campaign in Africa reflected a similar disregard for non-Christians. He not only antagonized Moslem leaders by his attempts to proselytize their followers, but he angered all Africans by his refusal to take any stand on the French atomic bomb experiments in the

Sahara. See *New York Times,* February 14, 1960, p. 59, and *Providence Journal,* January 26, 1960, p. 35; February 4, 1960, p. 4.

31. *Charlotte Observer,* October 23, 1958, p. 9-C.

32. *Look,* February 7, 1956, p. 51.

33. Reinhold Niebuhr, "Literalism, Individualism, and Billy Graham," *Christian Century,* May 23, 1956, pp. 641-642.

34. Billy Graham, *Peace with God* (New York, 1953), p. 50.

35. See Graham's radio message, "The Signs of the Times" (1957), published by the BGEA.

36. See Graham's radio message, "The Mystery of Iniquity" (1956), published by the BGEA.

36a. Dr. Graham, in commenting on this passage in a letter to me, indicates that he does not believe in the inevitability of atomic war because it is possible that human nature can be radically changed by divine aid. Atomic war is only inevitable, he indicates in his letter, if human nature is not radically transformed.

37. *New York Times,* January 26, 1958, p. 61.

38. *Christian Century,* August 7, 1957, p. 934.

39. See Graham's radio message, "Teen-age Vandalism" (1958), published by the BGEA. One of the surprising things about these suggestions is that Graham said "the federal government needs to do more" to help clean up the slums. Though he gave a negative twist to it by asserting, "It concerns me that we are willing to give billions to other countries abroad but are not willing to spend the necessary money here at home to clean up our slum conditions."

40. Ralph Lord Roy, "Billy Graham's Crusade," *The New Leader,* August 1, 1955, p. 8.

41. *New York Times* Magazine, April 21, 1957, p. 19.

42. *New York Herald Tribune,* May 12, 1957, p. 24.

43. "Hour of Decision," November 10, 1957.

44. "Hour of Decision," July 27, 1958.

45. *Charlotte Observer,* September 23, 1958, p. 4-A.

45a. Typical of these fundamentalist attacks upon Graham are the following pamphlets: Bob Jones, Jr., *How Accurate Are the Statements Made by Those Who Defend Billy Graham's Modernistic Sponsorship?* (Greenville, South Carolina, 1957); Ernest Pickering, *Should Fundamentalists Support the Billy Graham Crusades?* (Chicago, 1958); William E. Ashbrook, *Evangelicalism: The New Neutralism* (Chicago, 1956); James A. Stewart, *Ecumenical Evangelism?* (Asheville, North Carolina, n.d.).

46. See Carl F. H. Henry, "Theology, Evangelism, Ecumenism," *Christianity Today,* January 20, 1958, pp. 20 ff., and the answer to it by James DeForest Murch, "Trends in Protestantism," *United Evangelical Action,* March 1, 1958, p. 7. Murch remarks of Henry's and Graham's view:

"Eager advocates of 'the new evangelicalism' need to be on their guard lest they go too far in their quest for a wider fellowship" and become ensnared with "the Super-Church" and its "new ecumenical theology or 'Christology'" which is simply another form of liberalism.

47. See Graham's radio message, "Peace *vs.* Chaos" (1951), published by the BGEA. Dr. Graham, in commenting on this chapter in a letter to me, indicates that he believes I have exaggerated his relationship with the National Association of Evangelicals and neglected his more important association with the Southern Baptist Convention. I have perhaps been remiss in not pointing out that Dr. Graham is deeply devoted to his denomination and is active in his support of it, particularly in the foreign missions field. But my estimate of his career in this chapter is meant to look beyond denominational affiliations to the overarching movements of theological development and ecclesiastical relations within contemporary Protestantism. In this respect Dr. Graham's positive, extradenominational relationship to a new movement like the NAE may well be historically more significant than his ordinary relationship to his denomination. Only time will answer this question.

48. In an article entitled "What Ten Years Have Taught Me," published February 17, 1960, in the *Christian Century*, Graham explicitly stated that this individualistic emphasis in his theology had not altered over the years: "I am more convinced than ever before that we must change men before we can change society. The international problems are only reflections of individual problems. . . . Social sins, after all, are merely a large-scale projection of individual sins. . . ."

Index

THE WIND CHIME

Victorian Timeshift Mysteries

Alexandra Walsh

SAPERE
BOOKS

D1247842

THE WIND CHIME

Published by Sapere Books.

20 Windermere Drive, Leeds, England, LS17 7UZ,
United Kingdom

saperebooks.com

ISBN: 978-1-80055-305-7

To Al, Richard, Katy-Kitten and Martha-Moo
who have been with the chimes since the beginning.
Love you.

PROLOGUE

It was the sound of the wind chime that indicated the change. Every summer we waited for the soft tinkling of the seashells to lose their harmonious song and crash together discordantly. It signalled the end of another long, lazy summer. A return to reality and the cold, winter days when our family would once more scatter themselves around the world. Exploring their way through their lives, living their hopes, chasing their dreams, and waiting, watching, for the first hint of summer when we would find ourselves inexorably drawn back to the house on the cliff.

Every summer we parted on smiles, hugs, promises of a love which would last forever. None of us ever spoke the words we feared, we simply waited, noticing if there were any changes in ourselves, in each other. And, as the wind chime indicated another summer's end, we always drank a toast, a promise to return as soon as the air turned soft and golden. We would go back, back to the house on the cliff, to the home that kept our secrets and the never-ending ocean that covered our lies.

From the diary of Osyth Attwater, Cliffside, Pembrokeshire

PART ONE: WINDSOR, 2019

CHAPTER ONE

The door closed on the last guest. Amelia Prentice leaned on the front door, the bubbled glass smooth on her back through her elegant black dress. Closing her eyes, she took a deep breath, allowing her shoulders to slump as the waves of exhaustion, relief, and sadness she had been keeping at bay overwhelmed her. Releasing her red-gold hair from the bun at the nape of her neck, she shook out her unruly curls, feeling the rigid formality of the day slide away as each strand freed itself. Kicking off her shoes, she left them where they fell and padded along the hallway.

With her wide blue eyes and pale, heart-shaped face she had an elfin look which belied her age, making her appear younger than her thirty-five years. It had occasionally unnerved people at her job as a paediatric doctor in a large London hospital but, as she entered the large living room, she caught a glimpse of herself in the mirror and felt that today, she looked far older. Sorrow was etched around her eyes and her lips were thin and pinched.

"Here."

A large glass of red wine was thrust into her hand by her friend, Louise Smith. Three people remained from the mourners who had attended the funeral — Amelia's oldest friends, who had been with her during the last terrible years, the people she knew would always be there, no matter how bleak things became and how far she fell.

Louise led Amelia towards one of the old, comfortable sofas and pushed her into the cushions. "Sit, drink, don't think for a while," she instructed. "We've ordered a takeaway."

Amelia gave her a grateful smile. They had been friends since they were eleven years old and knew each other inside out.

Louise sat on the chair opposite and pushed her own black high-heeled shoes off before stretching out her feet and resting them on the lap of her husband, Richie, who was in the chair beside her. She ran a hand through her sharp, brunette bob and closed her hazel eyes, emotion overcoming her. Richie gazed at her, his brown eyes full of concern.

At the other end of the sofa was the final member of their group, Benji Taylor, who had lived opposite Amelia throughout their childhood. His hair was prematurely grey and cut in a short number two buzz cut. His blue eyes were solemn as he gazed at the photographs arranged on the mantelpiece.

Silence hung between them. Amelia did not have the energy to speak, and she knew her friends did not expect it.

Richie raised his glass. "To your mum," he said, his tone solemn, "one of the strongest, kindest, funniest women I have ever met."

Amelia raised her glass but the lump in her throat stopped her from replying.

"To Auntie Joan," said Louise.

"To Auntie Joan," echoed Benji.

Amelia managed to croak, "To Mum," but she was not looking at her friends, she was looking at the three framed photographs above the fireplace. "To Dad and to my darling Molly. You're together at last. Look after each other."

Her parents smiled benignly from either side of the photograph of the beaming, tousle-haired Molly. Her dark curls were bouncing and her hazel eyes sparkling, despite the fact that a breathing tube was discreetly taped to her nose and the background of the image showed she was sitting in a

10

hospital bed surrounded by machines. Out of the corner of her eye, Amelia could see Louise wiping away her tears.

"Thank you," said Amelia, after taking a large glug of wine. "You three have been incredible. I wouldn't have survived this without your support."

Benji leaned over and squeezed her hand. "Yes, you would," he said. "You're made of as much steel as your mum."

"It's difficult to believe she isn't about to walk through the door and invite us all to stay for something to eat..." began Louise.

"One of her incredible curries..." said Benji.

"They were the best," murmured Richie.

"With chips," added Louise. "She always said it was a nod to her Welsh heritage."

"Which was a joke," smiled Amelia, "because she was born in this house and has no Welsh heritage, apart from spending a few summers there when she was a child."

The story was old, familiar, comforting, and the four of them sat for a moment, each remembering Joan Prentice, and her remarkable zest for life.

"What will you do now?" asked Benji, topping up their glasses.

Amelia shuffled into a more comfortable position. "Sleep, cry, grieve, and then decide," she replied. "Mum's cancer was so prolonged, we had time to discuss things and she insisted I shouldn't be sentimental about the house. She showed me other houses nearby on estate agents' websites and said I should make use of the money."

"Do you think you'll sell?" asked Louise. "Your mum's always said her family has been here for generations."

"It's too soon to even think about it," replied Amelia. "The idea of selling feels very final and, anyway, where would I put

all the stuff?" She waved her hand around at the walls covered in her mother's paintings — those she had created herself and the many she had bought over the years — shelves and shelves of books, the baby grand piano and the endless framed photographs.

"You could put your stuff into storage, let the property for a year and go on an adventure?" suggested Richie.

"A gap year?" laughed Amelia. "Don't you think I'm a bit old to be dragging a rucksack around Thailand and Cambodia?"

"You didn't get the packing-light gene, love," said Benji, "you'd never get all your stuff in a rucksack. You'd need a couple of camels to carry everything."

Amelia threw a cushion at him, relieved her friends were behaving normally and not treating her as though she were made of glass and might break. The last few weeks had seen people adopting hushed tones whenever they spoke to her, expecting her to crumble and fall as she organised her mother's funeral — the third within two years.

A knock on the door indicated the arrival of their food.

"You stay there," commanded Louise as Amelia made to stand. "All you're doing for the rest of the evening is sitting, eating, drinking, and letting us look after you for a change. You've spent too long looking after everyone else."

Louise and Benji clattered up the hallway, bickering over who would pay, both racing to beat the other. Richie shook his head and raised his eyebrows at Amelia, an expression they often shared.

"Idiots," he sighed but it was said with love. "I paid for it when I ordered." He cleared a space on the table in preparation for the bags of food, then hurried to the kitchen for plates and cutlery.

Amelia sipped her wine, listening as her friends, familiar with the layout of the kitchen, gathered everything they would need and descended upon her once again.

"Curry with chips — although we do have rice too…" began Louise.

"Half and half, chips and rice, a Welsh delicacy," interrupted Benji, "in honour of Auntie Joan."

Amelia accepted the plate of food. She had not thought she would be interested in eating after the sadness of the day but as the smell of the spices filled the room, her stomach gurgled and she realised she was ravenously hungry. Leaning back, she began to eat, savouring the heat and flavour of the curry. For a moment they ate in silence, then she said, "Why do you think my mum used to say she had Welsh heritage when she didn't?" She prodded a poppadum so it shattered, using a piece to scoop up a mouthful of rice.

"Maybe it was many generations back," replied Louise, "a family tale passed down. Although, she was born here in Clewer, wasn't she?"

"As far as I know, in this very house, the front bedroom. My mum inherited the house from her mother, Susannah."

"And where was Susannah born?" asked Richie, dipping a chip into his curry sauce.

"I did ask Mum, but she was vague about it. She said she thought it was in Windsor, not necessarily in this house. My grandmother never talked about her parents much apart from their names — they were called Rose and Edward Tunley but Mum didn't know anything else. It's why I always found this Welsh connection so odd."

"You could research your family tree and see if there is any Welsh blood," suggested Benji. "Maybe you could do that instead of a bungee-jumping gap-year."

"Perhaps," replied Amelia, although the idea did not really appeal to her.

"Do you think you'll go back to work?" asked Louise.

Amelia shrugged. "Not immediately, thanks to Mum and Dad's life insurance policies. They've left me quite comfortable and Mum said there are a few other bits and pieces in her will, so I don't have to rush back and —" she took a deep breath and tried to lighten her voice as she finished — "I've had enough of illness."

"You're a doctor," said Benji, "it goes with the territory."

"Benji!" exclaimed Louise. "Shut up!"

"He's right," said Amelia, "it's the job but, after the last few years, I'm not sure I can face being around illness for a long time."

"You could always retrain," suggested Richie.

Amelia nodded, spooning more food onto her plate. "Perhaps, but first I need to recover. In fact, there is one project Mum left me."

Louise laughed. "Your mum loved a project."

"What project did she leave you, Aimes?" asked Richie.

"She suggested before I consider doing anything, even selling the house, I should go through the boxes in the attic."

"Did she say what was in them?" asked Benji, helping himself to more curry.

"No, I imagine it's old paperwork — you know how much Mum and Dad loved filing away receipts."

Richie placed his empty plate on the floor and picked up his glass. "Shall we have a look now?"

"Richie, no!" exclaimed Louise, and Amelia smiled, loving her friend for her protective nature. "It's been a long and emotional day, the last thing any of us should be doing is poking around in the attic."

"Why?" asked Benji, shovelling in the last few mouthfuls. "It's not like it's late or anything, it's only half past six."

"Aimes?" Louise questioned.

Amelia finished her second helping and balanced her plate on the low coffee table where the empty containers were stacked. Picking up her wine, she drained the glass and was suddenly overwhelmed with curiosity. "We could have a quick look," she said, taking herself by surprise.

"Come on then," said Richie.

Leading the way, Amelia hurried up the stairs to the small door, set at the top of a short flight of stairs that led to the eaves and the attic space of the large Victorian house. She opened the door and stepped inside, flicking on the light. She paused on the threshold, wondering if this was the right time but one of the many conversations she and her mother had shared echoed in her mind.

"*We're luckier than most,*" Joan had told her, squeezing Amelia's hand, "*we have time to talk, to come to terms with things, to say all the things we can think of, the good and the bad. We know how much we love each other and how much we always will, even when I'm gone. My darling, never regret my passing. We will miss each other fiercely but know that I'll never be far away. If I can send you a sign, I shall. Most of all, remember you are alive. You must live and we will be smiling and cheering you on. No regrets, my darling.*"

"Aimes, we can do this another day," Louise's voice cut through her memories.

"No," said Amelia, her voice a fraction too loud, "we're here now, let's see how big these boxes are and maybe bring them downstairs."

The attic space was divided into two rooms with a small landing between them. Joan had told her they were once used as servants' bedrooms. When she had been eight years old,

15

Amelia had taken a fancy to moving into the bigger of the two rooms, with its skylight looking up to the stars, but after a few nights under the whistling eaves, she had returned to her much larger bedroom below with its views over the back garden, nervous of the creaking. An old-fashioned, metal-framed, single bed remained in the larger room, along with a narrow wardrobe that housed her mother's abandoned coats. During their teens, she, Louise and Benji had raided the wardrobe of anything they deemed to be 'vintage' and wore it with great pride. The rooms were spotlessly clean and Amelia felt there was very little 'sorting out' to be done. Once again, she wondered why her mother had made the request.

"I was expecting cobwebs, trunks and secrets," said Benji, gazing around in disappointment. "It's as organised as when we came up here all those years ago."

"Where are these boxes?" asked Richie, looking around.

"Next door," said Amelia.

The second room was smaller and darker, with a tiny round window set high up in the point of the roof. It had been designed to be decorative, giving an attractive focal point to the outside of the house but it let in very little light. Turning on the light, Amelia pointed to the stack of brown cardboard storage boxes. "These are what Mum was talking about... Oh, where did that come from?" On top of the pile was an oblong, cream-coloured dress box. Amelia stared. "When I came up here a few months ago, that wasn't there."

"Is there anything written on it?" asked Louise.

"No, and it's sealed with parcel tape," said Amelia, lifting it up. "It's quite light." She gave it a tentative shake, but nothing rattled. "It's probably more paperwork."

It took them half an hour to carry the boxes downstairs. Her friends, now suitably primed with wine, teased and joked with

the comfort of people who have a shared history so extensive that they almost spoke their own language. Amelia listened, allowing the familiarity of their banter to wash over her, offering comfort.

Amelia and Benji — Benjamin Taylor — had known each other the longest. Benji's parents had bought the house opposite Amelia's when Amelia and Benji had been six years old. While Benji was at drama school, his parents had moved to Suffolk to retire but Amelia and Benji had remained best friends. Louise joined them when she and Amelia met at their all-girls' school. Richie was the last of the quartet to arrive and did so when he and Louise began dating at the age of 15. They had been together ever since, marrying when Louise was 27.

"What do you think is in them?" asked Louise as she placed the last box on the dining room table.

"Are we going to open them?" asked Benji, excitement sparkling in his eyes.

Richie reappeared with more wine and after topping up everyone's glasses, they all turned to Amelia who was circling the table, examining their hoard. There were seven boxes and each was sealed with wide brown parcel tape. A few had dates written on the top — 1976; 1985; 1994 — but the rest offered no clues.

"I'm going to open this one because it's the odd one out," said Amelia, touching the dress box. "It feels more significant."

Benji pulled his keys from his pocket and handed her the miniature Swiss Army penknife attached to it for her to slice through the tape.

"Are you sure about this?" asked Louise as Amelia slit the tape, freeing the lid of the box. "It's been a long day and…"

"It's alright, Lou," Amelia said. "Mum would never have directed me to something unpleasant. Whatever is in here, it's a gift from her."

Easing off the lid, she looked down and to her surprise saw photographs. Very old, blurred black and white images. The one on top was of a house. The many towers and windows adorning the property made it look as though it was growing out of the side of the cliff. Tiny figures stood on the veranda that wrapped itself around the property and disappeared into the grey sky. Amelia turned it over to find faded brown handwriting on the reverse.

"*Cliffside, Pembrokeshire, 1865*," she read, "*Penny Attwater, Eudora and baby Osyth.*"

"Pembrokeshire?" whispered Louise.

"Maybe your mum did have Welsh heritage," said Benji, a hint of awe in his voice.

Walking to a wooden bureau, Amelia dragged out a magnifying glass to examine the photograph more closely. The older woman was staring straight at the camera, a serene smile on her face and, unusually for the time, her hair was loose, an amorphous blur as the wind snatched at its glossy length. Beside her was a younger woman but there was enough of a resemblance for Amelia to assume they were related, possibly mother and daughter. In the younger woman's arms was a child but its features were blurred. It was as she moved the photograph away that she noticed there was someone else in the photograph — a boy was standing in one of the upstairs windows, gazing down at the women. His expression was one of such intense loathing that it caused Amelia to shudder, almost dropping the picture.

"What is it?" said Louise, hurrying to take it.

"There's a little boy in the window," said Amelia.

Her friends crowded around, studying the image.

"He's creepy," said Benji and the others nodded in agreement.

Richie looked at it last and after a few moments said, "The women look familiar."

"What do you mean?" asked Amelia.

"Look at it again. Don't you think the older woman looks like your mum?" he said.

Gazing at the serene woman as she smiled at her across time, Amelia felt a shiver run the length of her spine as she realised Richie was correct. The silence grew and eventually Amelia looked up. "But who are they?" she said. "And why did Mum never mention them?"

CHAPTER TWO

The chimes woke Amelia a few days later. Reaching across to her phone to silence the noise, she was halfway out of bed, her sleep-fugged brain going into automatic mode, before she realised it had been a dream. Her phone was off; she had not set her alarm. When she had gone to bed last night she had realised that, for the first time in two years, she was able to rest with no disturbances, no bleeping machines or cries for assistance or even the panicked moments when she had woken to silence expecting the worst. Nowhere to be. No one to wake up for.

Slumping back on her pillows, she stared at the blank face of her phone, trying to recall the dream and the melodious tune that had drawn her from sleep, but nothing came except a black void. Groaning, she rolled over and looked at her clock. It was 7am.

"So much for a lie-in," she sighed, throwing her phone onto the duvet beside her. Piling her pillows into a comfortable pyramid and leaning back, she gazed out at the bright spring morning. In the distance, traffic hummed as the town set about its business. A robin trilled from a nearby garden but in the house the ticking of the clock and her own breathing were her companions. Silence. No Molly, no parents.

Amelia sipped her tea, then felt a wave of despair wash through her. It had been a week since the funeral and, until today, her time had been full as she sent thank you letters, comforted her mother's friends and fielded phone calls. Yesterday had been the first day when the phone had not rung continuously, when there had been no condolence cards in the

post and no emails of support. Life was righting itself, the waves were closing over Joan's life, leaving no trace except in the hearts of her family and friends, as everyone returned to their usual day-to-day existence, adjusting to the loss, and moving on.

I'm alone, thought Amelia. *I have no blood relations. My parents are gone and my daughter died in my arms. My family are together somewhere else and I have no one.*

It was not her usual way to allow self-pity to swamp her but Amelia was suddenly paralysed by the loss of her loved ones. Her fear and isolation was so complete she felt as though she could no longer breathe without them. A tear rolled down her cheek and she allowed it to travel without wiping it away. Inhaling deeply, she thought back to her grief counselling after Molly's death, remembering the exercises she had been taught. Calming herself, she focussed on talking herself back from the panic. *These feelings are normal*, she thought. *They, too, will pass.*

Closing her eyes, she imagined her daughter. A smile replaced the tense line of her mouth as she conjured up her curly-haired child. Amelia would never forget the terrible day of Molly's diagnosis with rare Childhood Interstitial Lung Disease. The diagnosis covered a range of critical illnesses connected with the lungs but the prognosis for Molly had been grave.

She and Molly's father, John Josephs, had been devastated. Amelia had taken Molly to bed — it would be her daughter's last night in her own home for many months before her treatment began and Amelia had been determined to behave as normally as possible in order to keep Molly calm, something she had explained to John. He had stood in the middle of their living room, giving a terse nod of understanding but he had made no move to help. Amelia and Molly had gone through

the usual bedtime routine and an hour later when she had returned to the living room, knowing Molly was asleep, she had found the downstairs of the house in darkness with no sign of John.

In the kitchen was a scrawled note saying he could not cope with the diagnosis, Molly had never been planned, and he was leaving. It was at this point Amelia had felt her legs sag. Not through the loss of her relationship, although that was difficult enough to comprehend, but at the callous, thoughtless way John could treat his child. She could not remember it, but she must have called Louise because ten minutes later there had been a hammering on the door and Benji stood there, shocked. Louise and Richie arrived half an hour later and together the four of them had tried to make sense of the devastation unfolding around them.

Amelia wiped away another tear as she thought back to those days. Her friends had put their lives on hold for her and Molly. They had moved into the house and supported her through the first distressing months of Molly's treatment, working on a rota, so one of them was always with her. Molly, when she was home, loved having her auntie and uncles around. It was through Molly's treatment that Benji had met his partner, Doug, who worked as a nurse on Molly's ward, a story she delighted in hearing, insisting Benji tell it to her as though it were a bedtime story.

"Well," he would begin, taking her hand, "I walked into the ward looking for the prettiest girl and who did I find by her bed, helping to make her feel better, but the man who captured my heart."

Eventually, Amelia had realised she needed more help and with her parents offering their assistance, she had moved back to Windsor to be near them. She had not immediately gone

back to her parents' house, instead renting a cottage a few streets away, but soon even this proved too difficult and, one day, her parents had arrived on her doorstep and insisted she and Molly move in with them.

Two days later, they did. Amelia and Molly had been gathered in by Joan and Patrick, safe, protected, loved and supported as they prepared for the tragic but inevitable outcome of Molly's rare condition.

And I've been here ever since. Four years. What changes those years have wrought.

Throwing back her duvet, Amelia marched into the shower, continuing to ponder the past four years. *You're not the only one who's had it tough*, she reminded herself, *Louise and Richie are on their third round of IVF. Benji and Doug now care for Doug's mother who has dementia. Life throws these things at us, we might crumble for a while but with each other, we survive.*

Standing under the shower, Amelia focussed on the sound of the water rushing past her, breathing deeply, trying to clear her mind as she had been taught in grief counselling. The water soothed her and, reaching to turn it off, she heard it: the chiming sound from her dream.

It's a wind chime, she thought. As though in response, the chimes sang again. Someone must have hung one in their garden.

The boxes remained in the dining room where her friends had placed them on the day of the funeral. Amelia had been preoccupied with other things since then, but sitting at the table now, coffee mug in hand, she wondered what in particular it was that her mother had wanted her to discover inside them.

Amelia gazed around her. *This was my family home,* she thought. *Mum was born here, and I was one day old when she brought me home. All my childhood memories are within these walls, as well as some of my saddest adult experiences.*

The house was old and detached with a sizeable area to the front, half of which was now paved and led to a garage — an area that had proved invaluable over the years of struggling with Molly's wheelchair and, later, her parents' frailty. A large back garden flowed from the house, surrounded by well-tended shrubberies giving it an air of seclusion. It was the internal space that was remarkable though. Joan had been an amateur artist, and this showed in the interior design.

Amelia's eyes lingered on the many whimsical images her mother had painted of fairies and mythical creatures. Each painting contained a shimmering beauty that, as a child, Amelia had believed was because her mother painted with fairy dust.

"It's my secret ingredient," Joan had once whispered.

Wandering around, looking at her mother's paintings, Amelia's eyes strayed to the other pictures her parents had collected. She felt her life was in these works of art, remembering many of the markets and second-hand shops where they had been purchased, weekends spent travelling to auctions and antiques fairs, thrilling bidding battles and the excitement of each new purchase.

Molly had found them fascinating and would sit for hours, making up stories about the inhabitants. Amelia searched the walls until she located a pencil sketch entitled *Princess of the Fairy Rings.* She had been entranced with the image when she had been a child and Molly had loved it with equal ferocity so it had hung opposite her bed. Joan had returned it to the living room after Molly's death, positioning it so Molly's photograph appeared to be gazing at the image.

Amelia thought back to the days when Molly's bedroom had been the centre of the house, their aim to include her in everything, to never allow her to feel lonely or scared. One afternoon, Amelia had crept in to discover her father reading to Molly the less well-known fairy tales written by George MacDonald: *The Princess and The Goblin*, followed by the sequel, *The Princess and Curdie*. When Amelia had tucked Molly up that night, Molly had said, "Do you think the princess in the fairy ring is the same princess who met the goblin?"

"It's possible," Amelia had replied.

"Maybe she's the Windsor princess from the boats," Molly had laughed.

"Perhaps she is."

The letterbox rattled, bringing Amelia back to the present, and the local paper fell onto the door mat. On the front was a large photograph of one of the old-fashioned boats that continued to chug majestically down the River Thames giving tourists the chance to sample the luxury of a bygone era. Her daughter and father had loved the boats and it was these Molly had been referring to when she had been thinking about fairy-tale princesses. Staring at the image, Amelia felt a surge of energy and decisiveness.

Relieved she had found a way to occupy her mind and body, she hurried upstairs to grab her handbag, before heading out into the spring sunshine.

The boats were ranged along the waterfront and checking her watch, Amelia saw she was in time to catch the *Windsor Princess* and enjoy a two-hour cruise along the river. Molly had loved the old-fashioned vessels and had been a regular visitor, so it was bittersweet as Amelia made her way to the front, alone. The captain and his crew had sent a wreath to Molly's funeral

and when the staff saw Amelia in her usual seat, they nodded but did not comment, for which she was grateful, as tears never seemed to be far away and she did not want to break down in public.

As the water lulled her, the voice of the guide giving the history of the river washed over her. Although she had sat through the speech many times, she had never listened properly because she had always been concentrating on Molly. Then she heard a name that drew her full attention.

"...at which point, the company changed its name from Jacobs Brothers to Stone and Family. It was bought by Wellington Stone, a man of means, who was joined by an old friend and business partner, William Attwater, changing the name again to Attwater and Stone..."

Amelia felt her heart race. Attwater was an unusual surname but she was sure it was the name of the woman in the photograph she had found on the day of her mother's funeral. Eager to discover more, she leaned forward so as not to miss a word of the speech, but the guide had moved on, describing the first boats and tales of derring-do from the previous owner, Arthur Jacobs, who had saved over sixty people during his time as owner of the pleasure boats. Listening with great attention, Amelia willed him to mention William Attwater again but there was no more. Frustrated, she sought the man out after he had finished.

"Enjoy the talk?" he asked.

"Yes," she replied. "I was particularly interested in the Attwater and Stone families, do you have any more information?"

"I don't but Bob might. His sister, Anna, has discovered they're descended from them." He waved to another member of the crew, calling him over and explaining Amelia's request.

"Not much, I'm afraid," said Bob after Amelia has asked about the Attwaters. "My gran used to talk about them. Apparently, on the surface they appeared to be the height of respectability, but she once described them as 'having more secrets than Harpocrates'."

Amelia stared at him in surprise. "Did she know what kind of secrets?"

"No, she would shudder and shake her head, almost daring me to ask, which I did, and all she would say is: 'a secret at home is like rocks under the tide and they had more secrets than the sea has tides'."

A shout from above caused Bob to nod apologetically and hurry away. Amelia stared after him, intrigued.

CHAPTER THREE

"And you have no idea who the Attwaters might be in connection to you?" asked Richie, later that evening.

Amelia shook her head. They were in the living room with the fire crackling as a spring storm rattled the windows. The remains of yet another takeaway was stacked in a box in the corner and wine glasses were in hands, except for Louise. Benji and Doug were sprawled on the sofa.

"None whatsoever, or whether there even is a connection," Amelia replied. "I hadn't known the name before we found the photographs in the attic but now it keeps cropping up."

"Spooky," murmured Louise.

"Was there anything else in the box with the pictures?" asked Doug.

"Yes," replied Amelia, "a family tree. Handwritten but I didn't recognise the writing. The best thing, though, is the photographs have been annotated, so at least we have a rough idea of who is who. I did some basic research this afternoon, which has given me more information."

She hurried into the dining room, returning with the dress box and a notebook. Kneeling down, she cleared the debris from the coffee table and began to unpack the images, putting the picture of the house, Cliffside, in the centre. Louise knelt beside her and together they laid out the photographs using the new version of the family tree Amelia had drawn that afternoon, before Amelia flicked to her notes.

"Whether we're connected or not," said Amelia, "it's a wonderful collection of Victorian photographs, especially as we know the family was prominent in Windsor."

"What secrets did they have, though?" asked Benji, his face thoughtful.

Richie was studying the family tree. "This woman was called Penny Attwater, wasn't she?" he confirmed, pointing to the image of Cliffside.

Amelia nodded. "According to the family tree, she was married to Daniel Attwater." She pointed to a formal double portrait.

"If you took away the stern look and the dodgy mutton-chops, he's quite dashing," mused Louise.

"Agreed," replied Amelia. "Penny is stunning too, if you look past the hairstyle. They must have been a striking couple."

Louise reached out for the family tree and Richie handed it to her. She placed it in on the table, so they could all see it.

"Is that the younger woman from the house picture?" asked Doug pointing at a picture of a small woman with fair hair.

"No, that is Penny and Daniel's younger daughter," said Amelia. "The writing on the back looks as though it says Xenia?"

"It's a bit strange," said Benji, taking the photograph from Doug, "but I suppose it could have been a nickname."

"There's another image of Penny Attwater carrying a baby and it's marked as 'Thomasina (Sina)', I wondered if it might have transformed over the years into Xenia," said Amelia.

"It's possible," agreed Louise.

"Who's this? Even with all the Victoriana, he's hot," grinned Benji.

Amelia laughed. "He's Noah Attwater, eldest son and heir of Penny and Daniel. He's got a definite glint in his eye, hasn't he?"

"And this chap?" asked Richie.

"Blaise, second son of Penny and Daniel, with his wife Katherine —"

"Who looks uncannily like a younger version of Penny," added Doug. "Talk about marrying your mother."

"Weird, eh, and who are these two?" asked Louise holding up a picture of a boy and girl, he in a sailor suit, she in a ruffled sailor dress, both staring serenely at the camera, their blonde hair apparent in the old image.

"Solomon and Thomasina, who I think is Xenia," said Amelia. "They're twins."

"You can see the likeness," said Louise, staring at them intently.

Amelia sat back to assess the impressive collection and consulted her notes. "From what I discovered this afternoon, Penny and Daniel definitely had four children: Noah, Blaise, Solomon and Thomasina." She pointed to the pictures as she counted off the names. "But, there's also the other girl."

"The one from the photograph of the house," asked Louise.

"Exactly, who is called Eudora," said Amelia. "This is where it gets peculiar. Eudora only appears in the photograph of the house, and while I've found a few documents relating to the Attwaters and their boat business here in Windsor, there aren't many references to Eudora. The only place I've found her was in the census entries. However, there are three more images of Osyth, grown-up and when she was a little girl."

"Strange name," said Richie. "Even odder than Xenia."

"It was the name of a seventh-century saint," said Amelia. "I looked it up online. Her day is 7 October, and you should pray to her for protection of hearth and home. Last thing before bed, rake the ashes in the grate and mark them with a cross, then offer a prayer for protection from 'fire, water and all other

calamities' which is supposed to protect you for the coming year."

"Fancy," said Louise. Doug and Benji laughed.

Amelia placed the three images of Osyth side by side: one of her as a child, aged about three; another as a teenager in a formal pose; then one with a dark-haired man in a more casual pose with her hair tumbling around her shoulders. The clothes were unusual, she wore a dress of stripes and patterns, low on her shoulders, while her companion wore loose black trousers tucked into boots and a flowing white shirt.

"They look as though they're in costume," said Richie.

"She's pretty, isn't she?" said Louise after studying the image for a few minutes. "She reminds me… It doesn't matter."

Amelia understood why her friend had stopped herself before finishing the sentence. "Molly?" she asked.

"Yes, it's her smile. Sorry, Aimes."

"You know what we agreed, we would always talk about Molly. I'd rather she was remembered in our conversations every day than her becoming a taboo subject. I won't break."

Louise gave Amelia a one-armed hug, then returned to the photographs on the table. "So, where's Eudora and who's the creepy kid in the window?" she said. "None of these could be him because they all have fair hair and that kid had dark curly hair."

Amelia opened her laptop and logged into the genealogy website she had joined. "I've done some research into the Attwater boatyard, too," she said, bringing up the pages for them to read. "It was originally the property of the Stone family but in 1850 it became the Attwater and Stone Boatyard, then eventually Stone was dropped from the name and it was Attwater and Sons, which is what the guide on the boat said

this afternoon. It seemed the Jacobs family and the Attwater family married and the Jacobs name disappeared, too."

Richie topped up their glasses, Amelia noticed the quick glance he gave Louise. None of them had mentioned the fact she was not drinking. They had all been here before and it had become an unspoken bond between them — "Wait and see," Louise always said, with her fingers crossed.

"I checked the census records too," said Amelia. "In the 1861 census, I found Penelope Attwater, aged 34, which makes her estimated birth year, 1827 and she was born here in Clewer."

"Really?" said Louise. "Who else was living in the house?"

"They're in alphabetical order: Blaise Attwater, age eight; Daniel Attwater, age 37; Eudora Attwater, age 12; Noah Attwater, age 14; Penelope Attwater, age 34; Solomon Attwater, age six; Thomasina Attwater, age six; Matthew Isaac Stone, age 34." Pulling her hand-drawn family tree towards her, Amelia checked the names. "All the children, including Eudora."

"Who's Matthew Isaac Stone?" asked Benji.

"No idea. I didn't get much further than this," Amelia said, clicking on to the scanned image of the census page, enlarging it so they could read the details.

"Look," said Louise, "Matthew Stone is listed as 'brother-in-law' in relation to the head of the house."

"Would he be Penny's twin brother?" Amelia asked, after working the dates out. "Look at their ages."

"He could be. He's listed as a 'visitor'. He must have been staying with them," Louise said. "It says Daniel Attwater was a boat builder and proprietor employing eighteen men."

"Check the 1871 census," said Doug, his face eager.

Amelia clicked through several pages. "I can't find it," she muttered in frustration, then a thought struck her. "Maybe I should change the location. I'm going to add Cliffside and Pembrokeshire to the search." A moment later, she let out a yell of delight. "They're here," she said, opening the page.

"Who's living there?" Louise asked.

"Daniel Attwater, Penelope Attwater, Blaise, Solomon, Thomasina, Osyth — she's listed as 'granddaughter' to the head of the house." Amelia paused as she considered this. "Then who are these people: Katherine Stone and Kieran Stone — niece and nephew. They were all living at Cliffside in 1871, but where are Noah and Eudora? Or Katherine and Kieran's parents? They must have been Matthew Stone's children but where are he or their mother?"

"Let's concentrate on one thing at a time," said Richie, who was making his own notes. "I helped my dad with our family history and once you start searching through genealogy records you can get lost down a rabbit hole. Should we leave the Stones for the moment and concentrate on Noah and Eudora?"

"Good plan," said Amelia as she entered another search, hoping to locate the missing family members.

"Here's Noah. He's in Windsor working at the boatyard for his dad," said Louise.

"So, where's Eudora? Do you think she was married?"

"Probably," said Richie. "Sometimes connected names pop up…"

However, after a thorough search, nothing appeared.

"There is another possibility," said Amelia, "but this is a bit sadder. Perhaps the reason Osyth is with her grandparents is because her mother died?"

"Do you think Eudora's her mother then?" asked Louise.

"I assumed she was, but it would mean she was only sixteen when she gave birth."

"It would seem the most logical conclusion," Richie replied, "especially as in your photograph, Eudora is holding the baby."

"I'll search the death records," said Amelia, but again they drew a blank on Eudora Attwater. "After her appearance in the 1861 census, there seems to be no other mention of her."

Doug glanced at his watch. "Sorry to break up the party, my loves, but we need to head home…" he began but Benji interrupted him.

"Aimes, why don't you search for the house, rather than the people? It sometimes throws up new documents. It's a trick we use sometimes to clear through data online when we're trying to track people down for shows."

Amelia typed in the name: Cliffside, Pembrokeshire, and pressed search. "I don't understand," she muttered.

"Aimes, what's the matter?" asked Louise.

"Look," said Amelia. "It's a website for a retreat in Pembrokeshire called Cliffside. Look at the picture."

They all stared at the screen, incredulous. The holding shot of the website displayed two images of Cliffside, a colour picture of its present-day self and beside this, the Victorian image Amelia had discovered in the box.

Amelia pushed the laptop away. "How can I have the same photograph?"

CHAPTER FOUR

Amelia sat in the waiting room of the solicitor's office, studying a portrait of a short man with sparse grey hair and a benign expression. He wore an extravagant crimson waistcoat under his long frock coat, giving an air of eccentricity to the otherwise sombre painting. The plaque underneath read: *'Ernest Lovegrove'*. The company was called Lovegrove and Durant, and Julian Lovegrove, with whom Amelia had her appointment, was the fourth generation of Lovegroves to offer legal services. Julian had been a boyhood friend of her father. Amelia had grown up knowing him, his wife, Lily, and their three sons. He had attended all the recent family funerals in his capacity as friend rather than legal representative.

"Amelia, my dear," he said as she entered his thick-carpeted, wood-panelled office, "how are you?" He came out from behind his desk and hugged her. "You must miss them all terribly."

Amelia sat in the chair opposite Julian's desk and nodded. "The house is very quiet," she said, determined not to let her voice waver, despite the constriction of her throat.

"Please know you're welcome at our house anytime," he said, and she felt tears prick her eyes.

Noticing this and to allow her a moment to gather herself, Julian sorted through the folders on the desk. Amelia was grateful for his consideration and took several deep breaths to calm herself, watching as Julian's face changed subtlety as he moved into his professional mode.

"Now, you probably know the contents of the will," he said, his tone gentle but business-like. "However, there is one

35

codicil which I believe your mother never mentioned. When Joan's mother, Susannah Cowper died, she left your mother a row of nine cottages…"

"Cottages?" interrupted Amelia. "Where? Mum never said anything about cottages."

"There is a strange covenant that comes with them," said Julian, digging out another sheet of paper and passing it to Amelia. She glanced at it, but it was dense with legal terminology and she instead looked up at Julian for an explanation. "For some reason, the owner is not allowed to tell their heir of the existence of this legacy. I believe the intention was so that whoever was in possession of them could do with them as they pleased without recourse to spouses, siblings, or other family members. When the covenant was written, it was more problematic for women to have autonomy over their inheritances, so the secrecy clause was introduced."

Amelia stared at him in amazement.

"It's not something I've ever come across before," Julian continued, "and I'm not sure, if it had been tested in a court of law, whether it would have been legally binding, but it was never challenged." He smiled at her. "Hopefully it's a pleasant surprise. During the course of her lifetime, your mother sold two of the cottages but seven remain and these are now yours. You inherit them with tenants but, next year, they will reach the end of their tenancy agreements and you may do with the cottages as you wish. They garnered your mother a very healthy income. Your mother sold one cottage when she was pregnant with you as she wished to renovate your house, Maybank, and the other…" He hesitated.

"The other?" prompted Amelia.

"The other cottage she sold was the one you and Molly lived in, briefly. The property had become empty and your mother

had always planned to sell it but as you chose that moment to move back to Windsor while trying to retain your independence, she had the cottage decorated and made it available for you. Did you never wonder how your mother was able to find you a place to live so quickly or why the rent was so low?"

Amelia stared at him in astonishment. Her priority had been Molly, and when her mother had said she knew a cottage to rent only a few roads away from their home, Amelia had not questioned it.

"It was a few months later, when it became clear you needed their help, that your parents insisted you and Molly move in with them. Your mother put the cottage on the market and it sold within three days. A cash buyer."

"So that's where the money came from," sighed Amelia. "I'd had to resign from my job, but I was so worried about money, especially as we had to buy a bigger car to transport Molly and her wheelchair. Mum said she'd cashed in some Premium Bonds and sold a few things." Tears sprang to Amelia's eyes as she remembered. "When I tried to refuse her help, Mum said it was a forward payment on my inheritance. I was in such a state, I didn't really think it through. It was a relief to have one less thing to worry about."

Julian gave a sad smile. "Your mother was a remarkable woman," he said. "She retained the deeds to the cottages — apparently she planned to tell you where they were stored. However, we do have copies, should you need them."

Amelia barely listened as Julian read through the remainder of the short will, assuring her all the small personal bequests would be dealt with by his office as they were executors. Suddenly, her mother's request to sort out the already spotless attic made sense. No doubt the deeds to the cottages were in

the boxes. Aware he was winding up their meeting, another thought occurred to her.

"Do you know anything about a house called Cliffside in Pembrokeshire?" she asked. "Or a family called Attwater?"

Julian looked at her blankly. "No, I'm afraid not," he replied. "Not in connection with Patrick and Joan; however, I believe from one of the meetings of the local history society the Attwaters once owned the paddle steamers and pleasure boats on the river near Jacob's Island. They sold up long ago to the family who owns them now. Some of the boats are originals, dating from the days of the Attwaters but as far as I know, there's no connection to your family."

Amelia had not expected him to have any further information but she felt a twinge of disappointment, nevertheless.

Julian continued to explain the details of bequests until, eventually, the meeting came to an end.

"Thank you," said Amelia, as Julian closed all the folders and gave her an avuncular smile.

"My pleasure, my dear," Julian replied, "and really, Amelia, if there's anything I can do, either professionally or as one of your father's oldest friends, please ring me."

"Is this why you wanted me to go through the boxes in the attic, Mum?" Amelia asked her mother's smiling photograph as she marched into the dining room. From somewhere outside the wind chime sang, breaking the silence of the house with its joyful tunes and Amelia felt a sense of calm. "Well, Mum," she continued, "you promised you'd send me a sign if you could. How about giving me a clue as to which of these boxes you specifically wanted me to explore? Is it the deeds you want to show me, or something else?"

She was aware her behaviour was bordering on the irrational, but she did not care — her mother's illness had been prolonged and it had given them time to discuss the future, but never at any point had Joan hinted that she was leaving Amelia such a profitable legacy. The figures Julian had given her to peruse had astounded her and she realised she was in the enviable position of having a healthy private income. The fact that she owned Maybank, as well as the cottages, meant her overheads were low and her income sizeable. The shock of this unexpected good fortune was beginning to sink in. Amelia was convinced this was the reason her mother had been insistent on her clearing out the boxes in the otherwise spotlessly tidy attic.

Amelia placed her hand on the first box, looking up at the photograph again. "Well?" she questioned.

Walking from box to box, she did the same with each and was greeted, as she had expected, with silence, but as she placed her hand on the final container, the squattest and heaviest of the boxes, the sound of the wind chime rang out, sending an unexpected chill down her spine.

"You're kidding me," she muttered, pulling her hand away as though the box had burnt her. With great care, she replaced her hand, and the gentle notes of the wind chime filled the room. "OK, Mum, this one it is."

As she sliced through the brown parcel tape, dust filled the air, making her sneeze. Reaching inside, she pulled out a series of old-fashioned book-keeping ledgers bound in burgundy leather dating from 1830 to 1845, then another set bound in navy blue from 1860 to 1895. Even though she was intrigued, a wave of fear at what she might discover washed through her. Shaking her head, trying to dislodge this unexpected feeling,

she placed the ledgers on the dining room table and opened the first book.

Written in elaborate, copperplate handwriting were the words: *Accounts and rents for Attwater Cottages, Clewer Within, Old Windsor, Berkshire.*

"No!" gasped Amelia. "Attwater Cottages."

Flicking through the meticulous accounts, she ran her finger down the list of names of the tenants, their occupations, and the rents they had once paid. Nothing obvious stood out and as she examined them, each book followed the same pattern.

After checking a few, she put them to one side, returning to the remaining contents of the box. There was a series of neatly folded documents, each one bound with a faded ribbon of the type she had seen on wills and other legal documents. Opening the first one, she saw it was a deed to *Number One: Attwater Cottages.* Others followed, which she laid out on the table beside the account books. Then a thought struck her, and she lifted out the final pile of paperwork and books. *Were there any details about Cliffside?* Penny Attwater had been photographed outside Cliffside and the cottages were known as Attwater Cottages. The name Attwater seemed to be haunting her: did she have a connection to them? And, if she did, what was their connection to Cliffside?

Opening all the loose sheets of paper she found a myriad of bills, letters, general paperwork but no more deeds and nothing pertaining to Cliffside.

"Damn," she muttered.

Keying 'Cliffside' into a search engine, the website she had discovered the previous evening popped up and she began scrolling through it, hunting for more information.

"*Cliffside Retreat is based in the family home of Dr Edward Stone,*" she read. "*Built by George Stone, boatyard proprietor, and his wife,*

Eleanor, in 1832, the property has been passed down through successive generations. Opening as a retreat two years ago, the emphasis is on the feeling of a home-from-home."

Reading on, she was disappointed to see there was a biography of Edward Stone but no picture. However, further down, another photograph appeared, old and Victorian. A man with dark curly hair stared into the lens. He was leaning on a half column and held a sextant, and seated beside him was a small woman with dark hair and liquid eyes that seemed almost black in the ancient photograph. She held a bible on her lap. The caption read: *Matthew and Georgina Stone, 1863, at Cliffside.*

Amelia pulled back from the screen in surprise, knocking the pile of paper onto the floor. "Matthew Stone?" she muttered. "Penny Attwater's twin brother."

She stared at the screen for several minutes, studying Matthew's high-cheekboned face and wide generous mouth. He seemed to be struggling to keep to the serious expression required by the Victorian photographer. Georgina, however, looked haunted, her eyes glaring towards the camera, her body taut, as though, given the opportunity, she would flee.

Bending down to gather the documents she had knocked on the floor in her surprise, her fingers grazed against a hardback book, lost in the pile of papers. Pulling it out, Amelia felt herself shiver as once again the breeze blew her neighbour's wind chime and the room was filled with its melodious tune. The notebook was leather-bound and well-preserved. Amelia opened it.

In neat, violet letters were the words: *"These are the thoughts and dreams of Osyth Attwater, 1883"*, and underneath was a delicate pen and ink line drawing of a wind chime.

Amelia turned the pages and began to read.

PART TWO: PEMBROKESHIRE, 1883

CHAPTER ONE

The tale to be told began with love. A simple act, yet one carrying such magnitude it had the power to create a life as easily as it could destroy. The child, a daughter, did not ask to be born...

"Osyth, where are you?"

Osyth glanced over at her friend, Angharad Williams, who was curled in an armchair staring out over the crashing waves of St Brides Bay below. She did not respond to her grandmother's voice. After a moment of listening to see if footsteps would follow the call, she returned her concentration to the inkwell, dipping in her pen.

Cradled in the arms of her young mother she knew her fate. Her eyes, the deep green of a polished emerald were wise, belonging to an older soul, a life already lived. She understood her mother acted with love; she knew one day they would meet again...

"Osyth!" came the call again.

"You should answer," said Angharad.

"In a moment, I must finish this sentence..."

"Osyth, listen, the wind has changed direction." Her grandmother's voice floated up the winding staircase that led to the tower room above Osyth's bedroom. "Listen, Osyth."

This time the words hit their mark and Osyth felt the breath catch in her throat. "At last," she breathed.

Her heart beating with excitement, she ran down the narrow staircase to her bedroom below, Angharad scurrying behind her. Flinging aside the white linen curtains, Osyth struggled

with the sea-swollen wooden frames, forcing open the salt-stained glass to lean out and listen. Her eyes screwed shut against the roar of the wind and sea and she held her breath as the wind blew again. Above the call of the wild elements, she heard it, the fairy-like jingle of the wind chime on the veranda. Its tone was no longer discordant as it had been during the rattling chaos of the winter storms — this gust created a tune that was as harmonious as it was delicate. Every year it began this way, the signal they would all gather. It was a promise fulfilled, another spring blowing in on the tide.

"Did you hear it?" she asked Angharad who had joined her at the window.

"I heard the usual chiming," her friend replied, "but I never hear this change you speak about. Are you sure you aren't making it up?"

Osyth laughed. "No, of course not," she said, pulling the window shut. "Nain and Taid hear it too. So does Uncle Noah. In fact, he claims to hear it even if he's hundreds of miles away in Windsor."

Angharad looked sceptical. "Your grandfather will be calling you soon," she said straightening her skirt. "You'll need to leave for the station."

"Are you coming too?" asked Osyth.

"No, I have to help Mam. There's so much to do what with the rest of your family arriving and then the wedding in a few weeks."

The girls exchanged an excited look.

"It's hard to believe Katherine will be a married woman," sighed Osyth. "She's only a few years older than us but she'll have a home of her own and a husband."

It was a topic the girls had discussed at length, awed by this new turn of events. Osyth had been astounded when six

months earlier her cousin, Katherine, the closest to her in age in their vast and sprawling family, had shyly announced her engagement. The shock waves had reverberated through their kin for some weeks until the unexpected news had settled into everyone's mind and they had adjusted to the idea that Katherine would be leaving them.

"It's so romantic," Osyth sighed.

"Like a fairy tale," Angharad replied breathily, before allowing her practical nature to assert itself as the midday clanging of the grandfather clock echoed through the house. "You need to get ready, Osyth, and I must go downstairs." She walked over to Osyth's triple-aspect mirror on her new dressing table and checked her appearance.

"You look perfect," Osyth assured her, joining her friend by the mirror. The girls were of a similar height and slim build but Angharad had glossy straight brown hair and hazel eyes, while Osyth's was a storm of dark red curls winding around her head in diverse directions. "I, on the other hand, need to do something with my hair."

"Sit down, I'll do it," laughed Angharad.

Osyth grinned. If it was left to her, she would plait her hair down her back and leave it at that but as a young lady approaching her eighteenth birthday, she knew this style would be frowned upon, especially by her Aunt Xenia who was the height of fashion. Sitting down on the padded stool in front of her dressing table, she winced as Angharad began to brush her hair.

The spring sunshine streamed in through the five windows in Osyth's unusual bedroom as they chatted. Ever since childhood, she had loved her octagonal tower bedroom. Three large windows looked out across the majesty of St Brides Bay and the Celtic Sea, while two tall, narrow windows were

situated opposite each other on the panels of the tower closest to the house. One looked over the courtyard below while the other offered glimpses of the wood that spread out behind the house.

"Is that Kieran?" asked Angharad, as she pushed the last hairpin into the neat bun now nestling at the nape of Osyth's neck.

They squashed together, peering out of the window, watching as the slim figure of Osyth's cousin, Kieran Stone, emerged from the shadows of the trees.

"He was in the wood," said Angharad.

Osyth sighed and returned to the dressing table where she began putting away the remaining hair accessories. "The standing stones have called him," she said, and Angharad laughed.

"The standing stones?"

"Whenever Kieran is upset, he goes to the stones," Osyth explained. "We all have a place where we feel safe, where we can think and, for Kieran, it's the stones in the wood. They listen to him. For me, it's the cave on the beach where there's a fairy ring of shells on the wall. You prefer the dell by the kissing gate, where the beech tree stands and the roots are like a chair."

Angharad shook her head in mock despair. "Nonsense," she replied, her eyes twinkling. "I suspect he was in the wood because he has a surprise planned for Katherine."

"What surprise?"

"If Kieran hasn't told you, then I can't," she said and with a grin, she hurried from the room leaving Osyth wide-eyed but amused.

Osyth padded across the room to the narrow doorway that led up a short flight of steps into the attic space above her

bedroom. She had recently adopted this space as her private place to write. It had been her Uncle Blaise's idea — he had carried the table and chair up here, while Aunt Xenia had provided cushions and a pretty lamp. Blaise had also brought two other chairs and her grandmother had supplied blankets, so her friends could join her in comfort. The most important thing, however, was her portable writing desk, a gift from her Uncle Solomon, which sat in the centre of the table surrounded by her pen, ink and journal, another gift from Solomon. The attic had three round port-hole style windows and when the wind blew, Osyth liked to imagine she was on board a ship. Stowing her writing tools in the drawer, she was closing the glossy wooden top when another voice called up the stairs.

"Granddaughter, where are you?"

"Here, Taid," she called, using the affectionate Welsh term for her grandfather, Daniel Attwater.

"Did you hear it?" he asked as she hurried down the stairs towards him.

Tall and broad, Daniel Attwater was an imposing figure. Standing at over six feet tall and with thick blond hair, now sprinkled with grey, his understated but expensive clothes marked him as a successful man. In his late fifties, he looked younger thanks to the fitness he had gained after a lifetime spent working in the timber and boatyards that he had inherited from his father. His love of sailing had weathered his skin, causing his eyes to shine even more noticeably green in his tanned skin. Yet, despite the tailored jacket, the elegant white shirt, tucked into fitted black trousers and ox-blood-red riding boots that had been polished to a glossy sheen, there was a restlessness about him, a wildness that seemed to

shimmer as he smiled, his sparkling eyes as full of excitement as Osyth's.

"Yes, Taid," she exclaimed, "the wind chime has never been wrong. The chimes are singing their song of spring. It's the perfect omen!"

He opened his arms wide and she threw herself into them as she had been doing since she was a child, laughing as he lifted her off her feet, spinning her around, her legs flying high, until they were both dizzy.

"You're almost too tall for me to do that now," he said, lowering her with great care and steadying her before he removed his arms.

"I shall be eighteen years old next month," she reminded him. "A young lady, perhaps too old for such childish games."

Daniel laughed. "Never," he declared. "I still do the same to your grandmother and your Aunt Xenia."

"You would never dare," she laughed.

"What are you writing?" he enquired, casting a quick glance towards the staircase.

"A journal," she replied, her tone casual, "capturing the soul of this house, this family, myself." She struck a dramatic pose, reclining against the windowsill, laughter bubbling in her throat.

"You plan to rival your Uncle Solomon?" he asked, one eyebrow raised in amusement. "Will you send it to his periodical?"

"No Taid, it's not grand enough for Uncle Solomon to read," she replied. "It's my thoughts and, probably, it will remain for my contemplation alone."

"You come from a family of storytellers, Osyth," replied her grandfather. "Perhaps you will outshine us all."

Osyth shrugged. Even though she loved her grandfather, she was not prepared to share her secret dream of being a published author with him. Not yet, anyway. The only two people in whom she had confided were her best friend, Angharad, and her cousin, Kieran. The three of them had grown up together and there was a strong bond between them, something which this summer seemed to have intensified. It would be their last summer together — when the autumn winds blew in, they would be leaving their childhoods and the safety of the house on the cliff, the place where they had been free to cross class barriers and be friends.

Ever since their youth, they had sought each other, finding places to hide, to whisper and to plot. In the room under the house known as the cave; in the old chapel in the woods; in the sea cave; or in their endless complicated dens, built from branches and seaweed. More recently, they would huddle under the blankets in her attic talking about their plans for the future: for Osyth, an adventure which could inspire her to write a novel like those she admired by Ellen Wood, Ann Radcliffe, Rhoda Broughton, or Elizabeth Gaskell. Kieran wanted to be a doctor, an ambition that was soon to be fulfilled as he would begin his studies in September, while Angharad, aware of her status as the daughter of the housekeeper and the chief steward had declared she wished to make a good marriage and then, when she had status in her own right, she would fight for the rights of all women — rich or poor. It was an ambition that had made Osyth admire her friend even more.

"Angharad, you're so clever," she would often say to her friend, awed by her maturity, even though Angharad was only two months older than her. "I wish I had your courage and fortitude."

Angharad would blush but Osyth could see she was delighted by the compliment. It pained Osyth to think these days were numbered, even if part of her was secretly thrilled she would soon be entering the new and exciting world of adulthood.

"Well," said Daniel, bringing Osyth back to the present, "your forays into the world of literature will have to cease for the day." He consulted his pocket watch. "Are you aware of the time? Or would you rather remain here?"

"Remain here?" She was scandalised. "All I have to do is slip on my riding jacket and lace up my boots, then I'm ready to accompany you to the station."

"And you wouldn't rather ride in the carriage with your grandmother and Katherine?"

"There would be no room for my aunts," she replied. "I'd rather ride with you and Uncle Blaise on the horses. Bluebell is sure to have been saddled, she would be disappointed to be left at home."

"Very well, you and Bluebell shall ride with us, while the other ladies take the carriage. Although, I doubt any of them would be amused to know that you have referred to them collectively as 'The Aunts'. It makes them sound like old ladies."

Osyth grinned. "Then we mustn't tell them. Aunt Xenia will be furious if we don't take her horse, Cherry — she'll want to ride back with us along the cliffs."

"Thomasina is a married woman with twin sons — would it be correct for her to behave in such a manner?" asked Daniel in a mock-serious tone, using his youngest daughter's full name.

"Perhaps Thomasina Pettifer, the wife of the respectable timber merchant Mr William Pettifer might not, but Xenia

Attwater, child of Cliffside and the Pembrokeshire coast, definitely would."

"Unfortunately, until she arrives here, throws off her bonnet and shakes out her hair, she will be travelling in disguise as Mrs William Pettifer. Now, if we plan to meet the train, you must fetch your boots. Your grandmother has already called for the carriage — she's so excited to see everyone."

He replaced his watch in his pocket and hurried from the room. Osyth could hear him calling to her grandmother as he descended her tower stairs.

The tradition of the family returning to the house on the cliff every spring had been one that had marked the passage of Osyth's life. Every year, her many aunts and uncles, with her increasing number of cousins, flooded into Cliffside for a spring and summer of sunshine walks, midnight swims and tales told on the veranda under the watch of the wind chime. The family saw this as their guardian, a lucky charm drawing them home every spring. It had been hung in its place as sentinel by Osyth's great-grandmother, Eleanor Stone, and her Uncle Noah claimed he could hear it no matter where he was in the world.

This year, however, things would be different. Not only would they be celebrating a family wedding but, when the autumn breeze made the wind chime sing its note of warning that another year had turned, Osyth would be returning with her grandparents to the family's other home in Windsor to widen her social life and allow her to explore new avenues. Osyth knew this meant it was time to grow up, and part of her new life would be the tantalising and terrifying thought of finding a husband. Most of her life had been spent in Cliffside and the thought of her new adventure was both exhilarating and daunting.

But first, we have a wedding to enjoy.

Bending to lace up her sturdy riding boots, she became aware of the shadow.

"You may come in, Kieran," she called to her cousin and he entered on silent feet.

Four years older than Osyth, Kieran Stone was tall and angular. His raven hair was worn long to his collar and his brown eyes were so dark that his pupils were almost indistinguishable from the irises. His hair and eyes were thrown into stark relief by skin of such alabaster paleness it was almost luminous.

Osyth smiled up at him from where she was perched on her chair, lacing up her riding boots. "The wind chime has rung in the spring; it will be a beautiful ride to Neyland to meet the train."

"The wind chime sounds no different today than it does any other day," he said, laughing. "It's a clanging, rattling nuisance and one day I will throw it into the sea."

"Oh Kieran, you spoilsport," she replied. "It's a family tradition; we always hear the tune change around now."

"Your family."

"*Our* family," she replied, pulling on her riding jacket and sliding the mother-of-pearl buttons into their silken loops. "Will you be joining us?"

"No, Angharad has said she will help me put up some surprise decorations for the bride-to-be."

"How thoughtful. Was it your idea?"

"Yes, I thought of it this morning," he said, following her down the winding staircase that took them to the rest of the house.

"Would you like me to stay, too?" asked Osyth, torn between the thought of racing across the cliffs with her grandfather and uncle or staying here with her friends.

"We need you to ensure Katherine is distracted," he said. "It's an important task and you're the best person for the job."

They had reached the hallway; the large front doors were open, and the coach was waiting on the drive.

"It's a wonderful gesture," said Osyth, staring up at her cousin. "I didn't think you approved of this marriage."

Kieran looked uncomfortable, scuffing the intricately patterned carpet with his shoe, a pink tinge staining his pale face. "I didn't — I don't," he sighed. "Honestly, I don't know. Katherine is happy but it feels wrong to me. My feelings are unimportant, though. She is my sister and we only have each other, and this is my gesture of apology after our row the other day."

"Oh Kieran," said Osyth, reaching out to give him a quick hug, releasing him and stepping back, aware of his dislike of physical contact.

"Thank you," he said, his voice low. "Now, you must hurry — you don't want to be late meeting the train." He gave her a sharp bow from the neck, then turned on his heel and vanished.

Osyth sighed. *Poor Kieran*, she thought, *he really is a strange creature. How could anyone be unhappy about this marriage?* From outside she heard her grandfather calling her name, urging her to hurry. Grabbing her bonnet, she dashed towards the stables.

CHAPTER TWO

Laughter filled the house. Its rooms overflowed with people. The family was home, spilling from every corner; they were together again, and this year Katherine's wedding was driving the levels of excitement even higher. As the weather displayed its gamut of moods, from lashing rain and stormy seas to blistering heat and flat waves that barely had the energy to ebb and flow across the sand, the family members shed their sensible city selves and relaxed beneath the tunes of the wind chime.

When George Stone had built the house on the cliff, his wife, Eleanor, had hung up the wind chime, a trinket from a friend who had recently returned from India. One summer, Eleanor and her young daughter, Penny, had strung together strands of coral beads from a broken necklace that had once belonged to Eleanor's mother along with shells from St Brides Bay, enhancing the beauty of the object and encouraging its chimes. In return, they imagined it cast a spell of protection over the family. So began the tradition of gathering in the evening and telling each other stories.

A week after the family had arrived, Osyth followed them through the French doors on to the veranda with its carved gingerbread edging, full of excitement for her favourite part of the evening. Curling up in a chair under the wind chime, swathed in a soft woollen blanket, she snuggled down, full of anticipation. The party had begun with her grandmother announcing there would not be a formal dinner as the kitchen staff were too busy preparing for the wedding. Instead, it would be an indoor picnic. With the family serving and

clearing, Osyth and Angharad had taken it upon themselves to pour the drinks, although once the family had assembled to eat, Osyth's friend had melted away, disappearing to the kitchen.

Now, as Osyth watched her family settling themselves under the glow of the magnificent sunset, she wondered again about her friendship with Angharad. When she travelled to Windsor, Angharad would go with them as her companion. It had been her grandmother's suggestion and, although the two girls were delighted they would continue to be together, Osyth felt uncomfortable that her friend would be paid to be in her company.

As the chatter around her ebbed and stilled, Osyth pushed her misgivings from her mind and turned her attention to her family. Everyone was seated around the brazier, lit by her grandfather as protection against the chill of the sea air. They were sprawled on cushions and perched on chairs: Blaise and Katherine in the centre. Besides Blaise was his elder brother, Noah, with his wife, Hannah, cradling their youngest child, George, in her arms. The twins, Xenia and Solomon, their matching golden hair glinting in the dying rays of the setting sun were huddled together under a blanket, anticipating the chilly breeze from the ocean as the sun withdrew its fading embers. Xenia's husband William sat beside Daniel. Their twin sons, Caleb and James were asleep upstairs with Noah's children and Solomon's brood. Meanwhile, Solomon's wife, Marianne, lounged on a chaise, her pregnancy in its late stage evident under the exotic flowing robe Solomon had bought her on his last trip to India.

In prime position, nearest the brazier, sat Penny Attwater. Osyth's eyes drifted to her grandmother, admiring Penny's beauty, her fierce storm of red hair only gently marred by time.

There are so many of us, thought Osyth, *yet people are missing too.*

From her position in the corner near the house, she could see the only fault in their beloved wind chime. On one of the delicate strands of coral shells which hung between the silver chimes, a shell was missing. Osyth's eyes went from shell to shell as they all climbed together to meet at the top where the enamelled image of a sun reminded them to bless each sunrise and sunset, pausing when they found the gap. Closing her eyes, she whispered, "Mother, there are stories tonight, I wish you could hear them, too."

Many years ago, her grandfather had explained this shell had been taken by her mother, Eudora. "She loved the wind chime," he had explained. "This shell went with her. It was her promise to return to us one day."

"But she can't return," Osyth had murmured.

"I see my daughter every day," Daniel had said, hugging his granddaughter. "I see her in you, my darling."

The words came back to her and she wiped away a tear. Her mother, Eudora, had been gone from the family for so many years. She had missed seeing her siblings married, her nieces and nephews born, and her daughter grow up. It was at moments such as this that Osyth most missed her mother. Eudora's hair had been as wild and red as a sunset, a family trait she had passed to Osyth. Loved and loveable, was how Osyth's Uncle Noah had once described her.

Loved, loveable and lost to me forever, thought Osyth. Her mother's portrait hung in the Summer Drawing Room, painted when Eudora was sixteen years old. It captured a young woman full of life and laughter. Osyth found it hard to believe that less than a year later, her mother had died.

Katherine's laughter brought her back to the moment. Her cousin was alight with happiness, while Kieran hovered on the

edges. His chair was pushed back into the shadows but his eyes never left his sister, a bleakness on his pale face, as he watched her every move. Osyth had suggested he sit beside her but he had declined and she understood. Kieran was shy — he did not cope well in the hurly-burly of family gatherings, preferring to observe.

He and Katherine were the children of Penny's twin brother Matthew, who had died some years ago. Kieran and Katherine had been staying at Cliffside when it happened. With their mother, Georgina, already dead, they were now orphans, but Penny and Daniel had stepped in to look after them. Katherine had run into their open arms but Kieran had always been reticent.

"I have a special tale for Osyth," Noah's voice cut through her thoughts. "The Fae-folk invited me to their winter feast in their magical kingdom of Tylwyth Teg," he said, and a cheer erupted from the family. "For three days and nights I danced and drank and ate and sang in fairyland. I played tunes for the king, I danced with the princesses and I told them tales of Cliffside. They wanted to meet us all."

Laughter reverberated around the veranda.

"No doubt you spoke at length with the king?" Osyth suggested, her voice bubbling with amusement.

This was a tale Noah had been telling her since childhood, in those days her soul had drunk it in, believing each word as it had dropped jewel-like from his wide, smiling mouth. Despite the years separating them, there had always been a strong friendship between Osyth and Noah. An understanding, unspoken but potent in its promise: one day she would turn to him and he would help her. For now, he was content to tell her folk tales.

"I have a message from the Fae-folk for Osyth," he said, as the family gave their customary gasp before allowing a hushed silence to fall over the veranda, even the waves held their breath, climbing across the rocks, fighting the ebb of the tide to hear the message Noah was about to deliver. "When you have found the Dream Catcher the Fae-king has promised he will give you the answer to your question."

Osyth stared at Noah, her eyes wide. "And the king of the fairies himself told you this, did he?"

"The Fae-king, himself," Noah declared; then a harsh and furious voice cut through the relaxed atmosphere.

"When are you going to stop telling this stupid tale?" Kieran snapped from his shadowy hiding place. "There are no such things as Fae-folk. These are tales for children. You're a grown man, Noah, how can you tell such lies?"

The smile vanished from Noah's face but he did not respond, instead he shot his father a quizzical glance. Osyth watched as a look of understanding passed between them, before her eyes were drawn back to Kieran. He had pushed his way to the centre of the veranda, his face furious. Daniel stepped forward, placing a gentle hand on his nephew's arm, but Kieran threw it off.

"Enough, Kieran," Daniel spoke softly, "this is your sister's time, you know how she enjoys Noah's tales…"

"But they are lies," Kieran exploded, his voice a high-pitched eldritch screech. The spittle flying from his mouth with the force of his words crested in an arc like sea spray caught in the breeze. "He is a liar. A deceitful charlatan — but what can you expect from the spawn of an adulterous marriage between a lunatic and a scoundrel?" He spat at Noah's feet.

Osyth was not the only person who gasped, "Kieran, no!"

Katherine was on her feet.

"You're no better," he snarled turning on her, his hands reaching out claw-like towards her, "selling yourself into marriage, bewitched by our aunt, taking your inheritance and handing it to her..."

"Is that what you think?" his sister gasped, reaching out, her hand replacing Daniel's on her brother's arm.

Osyth winced, sure Kieran would throw off his sister's entreaties as he had dismissed his uncle's, but Katherine's touch seemed to bring Kieran to his senses, and for a moment, he hesitated. The words he had been about to fling into the night air seemed to freeze on his tongue and then he looked down into his sister's pleading blue eyes. For a moment he gazed at her in confusion, then his face cleared and a faint blush tinged his skin.

"Katherine," he said, his breath coming quickly as though he had been running, "I'm sorry. I'm sorry, sir," he said, turning to Daniel and giving him one of his sharp bows. "Aunt Penny, forgive me, please, my head, the pain is very bad this evening. I lost myself for a moment. Please excuse me, I must retire." Stumbling, he turned from the veranda, disappearing into the house.

"I'll go," said Solomon, extricating himself from under the blanket. "I'll see him safely to bed."

The silence was broken by a sudden breeze ruffling the wind chime, breaking the spell of Kieran's outburst; then there was a sob and they all turned to Katherine.

"Is that what people will think?" she asked, taking Blaise's hand and turning him to look at her. "We're cousins, Blaise. Will people be scandalised by our marriage?"

"Do we care if they are?" he asked, his face awash with love. "We love each other. We know the truth."

"But will it be enough?" she sobbed.

"Of course, it will," he replied. "Look at the scandal Mother and Father's marriage caused but they are respected now. People understood it was love. We will be the same, people will soon see our feelings are real."

Daniel seated himself beside Penny, their hands entwined.

"You haven't changed your mind, have you?" Blaise asked, his voice losing some of its confidence.

"No," Katherine replied, "but Kieran's words feel like a curse."

"There is no curse," Blaise replied, "there is only our love."

"Yes," she replied, "our love."

An uneasy silence settled around them, broken by Penny.

"We should retire," she said. "It's been a long day and we have much to do tomorrow. With luck, Kieran will be restored by a good night's sleep. We have all witnessed these turns of his before and he usually has no recollection of them the following day."

"Conveniently," muttered Noah to his sister Xenia, both of whom exchanged a frustrated look.

Penny ignored Noah's comment and stood between her daughter and her niece like a goddess with her handmaidens. "We shall accompany you to your room and I'll ask Mary to bring you some cocoa," she told Katherine. "Come, it may be a few days before the wedding, but Katherine is still our bride."

Taking Katherine's arm, Penny led her into the house followed by Xenia.

It was only when, several hours later, Osyth slid into her own bed that Kieran's words came back to her in all their terrible ferocity.

"What can you expect from the spawn of an adulterous marriage between a lunatic and a scoundrel?"

What had he meant? Was he referring to her grandparents?

She shuddered as she recalled the fury on his face that had rendered him unrecognisable.

"He was in the throes of one of his headaches," she reassured herself as she turned off her lamp. Below her, the wind chime sang its tune. "His words meant nothing," she whispered into the darkness, but somehow, she could not shift them from her mind.

CHAPTER THREE

Osyth walked across the wide expanse of the cove. The secluded beach at the base of the cliffs was reached by a flight of gently gradiented steps, carved into the stone, allowing an easy stroll down to the bay. A cool, green glow pre-empted the dawn as the lace-fringed waves washed over Osyth's bare feet. A woollen blanket around her shoulders kept away the chill while her embroidered white nightgown floated around her in the morning breeze. Throwing back her head and stretching her arms wide, she inhaled the salt-laced air, breathing in until she felt her lungs would burst. Turning in a slow circle, her mane of red curls danced like fire as she moved to the faint tune of the wind chime that serenaded her from above.

Checking no one was watching, she placed her blanket on the sand and leapt into the air before performing a series of cartwheels, springs and flips across the beach. Landing lightly, she giggled at the squiggles her acrobatics had created in the sand, before bending over backwards until her hands touched the ground, in a back bend, flicking her feet over into a standing position. Ever since she could remember, she had been able to perform these extraordinary tricks. Her younger cousins were both intrigued and terrified when she would lay on her front and lift her legs behind and over her body until her feet touched her head.

As they had grown up, she and Angharad had practised these moves, occasionally performing for the rest of the family on the long summer evenings. The two girls had enjoyed their tumbling but Osyth wondered if this, too, was something she would have to give up as she entered the adult world. The sea

rushed towards her and Osyth grabbed at her blanket, rescuing it in time from the icy ripples of the tide.

I will miss this when I'm in Windsor with Nain and Taid, she thought.

Osyth knew the river Thames would be nearby but no matter how mighty, it would never compare with the magic of her beloved ocean. In the days she had spent at her grandparents' house over the years she had seen the river and, while she agreed it was a beautiful stretch of water, in her opinion it lacked the wild and unpredictable nature of the sea. These moments spent alone with the sunrise, watching the waves change colour as they woke to a bright new day seemed to feed her soul and she knew this would be why she would always return home to Cliffside.

My mother loved this house, she thought, turning to admire the towers and turrets.

Weaving her way across the sand towards the sea cave and the strange ring of shells embedded in its wall, Osyth considered what she had seen in the moments before creeping through the slumbering house to the beach. Watching the darkness from her bedroom window for the tell-tale shimmer of dawn, she had heard a noise. Moving to the side window, she had seen Kieran, dressed in his suit from the previous night emerging from the wood. He had paused, checking there was no one around before beckoning to someone and, to her surprise, Angharad had emerged, a blanket wrapped around her nightgown. The two had whispered together, then Angharad had run to the kitchen door, while Kieran had walked to the front of the house and Osyth had heard the door open and click quietly shut.

Where had they been? And why had she been excluded?

Pushing her irritation with Kieran and Angharad aside, she decided to gather some shells for Katherine's breakfast tray in order to cheer her up. Despite the combined efforts of the women in the family comforting her, Osyth had heard Katherine's sobs through the night. The terrible words Kieran had flung out had left their mark.

With new purpose, she began searching the tideline for pretty shells. Her hoard grew quickly and, as she gathered a whirled wentletrap, washing away the sand to admire the creamy folds interspersed with veins of purple and red, she saw two figures in the distance, their heads bent together, deep in discussion. A moment later, they looked up and, waving, her uncles called a greeting.

"Good morning, darling," said Blaise as he and Noah reached her side. "You're up bright and early."

"As are you, Uncle Blaise," she replied. "I came down to gather these for Katherine in case she's still sad about last night." She folded back a section of blanket to reveal a cache of glittering shells.

"You're a sweet thing, Osyth," said Noah. "Katherine will be delighted."

"Have you spoken to her this morning?" asked Osyth.

"Mother has and she is well," said Blaise. "Kieran's outbursts always upset Katherine; she feels responsible for him."

"But she isn't, no one is," said Osyth.

"He's her brother and she feels his behaviour reflects on her, so she tries her hardest to protect him," continued Blaise.

"Protect him from whom?" asked Osyth.

"Himself, usually," sighed Noah, bending down to pull a brilliant white cockleshell from the sand, adding it to Osyth's collection.

"What do you mean?" asked Osyth, confused.

"When Aunt Georgina died, it was Kieran who found her," explained Blaise, "and both Katherine and Mother believe this has been the root of his problems."

"But how?"

"Uncle Matthew had been at work and they had been with their nanny, Gretel, but Kieran had sneaked away to find Aunt Georgina in her room. It was their ritual, apparently — before luncheon, he would creep down the stairs from the nursery to find his mother and they would spend time together. Sadly, on that day, when he ran to the bed, thinking Georgina was asleep, he shook her to wake her up but there was no response. When Gretel found him, he was laying on the bed beside his mother, holding her hand and sobbing."

"Oh, Uncle Blaise, that's devastating," said Osyth. "I had no idea."

"Kieran is sensitive, and losing both his parents when he was a child has made him different," said Noah. "Mother has always insisted we're gentle with him, allow him some leeway. He's family and it's up to us to protect him, even if he can be challenging on occasions."

Noah's words were tempered, but Osyth could feel the frustration behind them. Kieran was often rudest to Penny, and Osyth knew it upset Noah to see his mother abused in such a manner.

Noah skimmed a stone across the waves, then, trying to adopt a tone of casual indifference, he said, "Do you think Kieran's outbursts are becoming more frequent?"

Osyth was about to deny anything had changed but then she paused. Noah had never asked her opinion on such a serious subject before and, as he was treating her as an equal, she realised she needed to give an answer befitting this unexpected

rise in status from child to adult. Thinking back through the past few months, she asked herself the question again: had Kieran changed? As she considered the winter and spring they had spent at Cliffside, she realised with disappointment that his outbursts, which had once happened on rare occasions, had indeed increased in quantity and ferocity. Usually, the three of them — herself, Angharad and Kieran — were able to relax with each other, it was the only time he would ever be himself, but, recently, his manner had become more frigid, less accommodating.

"He has been more unpredictable since Katherine announced her engagement," she admitted.

"Do you think he's dangerous?" asked Noah. As he spoke the sunrise behind him caught the gold in his hair, giving him an ethereal look.

"Dangerous in what way?" asked Osyth.

"Would he hurt himself?" questioned Blaise.

Osyth stared at her uncle in horror. "No, never," she replied. "He becomes angry, but he is rarely violent and if he does lose his temper, he's likely to lock himself away."

"Has he ever hurt or threatened you?" asked Noah.

"No!" Osyth was alarmed. "Kieran and I have been friends since we were children."

"Are you still friends?" asked Blaise. "He has always been fixated with you, darling, and if he has become bothersome, you can tell us."

Osyth was about to splutter a defence of Kieran but again, she paused. Her uncles were concerned not only for her own wellbeing but for her cousin, too. Rather than react in her usual headstrong manner, she forced herself to weigh up her words before she replied as she had seen her grandmother, Penny, do on so many occasions.

"He is not bothersome," she replied, "but he is strange. I feel no fear but often I pity him. It is as though Kieran has cut himself off from happiness. He once told me that he would be betraying Aunt Georgina if he were to love Nain or any members of our family. He is loyal only to Katherine." She stopped, then as an afterthought added, "When he has been with Angharad and myself, he has often told us he blames his father for his mother's death. Was Uncle Matthew in any way responsible?"

"No," said Noah. "Uncle Matthew was a kind and gentle man; he was not involved in Aunt Georgina's death. Kieran is confused about his facts."

Osyth did not reply, instead she bent down to collect another shell, a shimmering black mussel.

"Yet he loves you," said Blaise, his tone curious.

"In Kieran's world, he and I are twin souls cast adrift in the family, part of you but not part of you," she replied.

"And do you feel like that?" asked Noah.

"No, I love you with all my heart and I am grateful that I have you because I no longer have my mother."

"Our beloved Eudora," said Blaise, hugging Osyth tightly. "You will always have us, my darling."

As he released her, the wind chime was caught by the sea breeze and the tune held them spellbound for a moment. The three turned, their feet leading them on the familiar route through the rivulets and rocks, towards the steps leading to Cliffside.

"Uncle Noah, may I ask you something else about Kieran?" Osyth ventured.

"Of course," he replied, "although whether or not I will answer will depend on your question." For once there was no

twinkle in his eye, no storytelling trickery. He was answering her honestly.

Osyth hesitated for a moment, then said, "The other things Kieran said last night, what did he mean?"

"Which piece?" asked Noah. "He said a great deal and most of it was hysterical nonsense."

"The horrible things he said about Nain and Taid, saying their marriage was adulterous…"

To her surprise, both her uncles grinned, and Noah laughed over the remainder of her sentence.

"It isn't that shocking," he said.

"Back then it probably was," mused Blaise.

"What was?" Osyth pushed.

"They were stepbrother and stepsister," explained Noah. "Mother's father, George Stone, had been a widower for many years and when his business partner, Aubrey Attwater, who was Taid's father, died, he and Aubrey's widow, Eleanor, became close. Eventually, they fell in love and married."

"Is that how Nain and Taid met?" asked Osyth, her green eyes wide with wonder.

"It is," said Blaise.

"And the spiteful names he called them?"

Noah pulled out his pocket watch and raised his eyebrows, as though he was surprised at the lateness of the hour. "There isn't time for the rest of the tale at the moment," he said. "Put it out of your mind for now. Perhaps you can persuade Father to tell it one evening when we're on the veranda."

"But Uncle Noah…"

"Another time, Osyth," he said, and this time there was a warning in his voice. Osyth felt a shiver run though her. Above her a gull screamed and for a moment the wind chime jangled discordantly.

"We must return to the house," said Blaise, forcing sunshine into voice. "I'm not sure if either of you realise it, but I'm getting married in a few days and there is lots to be done." Forcing a laugh, he held out his arm to Osyth, who linked hers through his, hurrying to keep up as Noah led the way back to the house.

Despite her smile and their carefree chatter as they climbed towards the house, Osyth knew there were secrets yet to be told.

CHAPTER FOUR

In art, Blaise could be bold. The colours on the canvas, the stories he dreamed to tell, the shapes, the forms, the creatures, all children of his own creation, transporting him to a land of magic and mystery. Like so many born to the legacy of the house on the cliff, throughout his life the changing tides of the sea, the call of the kingdom of the fae and the gentle songs of the wind chime haunted him, drawing images from his mind, to be captured on the broad canvases he built around himself like a fortress. Behind each image, he hid, allowing others to interpret what they wished from his swirling, ethereal works. Each unique, each unnerving in its beauty.

Osyth paused, dipping her pen in the ink, rereading what she had written about her uncle. Blaise was an artist and in the past few years his work had become more sought after. Next, she considered her cousin, Katherine, really her second cousin, but this always felt too cumbersome when describing their relationship.

There also lived a misplaced changeling at Cliffside. A child returned home by the fae through the twists of her mother's anguish. Katherine, the daughter of Matthew and Georgina, conceived through a moment of love but born to despair, with hair as red as her Aunt Penny's and eyes the same delicate blue. She was so similar to Penny that there were those who felt sure she must be her daughter and, in many ways, except for her birth, she was.

Reading back the words, Osyth wrinkled her nose, wondering if she had any right to comment on the people she loved. *No one will ever read it*, she reassured herself, then her eye caught a glimpse of the clock and she jumped to her feet. The wedding was a few hours away. She was to be attended by Anwen, a trainee lady's maid brought to the wedding by her Aunt Xenia.

"You can't have your hair flying everywhere," her aunt had exclaimed when Osyth had protested. "Neither can you have it in that wretched schoolgirl plait. You're a young lady, Osyth, and today you will look like one."

Osyth had laughed at her aunt's mock sternness. Placing her journal and pens in her writing desk, she walked across to the window where the waves were being whipped into white horses by the merry breeze. Below her, the wind chime sang a medley of joyful tunes, while snatches of conversations and laughter floated towards her. This afternoon, she would carry the train of her cousin's wedding dress. A white organza dress festooned with orange blossoms.

With a knock on the door, Anwen entered, her arms full of satin and tulle. Osyth stared at the dress. During her last fitting, she had been told that embellishments would be added, and she was fascinated to see the detailed embroidery and the swags of tiny silk flowers flowing down the back of the skirt. Anwen laid the bridesmaid's gown on the bed.

"The bride's gown is even more extravagant," she said, following Osyth's surprised eyes. "Now, Miss, if you would sit by the mirror, I'll begin with your hair. Mrs Pettifer has been very clear on how she would like it arranged. She has also asked me to pass on the message that when you're ready, you're to go to the bride's room."

Osyth sat before the large triple-aspect mirror and watched as Anwen laid out her hairbrushes and pins before unplaiting the heavy braid of her red hair and brushing it with long, firm strokes.

Over an hour later, Osyth felt exhausted, even though she had done very little except sit. Her hair was piled, folded and curled on top of her head, with ringlets of red fire framing her face. White flowers had been woven through the complicated style, glimmering like stars in a red summer sky. A hint of make-up had been applied; again, under her Aunt Xenia's rigid instructions: a wisp of powder and a pale pink shimmer on her cheeks and lips.

"If you would step into the gown, please," Anwen said, holding the shimmering oyster-coloured satin dress open. It slithered up Osyth's body, over the punishingly tight corset and Anwen fastened the long row of buttons down her back.

Taking a step back, Anwen scrutinised Osyth as she put on her matching satin slippers, the heel higher than she usually wore. Osyth waited, unsure whether to speak or move, rather intimidated by the efficiency of this girl who was not much older than herself. Walking around Osyth, Anwen made the occasional adjustment, tweaking the skirt, folding a loose curl back in with its fellows before allowing Osyth to at last face her reflection in the oval mirror.

"Oh my!" she exclaimed. "I look so much older." Her hand went to her hair. "Gwenhwyfar, the fairy of the white moon shadows, has danced through my hair leaving behind her white star flowers," she murmured, mesmerised by her appearance.

The woman who stared back at her was elegant, sophisticated and graceful. Her hair shone, the suggestion of make-up enhanced her features and the narrowness of her waist was a surprise.

Reaching into her bag, Anwen produced a wrapped gift. "Your aunt asked me to give you this when you were dressed," she said with a broad smile. "It's the finishing touch."

Unwrapping it, Osyth gasped. A bottle of White Rose fragrance from Floris of London, one of the most exclusive brands, according to Aunt Xenia, who knew about such things. A note attached to the bottle read, "*To our darling niece, a floral and elegant scent to enhance your beauty even further. All our love, Aunt Xenia and Uncle William*".

"A dab behind each ear will suffice," said Anwen, as Osyth gave a moan of delight before pulling out the exquisite stopper and inhaling the delicate floral blend with a deep sigh. Osyth waited until the maid had departed, then drenched herself in scent.

"My dear, you look stunning," exclaimed her grandmother when Osyth entered Katherine's room a few minutes later, "and you smell wonderful."

"Thank you, Nain," Osyth said, self-conscious in the formal clothes and unfamiliar heels. The cloud of scent seemed to envelope as she walked and she imagined a shimmering bubble surrounding her. "How's Katherine?"

"Radiant," replied Penny, pointing to the bride who was surrounded by her cousins. "However, I have a task for you. Would you run downstairs to Taid and ask him where he put the present we have bought for Katherine? He was supposed to bring it here but I suspect he's been distracted by checking on our guests."

"Where will he be, Nain?"

"In the winter drawing room; it's where the men planned to gather in order to calm Blaise's nerves."

Without a word, Osyth hurried from the room, stumbling as the weight of her skirts slowed her from her customary gallop to a demurer pace. Making her way through the house, her smile broadened. Cliffside had been transformed. Curtains of greenery and garlands of flowers interwoven with seashells and glittering models of fairies were draped around the house. The door to the winter drawing room was not closed but it was pulled to, and Osyth could hear the rumble of male voices. For a moment, shyness reared itself, then she scolded herself — these were her uncles and cousins. To ensure she did not interrupt anything, she gave a smart rap on the door. It immediately opened and her Uncle Solomon gave her a blank look before realisation made his eyes wide.

"Goodness me, Osyth, you look wonderful," he said, beckoning her inside. "Although, looking like that, I'm not sure I should allow you in, these men might not be able to control themselves."

Osyth was unsure whether to laugh. The idea that men would find her attractive was a new concept. "Is Taid here?" she whispered, glancing around the room which was full of smoke, brandy fumes, and men in dark coats, all speaking in deep, booming voices.

"Pa," called Solomon through the crowd and Daniel turned from where he had been speaking to a young man Osyth did not know. As her uncle had not recognised her for a split second, she wondered if her grandfather would be startled too. However, as Daniel stared at her, she watched, perplexed, as the colour drained from his face. Then he seemed to recall himself and hurried towards her.

"My dear," he said, taking her hand, "is there something wrong?"

"No, Taid, all is well. Katherine is radiant. Nain asked me to collect the gift for Katherine that you were supposed to take to her room."

"Is that the time?" He glanced over at the fireplace where a golden clock whirred. "We have been so engrossed in keeping Blaise calm, we quite forgot." He delved into his pocket and brought out a wrapped box. "It's a locket," he whispered, giving her a conspiratorial wink. "Please tell your grandmother that we shall be leaving for the chapel in ten minutes."

"Yes, Taid," she said, then because he was so pale, she added, "are you quite well?"

"Most robust, thank you," he said. "For a moment your appearance startled me. I thought you were your mother; dressed this way, you looked very similar to her when she married your father."

A lump rose in Osyth's throat.

"Sir, would you care to finish your drink?" The young man to whom Daniel had been speaking had approached. "My apologies," he said, flushing pink when he saw Osyth. "I had not realised the bride had arrived."

"Not the bride," said Daniel, "the bridesmaid."

Osyth managed a smile.

"This is my granddaughter, Osyth Attwater," said Daniel. "Osyth, this is our new assistant, Mr Frederick Meyrick. He's connected to the Bush and Meyrick families in Bangeston, near Pembroke Dock."

Osyth bobbed a curtsey as etiquette required, then muttering apologies, she hurried from the room back to Katherine. She already knew Mr Frederick Meyrick had recently begun to work with her grandfather and Uncle Noah. He was young and competent in his job in the office but Noah had told her his

real joy was to write poetry. Handsome, too, thought Osyth as she hurried up the stairs, blushing at her own forwardness.

After the wedding, the family and guests gathered in the summer drawing room. This was a series of rooms that could be opened into one large space by the removal of sections of panelling. The room overlooked the gardens and, beyond that, the cliff and the sweeping majesty of St Brides Bay.

The wedding breakfast was served and as the day progressed members of the family were ushered away to be photographed, a hobby shared by both Noah and Daniel. Arranged and posed by a photographer friend, they were determined to preserve the portraits of the family on this happy day.

And it has been happy, thought Osyth, watching as the bride and groom were encouraged into a traditional posture, both trying to keep their faces serious as was required by the photographer but struggling with fits of giggles. The most challenging image had been taken outside Cliffside in the gardens and featured the entire family. Osyth had been amused to discover it was the adults, rather than the children, who lacked the ability to follow direction offered by the photographer. Eventually, however, they had succeeded, and everyone was excited to see the finished picture.

They had all been concerned about Kieran and how he might behave during the ceremony, but he had been calm, walking his sister up the aisle in place of their late father, Matthew. Even now, Kieran was circulating, speaking to guests. Osyth, watching him exchange pleasantries with a friend of her grandmother's, felt a rush of pride. All day he had pushed his shyness and reticence about the marriage aside, welcoming guests, charming members of extended family, helping Penny and Daniel in any way possible in order to ensure Katherine

and Blaise's day was perfect. It was a far cry from his usual retreat to the side of a crowd where he would watch with hooded, nervous eyes.

Osyth smiled as an old family friend approached her and, following Kieran's example, spent a few moments discussing the weather and the newest piece of gossip about the royal family. Soon she would be required to go upstairs and help Katherine change. After this, the married couple would depart to a local hotel before catching a ferry to Ireland the following day for a month's honeymoon. From here, they intended to live in Paris for at least a year for Blaise to study with the artists he admired before visiting St Ives in Cornwall where there was a colony of like-minded painters. Osyth would miss Katherine but she was excited for her too, especially as they had invited her to stay once they were established in Paris.

Kieran arrived at her side and handed her a flute of champagne.

"Are you sure?" she asked in surprise.

"Your grandfather insists," he said.

Osyth glanced over at her grandparents who were standing with Xenia and William. They caught her looking and all four raised their own glasses. She returned the gesture and took a cautious sip of the champagne. The bubbles tickled her nose and the dryness on her tongue felt unfamiliar but not unpleasant.

"My sister is happy."

"Yes, so is Uncle Blaise," replied Osyth, then a thought occurred to her. Katherine was now her aunt. This struck her as funny and the sentence began to form on her lips, but Kieran was already speaking.

"Would my mother have approved of this match?"

"Kieran, I don't know," replied Osyth. "I'm sure she would have approved of Katherine being happy."

Noah and Hannah detached themselves from a nearby group and came towards them. Osyth smiled but beside her she sensed Kieran stiffen.

"You look very beautiful today, my dear," Noah said, kissing Osyth on the cheek. "There is no denying you are a young lady, not our little girl of the fairy rings anymore."

"It's a long time since I've been Osyth of the fairy rings," she laughed. "Although, they still appear each autumn. Every year when I stood in them, I expected a door to open into fairyland."

"Foolish…" muttered Kieran behind her.

"Not so," said Hannah. "There have been many studies made concerning the legends of the small folk in this area, a number claim that the fairy rings lead the way to the hidden kingdom of Tylwyth Teg, the land of the fairies. There are also tales of sailors seeing the green islands of fairyland not far from here, which date back to Mediaeval times. They appear in the mist, hovering above the water. These things cannot be entirely dismissed, Kieran."

"Your father is a minister of the church," said Kieran, looking at Hannah in confusion. "How can you believe such things?"

"There are many things in this world that can't be explained," she replied. "My father would be the first to tell you to consider every wonder placed before you on this earth because everything was created by our merciful God. There is even a tale concerning Jesus and the fairies."

"You jest," said Kieran.

"No, my father told it to me, would you like to hear it?"

"Yes, please, Aunt Hannah," said Osyth.

Hannah smiled, her grey eyes twinkling and began, "It was once believed that during our Saviour's time, there lived a woman whose fortune it was to have been blessed with twenty children," she began. Beside her, Kieran tutted but Osyth caught hold of his sleeve so he could not walk away. "As she saw the Blessed Lord approaching her home, she felt ashamed of being so prolific and, concerned he might judge her, she decided to conceal half her brood. When he left, she went in search of her hidden children but they were never seen again. It was said afterwards that their disappearance was a punishment from heaven for hiding what God had given her. It is thought that these lost offspring were taken to a new land which was hidden below the earth and they were the ancestors of the race of beings called Fairies."

Noah slid his arm around his wife's waist and kissed her cheek. "A wonderful tale, my dear," he said, then looked at Kieran.

Osyth was relieved when Kieran forced a smile.

"Thank you, Hannah," he said, "it was an interesting parable, and we are better able to understand the nature of the local legends. Now, if you will excuse me." He gave his usual sharp bow from the neck and hurried away.

"Don't be angry with him, Uncle Noah," said Osyth as they watched him disappear into the crowd. "He's trying very hard."

"I know, my darling," replied Noah. "He's doing very well."

"And now, Osyth, we must go upstairs to help Katherine change," said Hannah. "Noah, my love, you should fetch Kieran before you join your brothers and your father. He may need some help in the boisterousness of the crowd."

Upstairs there was well-meaning chaos in the wedding boudoir. Katherine stood in the centre as Penny directed people around her, helping her from her magnificent gown into a prettily embroidered travelling dress with matching coat. Osyth was delighted to find Angharad among the group of women.

"You are truly my daughter, now," she heard her grandmother saying to Katherine as she and Angharad took it upon themselves to fold up the frothy veil.

"May I call you Mother, or would you prefer me to continue to address you as Aunt Penny?"

"Whichever feels the most natural," Penny replied. "You are the best of all of us, Katherine, I know my son is safe with you."

"It's so romantic, isn't it?" sighed Osyth, and Angharad laughed.

"Will you be next, Osyth?"

"Perhaps," she replied. "After marriage, you have more freedom."

"Not always," replied Angharad. "If your husband is cruel, you might be kept a prisoner."

"You've been reading *Jane Eyre* again," Osyth said, grinning. "Anyway, I wouldn't marry anyone cruel and if they turned out to be awful, Taid and Uncle Noah would come to save me."

"Do you have anyone in mind, Osyth?"

"Not yet."

"What about the young man you were speaking to earlier? Frederick Meyrick?"

"I barely know him," Osyth said, but her glowing cheeks caused Angharad to burst out laughing. "What about you, Annie? Do you have any thoughts of a husband?"

"Perhaps," her friend replied but before Osyth could question her further, there was a flurry of excitement.

Moving downstairs in a shower of orange blossom, Katherine and Blaise were in the coach and, suddenly, they were gone.

Osyth and Angharad stood waving until they were the only ones remaining outside the wide front doors of Cliffside. The sun was sinking and as the family returned to the house, Osyth suddenly felt sad. Behind her, the wind chime sang soothing songs but as she had waved goodbye to Katherine and Blaise, Osyth felt she was bidding farewell to her childhood, and that left a bittersweet sadness in her heart.

PART THREE: PEMBROKESHIRE, 2019

CHAPTER ONE

Driving down the narrow lane and into the car park, Amelia watched as Cliffside loomed through the glowering clouds. A huge rambling house with towers and turrets; perched impossibly on the edge of the rocks, it seemed to defy gravity. Its many windows stared out over the crashing waves of St Brides Bay and, apart from the addition of the paved car park, it did not seem to have changed much since the Attwater's had been photographed on its veranda. As if to highlight the magnificence of the property with its strange eccentric beauty, the low, grey, drizzle-laden skies that had been Amelia's driving companions for the past hour cleared and a ray of May sunshine shone down, spotlighting the house.

"Astonishing," murmured Amelia.

Her phone buzzed.

"Are you there yet?"

"Hi Benj, yes, just arrived."

There was a pause. "Aimes, are you sure about this?" he asked. "I've been looking online and have found a couple of other places you could stay instead."

"Please, Benji, you know how important this is to me."

"But a few weeks ago you had no idea this place even existed, now you've dashed off to quite literally the middle of nowhere, to stay with…"

"It's a retreat," she interrupted, her voice simmering with irritation. "You've looked it up yourself and I know you rang them to check it's a real place."

"How do you know?"

"Doug told me."

"Turncoat," muttered Benji.

"This place is incredible. I'll send you some pictures, it's hardly changed at all. I'll call you once I'm in my room," she finished, refusing to allow his apprehension to exacerbate her own nerves. "And thanks, Benj, I'll ring immediately if I need you to book me somewhere else or ride to my rescue."

From the other end of the line, he gave a grudging laugh and they said goodbye.

Ever since Amelia had booked her two-week stay at Cliffside her friends had been trying to dissuade her. Each was concerned in their own way: Louise because she thought Amelia should be near home while she grieved, not several hundred miles away; Richie was more realistic suggesting she could wait a week or so and see if it still seemed a good idea rather than one born from an emotional response; and Benji was convinced it was run by a cult and Amelia was going to be kidnapped. When the others had asked why anyone would want to restrain her against her will he had merely sulked.

Amelia knew they meant well and understood their concerns but from the moment she had seen the picture of Matthew and Georgina Stone, she had known that visiting this house, which had unexpectedly appeared in her life, was the correct thing to do. Booking the suite, she had told herself if it was too strange, she could always leave, but somehow she knew this was where she was meant to be and, having read the beginning of Osyth Attwater's diary, she felt compelled to discover what had happened to her and the extended family of the Attwaters and Stones. The person who intrigued her the most was Eudora Attwater, who even after a more extensive search by Amelia, seemed to have vanished from the records.

Picking up the photograph which she had positioned on the dashboard of the passenger side so she could glance at it as she

drove, she opened her door and stood in the car park. The clouds were rolling in again, scudding from the wide-open bay as Amelia held the picture at eye-level, adjusting her position until the towers and turrets were lined up. Gazing at the picture and the house, she felt a thrill of excitement course through her.

Mum, you left me a mystery to solve, so here I am, on the trail of Penny, Eudora and Osyth Attwater. Did you know who they were? Was this your fabled Welsh heritage?

Then the blurred face of the small boy drew her attention and her eyes moved upward to the window where he had been standing. Instead of the long narrow pane, there was now a wall. Amelia shuddered, staring at the spot where the angry child had scowled at the world. *Who were you? And why were you so full of hatred?*

"Hello," said a calm male voice behind her, making her jump, "would you mind explaining why you have Aunt Caitlin's photograph and the reason you've taken it out of her library?"

Turning around, she was surprised to see a tall, broad-shouldered man with jet-black hair curling over his collar in a hairstyle that had echoes of the Edwardian era. His intense dark brown eyes held a fearsome expression. He was dressed in a battered wax jacket, jeans and riding boots, holding the leads of two black greyhounds, who wagged their tails.

"That picture is part of our private collection," he continued, "and should remain in the archive. It is not to be removed by anyone without permission."

Amelia stared at him. She had lost the ability to speak and she was unsure why. To her horror, he took a step closer with his hand outstretched, palm flat as though waiting for her to

place the photograph there. When she did not move, his eyes narrowed and he reached forward to take it from her hands.

"Excuse me!" she exclaimed, stepping back so she was out of his reach, his sudden lunge breaking the spell. "This photograph belongs to me."

The man's scowl deepened but he swallowed hard and when he spoke, his voice was calm. "The image you're holding is one of the few we have of the former inhabitants of this house…"

"Yes, I know," she interrupted, "*Penny, Eudora and Osyth Attwater*. It's written on the back."

"No, it isn't," he replied in the same calm but determined voice, "the inscription on the back says, *Cliffside, Pembrokeshire, 1865*."

Amelia fixed him with a look of icy disdain, then turned the picture around to show him the faded inky letters. He leaned forward and, as he read the words, his face was suddenly wreathed in confusion. Amelia raised her eyebrows but did not break the awkward silence.

"I'm sorry," he said, looking up at her, "I was mistaken."

With great care, Amelia slid the image back into a protective plastic sleeve, then into the front pocket of her handbag, before turning away from the man and walking back to her car. As she reached to the boot and removed her suitcase, she realised her hands were shaking. For the first time she wondered whether her friends had been correct: was her impulsive need to visit this unknown property a foolish one?

"I'll help you with that," the man said, appearing at her side, startling her.

"No, thank you, I can manage," she replied, her voice cool and authoritative. It was the tone she had used when confronted with belligerent or aggressive patients or their

families. It could usually halt people at ten paces, but this man seemed impervious.

"I insist," he said, and Amelia wondered if he was going to wrestle the suitcase from her grasp. "My name is Edward Stone," he continued, "this is my house."

Amelia did not reply but felt a strange thrill of emotion ripple through her. It was recognition. Quashing such thoughts, she continued to look at him in silence.

"You must be Dr Amelia Prentice, you are the only guest we're expecting today," he continued, his voice remaining level. "My apologies for our altercation. My Great-Aunt Caitlin shares the house with me, and she has a collection of family memorabilia that is extremely precious to her. As you must know from the website, we have a copy of the same photograph as you. I was upset to think someone would have taken it from her private library."

"If you had surmised who I was, which would not have been difficult as you requested the number plate of my car when I booked, and, as you've stated, I'm your only new guest today, how could I have coerced your aunt into giving me the picture when I have yet to step inside the house? Something which must have been apparent by the fact you probably saw me drive into the car park."

Edward Stone dropped his gaze, stroking the head of the taller of the two dogs, before responding. "Very well-reasoned, Dr Prentice," he said, his face neutral. "However, would you mind my asking where you got your photograph? It's obviously an original image, not a copy."

A gust of wind buffeted them, as the first drops of rain stung their faces, and Amelia considered her options. "Perhaps we could go inside," she said, feeling there must be a receptionist or other staff around as this man was unnerving her. Despite

his outwardly reasonable demeanour, she could sense his frustration — although about what she had no clue — and she did not think the photograph was the root of his irritation. "Then we can discuss this further."

He once again reached for her suitcase but when she jerked it away from his hand, he desisted, instead leading the way to the front doors, unclipping the dogs who bounded off through the house. "They belong to my aunt," he explained, "but she's too frail to walk them now."

They were standing in a well-lit square entrance hall that had been converted into a reception and waiting area. A woman in her early forties was seated at the welcome desk and she smiled when they entered. With long straight dark hair and striking brown eyes that were enhanced by her glasses, she exuded calm, confident control and Amelia felt a sense of relief.

"Dr Prentice," the receptionist began, "I'm Kerry. You've had a long journey! Let me book you in so you can get settled."

"It's OK, Kerry, you get off, you should have left twenty minutes ago," Edward Stone said, joining her behind the desk, "I've got this."

"No really, I'd rather she stayed," said Amelia and to her surprise, her voice had a tremor.

Kerry looked between them, startled. "Has something happened here?" she asked, her eyes quizzical as she glared at Edward. "What have you done this time?"

"Nothing," he exclaimed, his olive skin taking on a ruddy tinge. When Kerry raised her eyebrow, he seemed to crumple. "It was the photograph," said Edward, pointing vaguely towards Amelia's handbag. "Dr Prentice was holding up a picture of the house and I thought she'd taken it from the library."

"And how could she have done that when she's only just arrived?" asked Kerry, glaring. "Honestly, Eddie, we'll have no guests left if you keep shouting at people the moment they drive into the car park." Kerry turned to Amelia. "Dr Prentice, I can only apologise. Considering the less than warm welcome you've received, would you still like to stay here or would you prefer me to call some of the local hotels and arrange for you to move to one of those instead? Obviously, all expenses will be met by The Cliffside Retreat and you will be given an immediate and full refund."

Amelia paused. After the altercation in the car park, she had wondered whether or not to move on elsewhere.

"I can assure you, you will be completely safe," continued Kerry, "we take the security and wellbeing of our guests very seriously." Once again, she shot Edward a look of disgust.

Edward edged away from her, lowering himself into a chair out of Kerry's reach, giving Amelia an apologetic smile.

"Aren't you going to say anything?" Kerry asked, turning on Edward. "You caused this situation — the least you could do is apologise."

"I did!" he protested.

"Well, do it again!"

At this point, Amelia fought to stop herself from laughing. Edward Stone was almost cowering beneath Kerry's fury. Amelia wondered if they were married.

"Dr Prentice, I really am extremely sorry," said Edward. "It was a complete misunderstanding and I ask for your forgiveness. We will, of course, make a gesture of apology by offering you a discount on your stay."

Kerry gave a satisfied nod and turned back to Amelia.

"Fine," said Amelia, "I'll stay."

Edward looked relieved and Kerry beamed. After tapping in a few details, she placed Amelia's paperwork and welcome pack on the table. "Would you like to follow me?" she said, "and don't worry about your suitcase, one of the boys will bring it up in a moment."

Kerry shot Edward a final look of fury, but before they could leave, he asked, "The photograph? You were going to tell me how it came to be in your possession."

For a moment, Amelia hesitated, then she reasoned to herself that she was in a brightly lit house with Kerry beside her and probably more people nearby who could come to her assistance if she needed it. Slipping her hand into the front pocket of her handbag, she removed the photograph in its protective plastic sleeve and placed it on the reception desk. Kerry gasped and threw a bemused look at Edward, who did not notice but was instead staring at the image.

"May I?" he asked, indicating he would like to pick it up. Amelia nodded. She watched his eyes narrow as he read the inscription on the back.

"*Penny, Eudora and Osyth Attwater*," Kerry read aloud, leaning over to look. "Who were they?"

"Penny Attwater was born Penelope Charlotte Stone," said Amelia. "I've been researching her in the census records. Eudora was her daughter and Osyth was her granddaughter. Penelope was the twin sister of Matthew Isaac Stone."

Edward's head jerked up. "Matthew Stone?" He opened up the website and scrolled to the image. "This Matthew Stone?"

Amelia shrugged. "I would guess so," she said.

Edward stared at her in confusion. "Where did you say you got this?"

"It was with my mother's papers, I found it with a number of other pictures after she died."

"What was your mother's name?"

"Joan Prentice, *née* Cowper," replied Amelia but there was no sign of recognition from Edward.

He and Kerry continued to stare at the image, then he turned to the computer screen and tapped in some details. "Dr Prentice, you were supposed to have an assessment with me tomorrow morning but on balance, it would be more professional for you to see my colleague, Dr Melissa Forte."

"Why?" she asked.

"Because I think we might be related and as we both know, doctors can't treat members of their own families."

CHAPTER TWO

"He said what?" Louise's voice was shrill. Benji choked on his coffee.

"We might be related, so he'd get one of the other consultants to see me."

Amelia was sitting on the squashy blue sofa in her suite at Cliffside with her laptop balanced on her knees, the faces of her two friends gazing at her from their offices.

"Aimes, this is peculiar," Louise said.

"It isn't," Amelia replied, wondering how to explain the feeling of peace that had been stealing over her since her arrival at Cliffside, the strange sense of belonging. "It's very tranquil, like I'm staying with an exceptionally friendly family."

Benji made a noise of disbelief and rolled his eyes at Amelia.

"Unusual," said Louise with a concerned expression, but then she forced a grin and Amelia knew the moment they had finished the call they would be deciding whether or not to drive down and rescue her.

"What are you doing today?" asked Benji. "I assumed you'd be in group therapy or stroking healing llamas or something."

Amelia laughed. "Nothing so exciting," she replied. "I'm having my assessment with Melissa Forte in a minute, then it's my decision how much counselling or therapy I attend." Her eye caught the time. "Better go, guys, I don't want to be late for my one and only scheduled appointment."

They blew kisses and vanished. Amelia snapped her laptop shut and put it on the coffee table, looking around the room that was to be her home for the next few weeks. Her suite in the tower was spread over several floors and comprised an

octagonal-shaped bedroom with the en suite tucked into the attic room above, while below was a living room with kitchenette. After her strange meeting with Edward Stone the previous afternoon, Kerry had insisted on showing Amelia to her rooms.

She had led the way along the winding central corridor of Cliffside from which rooms opened to either side. A vast and comfortable living area overlooking the bay took up one side of the house, while smaller, unevenly shaped spaces span off the other. Amelia glimpsed a study with book-lined walls, a small sitting room, and a larger L-shaped room, but with only a cursory glance, she could not tell what purpose it might serve. The thing that had struck her most was that none of them looked like traditional treatment rooms, there was no standard low-budget, uncomfortable seating; no whiteboards, no seminar spaces. Every room looked as though a family lived here.

"Down there is the honesty bar. The room is carved into the rocks and opens on to a garden below the veranda," said Kerry, pointing to a narrow stone staircase.

"A bar?"

"Yes, I know, it is quite unusual, but we deal mostly with people who have depression and bereavement issues. We're not an addiction clinic. This is a small retreat for people who often need a rest and a chance to escape and talk in confidence rather than intense therapy. The relaxed atmosphere and homeliness helps."

"I've never seen a wellbeing clinic quite like this before," Amelia had admitted. "Have you been open long?"

"Two years," replied Kerry. "It's quite an experimental approach but Edward has to work within certain boundaries. He was determined to create a place that was more like a home-from-home rather than a sterile clinic or an overpriced luxury hospital that resembled a hotel."

"Boundaries?"

Kerry paused, as though considering whether or not she was being indiscreet, then said in low voice, "Edward doesn't own the whole house. Half of it belongs to his Great-Aunt Caitlin and she loves it as it is. Edward would never want to upset her, so he agreed to leave the décor."

"How has he been able to turn it into a retreat?"

"Caitlin knows Edward has to make the house pay its way, so she agreed to his idea of an experimental clinic. She's very elderly now and keeps to her wing of the house most of the time but when we're quiet, she'll settle herself in the Summer Drawing Room, the big room overlooking the sea, and work on her book."

"Her book?"

"Yes, she's writing a family history. Edward said it's a bit rambling, but it keeps her happy."

Before Amelia could question her further, they had arrived at the foot of a wide wooden staircase with a bright red runner down the centre.

"This is you," said Kerry, her eyes twinkling. "This is my favourite part of the house. You have the entire tower to yourself and the view is spectacular."

As Kerry had been giving Amelia the tour of her suite, there had been a knock on the door and a tall blond man deposited Amelia's suitcase on the bed.

"Thanks Dave," said Kerry smiling. "This is my husband, David," she added.

"Oh, I thought maybe you were…" Amelia let her comment fade away, but David finished it for her.

"Married to Edward?" He laughed. "He's my best friend, we all grew up together. Were you telling him off again?" he asked Kerry, who gave an innocent shrug. With a laugh and a rueful shake of his head, muttering something that had sounded like, "Poor bloke…" David had waved goodbye and disappeared back down the stairs.

"I'm heading off in half an hour," Kerry had said, "but there's always someone around if you need anything. All the details are in your welcome pack." She had pointed to a bright lilac folder she had placed on the coffee table. "Dinner is included, and you can either eat in the main dining room or the bar or have it sent up to your room, whatever makes you feel most comfortable. Now, we'll leave you to get settled but please remember, we're here to look after you, so anything at all, just call reception."

Amelia had nodded, overwhelmed by the warmth of Kerry's welcome. The long journey and the strange incident when she arrived were beginning to make themselves felt and it was with relief that she took the keys and said goodbye to Kerry. She had eaten in her room that night and gone to bed early. It had been an entirely new experience to be lulled to sleep by the sound of the waves crashing on the rocks below the house. The sound of the wind chime had been both unexpected and familiar and she made a note to buy herself one when she eventually returned home.

Taking one final glance in the mirror at her appearance, she clattered down the stairs. Entering the main corridor of the house, she allowed the peace of the house to calm her. Low

voices murmured from the Summer Drawing Room but she bypassed this, searching for the study where she was to have her meeting with Melissa Forte. Even though there were other guests, Edward and his staff seemed to have developed a system where no one strayed into anyone else's space. Yet, the place remained welcoming and friendly. More like a perfect flat-share situation, thought Amelia.

To her delight, the study was the book-lined room she had glimpsed the previous day, although it was one of the few rooms that did not have a view of St Brides Bay. Instead it looked out towards the woods that spread away from the house. Browsing the shelves, she saw there was a strange mix of old and new titles. One bookshelf was protected by glass doors and this seemed to house the older, more valuable books. There were a number of battered copies of Charles Dickens' titles, the most well-thumbed of which was *Oliver Twist*, and other more pristine volumes by female writers from the Victorian period including Elizabeth Gaskill, Ellen Wood, Ann Radcliffe, and Rhoda Broughton.

On another shelf was a huge tome entitled *Folk-lore of West and Mid-Wales* by Jonathan Ceredig Davies. Wondering if Osyth had ever fulfilled her dream to be published, Amelia had searched for her online but had been unsuccessful in discovering any written works. Now she was in the house where Osyth grew up, she wondered whether there might be something. Unfortunately, a search of the shelves left her empty handed, but her eye was caught by a row of well-worn hardbacked books. To her delight, they were copies of the George MacDonald books both she and Molly had loved but before she could lift them from the shelf, a movement outside the window caught her attention.

Gazing at the close-planted trees swaying in the breeze, there was nobody in sight and she decided it must have been her imagination. As she gazed at the trees, the comments Osyth had made in her journal came back to her and she wondered if the standing stones had survived, the ancient monuments that had held such a fascination for Kieran Stone. *Was he an ancestor of Edward's?* she mused. In the distance she heard the wind chime and wondered again where it hung. Her thoughts were interrupted by a woman's voice.

"Dr Prentice, I'm Melissa Forte."

Amelia turned. A woman of medium build with light brown hair drawn up into a ponytail was smiling at her. She was casually dressed in indigo jeans, a flowing red jumper and black ankle boots.

"Edward has asked me to do your first assessment," Melissa continued with a smile and gestured towards one of the armchairs. "We try to keep things relaxed."

Wondering again if this was good idea, Amelia took the seat Melissa proffered, trying to pull her attention away from the wood and the wind chime but a movement near the tree line caught her attention again.

"Is something wrong?" asked Melissa, following Amelia's gaze.

"I thought I saw something," Amelia said, hurrying back to the window. "There, look."

A stooped figure in a black cloak was vanishing into the wood.

"Nothing to concern yourself with," said Melissa, joining Amelia. "It's Caitlin, Edward's great-aunt."

"But isn't she very elderly?" questioned Amelia. "Should she be going into the wood unaccompanied?"

"Caitlin is an independent soul," replied Melissa, her tone clipped, "she has always walked in the woods and, she tells us, she always will. If you'll excuse me for a moment, I'll make Kerry aware Caitlin is outside, so she can keep an eye on her."

Melissa vanished and Amelia returned her gaze to the wood. The woman remained in the trees but she was looking at the window, staring at Amelia. As their eyes locked, a look of terror flashed across Caitlin's face. Stepping back, she vanished into the shadows of the trees.

CHAPTER THREE

Amelia woke to the first glimmers of the sunrise. It looked so inviting that she was compelled to drag on some clothes before running down to meet it on the beach. Stopping, she turned her eyes to admire the majesty of the horizon as the sun climbed into the awakening sky, breathing in the heady scent of the salty air. Above her, gulls cried, their faraway call sounding like laughter, while at her feet, the white-edged waves hissed and sang, inviting her to enjoy the beauties of their bay. Inhaling the sharp tang of the fresh air was like a soothing balm easing the nervous tension in her shoulders. A feeling of unexpected peace and belonging rippled through her, enveloping her like a gift from nature.

Amelia had been at Cliffside for a week and was beginning to feel the benefits of her daily sessions with Melissa Forte. At first, when they had discussed bereavement, Amelia had hidden behind her professional face, responding to things as a doctor, rather than a mother or daughter. It was how she had coped through the years of watching her family succumb to an array of illnesses which she had been powerless to prevent. Then one morning, she had opened up.

"I feel so guilty, even with my medical training, that I couldn't save any of them," and suddenly her defences had broken and she had cried. Not the exhausted and stress related tears she had cried during the funerals but real, deep, heart-wrenching sobs. It had been a turning point. She was no longer waking in a blind panic, thinking she had missed a cry from Molly or her parents. Instead, she was able to look at the photographs of her lost family and smile at them, rather than

shudder with guilt, despair and grief. Since then, she had spent an hour with Melissa each morning and, after that, she would see how the mood took her. The only definite decision she had made was to extend her stay for another two weeks.

To her surprise, she had not seen Edward since her arrival. He was, according to Kerry, away on a course. Part of her was frustrated because she had hoped to be able to ask him about the Stone family. Neither had she glimpsed the mysterious Aunt Caitlin again, although she had seen David walking the two greyhounds on the beach as a favour to Edward while he was away.

Now Amelia was away from the sheltered warmth of Cliffside, she realised a vest top, fleece, leggings and trainers might not be substantial enough against the weather.

Better run to warm myself up, she thought. She jogged gently across the sand before briefly stopping. *Osyth Attwater stood here. In the run-up to the wedding she collected shells for Katherine's breakfast tray.* She continued at a gentle pace along the waterline, while the question, which was recurring with increasing intensity, dashed across her mind: *Osyth, who were you to me?*

The journal was engrossing and, from the description in the diary, Amelia wondered if she was sleeping in Osyth's old bedroom. It matched many aspects of her rooms, particularly the views over St Brides Bay from the main windows and the wood behind the house from the tall, narrow ones on the other side of the tower. It was a thought that appealed to her. Whoever Osyth Attwater had been, she had loved this house, her early journal entries had made that clear. The connection Amelia was developing towards the diary and the woman who had written it was visceral, and like Osyth, she was becoming increasingly concerned and intrigued about all the secrets that seemed to tumble towards them out of thin air.

Upping her speed a little, enjoying the feel of the wind stroking her face, she thought back over what the diary had told her. Osyth had been close to Angharad Williams, who had grown up with her at Cliffside, and they were a trio with Kieran Stone. Amelia was wondering again if Kieran was an ancestor of Edward's when a rush of barking and splashing drew her from her thoughts. The two black greyhounds pounded towards her.

"Hello babies," she said, bending down to stroke the two dogs who were dancing around her in excitement, "are you on your own? Or are you with your Uncle David today?"

"Lara! Nero!" Edward's voice rang out from behind the small outcrop of rocks.

"They're here!" she shouted as he hurried into view. Edward was wearing a fisherman's jumper, jeans and wellies. The look suited his unruly hair and dark eyes and, to her surprise, Amelia felt a small jolt as he smiled at her.

"Thanks," he said, walking up to where the two greyhounds were playing chase in the shallows. "They can't get off the beach but I don't like it when they're not in sight. These rocks and tides can be treacherous."

Amelia watched the dogs bounding and jumping, running backwards and forwards to Edward, checking he was nearby and occasionally rushing to her with a cheeky bark and wagging tail.

"Molly would have loved a dog," she said. "We discussed it at length but it was never viable — she was in hospital more than she was at home. It's a shame though, we had dogs when I was growing up and they are wonderful creatures."

"They're pure love," said Edward, and she turned to look at him in surprise. "What?" he laughed. "Did you think my dark medical heart wouldn't allow me to appreciate pets?"

"Sorry," she said, "I don't know why I'm surprised, it's clear you adore them, and they worship you."

"Aunt Caitlin has had them since they were puppies, so they're family. How are you settling in?"

"Very well, thank you," said Amelia. "Melissa has helped me more than I thought possible. Guilt and grief are so intertwined it's easy to lose yourself as you try to make sense of death."

"Dr Prentice…"

"Amelia, please," she interrupted.

"Amelia, I'd already read your case notes before I decided it would be unsafe to treat you and may I offer my sincere condolences. You and your family have suffered unbelievably."

Amelia felt the sting of tears but she blinked them away. "Thank you," she said.

"And, please let me apologise again for my behaviour when you arrived," he said. "I was in a foul mood. My girlfriend moved out last month, and she took an awful lot of things that weren't hers, some of which are family pieces. Seeing you standing there with what I thought was another family belonging, I irrationally thought you'd been stealing things too. Although, I also just wanted to shout at someone. The break-up with Ella has been so very reasonable and considerate throughout. Sometimes being able to see every side of every argument is frustrating when all you want to do is let off steam and shout."

Amelia could not help herself. She laughed. "Apology accepted; I understand the strain of always being reasonable. I've spent years being polite and calm, when all I wanted to do was scream like a banshee at people and demand they make my family well again."

He gave her a complicit nod. "Medical calmness has a lot to answer for," he sighed, before noticing her outfit. "Am I interrupting your run?"

"No, I really came down to watch the sunrise. I'm happy to walk the dogs with you, if it isn't an intrusion?"

"Not at all, I was going to warn you to be careful. The tide has turned and the other side of the beach can get cut off very quickly. Their freedom is about to be curtailed because of it. It's not worth taking the chance in case one of them decides to bolt. You see the cave?" He pointed to the outcrop. "If the tide has turned, make sure you're this side of it, otherwise we'll be calling Air Sea Rescue."

"Thanks," she said. "It was in your welcome pack but I have to admit, I'd forgotten."

"Don't worry, we would have sent someone to fetch you long before you were in danger. We monitor it very carefully."

Their cautious, too-polite conversation made Amelia think of a dance in which neither of them were sure of the steps: a move forward, one to the side, back a pace, but it was not unpleasant and she wondered if it was the shadow of a potential shared family that hung unspoken between them. She wanted to keep talking to Edward, not only to discover more about the Stones, but because his presence felt familiar, as though they had done this before. She was enjoying the sensation.

"Was your mother's death the reason you booked the grief counselling?" he asked, before putting his fingers to his lips and whistling to the dogs who streaked back across the sand towards them. He clipped on their leads.

"Partly. As you know from my notes, she's the third member of my family I've buried in two years," Amelia replied. "My mother, Joan, died from pancreatic cancer; my father, Patrick,

from heart disease, but before either of them, there was my twelve-year-old daughter, Molly. She was born with a rare lung condition for which, unfortunately, there was no cure. She died three days after her twelfth birthday." Tears welled in Amelia's eyes and she looked away from Edward's sympathetic face, staring again at the glistening seawater. "She died at home, then six weeks later, Dad died."

The silence between them grew. Amelia could not find the words to continue. Her strength had carried her through; the need to care for Joan, to pay a final beautiful tribute to first Molly, and then her father, had stopped her thinking or feeling; but now as she walked with a stranger in the shadow of a house hundreds of miles from home, the reality of all she had suffered in the previous two years overwhelmed her anew. Tears welled in her eyes as she thought about her daughter, the fragile child who had never been able to live life to the full, who would never have been able to run across this beach or chase the dogs because her cruel illness had made her too frail. It seemed so unfair, such a waste of an innocent soul.

"While Mum was ill, we discussed anything and everything," Amelia found herself saying. "She suggested I sort out the boxes she had left in the attic. It's where I found the photograph of Cliffside. It's the real reason I came here. She sent me on this quest. So, here I am, following in the footsteps of Osyth Attwater. It's odd to think she stood here on the brink of womanhood in 1883 and captured the moment in her journal for me to read... What?"

Amelia paused when she realised Edward had stopped.

"You have her journal?"

"Yes, and other photographs with more information about the Attwater family," she said. "A family tree, too, although I have no idea who drew the original."

"Have you read the diary?"

"Not all of it," she admitted. "The writing is challenging but I'm slowly managing to transcribe it. Why?"

"My Great-Aunt Caitlin has been writing a book about our family history. She keeps telling me someone has to unravel the secrets and finally reveal the truth."

"About what?"

Edward shrugged. The sun had risen behind them, changing the breeze from cool to sensuously warm with the promise of a sparkling day to come.

"There are more diaries or journals, as Osyth refers to them," Amelia continued, "although I only have one. I've been adding my own research, too."

They had reached the steps.

"You know, we're sort of in this together," Edward said, "it seems only fair I help." His voice faded away in uncertainty.

Amelia looked at him, her expression curious. "What do you mean, 'in this together'?"

"We must have a link somewhere, otherwise why would we both own a copy of the same photograph of Cliffside?" he said.

Amelia could not think of what to say. This mission was hers; it had been her mother's last request and she was unsure if she was ready to share it with this unpredictable man.

"I'm free today — perhaps we could compare notes," suggested Edward, and Amelia was amused to see his cheeks flush.

"I've got a session with Melissa at 9am," she replied, to give herself some more time to think. Edward was a Stone, so he was more likely to be connected to this mystery than herself. Perhaps it would accelerate her discoveries if they worked

together. Suddenly, she was nodding. "We could meet afterwards."

"In the study about 11am?" he suggested, and Amelia smiled her agreement.

They had reached the side door of the house. Edward gave her an oddly old-fashioned bow from the neck and disappeared down a passageway that led to the private side of the house, leaving Amelia bemused at her decision.

A few hours later, Amelia wandered around the study, her research laid out on one of the tables, her nerves taut with anticipation. While she waited, her interest once again returned to the bookshelves and the George MacDonald books she had read as a child. They were not fashionable fairy tales and she was always intrigued when she saw them on someone else's bookshelf. Selecting the copy of *The Princess and The Goblin*, she opened the well-worn cover and smiled. Osyth Attwater was written inside beside the sketch of a rose. Replacing it, she turned to the sequel, *The Princess and Curdie*. Once again, Osyth's name was inscribed inside the cover but as she flicked through it, Amelia realised there was something odd about the book. Halfway through, a section had been cut out and a key was hidden within the pages.

"I'll show you mine," Edward said as he walked in carrying a box, "if you show me yours."

She jumped, slamming the book shut, smiling at his feeble double entendre, as she shoved it back on the shelf.

"What are you looking at?" he asked but his tone was friendly, rather than accusatory.

"George MacDonald fairy tales," she replied, in response to his quizzical expression. "You don't see them very often but my mother read them to me and I read them to Molly."

Edward glanced at them but Amelia could tell they held no interest and, for reasons she could not explain, she decided not to tell him about the key. Instead, she pointed to the box he had placed beside her own research. "You have other photographs?" she asked.

"More than that."

"More?"

"Diaries and letters from Caitlin's collection."

"Really?"

Edward smiled. "Please don't be offended but I haven't mentioned you to her yet," he said. "I thought it would be better for us to discover if we do have a connection before we get her excited. Caitlin is always talking about our lost family and I don't want to get her hopes up if this turns out to be nothing more than a series of odd coincidences."

"Lost family? What does she mean?"

"I'm not sure. She's very possessive of her research but if we discover you are connected to us, then perhaps she'll share some of her secrets."

Amelia wondered whether or not to mention the fact she and Caitlin had encountered each other from afar but as the old lady did not seem to have mentioned it to Edward, she decided not to worry him either, although the look of terror on Caitlin's face was one that continued to haunt Amelia.

Edward rifled through the paperwork in the box while Amelia watched him with interest: was this man her cousin? She had thought she was alone in the world. Both her parents had been only children. Was it possible she was about to discover she did have blood relatives, after all?

"You're descended from the Stone family?" she confirmed, wandering over to the table and gazing at the selection of images he had placed there.

"As far as I know, yes. Matthew Stone is an ancestor. The image on the website," he said by way of a reminder.

"From checking the census records, I've discovered Penny Attwater was born Penelope Charlotte Stone," Amelia continued, pointing to the picture she had laid down, "and Matthew Isaac Stone was her twin brother. The caption on your website suggests he married a lady called Georgina, although we'd have to check the records to discover her maiden name, unless it's in Caitlin's notes. Why don't you look at my research, while I look at yours, so we can see if we crossover anywhere other than with the photograph of Cliffside?"

Edward gave a nod and they swapped positions in order to study each other's faded Victorian images. Amelia felt her breath catch in her throat as she saw the familiar image of the house, then the formally posed picture of Matthew and Georgina. Scanning down, the next two images were of children, a boy and a girl, their postures as unyielding and rigid as those of the adults. The girl, like the man, had a softness around her eyes and a serene air. Her long hair was tied in a plait, while the curls of the boy stood up around his head as though they were charged with static electricity, his dark eyes staring at the camera in barely concealed fury.

A small gasp of recognition escaped Amelia. "It's him," she said, "the child in the window."

"What child?" asked Edward, looking up from Amelia's notes.

"The angry little boy in the top window of the picture of the house."

"There isn't a child in the window," he said in confusion.

"Yes, there is," she replied, sliding her copy of the photograph towards Edward.

He leaned over her, his eyes widening in surprise. "He looks murderous. Look though, this is my copy. He isn't here."

Amelia stared at the image in bemusement. The window in Edward's version of the photograph was empty. "But that's impossible," she replied.

"And you think this might be him?" asked Edward, pointing to the photograph of the boy staring up at him from his own family pictures.

"Yes, it's the hair mainly, and the eyes." She shuddered — she did not like to say that they looked soulless, as though this child was a phantom. "Do you know who these people are?"

Edward picked up an old-fashioned school exercise book and flipped through the pages. "According to Caitlin's notes," he said, re-joining Amelia at the table and showing her the swirling writing, "he is Kieran Stone, son of Matthew Stone and Georgina Viner, which must be her maiden name. The little girl is their daughter, Katherine."

"Kieran and Katherine!" exclaimed Amelia, selecting an image from her own photographs. "This is Katherine Stone grown up. She married her cousin, Blaise Attwater."

Edward stared at her in surprise. "I've read those names," he said, flicking through the exercise book. "He was an artist, I think, but I didn't know they were cousins."

Amelia's heart pounded with excitement. "Kieran and Osyth were friends, as well as second cousins. She writes about him in her journal. Kieran and Katherine's parents died while they were young, and they were brought up by Osyth's grandparents, Penny and Daniel Attwater. Penny was their aunt." She pointed to the relevant pictures.

"How did their parents die?" he asked.

"I don't know," she said, pulling her laptop towards her and opening her research, "but I have them listed as living here at

Cliffside in the 1871 census, where they are described as 'niece' and 'nephew' to the head of the house, who was Daniel Attwater, the husband of Penny Stone. According to the census, Kieran was ten years old and Katherine was eight." Opening a new tab, she keyed in the name Matthew Isaac Stone, and, after scrolling through, she found a death record. Edward pulled a chair up beside her. "He died in 1865," she said, "but we'd have to order a death certificate to discover the cause, which will take a few weeks to arrive."

Edward pulled his wallet from his back pocket and handed her his credit card. "I'll pay," he said.

Amelia shook her head and pushed the card away. "No, I will," she said and clicked the button to order the certificate. She was about to return to the documents listed, when Edward, who was continuing to flick through Caitlin's notes, asked, "Shall we try Georgina Viner?"

"No problem," she said, keying in the new search. "I know Georgina died young. Osyth claims Kieran was a child when he discovered his mother, dead, in her bedroom."

"Kieran found her?" he asked. "Her son?"

"Yes, Blaise told Osyth."

"How awful," said Edward, picking up Amelia's photograph of the house, "no wonder he was full of rage."

"Here's the record for Georgina's death. I'll order the certificate."

A curious expression crept over Edward's face. "Would you be prepared to do a DNA test?" he asked.

Amelia stared at her screen, thinking about his request. It was not something she had considered but she felt it could do no harm and it might solve the mystery her mother had left her to unravel. "Yes," she replied, "it would be interesting."

Edward grinned, looking years younger, his dark eyes sparkling. "I'll order the kits," he said, "no arguing, and I'll ask Caitlin to do one, too."

Amelia felt a rush of excitement. This was more than she had expected from Edward when he had suggested they pool their research. Grinning to herself, a surge of happiness bubbling through her, she felt justified in her decision to follow her instincts and visit Cliffside.

Then, a shadow loomed over her and, looking up, she jumped, letting out a yelp of surprise. What she had taken to be a bookcase was a hidden door. Framed on the threshold was Caitlin. She would once have been a similar height to Amelia, but age had shrunk her. Her silver hair was in a neat bun at the back of her neck and her piercing, furious blue eyes pinned Amelia to the spot.

"You," she snarled, raising a gnarled finger, pointing at Amelia. "You've come back, have you? Come to take what you always thought was yours by right? Well, you can't have it. I'm the only one who knows where it is, and I will never tell you. You were a devil then, and time won't have changed you, you foul creature!"

Then she turned, slamming the door behind her, leaving Amelia and Edward in stunned silence.

PART FOUR: BERKSHIRE, 1883

CHAPTER ONE

Children crave guidance. They need teaching but their hearts and minds can only be shaped as far as they will allow themselves to bend. In the house on the cliff, two families merged, skipping generations to muddle ages, blurring the lines of the past, each family blending together, until to an outsider, it was impossible to see where the boundaries of each relationship began or ended. The confusion of the loud, rambling inhabitants breathed life into the old house. Each day was welcomed with shouts of joy, tears of despair, mixed blessings of love and hate as siblings fought siblings fought cousins fought aunts fought uncles fought parents. Age did not matter, together the family created its own rules and kept itself safe within the walls of its love...

Osyth broke off from the sentence as she coughed. For the past week she had been in bed with a cold. Today was the first time she had been up and dressed, and, while she felt better, a persistent cough was irritating her.

"Here's some more honey and lemon, Miss Osyth," said Betsy, her grandmother's housekeeper, another member of staff whom Osyth had known since her childhood and regarded as family. Osyth wondered if Betsy had special fairy powers because she managed to appear whenever a coughing fit began.

"Thank you, Betsy," she said, when she was able to speak again.

"Your grandmother said you weren't to tire yourself," Betsy said, looking at Osyth's writing desk with concern.

"I'll just finish this sentence, Betsy," Osyth replied, returning her concentration to her inkwell, and dipping in her pen, "then

113

I promise to put it away. It's more tiring than I'd imagined. Perhaps you could ask Harris to light the fire in the drawing room? I think I'll rest in there and look through the books Uncle Solomon sent me."

"A wise idea, Miss," said Betsy, gathering an empty cup and the discreet pile of handkerchiefs Osyth had left by the door. "If you're not down there in ten minutes, I shall come and fetch you."

Osyth managed a smile before turning back to her journal.

One child, Osyth, was alone. The abandoned daughter of the missing Eudora and her mysterious fairy lover, the mystical child who longed to return to the green islands of her fae-kin. There was no doubting Osyth was a true member of the house on the cliff. Her hair shone the same vivid colour as her mother's and her grandmother's, the red of the setting sun on a clear summer's evening. Only her eyes picked her out as unusual. She viewed the world through eyes of such depth and intensity, their mossy green smoothness could often look black with the constantly shifting currents of her moods. Penny and Daniel loved the serious, silent child who was so different from her lost mother. Eudora had laughed and smiled, bewitching friends and strangers alike with her twinkling blue eyes and her sunshine smile.

Osyth finished the paragraph, rereading it and wrinkling her nose. She was too tired to know whether she liked what she had written or not. The idea of laying on the wide comfortable sofa in front of the drawing room fire was suddenly very appealing. Stowing her journal and pen away, she picked up her battered copy of *The Italian* by Ann Radcliffe and made her way through the unusually quiet house.

Her grandmother and Angharad had gone shopping. She had felt too tired to join them, which was a shame as Angharad was

having a dress fitting and she had wanted to be there to share her friend's excitement. Her grandfather was away with Uncle Noah. Much to her chagrin, they were spending a few days at Cliffside on business matters.

"Even if you were well, I wouldn't take you," Daniel had said when he had visited her sickroom the morning he was leaving. "We will be there only a few days and we will be at the boatyard all day."

"But Taid, I could stay with Mary…"

"No, Osyth," he had said firmly. "Maybe next time. It's more important that you recover."

They would be home later that evening and Osyth was looking forward to hearing the news from Cliffside. She was enjoying being in Windsor and visiting her uncles and aunts in London, but her heart ached for the roar of the ocean. The river offered some solace, but it did not have the intense elemental pull of the crash of the turning tide at the base of the cliff.

Flopping down on to the sofa, she sighed and stretched out full-length in a position she would never have adopted if anyone else had been in the room. The pile of periodicals and books her uncle had sent had been placed on the table beside the sofa but she did not have the energy to read them, instead she removed the letter from Kieran that she had been using as a bookmark. Laying on her back, she tucked her elbows into her sides until she was in a comfortable position and began to reread it, thrilling at the news of his exciting life as a medical student:

You would never believe the things I am learning but they are not suitable for me to write about because they could be construed as shocking. I do not suppose for one moment that you would be upset, dearest Osyth, but for the

sake of propriety it would be unseemly. When we see each other, I will tell you more...

There was a timid knock on the door and Betsy peered into the room. "Are you awake, dear?" she asked.

"Yes," Osyth replied, scrabbling into a more dignified position.

"The young man who works with Mr Attwater is here with the paperwork your grandfather requested," she said. "Do you feel well enough to see him for a few moments or shall I suggest he return later?"

"Did he leave his name?" asked Osyth, excitement bubbling inside her.

"Here's his card."

Osyth glanced down and suppressing the smile that fought to light up her face, she attempted insouciance. "Mr F Meyrick," she said. "We've met on a number of occasions. Give me a moment to tidy myself, then please show him in, Betsy. Could you also send in some tea with crumpets? It's a very cold day and we must take good care of him."

Betsy retreated and Osyth flew to mirror that hung in the corner of the room, pinching her pale cheeks to try and give herself some colour. Luckily, her hair was neat for once, and she was wearing a pale green tartan dress that suited her colouring. The tawny silk scarf she had placed around her shoulders gave a hint of warmth to her pale face. She was also delighted that in a moment of boredom earlier she had put on some of her precious Floris White Rose fragrance to cheer herself up.

Seating herself in her grandmother's chair, she opened *The Italian* again, but she was too nervous to read. Ever since she had arrived in Windsor at the beginning of September she had

been becoming increasingly fond of Frederick Meyrick. When they had met in the summer at the wedding, they had barely exchanged more than a few words. However, her grandparents were prolific at entertaining and Mr Meyrick, as the cousin of a baronet who was a neighbour from their home in Pembrokeshire, as well as an employee in the offices at the boatyard, had been invited to a number of their dinners and soirées. Osyth had noticed her grandmother usually sat them near each other and a tentative friendship had begun to form between them. To Osyth's irritation, they had rarely been alone for more than a few moments, so their conversations had always been superficial.

"I know nothing about him," she had lamented one night to Angharad. "He might be engaged or even married."

"It's unlikely," her friend had replied, "or someone would have mentioned it."

"How do I know what he feels about me?"

"He blushes every time he speaks to you. He gets flustered, stammers and drops things. I would say these are all conclusive evidence that he likes you."

"Really? Perhaps he wants to be friends."

"If you ask me, I think he's interested in more than friendship."

Since then, Osyth had included a request in her prayers each night asking to have the opportunity to spend some time alone with Frederick. It seemed her wish had been granted.

When Betsy knocked, she was pretending to read and made a show of looking up when Frederick was announced.

"Miss Osyth, Mr Frederick Meyrick to see you."

"Frederick," said Osyth, rising in as good an imitation of her grandmother's elegance as she could manage. "What a wonderful surprise."

"Miss Attwater, Osyth, I hope this isn't an intrusion," he managed and Osyth was delighted to see a pink tinge creeping up his cheeks, his words tumbling out in a rush. "I know you've been ill and I wouldn't want to tire you."

"Not at all, I am quite well," she replied. "Although, you will have to make do with only my company. My grandmother and Angharad have not yet returned from their shopping expedition."

The door opened and Betsy ushered in her daughter, Ethel, who was carrying a tray of tea. Once it had been arranged to Betsy's satisfaction, she smiled at Osyth, then ushered Ethel away. Pouring tea and serving Frederick with a hot buttered crumpet kept Osyth focused, and she felt her nerves melting away.

"Angharad is having a dress fitting," she explained, "and then Nain wanted to take her to the new teashop."

He sipped his own tea, then bit into the buttery crumpet before speaking. "Osyth, may I ask you something?" he said.

"Of course."

"Why do you call your grandparents Nain and Taid?"

"It's Welsh for grandmother and grandfather," she explained. "I was born in London but my mother returned to Cliffside when I was only a baby."

"And your father?" he asked, then blushed. "I'm sorry, this is very nosy of me. Please don't feel you have to answer, but I'm intrigued. Noah told me you were an orphan and had been adopted by your grandparents?"

Osyth placed her cup on the table beside her and smiled. It was not often people asked her the details of her past but she enjoyed talking about it. The story was, in her opinion, extremely sad, but also wonderfully romantic. "My mother was Eudora Attwater — she was Nain and Taid's second child,

after Uncle Noah. She was impetuous but loveable and while she was staying with some friends in Ireland, she met my father, Egan O'Reilly. They had a whirlwind romance and were married a few months after they met. My father worked for a shipping company and, shortly after I was born, he embarked on a voyage, but the ship and all hands were lost. My mother had taken me to stay with Nain and Taid at Cliffside and she was said to have been so broken-hearted by the news, she never recovered. She caught a chill and three weeks after the news of my father's demise, my mother died, too."

"Oh, my dear, I'm so sorry," gasped Frederick.

"Really, you have no need to be upset on my behalf, I don't remember my parents at all. Nain and Taid adopted me."

"But what about your father's family?"

"He was an only child and his mother was his one living relative. She was elderly and died six months after my father went missing."

"What a dreadful tale."

"Yes, it's very sad but my life has been happy and I've had all my aunts, uncles and cousins to look after me. Nain and Taid adopted me under their surname but when I was old enough to understand they asked if I would prefer to use my father's name. I declined. I didn't want to be the only O'Reilly in a houseful of Attwaters and Stones."

They sipped their tea and Osyth offered Frederick another crumpet.

"Your family is very confusing," said Frederick, after a pause. "There are so many of you."

"When you're part of a huge family, you don't notice because everyone is an individual but I suppose, looking in, it must be very muddled," she said with a smile. "It doesn't help that Kieran and Katherine were brought up by Nain and Taid, too."

"Where do Kieran and Katherine fit in?" Frederick asked, and Osyth noticed a definite hardening of his tone when he said Kieran's name.

"They're also orphans," she said. "Their father was my Great-Uncle Matthew, Nain's twin brother. His wife, Georgina, died and Matthew took Kieran and Katherine to Cliffside to be with his sister while they grieved. Shortly after that, my mother died, then there was an accident and Matthew died too. Nain told me it was a terrible time."

"What sort of accident?" Frederick sounded horrified.

"I don't know," admitted Osyth, "no one has ever told me the details and if ever I've asked, they've said I was too young or it was the wrong time to discuss it. In the end, I stopped asking. It upsets Nain and I would never want to hurt her. What about you, Frederick? You know so much about my family, but it seems to be all we ever speak about. Do you have a large family?"

"Not really. In my direct family there is only my mother, Sybilla, and myself. My father died when I was four years old."

"How sad."

"I don't really remember my father," admitted Frederick. "He left my mother comfortably off and she lives with a companion in Kent. Papa was distantly related to the Meyricks who lived at Bodorgan House in Anglesey and their cousins who once lived in Bush House, which is in Pembroke Dock, not far from Cliffside. The Meyricks now reside at Bangeston Hall. I don't know the full twists and turns of the family history but I know we have a connection to the Devereux family at Lamphey Hall. The current baronet and MP for Pembrokeshire, Sir Thomas Charlton, took the Meyrick name by Royal Charter so he could inherit the estate. We're fourth

cousins, or something like that, and he and his wife, Mary, have always been very kind to me."

Osyth absorbed this information. The Meyricks were colleagues of her grandfather's. The land which Daniel owned had once belonged to Frederick's family but her grandfather had purchased it from them a few years earlier when he decided to develop docks in Pembrokeshire, as well as Windsor. "Is the Meyrick connection how you began working with my grandfather?" she asked.

Frederick placed his cup on the table beside him and shifted nervously in his seat. "It was through your uncle, Solomon," he said, after some awkward fidgeting. "I write poetry, you see. I sent some to his periodical and he suggested we meet. My work wasn't terribly good but he was very encouraging and gave me some advice, then he asked me how I was earning a living. I was planning to work for a shipping agent in the East End of London but he asked if I would be interested in a role with his father's company. A few days later, I met with Mr Attwater and Noah and they offered me a position as a clerk."

Osyth silently thanked her Uncle Solomon with all her heart for taking an interest in Frederick and drawing him into their circle. Solomon had done this before with other young men but never with such success as Frederick. Usually they remained shadows in the background, known only by their names while Solomon mentored them, until they melted away to be replaced with another hopeful artisan.

"You probably think I'm foolish for writing poetry, catching dreams…" Frederick murmured, blushing to the roots of his light brown hair.

"No, I think it's wonderful," Osyth said. "If it isn't too bold, I write too —"

However, before she could confide further, the door burst open and her grandmother walked in with Angharad a few steps behind, both pink-cheeked from the icy December air.

"Mr Meyrick," exclaimed Penny, throwing an amused glance at her granddaughter, "how wonderful to see you. I do hope Osyth has been entertaining you."

"Mrs Attwater, how do you do?" said Frederick, leaping to his feet and once more looking flustered. "Mr Attwater requested these papers and I wanted to deliver them personally to ensure their safe arrival."

"He will appreciate your efforts…" began Penny as Frederick brandished a leather case, before placing it on the table without looking at what he was doing, so overwhelmed was he to be surrounded by women. It hovered momentarily on the corner, before tipping onto the floor. Osyth and Angharad both leapt forward to catch it but the folder fell, strewing its contents across the patterned carpet.

"My apologies," stammered Frederick, taking the pages from the two girls as they gathered them together.

Penny laughed. "Why don't you take a moment to reassemble your papers. Use Daniel's desk," she said. "I'll call for more tea."

Osyth and Angharad exchanged a grin, then Osyth saw a stray piece of paper near the fire. "Here's another one, Frederick," she said, scooping it up. She turned it over and saw it was a list of figures — payments, she thought, glancing at the pound signs, then as she reached over to hand it to him, the name at the top caught her eye: *Payment for Mrs E O'Reilly*.

"Thank you, Osyth," he said with a grateful smile. "This will only take a moment."

Osyth returned to the sofa, having given up her grandmother's chair now Penny had returned, her mind racing. *It must be a coincidence*, she told herself. *There must be more than one Mrs E O'Reilly in the world*. It was an eerie thought, though, that her grandfather dealt with a woman who bore her late mother's name.

"Osyth, my dear, are you quite well?" Penny's concerned voice broke into Osyth's racing thoughts. Her gentle hand was on Osyth's forehead. "You've gone awfully pale, though you don't feel feverish. Perhaps you've overdone things."

"Yes," murmured Osyth, wondering whether to question her grandmother, but before she could speak, Penny had taken charge with her usual calm efficiency.

"Angharad, would you take Osyth upstairs to rest, please?"

Osyth felt her friend position her hand under her elbow and help her rise to her feet. Her head cleared and she turned, her smile apologetic. "Thank you for a pleasant afternoon, Frederick," she said, then allowed Angharad to lead her out of the room, her mind full of what she had read, somehow unable to dismiss the name from her mind.

CHAPTER TWO

As Osyth stared out of the window, familiar sights came into view. The castle in the distance, the flash and glint of the river and the labyrinth of roads and alleyways making up the busy warehouses and manufacturing area of the town that led down to the boatyard owned by her grandfather. Their coach pulled away from the pungent smell of the river, heading for the centre of Windsor and the offices of Lovegrove and Durant, the family solicitors. Osyth gazed out at the black trees, their outline harsh against the frosty day and the low grey skies. The December weather was bleak, bringing freezing rain and soupy fogs.

Whenever she travelled through Clewer into Windsor, she could not help but imagine how it would once have looked. Ever since Daniel had told of the ancient notoriety of the area where her grandparents' large house was situated, she had been fascinated. Once famed for its alehouses and brothels, the roads had been dangerous to walk at night but now they were residential and Maybank was an imposing detached villa situated in a large, landscaped garden. A small island of family life within the past shadows of dark deeds.

Respectable, she thought, *we are respectable*. In fact, discovering her grandparents had been step-siblings before their marriage had given Osyth a thrill of excitement. It had been the first suggestion that her grandparents were, perhaps, more interesting than she had imagined. To her, they had always been a normal, contented married couple with a successful family business. Part of their year was spent in Windsor, the rest at Cliffside. Her grandfather occasionally travelled for

work; her grandmother sat on local committees. Osyth was beginning to understand that she wanted more than this sedate way of life. Uncle Noah had once described Eudora as having a restless soul, and Osyth wondered if she had inherited something similar from her mother.

Her mind drifted as the carriage jogged along, toying with the name, Mrs E O'Reilly. It had been haunting her ever since she had seen the list of payments on the document Frederick had dropped. She glanced across at her grandmother who was staring out of the opposite window, lost in her own thoughts. The silence between them was companionable. Neither had ever felt the need to fill the void with unnecessary chatter.

It will soon be Christmas, thought Osyth, as the brightly decorated shops of Windsor came into view. *Kieran will be home in time for his twenty-first birthday.*

She wondered if this would be the last Christmas he would ever spend with the family. With his birthday would come his inheritance, which included his parents' home, a tall town house on Richmond Green in Surrey. In his last letter he had told Osyth he would be opening up the house again and using it as his permanent residence: *You and Angharad will always be welcome…* He had made no mention of the rest of the family.

It was odd for Osyth to think that Kieran would soon have independent means. She knew from listening to her grandparents that he would inherit not only the house, but also a quarter share in the Attwater and Stone Boatyard. The business had been a partnership between her great-grandfather, George Stone and Taid's father, Aubrey. When George had died, his half of the business had been divided between Penny and Matthew, although the bulk had gone to Matthew. In his will, Matthew had divided his share equally between Kieran and Katherine.

As their official guardians, Penny and Daniel had kept the money for Matthew's children in trust. Katherine had inherited hers on her marriage to Blaise and Kieran would inherit a large sum from his mother as well as the house and money from his father.

Things are changing, Osyth thought and, while she was happy for Kieran, she was sad for herself.

"What's Angharad doing today?" asked Penny, cutting into Osyth's thoughts.

"She's gone to the library," replied Osyth. "You know what an avid reader she's become in the past few months." She did not mention to Penny that Angharad had an admirer at the library who was courting her in a gentle manner. Even Osyth had not yet met this mystery gallant but Angharad had promised that soon, all would be revealed. "Incidentally, Nain, is there any chance she'd be able to come with us tomorrow? She could wear my blue gown."

The following evening there was a Christmas party at St Leonard's Hill, the nearby manor house that was owned by Sir Francis Tress Barry, a businessman, baronet and amateur archaeologist. As an old friend of Daniel's and a sponsor of Solomon's magazine, the family had been invited. It was to be a spectacular event, designed to show off the magnificent renovations that had recently been completed.

"Darling, you know why Angharad wasn't invited," said Penny. "After all these weeks, you're the only one who is not adapting to this situation. You and Angharad may have grown up together at Cliffside and be the best of friends — and we all see her as part of the family — but, in reality, her mother is my housekeeper. Her official role is your companion, and companions are not invited to illustrious parties hosted by baronets like Sir Francis Tress Barry. I'm sorry, Osyth."

Osyth sighed. "It's seems so unfair," she said.

"Does Angharad want to come?" asked Penny.

"No, she was horrified when I suggested asking you and Taid."

"There you are then," said Penny with a certain finality.

The coach rumbled on and Osyth continued to mull over the social inequality in her and Angharad's friendship. It had always bothered Osyth but while they had been in the wild and rambling house perched on the edge of the cliff, it had been less pronounced.

"When I'm married, like Katherine," announced Osyth, as they turned into the busy main high street where their destination was situated, "I'll find Angharad a wonderful husband of equal status, so we can spend all our time together."

"You're a terrible romantic," laughed Penny. "Perhaps Taid and I should have stopped Noah and Solomon filling your head with tales of fairies and courtly love."

"Their stories are what has given me such great compassion," Osyth protested with a glint in her eye. "Would you want me to be hardened to other people's sorrow, Nain?"

"Not so much a fairy princess as a little devil," replied Penny, her blues eyes twinkling with mischief. "Although, we must both pretend to be women of considerable seriousness for the next hour."

"Is this my surprise?" asked Osyth. "To be sensible for an hour."

"No, but you will want to keep your wits about you while the details are explained. This is a secret between us and we will only be able to discuss it when we are alone, so you must pay attention."

Intrigued but assuming her grandmother was joking, Osyth followed Penny into the offices of Lovegrove and Durant. She had been here before, when her grandfather had needed to deliver some papers. It had been many years earlier but the offices had not changed. A large aspidistra dominated one side of the black-and-white tiled vestibule. A young man seated at a desk leapt from his feet and ushered them into the waiting room, and they had barely made themselves comfortable when Mr Lovegrove hurried to meet them.

"Mrs Attwater, Miss Attwater, what a pleasure."

Ernest Lovegrove was short with a round mound of a belly that was extravagantly upholstered in a waistcoat of crimson. A pair of dark trousers and long frock coat calmed some of its exuberance, but the brilliant peacock-blue cravat competed with the festive red to see who could be the brightest. Osyth had always liked Ernest Lovegrove, taking great delight in the eccentricity of his clothes.

"Such a cold day," he pronounced, "but the fire is warm in my office and Jones will bring in tea. We have serious matters to discuss but there is no legal reason why we cannot do so in comfort."

Osyth and Penny followed the waddling figure of Ernest Lovegrove and were soon settled in chairs opposite his desk where a cream-coloured cardboard folder tied with pink legal ribbon waited. Osyth glanced at her grandmother who was watching the solicitor with eager eyes. Osyth reached out and squeezed Penny's hand. "Why are we here, Nain?"

"An early Christmas present for you, my darling. It would have been your mother's but she has no need of it and you might."

"Would you like me to explain, Mrs Att—"

"Penny, please, Ernest," she interrupted. "We have known each other for so many years and I appreciate your discretion in this delicate matter. Osyth knows nothing about this and, at present, doesn't need all the details. I will tell her those when she is older. For now, let's impart the exciting information."

Osyth looked from one to the other in bemusement.

"Very well." Ernest removed a sheet of paper from the folder and beamed at Osyth. "In a short while, I shall be asking you to sign this document. It's nothing to be alarmed about, in fact, it's a pleasant task but first I must explain the circumstances so you are fully conversant of how this bequest works."

"Bequest?" asked Osyth, alarm filling her. "Nain, are you dying?"

"No, darling, no," Penny assured her. "It's a legal term. This is something I've chosen to give to you today as it may be of use." She nodded to Ernest to continue.

"When your great-grandmother, Laura Stone, as she became with her marriage to Penny's father, George Stone, died, she left substantial property. It had been given to her by her mother and she wished it to continue down the female line of the family. She was rather a modern thinker and felt the men were given too many things by right, so she tied this section of her property into a more complicated legal framework. It did not have to pass down a direct bloodline but it always had to go to a woman. As she had no daughters and only one living son, your grandfather, Daniel Attwater, she looked to her stepdaughter, who was also her daughter-in-law."

Osyth looked at Penny. "You, Nain?"

"Yes, my dear. Laura was a sweet and gentle woman; I could not have asked for a kinder or more loving stepmother. When she became my mother-in-law too, I was doubly blessed."

"A charming woman," Ernest agreed, his face momentarily taking on a sad and respectful expression. "Also, an intelligent one. She passed the properties to your grandmother; however, it was done with a certain amount of skulduggery and even now, your grandfather has no idea of the size of this bequest from his mother to his wife. He is a sensible man and decided not to investigate. He trusted his mother; he trusts his wife."

"You have property in your own name?" asked Osyth, surprised.

"Oh yes, and with the introduction of The Married Women's Property Act last year in 1882, even if he wished to challenge my right to own property, he has no grounds."

"Where is it?"

"In Clewer, not far from Maybank. A row of cottages, well, three rows to be exact, although over the years, a few have been sold. There are eighteen left."

"Eighteen cottages?" said Osyth, staggered. "Why did you never tell me, Nain? I thought we told each other everything."

"Your grandmother wasn't at liberty to reveal this particular secret," said Ernest. "There is a strange covenant that comes with them. The owner is not allowed to tell their heir of the existence of this legacy. It is something purely for the owner, so that whoever is in possession of them can do with them as they please without recourse to spouses, siblings or other family members. Until last year, it was problematic for women to have autonomy over their inheritances, which was why the secrecy clause was introduced. It's not something I've ever come across before," he continued, "and I'm not sure, if it had

been tested in a court of law, whether it would have been legally binding but it has never been challenged."

Osyth stared at him and as the silence grew, he shifted in his seat and said, "Hopefully, this is a pleasant surprise."

For a moment, the words did not make sense, then realisation began to creep into Osyth's mind. "Nain," she said, turning in her seat until she was facing her grandmother, "are you giving me these cottages?"

"Yes, my dear."

"Why?"

"You are now eighteen years old and, apart from the allowance which Taid and I give you, you have no other income. Your mother was very young when she died and your father was at the beginning of his career — the few pounds he left went to his mother. She left a small amount in trust, which will come to you on your twenty-first birthday, but I wanted to ensure that, no matter what happens to Taid and I, you have the financial means to support yourself. Ours is a large family and the bulk of Taid's business assets will pass to Noah, Blaise and Solomon. Xenia is in a good strong marriage and William has already arranged things so she will never want for anything, but for a long time, I have worried about you, so I contacted Ernest and asked if the properties could be transferred into your name when you were eighteen. He has checked and there is no reason why not. Once the transfer of ownership is made, you will have a substantial income from the rents of the cottages and, should you ever need capital, Ernest will help you to sell one or more of the properties. This makes you a woman of some substance."

The next hour passed in a blur as Osyth signed several documents and was shown the extensive account books. When they finally left, gasping as the biting cold hit them after the warmth of the office, Penny squeezed her hand. "You understand that you can't tell anyone about this," she said as they settled themselves back into their coach. "Not even Angharad and certainly not Kieran."

"But they're my friends…"

"My darling, as you've said yourself, you're no longer our Princess Osyth of the Fairy Rings. You are a young lady and, since signing the papers, a wealthy one. I applaud and encourage your writing and your imagination but the time has come for you to begin edging your way into the adult world. Life is not a fairy tale, Osyth. There will be unhappinesses along the way. You have great inner strength but never be afraid to ask for help."

"Not telling them feels like lying," Osyth said, then regretted the bluntness of her tone. She did not want her grandmother to think she was not delighted and appreciative of the gift she had been given.

"Secrets sometimes feel like lies, but, you must remember, everyone has secrets, Osyth; some small, some large and we weave them into the fabric of our existence. Perhaps you should know the full history of the cottages. Then you will understand." Reaching across, she took Osyth's hand and tucked it under the blanket. "Taid's mother was born Laura Jacobs, the daughter of another boat manufacturer. Unfortunately, Laura's father suffered poor health and was forced to sell the business, which he did, to Aubrey Attwater, Taid's father. It was a messy affair and my father, George, who was Aubrey's business partner, was unhappy with the way it was handled. It left poor William Jacobs almost penniless.

132

Father stepped in and renegotiated, offering the man a pension, which he accepted. However, what Father hadn't known was that part of the agreement was for Aubrey to marry Laura, William's only child."

"How awful," exclaimed Osyth. "How could your father have been in business with someone so unpleasant?"

"We are not always able to choose the people who inhabit our lives," said Penny. "My father and Aubrey had both inherited their shares of the Attwater and Stone Boat and Timber Yard from their fathers, who had been firm friends. Unfortunately, their sons could not have been more different in temperament. However, they were both professionals and somehow my father was able to discover a way to work with Aubrey."

"Did Laura have to marry him?"

"Sadly, yes, despite the eighteen-year age gap between them," said Penny. "Aubrey was a cruel man — he didn't see Laura as a person, he saw her as an attractive asset and someone to give him heirs. They had four children, two girls and two boys: Emily, Mary-Ann, Lucas and Daniel, your grandfather. Sadly, both girls died before their second birthdays and Lucas was killed in a boating accident. Your grandfather tried to save him but he wasn't able to reach him in time. He's never really forgiven himself."

"Oh, Nain," gasped Osyth. "How awful."

"Laura was devastated but Aubrey's response was that she was still young and they could have more children. For several years, Laura suffered great unpleasantness and cruelty at her husband's hands. Laura was in fear for her life and when Daniel once tried to step between his parents, his father beat him with a walking stick."

Osyth stared at her grandmother, repulsed by her words.

"It was while Aubrey was away on a business trip that Laura received a letter saying she had inherited the cottages from her Aunt Lucy. She spoke to Mr Lovegrove's father and asked if it would be possible to keep the legacy a secret. He was no friend of Aubrey and agreed. Laura sold two of the cottages in order to have a fund of cash, which she left lodged with the solicitor, in case she or Daniel ever needed to get away from Aubrey."

"What happened?" asked Osyth.

"Shortly after this incident, Aubrey died from apoplexy, so Laura was free, but she left the secrecy clause in place. Four years later, my beloved mother, Eleanor died. By then, Father had taken Daniel into the company, even though he was only fifteen years old. Eventually, after spending time together, Father and Laura fell in love and decided to marry."

"Were they happy?"

"Yes, very. Father died before Laura but they had many happy years together."

"And Laura left the cottages to you," confirmed Osyth. "Were you ever in need of help, Nain? Is that why she chose you?"

For a moment, Osyth thought her grandmother hesitated, but then Penny smiled, shaking her head.

"No, my darling, Laura left them to me because I was her stepdaughter and her daughter-in-law. Taid has always been a wonderful and kind husband."

The carriage arrived outside Maybank.

"Our trip today must remain a secret," said Penny. "You are not lying to anyone, Osyth. You are merely making an adult choice to keep your business to yourself. It is a lesson and a skill that will serve you well if you're able to master the technique. You do not have to share everything you think or

feel with those around you; in fact, it is sensible if you don't. Now, let us go inside and prepare for our guests."

"What guests?" Osyth asked in surprise.

"Blaise and Katherine are due to arrive this afternoon as a surprise for Kieran's birthday," Penny said. "They will also be spending Christmas with us."

Beaming with excitement, Osyth climbed down from the carriage, her mind whirring with all she had discovered on their clandestine trip.

CHAPTER THREE

Osyth was standing on the deck of her grandfather's newest boat.

"The *Windsor Princess*, named for you, my darling," Daniel had said, handing her a bottle of champagne to smash across the hull before she and the rest of the family boarded for a cruise down the Thames.

Yesterday evening had been the Christmas party at St Leonard's Hill, the nearby manor house owned by Sir Francis Tress Barry and it had been an exciting whirl of laughter, dancing and sophistication. Dressed in a spectacular gown of sea-green silk, her first formal gown, Osyth had felt transported to another world. The dress, cut wide across the top to reveal her shoulders, was covered with swathes of tulle, held in place by tiny silk flowers while the skirt fell to the floor in a column of frothing ruffles. Wrapped in the scent of her beloved White Rose, Osyth imagined her dress was a wave from her beloved St Brides Bay made manifest in silk.

To her delight, Frederick Meyrick had been among the guests and they had spent a happy evening caught up in the festivities. At one point, he had shyly suggested she call him Freddie.

"All my friends do, and I hope we're friends," he had whispered, squeezing her hand as they waited for ices.

It was as Osyth and her family were leaving that Freddie had pushed a letter into her hand.

"It had been my intention to deliver this to you tomorrow but as you are here, this may put your mind at rest on our mystery."

A few days earlier, under the guise of fetching more ink from her grandfather's study, Osyth had instead searched his desk, but she had discovered no further clues as to the identity of Mrs E O'Reilly. Boldly, she had written to Frederick asking if he would help, convinced he would be able to reveal more. Curious, but not wishing to draw awkward questions from her grandparents, Osyth had waited until she was in bed before reading Freddie's note.

My dearest Osyth, it has been difficult to search too far but from the records I have been able to check, apart from that one sheet of payments, there seem to be no other records pertaining to Mrs E O'Reilly. When this occurs, it is often because the customer placed one order which has then been paid in full and no account was necessary or the account, having been settled, has subsequently been closed. I hope this in some way answers your question, however, I will continue to search.

Yours, Frederick

This had not helped Osyth because she had been certain payments were being made to Mrs E O'Reilly rather than the other way around.

Osyth gazed into the murky river water, letting her imagination wander. *The child was happiest left to play alone, entering a world of her own creation where fairies sang, waited on by fleets of magical servants. Knights on winged horses kept them safe and, when the sun had set, tales were told by bards as they feasted at the table of the Fae-King. Violet Devas of the Eastern provinces sang their ethereal songs in order to maintain the structure of all that is. While the Ellylldan — the tiniest of elves — blew on their pipes of mischief, calling to their beautiful cousins, the Gwragedd Annwn, the water maidens, as they rode their white stallions across the peaks of the waves. In her enchanted world, Osyth was a princess, the heir to the kingdom, waiting for the return of her*

mother before they both took their rightful places on the golden thrones she imagined in her dreams.

"My mother, the fairy princess," Osyth said aloud. "The loved and loveable, Eudora Attwater, gone forever."

Rain pattered on Osyth's umbrella as she delivered these words to the glowering clouds. The winter breeze swirled around her while the less pleasant smells associated with a working river — diesel fuel, chemicals and the distinct tang of sewage — drifted past.

"Darling, why don't you come into the stateroom? It's freezing up here."

Uncle Noah was beside her, draping a woollen shawl over her coat.

"I was talking to the waves," she said, tucking her hand under the arm he proffered.

Noah gave a complicit smile. "Did they reply?"

"Not yet," she said, "although we were discussing the Dream Catcher and that is an answer which may take some time to consider."

A look of confusion crossed Noah's face. "The Dream Catcher?"

"From the story you've been telling me since I was a child," she reminded him. "The Fae-King will give me the answer to my question when I find the Dream Catcher."

"Osyth, my dear," said Noah, his tone gentle and not without concern, "it was a story, there are no Fae-Kings and no Dream Catchers."

"Which is all you know," laughed Osyth as they entered the warmth of the stateroom and she hurried over to join Xenia and Penny.

"Hello sweet one," said Xenia, drawing Osyth closer to the fire. "How was Isis?"

"As beautiful as ever," Osyth replied.

"You two, with your talk of river goddesses," laughed Daniel, kissing Penny on the cheek as he joined them. "What about the river gods?"

"They were there too but the goddesses are more understanding to discussions of a female nature," replied Osyth.

Behind them, there was a gale of laughter and they turned to watch as Noah's eldest son, Alvar, showed off his new party trick — juggling three small rubber balls — to the admiration of the rest of the family.

Yet there are two of us missing, thought Osyth.

Angharad was on her way back to Cliffside after receiving a letter telling her that her mother, Mary, had fallen and was ill in bed. Osyth was sad to say goodbye to her friend, who would remain at Cliffside for Christmas, and for an unspecified amount of time afterwards, depending on her mother's health, but she understood and was desperate for news of Mary, too, who had been like another mother to her during her childhood.

Kieran's absence, however, had caused discord throughout the entire family. His twenty-first birthday had been celebrated with a small party a week earlier. Blaise and Katherine had returned from Paris as a surprise, which, at first, Osyth had thought had pleased Kieran. He had been friendly and calm, telling them about his medical studies and his growing interest in the pharmaceutical lessons, particularly the creation of tinctures, syrups and medicines. He appeared to be making the same level of effort he had employed at Katherine's wedding but Osyth knew him well enough to know he was fighting to keep control of his temper.

"Kieran, please tell me what's wrong?" she had said as the party had drawn to a close.

He had turned his strange dark eyes towards her and this close, she had realised he looked different. His always pale skin seemed almost translucent and there had been violet shadows under his bloodshot eyes.

"My birthday is tomorrow," he had informed her, "and I will take possession of my parents' house. I have already instructed staff and intend to use this as my permanent residence. You will always be welcome, my dear Osyth, but apart from Katherine, there are no other members of this family whom I will admit. I shall not be returning to Maybank for Christmas; in fact, if possible, my intention now is to distance myself from the Attwater family."

"But Kieran…" she had begun, only to have him interrupt.

"My life is my own," he had said and an edge of harshness had entered his voice. "I wish to live it away from these people. You are not safe here, and when you realise you reside among liars, thieves and lunatics, the door to my house will be open and waiting for you. It will be your place of sanctuary where I shall always protect you."

"You don't mean it," she had said, feeling tears welling in her eyes. "What about us: you, me and Angharad? Our friendship?"

Kieran had given her a look of mingled pity and scorn. "You are no longer Princess Osyth of the Fairy Rings," he had snarled. "The time has come to grow up. Our lives have moved on irrevocably. When you discover the things I have learned about your beloved grandparents, you will not want to be in their company either. Remember, Osyth, my home is your home."

"What do you mean?" she had demanded but Kieran refused to elucidate.

He had left the following morning, clearing his belongings from Maybank and sending word to Cliffside for his remaining items to be delivered to Richmond. No one, not even Osyth, had heard from him since.

Osyth's mind wandered to her trip out with her grandmother. Part of her was delighted with the legacy bestowed upon her, it gave her a feeling of confidence and a growing sense of wonder at the freedom the income from the rents would provide, but the thing that nagged her was the very fact it was clandestine. Her grandmother had kept this secret for years, so had Osyth's paternal great-grandmother, Laura Jacobs.

Secrets lead to lies, thought Osyth. *What other secrets has Nain kept? And what did Kieran mean when he spoke of liars, thieves and lunatics? I wonder if they think me simple with my tales of the fairy-land*, she mused. *Time to grow up, that's what everyone keeps telling me. Put my stories and my beliefs behind me. But the first task in my quest to maturity will be discovering why Kieran holds Nain and Taid in such disdain.*

A few days later, Osyth was curled in the chair in the small sitting room off the drawing room where her aunts and uncles were playing a noisy parlour game. Her younger cousins had returned to the nursery for their tea.

Snuggled up with the new book Uncle Solomon had given her for Christmas: *The Princess and Curdie* by George MacDonald, her eyes were heavy. This was the sequel to one of her favourite stories, *The Princess and The Goblin*, which she had first read when it was published in instalments in the magazine *Good Words for the Young*. They were thrilling tales

about a princess who befriends a miner, Curdie. The first tale had been packed with creatures and adventures, and this book was already drawing her into its magical realm but the heavy Christmas lunch was making her sleepy and she knew it would not be long before she succumbed.

Whispered voices woke her and, for a moment, as her eyes adjusted to the gloom, she was unsure where she was, wondering if the princess and her friend Curdie from the book had joined her. Then she remembered she was in the small sitting room. The lamps had not been lit and the only light came from the fire so with the blanket pulled over her, her chair was concealed in darkness. Not wishing to be caught eavesdropping, her first instinct was to alert the whisperers to her presence but before she could speak, she heard her name and paused.

"Do you think Kieran's told Osyth?" Xenia said, her voice low, urgent.

"No," replied Blaise.

"Would it be wise to inform her?" Solomon said, and there was a pause. It was no surprise to Osyth when she heard Noah reply. He was the eldest and his siblings always deferred to his wisdom.

"When the time is right," he said, "the information would be better coming from one of us rather than the garbled and warped interpretation Kieran will tell her."

Osyth held her breath and listened hard. They must have secreted themselves in here for one of their family conferences, something she knew her aunt and uncles held on a regular basis.

"Do you think he would dare?" asked Blaise.

"Does he even know what happened?" Xenia's voice was angry.

Noah spoke again. "When we had our meeting with Ernest Lovegrove for Kieran to receive the full details of his inheritance, there were certain things that needed to be explained to him. It transpired he did not know or had never understood the methods by which his parents died and he was shocked when the truth was revealed, particularly his mother —"

"How could he not know?" interrupted Blaise, his voice ringing with contempt. "Katherine knows and she is younger than Kieran."

"His reaction was so strong; it was plain he wasn't acting. This is why he's so angry and refused to come for Christmas."

"Perhaps Kieran chose to forget," said Solomon, his tone reflective.

"Chose to forget?" Xenia sounded incredulous.

"It can happen," said Solomon. "Wise men of science who study the patterns of the brain and people's moods claim we can wipe away large parts of our past if it is too distressing."

"You and your modern thinking," said Xenia but her tone had softened.

"Whether this is the case or not," said Noah with a bite of impatience, "Kieran has been using his time to research asylums. The fact he is training as a doctor has given him access to information we had not anticipated."

"Who?" asked Blaise, his voice hoarse.

"Mother."

There was a collective gasp.

"Does he know?" Xenia asked.

"Not everything," Noah replied, "certainly not about how his own mother, Georgina, is linked to our mother. If the news of how Georgina died has upset him, then the time leading up to Georgina's marriage to Matthew will disturb him even more.

143

He already irrationally blames our mother for all the terrible things that have happened in his life, if he discovers the true circumstances, it is not only his life he could ruin. This is why I wonder whether it might be time to tell Osyth…"

"No, we can't," said Solomon. "Not yet."

"Why not? She will have to know one day and it would be better coming from us," said Blaise.

"Surely, these are decisions for Mother and Father," suggested Xenia.

"Of course," replied Noah, "but we must be there to offer our support. Neither are as young as they once were and it is our responsibility to ensure Osyth is protected. When Eudora was taken, young as we were, we all swore an oath to ensure her daughter's safety."

From the hallway, Penny's voice called them.

"Should we tell Mother and Father that Kieran has discovered Mother was in hospital?" asked Xenia.

"I believe we should," said Noah, "but we'll wait until the New Year. Kieran has made his feelings clear for now, he won't be able to contact Osyth or, God forbid, Mother, before January. We should discuss it then."

The door opened and Osyth pulled the blanket further over her head. A moment later the room was once again plunged into darkness as her aunt and uncles left. As she lay with her new book of stories clutched to her chest, she wondered if she had indeed fallen through a fairy ring into Tylwyth Teg, where all she thought she knew had been turned upside down and the world was new and confusing.

CHAPTER FOUR

"Fairy maiden, draw near to me,
  Take me far below the sea,
  Water maiden, wild and free,
  With the fairies of the deep..."

Osyth's voice was low as she reached back into her childhood to the familiar comfort and safety of the tune, turning the usually cheery melody into a funeral lament. It was the song she would sing as she cast her spell to bring the family home every spring. Gripping tightly to the carved wooden handrail around the veranda she would silently begin counting to one hundred, stopping at intervals of ten to whisper with a passionate fervour: "I wish the family would come home today," which she would alter occasionally to: "I wish Uncle Noah would come home today."

After her grandparents, Noah was the person she most loved and admired. When she had grown impatient that her wishes had not been granted, as they often were in her beloved fairy tales, Noah had solemnly explained that she must allow the magic of nature to take the time it needed to grant the wishes cast upon its broad shoulders. Osyth worshipped her Uncle Noah, and had often scolded herself for forgetting this important lesson. *But what would my wish be today?* she thought.

Osyth sighed. Even though she knew it was time to acknowledge her secret spell had been nothing more than a childish game, she was unable to jettison all her magical beliefs.

"Fairy maiden, full of glee,
I'll tell my secrets for you to keep..." she continued, and to her surprise, Noah's deep baritone rushed across the room to

envelope her in the tune, making her jump as he matched his voice to her solemn interpretation.

Osyth turned from her vigil by the window to stare at him in surprise but, looking at his smile, she upped her tempo and they sang the remainder of the song together.

"Water maiden, promise me,
You'll keep them safe in the deep blue sea."

They were in Noah's office, a place Osyth usually found exciting and exotic with its scent of timber, oil and river water but which today felt cold and spare. He worked in the loft above the boatyard with Frederick, now training to be his assistant, in the room outside. Daniel's offices were in another building on the opposite side of the yard and were far more luxurious. Noah preferred to be here, though, where he was equidistant between the boats and the timber yard, at the heart of the business. He would often tell Osyth how the call of their workmen, the screech of the saws and the smell of the sawdust mingling with the often unpalatable stench from the river were the best way for him to remind himself he was alive.

"How do you survive without the ocean, Uncle Noah?" Osyth asked, returning her gaze to the Thames as it flowed below the window.

"I can't live without it for long," Noah replied. "When I'm not near the sea, I have to be content to hear the waves that crash in my heart. You must learn to hear them, too. Being in this office helps, with the noise and the bustle. If I can't have the ocean with the seaweed and the salt, this is a reasonable substitute." He joined her by the window and placed his arm around her shoulders. She leaned into him, feeling his solid familiar warmth. "It's the same with the wind chime," he continued, stroking her hair, "it's in our blood, Osyth; if we listen hard enough, we will hear its tunes, no matter where we

are in the world. We must never let the tunes of the wind chime die. If we do, we lose our souls."

"Not Kieran, though," she said, tears rolling down her cheeks.

"No, my darling, not Kieran." He led her to the chair by the fire and rang the small brass bell next to his blotter. A moment later, Frederick Meyrick appeared, his face falling as he noticed Osyth's distress.

"Run out for some refreshments, please, Freddie," said Noah, handing him some coins. "My niece is in need of our help this afternoon."

"Of course, I'll be as quick as possible."

Osyth listened as Frederick's footsteps crashed across the outer room and down the wooden staircase.

Noah sat down in the vast captain's chair opposite Osyth, a letter sitting in front of him.

The letter had arrived that morning, addressed to Osyth and full of excited words as well as apologies as Angharad confessed her secret beau was Kieran and they had eloped the day after his twenty-first birthday. They were now married and living in Kieran's house in Richmond. While it had caused consternation, there had been a certain amount of relief too. Angharad's departure before Christmas had not been questioned until the New Year when a letter had arrived from Mary with a worried statement that Angharad was not at Cliffside and had not been there at Christmas.

The families in Windsor and Milford Haven had spread the word far and wide that Angharad had disappeared. It was assumed she must have eloped with her mysterious stranger and Osyth was questioned intently. However, she knew nothing about the man who had been wooing her friend and

was as worried as the rest of the family. After a tense few days, this letter had arrived.

"They have both betrayed you," said Noah.

"Especially Angharad," Osyth sobbed. "We were friends. I helped her to meet her secret beau by pretending she was at the library. I didn't expect that mystery lover to be Kieran or that they would elope."

"While I am angry with them for causing you such distress, Angharad remains your friend, my darling," Noah said. "She has been part of our family since she was a child. We've watched her grow up and her safety is as important to me as yours. Although you may not believe it, she needs your help more than ever now she is married to Kieran."

Osyth made a contemptuous noise. "What do you mean?" she asked, wiping away her tears.

Noah toyed with the letter, his expression serious, then took a deep breath and reached across to take Osyth's slim white hand. "Mother, Father and the family have discussed this and we have all agreed, whichever of us you were to turn to was to tell you what transpired in the offices of Lovegrove and Durant on the day Kieran received his inheritance."

Osyth's breath caught in her throat and she wondered whether he was poised to tell her more about the tense conversation she had overheard on Christmas Day concerning Kieran and her grandmother.

"These are serious issues, Osyth, and it wouldn't be kind of me if I didn't ask you if you truly wish to hear these family secrets?"

Noah's words chilled her. Her emotions were conflicted: it was satisfying to no longer be fobbed off with the excuse that she was too young to hear the stories of the past but she was nervous of what she was about to discover. Biting her lip, she

took a deep breath. "May I ask you a question before I reply?" she said, and Noah nodded. "Will what you are about to tell me help in my understanding of Kieran and Angharad's actions?"

Noah thought for a moment before responding. "I believe it will," he said, then his voice hardened, "it will also, I hope, protect you in any future dealings you have with them."

Unsure what Noah meant, she asked instead, "Do you hate Kieran, Uncle Noah?"

"No, I don't hate him," he replied. "I find him strange and brittle. His rudeness to my mother tests my patience to its limits. However, my feelings for Kieran have always been concern rather than dislike. He has always believed certain things, none of which are true, and on this incorrect information, he has spent a lifetime forming opinions from which he will not be shaken. He has told himself these lies so many times, he has come to believe that his version of events is real and that everyone else is colluding to deceive him."

"What do you mean?" Osyth stared at Noah. The afternoon was becoming increasingly unpleasant and she wished now she had listened to Penny's entreaties to stay at home.

"He deludes himself, Osyth, he always has," said Noah, his tone exasperated, then on seeing Osyth flinch he softened his voice. "Kieran is an unhappy man. We have all been concerned for his health for many years. While he was a child under Mother and Father's guardianship, we could help, but he is of age, so we are no longer able to intervene."

"Do you mean his headaches and the funny turns?"

"This is part of the problem but his increasing anger and flashes of violence have long concerned my father," he said, "which is why Father behaved as he did on your behalf."

"On my behalf...?" Osyth's voice tailed away, bemused.

Noah took a deep breath as though he did not want to say the next sentence. "You see, my darling, after Kieran had signed the paperwork giving him control of his house and money, he asked Taid for your hand in marriage."

"What?" she gasped.

"He said there was a precedent already set with Katherine and Blaise. He could see no reason why you could not be married immediately, all he needed was Taid's permission because you are under twenty-one." He paused. "My darling Osyth, has Kieran ever discussed this with you? Did you have an accord? Did you know he was going to ask Taid to marry you? You may be entirely honest with me."

"Uncle Noah, no," she gasped, horrified. "Kieran has never mentioned such feelings in my presence and we certainly had no understanding." She felt sick at the thought. Kieran was like an older brother. "I have never felt that way about him," she stammered.

Noah leaned back in his chair and sighed. "Part of me is relieved but I am also saddened," he said. "Mother, Father and I have long been concerned about Kieran's interest in you. His attention seemed overbearing, possessive. In your eyes, you and he have always had an innocent friendship but his emotions have shown on his face for many years and they have caused us all some disquiet."

"But, if he loves me and wanted to marry me, why did he elope with Angharad?" asked Osyth, her mind whirring in confusion.

"A question we have discussed but to which we, as yet, have no answer," said Noah. "While Mother and Father are relieved to know Angharad is alive and respectably married, it does not alleviate our fears for her safety, particularly as Kieran's strange moods have been intensifying in the past year."

Despite wanting to defend him, as she had often done to other members of the family, Osyth could not deny Noah's words. "Yes, they have become more troubling," she said in a quiet voice. "I'd hoped that when he was occupied with his medical studies, he might be able to control his moods better."

"As did we all, darling, as did we all," replied Noah, "but it appears Kieran has been planning his escape from our family for a long time. Father and I thought that when he took possession of his parents' old home, he might wish to sell the property and buy somewhere with fewer sad memories but he has employed a staff and he moved in on the day he signed the documentation."

"Did Aunt Georgina die there?"

"Yes."

"Perhaps being there will bring Kieran some peace, some closure from her horrible illness."

Osyth was startled to see the pallor on Noah's face.

"Georgina did not die from an illness," said Noah. "Not in the way you think of illness, anyway."

"What do you mean?"

Noah walked over to his desk and removed a cigar from the cedar-lined box, taking his time to light it before he returned to the fireside. "Georgina's life had never been easy, although, when she met your grandmother and then, through her, Matthew, she became much calmer and happier."

"She was Nain's friend first?" Osyth asked, intrigued. The story of how Matthew and Georgina had met was one she had never been told.

"Yes, and we think this is the reason Kieran believes Mother is responsible for all the sad things which befell him and Katherine when they were children."

"You mean the deaths of Matthew and Georgina?"

"Yes."

"But why? What happened?"

A knock on the door interrupted them and Osyth was unsure which of them was more relieved, herself or Noah. Frederick came in carrying a box of cakes which he deposited on the space Noah cleared on his desk before returning with a tea tray. He smiled at Osyth. "My apologies for having taken so long but the first shop didn't have any of the cherry cakes that I know are your favourite, Osyth," he said, blushing to the roots of his hair. He hovered for a moment, then hurried from the room.

Relieved by the distraction of refreshments, Osyth was measured in her movements as she laid out the cakes and poured tea for herself and her uncle, wishing the process to be as elongated as possible. Both seemed to find respite in the ordinariness of this ceremony because when they were seated again, their voices had lost the previous panicked breathiness so unlike their usual demeanours.

"Freddie is a fine young man," said Noah, a hint of the usual sparkle in his eyes. "He is fond of you, Osyth."

"His company is very pleasant," she replied, feeling her cheeks go pink. "I like him."

Noah nodded in satisfaction, put a small cherry madeleine in his mouth in one bite and sipped his tea. "Osyth, this is not a pleasant tale," he warned, but Osyth felt relief that he sounded more like himself. His storytelling voice hovered at the edges of his words. "This is not a myth about the fairy kingdom of Tylwyth Teg. There are no magical doors in standing stones, no golden staircases leading below the earth from the fairy rings. What I am about to tell you is real and, unhappily, it is tragic. Are you sure you wish to uncover this secret?"

Osyth's heart pounded. In her mind she heard the echoes of her family: "It is time to grow up Osyth", "Leave fairyland behind", "You are a young lady of means now". She was determined to prove she was worthy of their trust but it was with some trepidation that she nodded, indicating for her uncle to continue his tale.

"It begins with your grandmother," said Noah. "When she was eighteen, her mother, Eleanor, died unexpectedly. They were at Cliffside and Mother had been nursing her. My grandfather, George, and Matthew were travelling to be with them but they arrived too late. Mother was devastated. She and Eleanor had been very close, more like sisters than mother and daughter. Left alone, unable to bear her grief, Mother went out on to the veranda and stood below the wind chime, trying to gain her usual comfort from its songs but she was so lost, it did nothing to soothe her broken heart. She walked from the veranda and down on to the beach. She was missing for three days and when Matthew finally found her hiding in a cave near Newgale beach, she either would not or could not talk."

"Oh, Uncle Noah, how awful for poor Nain."

"It was a terrible time. Mother was frozen with cold and for nearly a fortnight it seemed she might not survive her ordeal. However, she was young and strong and her body recovered, but she still would not utter a word. Eventually, George and Matthew were so desperate to help her, they had her committed to an asylum."

Osyth gasped.

"They meant it with love. They were assured by her doctors that such places were communities of peace, a haven of calm to help her recover. For a while, this seemed to be the case but Mother was unhappy being locked in a building so far from the sea and, eventually, the staff began to accuse her of wilfulness,

153

deceit and deliberate awkwardness. She was placed in a room with another girl of a similar age who also refused to speak and left to their own devices. Food was given to them three times a day but they were locked in their miserable room the entire time. George and Matthew knew nothing of this treatment or they would have removed her immediately."

"What happened?"

"I don't know all the details but the tale Mother has told is this: that girl was Georgina. She had been sent to the asylum by her uncle."

"Where were her parents?" asked Osyth.

"Georgina's mother died giving birth to her," said Noah. "She was brought up by her father and he was a cruel man. He blamed his daughter for the death of his wife and would beat her regularly as punishment."

"No!"

"When she was fifteen years old, Georgina had a child," continued Noah, his face bleak. "The child died but it has been suggested that her father was also the child's father."

As the ramifications of this statement seeped into Osyth's mind, she felt revulsion.

"Shortly after this, Richard Viner, Georgina's father, died. He fell and hit his head on the stone floor and never recovered."

"So, Georgina was free?" asked Osyth hopefully.

"Alas, no, her uncle became her legal guardian and he was almost as cruel as her father. He tried to take out a special license to marry her so he could appropriate her inheritance but she managed to seek enough help to halt this action. However, rather than making her safe, her actions caused her uncle to have her declared insane and she was committed to the asylum where she met Nain.

"As the days passed, they began to trust each other and one day, Georgina told Mother her name. Mother replied and once they had both begun speaking, they became friends and were able to help each other recover. When George and Matthew were invited to view a ball at the asylum, they removed Mother and Georgina because they were so horrified at what they saw."

"A ball?"

Noah gave a twisted smile. "Every Monday, the asylum held 'The Lunatics' Ball'," he said, his voice laced with disgust. "Sponsors and well-to-do dignitaries could come and view the inmates of the asylum as they were led into the hall and forced to dance for hours at a time. It was thought to be therapeutic and to create an illusion of normality for the patients but Mother claims it was the most humiliating experience of her life."

"But why did George and Matthew go to such a dreadful spectacle?"

"For some months, they had suspected their letters were not reaching Mother and they had received none in reply. The custodian of the asylum assured them Mother was well and their interruption would hinder her recovery but they didn't believe him. This was their only way to try and see Mother and the moment they did, George insisted she be handed over into his care."

"And was she?"

"After some arguing, she was allowed to leave with them and she insisted on bringing Georgina. She had recently turned twenty-one, so was no longer under the guardianship of her uncle. George hired a private nurse and took them home to Cliffside, where they helped each other to recover. He also arranged for Georgina to be legally placed under his care, so

her uncle could not retrieve her or her money. It was while she healed that Matthew fell in love with her."

Osyth was shaken. For years, she and Angharad had swooned about romances with tales not dissimilar to the one Noah had revealed. Heiresses imprisoned by wicked uncles, saved by dashing heroes, but the grim reality of the combined tales of both her grandmother and her great-aunt made her shudder.

"What happened to Georgina?" she asked.

"Matthew and she were married. They were happy for a number of years but her melancholia returned. She suffered greatly with pains in her back and her shoulders, as well as the internal scars left from the beatings administered by her father when she had been a child." Osyth gave a whimper of horror but Noah was determined to finish. "And for this she took laudanum."

Osyth stared down at the cold dregs in her cup, not wanting to hear the end of the story.

"On the day she died, she had been suffering greatly and the doctor believed she accidentally took too much of her medicine."

"It was an accident?"

"We will never know but we hope so for the sake of Matthew, Kieran and Katherine," sighed Noah. "Blaise, Solomon, Xenia and I have never been convinced. Georgina suffered with fears and demons, she was an unhappy woman and we have often wondered…"

The sentence hung in the air and Osyth sat, frozen with shock.

"And Nain?" she asked.

"She has been strong and well in mind and body ever since," said Noah. "Her life wasn't easy. There were many who

shunned her when she returned to Windsor because her condition was seen as shameful. Taid was working with George by then and he helped Mother to regain her confidence. Mother always says it was love at first sight for them both but it took the worst storm the Pembrokeshire coast has ever seen to bring them together. Although, that is a tale for another day."

Intrigued though she was, Osyth was relieved. It was enough having to deal with the monstrous images Noah had conjured with the story of Georgina. It must have been this her uncles and aunt had been referring to during their whispered conversation on Christmas Day.

"Does Kieran know this story?" she asked. "Is this why you've told me it today?"

"He does but he believes that his mother was brought to Cliffside against her will, that she was unhappy in her marriage to Matthew and that it was Mother who was instrumental in forcing Georgina into this cursed union. Kieran thinks his mother killed herself rather than continue living in misery."

"But how could anyone who knows Nain think she would behave in such a terrible manner?"

"As I said earlier, my darling, Kieran doesn't always see things the way other people do. He twists the story around to suit his own beliefs and, in doing this, he becomes a danger to himself and others, which is why we are so concerned for Angharad."

Osyth stared at Noah in despair. "What can we do?"

"Angharad is Kieran's wife, there is very little we can do now, but I would suggest, if you feel you are able, that you write to her and offer the forgiveness she has requested. There may come a time when she needs you and your friendship could be the thing that saves her."

PART FIVE: PEMBROKESHIRE, 2019

CHAPTER ONE

Amelia picked her way through the crowd, enjoying the excited chatter as she made her way to a good vantage point. The local news and all the staff at Cliffside had been discussing nothing else but the huge event that was taking place in the nearby village of Dale — the raising of a seventeenth-century wreck which was to be housed in a purpose-built museum. As she was around on such a momentous day, Amelia felt she should at least take a look. A family moved and Amelia stepped into their vacated space, giving her a clear view of the temporary pontoon. The archaeologists, divers, engineers and other members of the team were milling around on the sea-drenched boards, shouting instructions and adding to the palpable tension in the air, eager for the moment they would lift the vessel.

In the distance, Amelia glimpsed Edward Stone with Melissa Forte talking animatedly to David and Kerry. A man with dark curly hair joined them for a few moments, before returning to the pontoon where a woman was calling him, indicating they needed to get on the crew boat.

"Coming Perdita," he called, his voice floating over the noise as he raced down to join her.

Amelia pulled out her binoculars and watched as the crew boat chugged away from the pontoon heading for the salvage site. The woman, Perdita, was surrounded by people and the man with curly hair slid his arm around her waist. Another woman of similar build but with a mane of fiery red hair stood beside her, while next to her was a taller man with light brown hair, who seemed to be in charge.

Looking around at the crowd, Amelia waited for the usual pangs of loneliness to twinge at her heart but, to her surprise, nothing came. Instead she felt a peace, as though she were home. It was a feeling so unfamiliar that it unnerved her. Trying to distract herself, she fixed her binoculars to her eyes again, focusing on the other boats and the huge rig that was being used to winch the ship from its watery berth.

The previous day, Edward had invited her to join him and Melissa but she had felt awkward. When she had been working as a doctor, it would have felt strange to go to a social event with a patient. Even without this barrier, while she admired Melissa's professional knowledge, she found her personality cold and would not have chosen to spend time with her outside the treatment room. As for her relationship with Edward, she was unsure how to even classify it. Friendship was too strong a word, acquaintance seemed dismissive, and there was the possibility he might be her distant cousin.

Amelia shifted her binoculars to Edward and Melissa. She was uncertain about their connection as well. Melissa seemed very at home at Cliffside but whether there was something other than friendship and professional respect between her and Edward, it was hard to tell. Watching them now, she noticed Melissa's hand often strayed to touch Edward's arm or hand and she stood close enough for their shoulders to brush but he seemed oblivious to her overtures. Relief washed over her, then she laughed at herself. It was none of her business.

The crew boat had moored and Amelia wondered how long it would be before there was anything to see. Her plan for the day was to visit the Pembrokeshire Archives, where she had made an appointment to view a series of documents concerning the intriguing Attwater family. After the startling revelations of Osyth's diary, Amelia's heart had broken for

both women: for the abuse Georgina had suffered and, more personally, for the breakdown Penny had endured after her mother's death. Amelia had teetered on the brink herself when grief had consumed her.

These events combined with the bequest Penny made to Osyth of the three rows of cottages had sent shivers down her spine. Amelia had checked them on the Land Registry website and she discovered her cottages were among this far larger collection. What had happened to them between Osyth being given them and her mother inheriting them? Osyth's solicitor had explained to her the inheritance did not have to pass down a bloodline, so it was still possible the Attwaters were not actually her ancestors. *There is a simple solution — trace my family tree and see whether we crossover somewhere.* Yet, somehow, she could not quite face that. There was a shadow over her growing attachment to the family and her need to belong to it. While a family tree might confirm her attachment, it might also destroy her hope of claiming kinship. Instead, she had decided to continue to unravel the lives of Osyth, Eudora and Penny before she tried to write herself into their story.

Deciding there would be nothing more to see for a few hours, particularly as storm clouds were rolling in, Amelia decided to keep her appointment at the archives. As she was packing up her binoculars, she heard Edward calling her name.

His dark hair, usually so well tamed, was being blown by the wind and he cut an impressive figure as he made his way through the crowd towards her. With his Aviator sunglasses, crisp white shirt, blue jacket and dark jeans, she could not help but notice a number of women glance appreciatively in his direction.

"Looks as though the weather might cause a few delays," he said. "Stuart was saying they'd planned for rain but if the wind increases much more, they'll have to wait until it's calmer before they risk bringing her up."

"Do you know them?" Amelia waved towards the crew boat.

"Everyone knows everyone around here." He laughed. "I was at school with Stuart and his younger brother, Kit."

Fat raindrops began to fall and Amelia pulled up her collar.

"Were you leaving?" asked Edward, putting up the golfing umbrella he was carrying, covering them both.

She explained about her prior arrangement, then said, "Would you like to come?" The question was out before she had thought about it and she wanted to bite her tongue. Now there would be the awkward moment of refusal but to her surprise, Edward's face lit up.

"Really? You wouldn't mind?"

"Of course not," she said, unsure why this made her feel so happy. "Do you want to follow me in your car?"

"Melissa brought me, so I'll have to come with you, if that's OK."

Hearing her name, Melissa walked over to join them. She smiled at Amelia. "Shall we head back?" she asked Edward, a hand on his arm.

"I'm going into town with Amelia," he replied and Melissa's smile flickered with irritation before reverting to normal.

"See you later then," she said and disappeared into the crowd.

Edward took Amelia by the arm and guided her towards the car park.

"Actually, Amelia, I'm glad we bumped into each other. I wanted to apologise about Caitlin's behaviour."

"Really, it's fine," said Amelia. "She wasn't herself. We both know how debilitating urine infections can be in the elderly. In a way, it was good she shouted at me because it alerted you to the problem. How is she?"

"Much better. She should be home from hospital in a few days." He climbed into the passenger seat, pushing the chair back to accommodate his long legs.

Amelia edged into the queue of cars, full of people who, like them, had fled the rain.

"The awful part is my not noticing," he said, biting his thumb nail.

"Perhaps I should have spoken up earlier," admitted Amelia. "Her growing infection would probably explain why she looked so scared when she saw me the first time."

"What do you mean, the first time?"

"It was during my assessment with Melissa," said Amelia. "Caitlin was going into the woods and she saw me standing at the window. She stopped and the expression on her face seemed to be fearful. I'm sorry, Edward, I should have told you at the time."

"But why would she be scared?" he mused. "She loves having guests in the house. I have to put strict limits on her or she'd be chatting to everyone all the time."

"She was ill," replied Amelia, her tone practical. "Let's not look for mysteries where there aren't any. We're going to have plenty to unravel at the archives."

"True," he agreed. "There was a bit more to Caitlin's outburst though."

"What do you mean?"

Edward shifted nervously. "Before the antibiotics began to work, she ranted at me, too." He sounded hesitant.

"What about?"

"She called me Kieran and you, Eudora," he said. "Told me we were an evil pair who deserved each other after all the damage we'd done."

"Really? But she isn't old enough to remember them."

"I know and anyway, from the dates we've discovered for them, Kieran was only a child when Eudora died. We know that from the image you have of him scowling down at his aunt and his cousin."

"True," murmured Amelia.

"Caitlin had been reading her notes from her book on the family..." Edward continued.

"Which explains everything," concluded Amelia, interrupting him in relief. "She was confused because of the infection and, having been looking at her notes, she thought... Well, I don't like to presume." She was finally free of the car park and as she took the road out of Dale heading towards Haverfordwest, she said, "I've come to the end of Osyth's journal."

For the rest of the journey, Amelia updated Edward on all she had read.

"The Lunatics' Ball," he said. "Do you think it was meant with misguided kindness?"

"Probably," replied Amelia, "and maybe for some people it was a joy but for others, it was a torment to be endured. Charles Dickens was an advocate of it, as were many other reformers and philanthropists. It chills me though."

"Yes, I find it unnerving, too."

"It was said to be a way of recreating normality for the patients but whether they wanted to or not, they were made to attend, dancing to dirge-like music, slowly waltzing around while others observed. It's like life, we all drift around, spinning in circles, watched by others, thinking we have

control until, bam, we're hit with something unexpected. Yet somehow we keep on dancing through our lives, drifting around the ballroom at the lunatics' ball."

There was silence. Amelia turned a wan smile to Edward, expecting to see concern on his face, but the look of understanding he gave her was heartening.

"Come on," he said, his voice gentle. "Let's see what else we can discover. Perhaps we can find out about the love story between Penny and Daniel. It might give us some hope."

CHAPTER TWO

The records Amelia had requested were delivered by one of the smiling helpers, all of whom seemed to know Edward and Caitlin. After Edward had answered her enquiries about his aunt's health, the woman departed, giving Amelia a curious smile.

"You really do know everyone, don't you," Amelia muttered.

"It's the penalty of growing up in a small area, especially when your father was the local GP."

Amelia turned a few pages of the history book in front of her, flicking through to the pages about another nearby house, Scolton Manor. Once home to the Higgon family, who boasted three High Sheriffs of Pembrokeshire in their ranks, Amelia wondered if the Attwaters and the Higgon family had socialised.

"You don't speak about your parents much," she said, as she examined a picture of the manor.

"There's not much to say," Edward replied, sifting through a pile of local history magazines. "Mum and Dad separated when I was young and I spent my time split between the two. Mum remarried and moved to Spain. She's still there and, sadly, Dad died three years ago." There was a pause and then Edward continued, "He had Motor Neurone Disease. His decline was swift and brutal."

"I'm sorry," Amelia said, reaching out and covering his hand with hers.

"Thank you," he said. "That was when I inherited his half of the house."

"Was it difficult, inheriting only half?" she asked.

"No, it's always had a shared ownership, according to Caitlin. When I was little, she showed me her stash of family wills, explaining that two members of the family always held joint custody of the house on the cliff. It was thought to be a way to safeguard it for future generations. It isn't a legal requirement — it was a family thing. Caitlin has already told me she'll be leaving me her half because she doesn't have any children, so for the first time since it was built in 1832, it'll have one owner again."

Amelia looked down at the magazine he had open which showed an old image of another nearby stately home, Marquess House, but there were few details listed except for the fact it was bought and renovated in the 1880s.

"Are you looking for anything in particular?" Edward asked, closing the magazine and pushing it away.

Amelia showed him the list she had written: *find other prominent families, social events, local clubs and societies, lists of gatherings, personal notices in local newspaper.*

"I want to see how the Attwaters fitted into the local area," she explained. "After Penny returned from the asylum, she was shunned at her home in Windsor but I wondered how people here reacted. This seemed to be the place that held her heart, which is why I've requested information about other prominent families. If the Attwaters and Stones were affluent employers, they would have been part of the social hierarchy. When Noah was telling Osyth about Penny's recovery, he said that Daniel Attwater was working with George Stone and it was Daniel who helped her to regain her confidence but it took a storm to bring them together."

"A storm?"

"Strange, isn't it? It's on my list. I want to look up any violent weather around the mid-1840s."

Edward logged into the monitor beside him and pulled up a website. "It's one of the local diving clubs," he said. "They've put together a list of all the wrecks that were lost around this coastline. It doesn't necessarily state storms but ships don't usually sink when the sun is shining, not unless they're really inexperienced or unfortunate. Do you have a date?"

"Noah Attwater was Penny and Daniel's eldest son and he's listed in the census records as being born in 1847," said Amelia, "so at least a year before that, I'd guess."

"We could look for a marriage certificate for Penny and Daniel," Edward suggested.

"I'll do that, you look for storms."

Amelia put the pile of local history books and magazines to one side. It was with a thrill of excitement that she keyed in her password to the genealogy website and began scrolling down the marriage records. After a while, she gave a small triumphant cry. "We're in luck," she said, "there's an image of the actual certificate. They were married in May 1847 at a chapel in Milford Haven. They were cutting things fine; Noah was born in July 1847."

Edward raised his eyebrows. "Penny was seven months pregnant," he said. "I should think it was a huge scandal. Do you think Daniel was made to marry her?"

"No, I don't think so," replied Amelia. "Noah claimed his parents had fallen in love at first sight."

"Why did they wait so long?"

"Perhaps the marriage was delayed because by then they were stepbrother and stepsister. Do you think this could be the scandal Blaise mentioned? Osyth writes about it in her diary."

"Really?"

"You have scandalous ancestors," she murmured.

"They might be yours, too, so don't get too smug," he riposted, and Amelia laughed.

"I'm going to search for some of the local families mentioned in the books," she said, logging out of the genealogy site and into the archive's database. "We might be able to find some interesting references."

To her delight, she discovered the archive had copious documents concerning the Higgon family at Scolton Manor, although there was nothing for Marquess House. Widening her search, she found Frederick Meyrick's family in Pembroke, and read a brief outline of their history. Browsing through the listings, she ordered the documents which seemed most relevant before returning her attention to the Attwaters and Stones. Again, a list of deeds, wills and other legal documents popped up. The majority of them seemed to refer to Penny's father, George Stone. She nudged Edward and pointed to the original plans of Cliffside which could be ordered.

"We have some at home," he replied. "They're in Caitlin's archive."

"Do you think she might let us look?"

"Who knows? She's strangely possessive of all the family paperwork."

Amelia returned to her search, wondering if once Caitlin was well again, she might be persuadable. *Perhaps if I offer to share my transcript of Osyth's diary*, she wondered. Hovering the cursor over the list, she was about to click into another potential search when something caught her eye: *Settlement on the marriage of Daniel Philip Attwater and Penelope Charlotte Stone*. Making a note of the archive number, she hurried over to the desk and added it to the list she had requested.

More people had arrived and she was surprised when she returned from submitting her document request that Edward had changed monitors, moving them to a corner where he could sit with his back to the room.

"Who are you avoiding?" she whispered, taking the seat next to him.

"No one in particular," he replied, "but some of the ladies who have just come in were patients of my father. They know I'm a doctor too and quite often start telling me about their ailments."

Amelia stifled a giggle.

"Don't laugh," he said, pretending to glower at her, "or I'll tell them you're a doctor too and they can give you a three-hour description of their bunions."

He huddled down and she pulled her chair in next to him, whispering about the documents she had ordered. Outside, the wind howled and the rain clattered against the window. It felt cosy and intimate being closeted in the corner together and once again she was suffused with an unexpected feeling of peace.

"Any storms?" she asked.

"Actually, yes, on 13 October 1846 an unidentified sailing ship sank in St Brides Bay, which would suggest rough weather. If Noah Attwater was born in July 1847, then October could be a possible conception date."

"How would these events be connected though?" said Amelia. They stared at the notes they had strewn across the table. "Would it be worth checking local papers?"

"Maybe," he said.

Amelia was about to return to the monitor when her documents arrived.

"The marriage settlement is missing, I'm afraid," said the archivist as she placed the folders on the table in front of Amelia. "We'll keep looking but it must have been filed incorrectly. If we don't manage to track it down this afternoon, leave your number and we'll get in touch if it materialises."

Disappointment stabbed at Amelia's heart. The marriage settlement was the one she had most wanted to read.

"They might find it," said Edward, squeezing her hand. "Why don't you check these and I'll see if I can find anything in the newspaper archive, although I think the biggest database is held at the National Library of Wales in Aberystwyth."

Putting on the gloves left by the archivist, Amelia gave a nod of agreement but she was frustrated. The discovery of the marriage settlement in the index had been like a siren call from the past but she was being denied its secrets. Doing her best not to sigh, she turned instead to the documents she had called up about Scolton Manor and began to read. There were details of colliers, accounts, legal dealings with tenants, which while interesting did not help with the story of Penny and Daniel. Turning to another folder, she saw this one contained personal correspondence. A thrill ran through her — this was the first time she had ever done anything like this and she could not believe how excited she was at the thought of reading a letter that was written over a hundred years ago.

A transcript was beside it but Amelia turned to the original and within moments was transported to another world as the words reached out to her across time. She imagined the woman who had written it, her pen scratching across the paper as the fire crackled in the grate. The letter was in response to a thank you letter sent by Laura Stone, who Amelia realised was Daniel's mother, formerly Laura Attwater, and then the wife of Penny's father, George. It seemed Laura and George had been

to a birthday party at Scolton Manor, accompanied by Matthew and Georgina. *Where were Penny and Daniel?* she wondered but as she continued to read, her breath caught in her throat.

It was with relief that we heard your son, Daniel, is recovering. What a brave young man to have tried to help those poor people when their yacht was caught in the storm. They could not have been local, no one from Nolton Haven or thereabouts would have risked trying to land on your cove on such a treacherous night. The rumour has reached us that it was your stepdaughter, Penelope, who raised the alarm and was instrumental in nursing him through the night. That was a lot of responsibility for the poor girl when we were safely at Scolton enjoying our gathering.

Amelia copied out the letter into her notebook and noted the date: 17 October 1846. "Look," she whispered, nudging Edward. "The family was at a party at Scolton Manor on the night of the storm but Penny and Daniel had stayed at home."

Edward scanned the transcript. "I've found this, too," he said and moved aside so she could read the newspaper. "The storm blew down an oak tree and blocked the roads from Scolton Manor. The Stones might have been forced to stay the night. Look at this." He flipped through the printouts he had made and shoved one across at her. There was a small piece entitled: *Local Man Risks Life.*

Daniel Attwater, stepson of local businessman, George Stone, last night put himself in danger when he tried to rescue an ailing ship trying to make land on the Cliffside Cove during the storm on Saturday. The vessel was owned by John Smith of Slebech who drowned, despite Mr Attwater's efforts. Another man, Dai Jones of Prendergast, survived and has been charged with smuggling tea and tobacco. Mr Attwater saw the ship was floundering and ran down to help. The yacht was lost with full cargo.

"No mention of Penny," murmured Amelia. "What do you think really happened?"

"Do you think Penny could have saved Daniel?" asked Edward.

"How?"

The archivist approached, smiling. "You've had a bit of wasted trip, I'm afraid," she said. "The document you requested was only ever on loan and it should have been removed from our index when it was returned to its owner." Her brown eyes twinkled as she glanced at Edward, who was studiously ignoring her, his attention entirely on his computer screen. Amelia was embarrassed by his blatant rudeness and wanted to pinch him.

"Caitlin?" asked Amelia and the archivist nodded, handing her a copy of the loan docket which she had discovered.

"Hope Caitlin feels better soon," she said to Edward's back, then she bustled away.

"Sorry I didn't look up," he said when the woman had taken her seat behind the enquiries desk again. "She keeps trying to set me up with her daughter."

"Really?" replied Amelia, agog.

"Never going to happen," he muttered. "She's not my type. But," he continued, "perhaps we should check Caitlin's notes?"

"Which is a great idea," said Amelia, "but Caitlin's in Withybush Hospital. It's a bit rude to start rifling through her papers the moment she's out of the way."

Edward pulled a face. "Haven't you ever done anything against the rules?" he whispered, nudging her with his shoulder. "Come on, let's go and have a quick look. She doesn't need to know."

173

Amelia was unsure but as he piled up the books and returned the documents to their folders, a sudden wave of curiosity flooded her. Osyth's diary had brought her this far, did Caitlin hold the clues to the next chapter of the Attwater mystery?

"Come on then," she said, "but if she finds out, I'm telling her it was all your idea!"

CHAPTER THREE

Driving along the twisting lanes, the rain beat down and the wind whistled around the car, buffeting it on the open stretches of road. A text pinged and Edward informed Amelia that the raising of the wreck had been postponed until the following morning due to the weather.

"Will you go?" she asked as they pulled around the tight bend into Cliffside.

"Probably," he replied, in the clipped manner to which she was becoming accustomed. "I'll drive us tomorrow, if you like."

"What about Melissa?" she asked, unable to help herself. "Won't she want to come?"

"Doubt it," he replied. "History isn't really her thing. I was surprised when she offered to drive me this morning. Park over there and we can go in the side door."

They walked into the private wing of Cliffside. This was furnished in a similar style to the public rooms but there were more personal belongings: pictures on the walls, coats on pegs, wellies by the door and the two excited greyhounds, weaving their way around Amelia and Edward's legs. Amelia breathed in the smell of cooking.

"Slow cooker," said Edward in response. "I put it on earlier because I wasn't sure when I'd be back."

He led the way along a winding corridor and into a large sitting room, where a dining room table dominated one end. The view looked out over the garden and the west side of the bay. To Amelia's immense excitement, there were French doors leading to the veranda. From the moment she had

arrived, Amelia had wanted to stand on this ancient viewpoint, to witness St Brides Bay as Osyth had seen it. Her other desire was to examine the wind chime, to finally meet the guardian of the Attwater family, whose melody had been punctuating her days for the past few weeks. It was unlikely to be the original hung by Eleanor Stone but she hoped it might be similar. It had, therefore, been a huge frustration for her that, while the veranda dominated the back of the house, guests were not admitted to it.

"Health and safety," Kerry had said with a wry smile when Amelia had questioned this. "If we allowed guests on to the veranda our insurance premiums would treble."

Amelia had not realised she was gazing with such intensity at the rain-spattered doors until Edward's voice broke through the noise of the crashing waves and the jingling chimes. "I'd suggest you take a look," he said, nodding towards the French doors, "but you'd be soaked in seconds."

"Maybe later?" she asked, and he grinned in response before ducking out of the room.

The dogs had taken up what were obviously their usual positions either end of one of the two large dark pink sofas. Amelia wandered around the room, pausing to look at the photographs. There were framed images on nearly every surface, some very old and others of the current residents of Cliffside. There were several of a sullen-looking teenage Edward and she was examining an official photograph of him in mortar board and robes clutching his degree with a sparse moustache when he returned carrying several box files.

"Facial hair and I are not friends," he said, scowling at the picture. "You'd think with hair as dark as mine it would be thick and luxuriant but no, weedy and pathetic."

Amelia laughed, joining him on the empty sofa where he commenced to sort through Caitlin's notes. "Are you sure about this?" she asked, uncomfortable with what seemed like an invasion of Caitlin's privacy.

"Live dangerously, Aimes," he muttered and she felt a small jolt at the casual way he used the nickname she associated with her friends and family. She was not even sure she had even told him this was what they called her. "What Caitlin doesn't know can't hurt her," he continued. "Here it is." Pulling out a large, leather-bound, burgundy notebook, he turned to her, grinning. "Treasure," he exclaimed. "This is the book Caitlin has been writing for the past ten years." Edward opened the book and read: "'*A secretum in domo similis saxa sub gurgite*', or, in English, 'A secret at home is like rocks under the tide'. I don't know if it's the Stone family motto but Caitlin likes to use it on letterheads."

A chill ran down Amelia's spine. "What did you say?" she asked, her voice unexpectedly hoarse. The words of Bob, the man from the *Windsor Princess*, the vessel she had since discovered was named for Osyth, echoed around her mind. His mum had lived in Windsor all her life and her family had known the Attwater and Stone families and when describing them had said: 'A secret at home is like rocks under the tide and they had more secrets than the sea has tides.'

"What's the matter?" asked Edward.

"That phrase," she said, "I've heard it before." She explained.

Edward frowned in confusion. "Who was this man?"

"He worked on the boats at Windsor that were once owned by the Attwater and Stone boatyard."

Edward snapped the book shut and folded his arms possessively around it. "Tell me about the boats in Windsor," he said. His tone had gone from excited to wary.

"There's nothing to tell," she replied. "Dad, Molly and I used to go on them but beyond that, we have no connection. It was only after Mum died that I went on Molly's favourite boat to think about them all, and for the first time, I listened to the talk properly. They mentioned the Jacobs family who were connected to the paddle steamers, then the Attwater and Stone boatyard who had bought the Jacobs' boats. I'd only just discovered the photographs and heard the name Attwater for the first time, so it made a connection and I talked to one of the crew afterwards."

She knew she did not have to justify herself to Edward but the look of suspicion on his face was making her feel as though she had done something wrong.

"Why didn't you mention this before?" he asked.

"I'd forgotten all about it."

"It's odd," said Edward and for a moment she wondered if he was going to change his mind and ask her to return to the public side of the building. Then, to her relief, he unfolded his arms and placed the book on his lap where they could both see it. "Shall we have a peek?"

Amelia held her breath as he began turning the pages. Caitlin had beautiful handwriting and Amelia was desperate to read her version of the Attwater story, but Edward did not pause. He kept turning the leaves, searching for a specific page.

"Here," he said, "thank goodness Caitlin has laid it out in chronological order."

Penelope Charlotte Stone married Daniel Philip Attwater on 23 May 1847 in a quiet service in the Chapel-Through-The-Woods. The witnesses were George and Laura Stone, Matthew Stone and Georgina Viner. The reason for the delay in their marriage was due to Penelope and Daniel who felt, after she had saved his life, their love was strong enough to survive without the convention of a legally binding contract. However, from reading the letters between Penelope and her stepmother, Laura, it seems the young couple were eventually persuaded to bow to conformity, much to the relief of their parents.

From what I have been able to ascertain the romance between them began on the night of a terrible storm. George, his wife Laura, Matthew and Georgina were all attending a birthday celebration at nearby Scolton Manor, Penelope had chosen to remain at home. She mentions in one of her letters how her continuing recovery made her feel uncomfortable in certain circles. Daniel, who was travelling from the family home in Windsor, had been delayed by the weather and arrived too late to join the rest of the family at Scolton Manor.

Penelope and Daniel had been friends before her father married his mother. Daniel seemed to understand Penelope's grief and her feelings of irrational guilt that she was unable to save her mother. When he had been younger, his brother, Lucas, had fallen from one of the family boats and, despite Daniel's best efforts, Lucas had drowned. He, too, suffered bouts of what we would now call survivor's guilt.

The young couple were on the veranda watching the storm when Daniel saw lights out to sea and realised there was a boat in distress. Running down to the cove, he plunged into the water but was unable to rescue both men. One drowned and as he was pulling the second to safety, the tide caught Daniel and washed him back into the water. Penelope was making her way down to the beach and watched in horror as he was swept away. She shouted for help from the Cliffside staff, then slipping and sliding on the rocks, she began searching for Daniel.

Daniel was clinging to a piece of wreckage from the boat and Penelope waded into the sea herself. Using all her strength, she dragged him away from the rocks and was joined by the men from the house. Between them, they were able to pull Daniel to safety. He was soaking wet, freezing cold and exhausted.

Penelope took charge, sending for the doctor and having the housekeeper put the other man into a bed in the staff quarters. She writes how throughout her organisation of events she was plagued with horrible flashbacks about her mother's death as well as dark thoughts about Lucas's death.

Leaving the housekeeper to monitor the shipwrecked smuggler, Penelope took over Daniel's care, determined he would survive. No matter what she tried, Daniel could not get warm and, in desperation, fearful for his life, she sent the staff away, saying she would nurse him, before climbing into bed beside him, convinced her body would warm his and save his life. Eventually, they fell asleep and by morning, Daniel was recovering, so Penelope slipped from his bed before she caused a scandal among the staff. However, it seemed this was the beginning of their relationship. They were both what we would refer to as 'bohemian' and, even back then, seemed unbothered by convention. However, they were wise enough to know if they declared their love too publicly, there might be familial objections, as they were stepbrother and stepsister. There was no biological link.

When Penelope realised she was pregnant, they knew they would have to approach their parents with this news, yet they remained adamant marriage was not a state they wished to adopt. Eventually George and Laura were able to persuade them to wed, if not for their sakes, then for that of their child. The difficulty of being born illegitimate would far outweigh the scandal of step-siblings marrying.

Amelia and Edward stared at each other in surprise.

"They were ahead of their time, weren't they?" laughed Edward.

"Definitely!"

Amelia allowed the words transcribed by Caitlin to wash over her. True love, love at first sight. Every corner she turned in her research, the family in the house on the cliff talked about love, yet the story Osyth was telling in her diary was one of lies and dark secrets. *The two could exist together though. We keep secrets from those we love in order to protect them. At least, that's what we tell ourselves.*

"It's hard to believe the two stiffly posed people in your photographs once created such a scandal," said Edward, closing the book and leaning back into the sofa.

"They seemed to have love to spare, as well," said Amelia, slumping back beside him. "They had five children of their own and they adopted their granddaughter, as well as Penny's niece and nephew."

"No wonder this is such a big house — they needed all that room and more once their children grew up and began families of their own."

"Except Eudora," said Amelia.

Outside, the storm had blown itself out and the sun was shining again from a soft blue sky.

"Fancy walking the dogs with me?" Edward asked. "It's high tide, so I'll take them through the woods, we can go to the chapel and you can see where Penny and Daniel got married."

"Really?"

"Yes, and if you want, we could come back here afterwards, eat the incredibly delicious stew I've made and check the letters that Caitlin drew her story from."

"Why? Don't you believe her?" asked Amelia in surprise.

"Yes, but we might spot something new."

Twenty minutes later, having run to her room to fetch her walking boots, Amelia and Edward made their way along the red earth into the wood at the back of the house. Nero remained on the lead.

"He doesn't like going for walks," explained Edward, stroking the dog's ears. "He can cope on the beach but he gets nervous in the wood and is much happier on his lead."

"What about Lara?"

"Cheeky paws will cry and sulk if you keep her shackled. She'll also ignore us until she's ready to come home." His words were full of laughter and love.

Amelia released the excited dog from her lead and watched her sprint off, tail high.

The afternoon shadows undulated across the floor. Rooks and jackdaws squawked, while in the distance Amelia was sure she could hear a woodpecker.

"Are there still standing stones?" she asked, following Edward and Nero down the narrow path.

"Yes, in the centre of the copse. Why? Do you fancy finding your way into fairyland or Tylwyth Teg, as it's known in Welsh mythology. Standing stones were thought to be doorways between worlds."

"Really?"

"There's a story about these stones, my father used to tell it to me. Do you want to hear?"

Amelia nodded, intrigued. Edward grinned, then cleared his throat, and began: "There were two young men, one the son of a wealthy farmer, the other his servant, who, despite the difference in their status, were brought up together as they were the same age. They were as close as brothers. They met

suitable young women and married in a joint ceremony. Not long after the wedding, the two men went hunting. They came to the stone circle and the servant walked into the trees to flush out game but as the birds rose high and the deer skittered towards the son, there were no shots. Eventually, the servant returned to discover the stone circle was empty. He called for his friend but there was no response. He searched and searched, finally returning home, hoping his friend would be waiting at the farmhouse but no one had seen him.

"A search party was raised but after days and days of looking, there was no sign of the son and the family began to believe he had been spirited away to Tylwyth Teg, the land of the fairies. It was well known that the central stone in the circle was the gateway between the worlds. The missing man's wife then discovered she was expecting a baby, as was the servant's wife, and in due course they both gave birth to sons. These boys also became friends, grew up and married. The son of the missing man moved into the farmhouse and he, too, had children. Of the lost man, there was never a sign.

"Then one day, an old man appeared at the doorway of the farmhouse. Without knocking or waiting for an invitation, he let himself in and sat in the master's chair by the fire. 'Who are you?' asked the woman.

"'This is my house,' the man replied. 'Who are you? Where is my wife?'

"The woman stared at him in fear and ran for help. The servant, now an old man, hobbled to see the stranger. They recognised each other and embraced. 'You are so old, my friend,' laughed the restored man. 'I have been gone but a night, where I danced with the fairies in Tylwyth Teg.'

"'My friend, you have been gone for fifty years,' replied the servant. 'This lady is your daughter-in-law and these are your grandchildren. Your son and my son have gone hunting.' Tears sprang into the old man's eyes and he reached out for his friend, then died in his arms.

"Sometime later, the daughter-in-law of the missing man had more visitors. A group of little people in exquisitely jewelled clothes knocked on her door and when she invited them in, they refused, instead telling her that because of her harsh treatment of their friend, who returned home to die, the house would be forever cursed, unless she laid a wreath of white roses at the centre of the stone circle every midwinter."

As Edward finished the tale, Amelia felt a shiver run down her spine.

"Do you lay flowers?" she asked and to her surprise, Edward nodded.

"Ever since I can remember," he said. "Chapel or stones first?"

"Chapel."

They wandered through the trees, discussing all they had discovered, called Lara to heel and when she was safely on her lead, Edward opened the wrought-iron gate into the graveyard that surrounded the chapel. Most of the stones were ancient, some leaned at odd angles and a few had toppled into the grass. More were stacked beside the old wooden door. To Amelia's surprise, Edward pulled a large metal key from his pocket.

"Is the chapel yours?" asked Amelia and he nodded.

"It was decommissioned about forty years ago and when it was put up for sale, Dad and Granddad decided to buy it. They were worried it might be turned into a holiday home and it was a bit too close to the serenity of Cliffside to have ever-

changing neighbours. We keep up maintenance on it and I've recently been considering converting it so we can offer accommodation with more privacy if people prefer. It'll be a huge expense though, so it's a long-term plan."

Inside, the building smelled of cold and damp. The whitewashed walls had bubbled in places and, apart from a large granite font towards the rear, it was empty. A few stained-glass windows showed simple biblical scenes — Daniel in the lion's den and Moses in a basket — but the general air was one of forlorn neglect.

"The altar was there," said Edward, pointing vaguely, "and we have the records of who's buried where under the floor but from what I can remember, none of the Attwaters or Stones are here. We have the full burial, marriage and christening records somewhere. Perhaps we should take a proper look now we're on our expected quest."

Disappointment flowed through Amelia. In her imagination, she had seen a perfect, white-walled, pristine chapel with polished pews and bright, hand-embroidered hassocks. This dilapidated shell was strangely upsetting. She leaned down and stroked Nero who was leaning on her leg, trembling, his tail down. "Come on," she said. "Let's go, Nero doesn't like it."

Making comforting noises to the nervous greyhound, she hurried from the chapel, relieved to regain the warmth of the evening air. Amelia wandered with Nero across the grass, her eyes raking the inscriptions on the headstones, looking for familiar names but there were none. Edward and Lara caught up with them and they headed back to the wood.

"We could have a drink on the veranda when we get back," he announced, smiling, and once again Amelia was struck by the quicksilver moods of the man. Sullen to sunny in a matter of minutes and yet, she sensed that at his core, he was a caring

person. One only had to see how well he looked after Caitlin and the obvious affection between them to understand that but his brusqueness was challenging and she wondered if the upheaval in his childhood had scarred him more than he was prepared to admit.

"I'd like that very much," she replied.

"Good. Standing stones, then wine on the veranda. Come on kids," he said to the dogs. Moments later, Lara streaked off into the trees, Nero huddled closer to their legs and Amelia passed his lead back to Edward.

"We've had him since he was a puppy," said Edward, "and nothing bad has ever happened to him but he's such a shy dog. He's happiest in his garden, on his sofa or, if he's feeling brave, on the beach."

In the distance, Lara began to bark, then she yelped.

"Oh no," groaned Edward, "what's she done now? Come on, Nero."

He began to run, Nero trotting by his side, Amelia following. Lara continued to yelp and a few minutes later, they found her, standing on the edge of the stone circle. She was unhurt but her back leg was caught in a tangle of ivy. Her high-pitched yowls stopped when she saw Edward.

"Come here, little one," he said, handing Nero's lead to Amelia. He bent down, clipped on Lara's lead and began to untangle her back leg.

As he worked, he kept up a stream of gentle murmurs in order to keep her calm, while she occasionally licked the side of his face. Reassured Lara was unharmed, Amelia and Nero wandered towards the ancient circle. The swishing of the wind in the leaves mingled with the distant roar of the ocean and the faint tunes of the wind chime to create a mystical backdrop as Amelia and Nero walked around the sombre stones. There

were five standing, while three more lay broken on the ground. A flat stone was set in the earth at the centre of the circle. *The entrance to Tylwyth Teg*, she thought, *the place where Edward lays the white roses.*

Amelia put a tentative foot on the stone, pulling it back, then laughing at herself. Taking a deep breath, she stood on it and began slowly rotating, her eyes closed, breathing in the scent of the wood, trying to reach a sense of the long dead Osyth, Kieran and Angharad. The children, then the teenagers, then the married couple, who had once played here. *Especially Kieran*, she thought, *an angry child and a desperate man.* The leaves whispered and for a moment she felt she could hear them, laughing, calling to each other. Then Edward called her name, his voice urgent.

Opening her eyes, she glanced over. Lara was free, standing beside him, wagging her tail but Edward continued to kneel down, clearing away the clumps of ivy.

"Amelia, look."

Hurrying to his side, she dropped to her knees beside him. Nero and Lara between them.

"What is it?"

"It's a headstone," he said.

"It must be an animal's grave," she replied. "People often used to bury horses and mark them."

"Maybe, but this is a significant place. No local would bury a pet on the edge of the stone circle. It's a sacred site."

Edward reached into his pocket and pulled out his water bottle, scrubbing with his fingers to remove the mud and reveal the engraving. Amelia fished a wodge of tissues from her pocket and began to help, wiping the years of grime away from the letters, a sense of urgency enveloping them both. The

two greyhounds stood silent by their sides, as though sensing this was important.

"No," gasped Amelia as words began to emerge from the years of natural detritus. "No, it can't be."

"Why was she buried here and not in the graveyard?"

"*Eudora*," read Amelia, tracing her fingertips over the words, "*loved and loveable, our changeling princess who went home to the fae. 1849–1884.*" Amelia's voice petered out, then she turned to Edward. "Osyth says in her diary that her mother died in 1866. What do these dates mean?"

PART SIX: WINDSOR, 1884

CHAPTER ONE

As Osyth stared down at the letter, tears flowed noiselessly down her pale cheeks and her heart was filled with confusion. The fairy-tale love story with its bittersweet ending that had sustained her throughout her childhood years was slipping away. All she had believed was a lie. Her heart, whose beat had once known only love, now felt the pain of secrets with their bitterness and hatred, the dark twins of her fertile imaginings.

My Dearest Osyth, it is with great delight that I am able to solve the mystery we encountered last winter. You were intrigued to discover the identity of a client named Mrs E O'Reilly. Last week, while your grandfather and Mr Noah were away, the bank requested a meeting, which I had been authorised to oversee. While we were discussing the many aspects of the boatyard (none of which I will tire you with) Mr Cosgrove confirmed the regular monthly sum had been paid and collected as was the usual arrangement. It appears this is an understanding of many years, and the money is paid to an account on the Continent. I was unable to discover the exact location but it is collected regularly by a Mr Egan O'Reilly. It is a payment that is made to his wife. I hope this alleviates your curiosity.

With my greatest regard,

Mr. F. Meyrick

"No," Osyth muttered, confusion coursing through her. "No, this cannot be, they can't have lied to me all these years. Frederick must be mistaken." Her mother was the wife of Egan O'Reilly, but both her parents were dead, so who were the people receiving money from her grandfather every month? "Nain," she gasped, searching for a release from the

dark new world in which she found herself. "Nain will know." Like Altheia, the fairy of revelation from the tales of her childhood, her grandmother would be able to pull aside this strange illusion and reveal the truth.

Gathering her skirts in her hand, Osyth hurried from her bedroom and down the stairs. At this time of day, Penny was usually in the morning room catching up with her correspondence but when Osyth opened the door, the hearth was cold and there was no sign of her.

"Your grandmother is unwell," said Betsy as she bustled past. "She requested we leave her to sleep until lunchtime."

"Do you know what's wrong?" asked Osyth, concern for her beloved Nain momentarily pushing aside the boiling confusion created by Frederick's letter.

"One of her headaches," replied Betsy. "She has had some hot tea and a bite of toast but now she would like peace and sleep, then she will be restored to her usual self."

"Thank you, Betsy. Please send her my love when you check on her later."

Betsy nodded and continued down the corridor towards the kitchen.

Osyth's grandfather was away, as was Noah. Her mind flickered towards Xenia but she, too, was out of town, staying with William's family in Norfolk.

Uncle Solomon, she thought. *He will know. He knows everything.*

An hour later, she sat on the train heading towards London. Betsy had been horrified when she had informed her of this plan.

"You might be kidnapped," she had said, her voice shrill.

"I shan't!" laughed Osyth. "I've visited Uncle Solomon many times at his offices."

"Young ladies do not go out alone!"

"Oh Betsy, you're so old fashioned."

However, now that Osyth was alone on the first-class train from Windsor to Waterloo, her nerves were thrumming and her heart was beating faster than usual. The letter was in her reticule, which she clutched tightly with her gloved fingers. In order to persuade Betsy not to wake Penny, it had been agreed that the groom, Bobby Andrews, a long-time member of the Attwater staff, would accompany Osyth to the railway station, where he would ensure her ticket was a return and would ask the guard to see her safely into a hansom cab when she arrived at Waterloo.

Solomon's offices were in Fleet Street and Osyth had visited them with her grandparents. He ran a magazine and published literary works and art. Many considered his choice of authors to be risqué but Solomon always shrugged and said, with a wink to his niece, "What's the point of living if there isn't a little risk?"

As the journey passed and nothing untoward happened, Osyth began to relax and enjoy the thrill of her clandestine adventure. Once again, her thoughts moved to the letter, which seemed to glow hot through the fabric of her reticule. Its words had shocked her but she was convinced Frederick was mistaken; there would be a logical and simple explanation for this monthly payment. To think otherwise sent a strange shiver of fear through her heart.

Her thoughts were interrupted by the train's arrival at Waterloo. The guard brought a porter in full livery and passed Osyth into his care. Guiding her through the milling crowd, the man whistled for a cab and helped Osyth inside.

"He's not here," said the man leaning over the inky pages, half an hour later as Osyth stood breathless with nerves in her uncle's office. "We're not expecting him today."

Osyth stared at the man and the adrenaline that had brought her this far seemed to ebb away.

"Oh," was all she could manage.

"Was he expecting you?"

"No, it was a surprise," she replied. "He's my uncle and he said to come to him if I ever needed anything."

The man's eyes flicked up and down her. "You're the daughter of his missing sister, aren't you?"

"She isn't missing, she's dead."

"Right, yes, my mistake," he said, turning away and scribbling something on a scrap of paper. "This is his London flat. It isn't far. I'll get one of the boys to put you in a cab."

A short time later Osyth was standing outside a tall townhouse in Gerrard Street. Checking the address, she took a deep breath and walked up the stairs to the red front door. It was a few moments before there was a scrabbling with the chain and it opened to reveal a beautiful young man, not much older than Osyth. His dark hair curled over his collar and his wide brown eyes gazed at her with curiosity. Osyth stared back taking in the dazzling peacock blue silk dressing gown he wore over a bare chest and cream trousers.

"Yes?" he asked, his tone amused, when she continued to gape.

"I'm sorry," she stuttered, looking at the address on the piece of paper and wondering if this were a cruel joke. "This must be the wrong place…"

"Who were you looking for?"

"My uncle, Solomon Attwater."

The young man smiled, then he took her hand and ushered her inside. His skin was soft against her palm as he drew her into the hallway. She wondered whether she should turn and flee but it was too late, the young man had shut the door behind her and flipped the chain back in place.

"He is dressing," he said in his heavily accented voice. "Come, I shall call him and then you shall join me for coffee. We will wait together."

Tucking Osyth's hand under his arm, he led her down the wallpapered hallway past the marble and wrought-iron staircase to a sunny room looking out over a small garden, with views of the backs of the shops and houses opposite. Doors opened onto a balcony and a parrot squawked on a perch. Several chaises, covered in silken throws and elaborately decorated cushions took up one corner of the room. On the other side was an easel with a painting resting on it, a raised platform and a variety of artist's props. The painting was covered with a red cloth.

"I call him," said the young man whose soft, exotic accent made Osyth think of blue skies, sunshine and the smell of spices. "Sit, be comfortable. Ulysses will entertain you." He pointed to the parrot, before smiling and drifting from the room.

Osyth stared around, unsure what to make of this strange situation. This must be the flat Solomon often referred to but she had not known he had a foreign servant. Marianne, his wife, and their three children lived in Hampshire, coming to town rarely. Osyth walked over to the easel and was about to lift the cloth covering the painting when her uncle strode into the room.

"Osyth, my dear." His face was full of concern and she dropped the silken covering, running into his open arms. Now

he was here, she felt safe and, to her surprise, tears welled in her eyes.

"My sweet girl, what has happened?" he asked, leading her to the chaise by the fire. "Does your grandmother know you're in London?"

The young man hurried in carrying a tray with a jug of hot, fragrant Turkish coffee.

"Thank you, Drake," said Solomon. "Give us a minute alone, please."

"Of course," Drake replied, gliding away on silent feet and disappearing up the stairs.

"Sit, drink," said Solomon, "then tell me."

Osyth sipped from the small handleless cup he pushed into her hand. Wrinkling her nose, she choked on the thick, gritty liquid. Solomon dropped more sugar into it, stirring it with a metal spatula. This time the sweetness made the aromatic spices more palatable. As it slid down her throat, she felt its intensity bring her drifting senses back into focus. Replacing the cup on the tray, she reached into her reticule and pulled out the crumpled letter.

"It's a note from Frederick Meyrick," she said, passing it to her uncle.

Solomon smoothed it out, his face expressionless. "Perhaps you had better explain, Osyth," he said.

Taking a deep breath, she told him all that had happened.

"And this arrived early this morning from Frederick," she said. "Please don't blame him. This is all my fault but I don't understand…" Her voice petered out.

"Oh, my darling girl," sighed Solomon. "It's no wonder you were upset, but I suspect this is an unhappy coincidence. Pa will be home today and as it's a Friday, I imagine Noah will be

joining you for dinner. Shall we visit too and perhaps between us we can untangle this misunderstanding?"

"Really?" asked Osyth, feeling her heart lighten for the first time since receiving Frederick's letter.

"Of course," Solomon replied. "If you will be patient while I send a telegram to Mother so she knows you are safe, then we can have some lunch before catching the train to Windsor. Drake will pack me a bag and I shall stay for the weekend."

"Thank you, Uncle Solomon," Osyth said, feeling the tension lifting from her shoulders. She looked properly around the sumptuous room. "I didn't know you painted."

"I don't," he replied, his usual easy grace flowing back through him as he leaned back, languid and amused. "Drake is the artist."

"I thought he was your servant," she said.

"He's my friend," replied Solomon. "This house is far too large for one and it gives me peace of mind to know he is here, when I am not. We have an arrangement and he looks after me when I do stay. The rest of the time, he paints."

"Will I have seen any of his work?"

"Not yet, my dear, he is young and developing his style but one day he will be a big star."

"May I see the painting he is working on at the moment?"

"Perhaps another time," replied Solomon. "The subject matter is not what I would be comfortable with my niece viewing, especially in my own home."

"Why? What…?"

"He paints nudes," whispered Solomon, a knowing smile on his face and Osyth blushed.

Lunch with Solomon had been a treat, followed by shopping in Regent Street, then the train home to Windsor where her grandparents and Noah were waiting. Her apologies had been profuse and Daniel had explained the strange reference to a Mr E O'Reilly.

"It is pure coincidence and there is no connection to your father," he had assured her. "The reason we pay a lump sum every month to them is because they were once shareholders in the company, many years ago, when my father was alive. He was not a good businessman and he borrowed a great deal of money from the O'Reillys. We are still repaying the debt."

After that, the evening had passed pleasantly, with Noah regaling them with tales from his latest travels on behalf of the boatyard, before Penny had asked Osyth to walk her up to her bedroom.

"My darling, I am so sorry you were upset today," Penny said as they climbed the stairs. "You know how much Taid and I love you. We would never wish you to be as confused as you were today."

"I know, Nain," Osyth said. "I'm sorry. It was an overreaction but there seemed to be no logical explanation."

"In future, please ask us first."

Penny flinched in pain.

"Nain, what is it?" Osyth asked.

Penny smiled. "The aches and pains of old age," she said. "Nothing to worry about, but it has been a tiring day. Perhaps you could help me into bed."

"Is this my fault?" Osyth asked, walking with her slowly to the vast bed.

"No, my dear, my head and back have pained me all day, this is not your doing. Now, if you would be kind enough to pass me my book, I shall read for a while before sleeping."

"Good night, Nain," Osyth said and leaned over to kiss her grandmother on the cheek.

"Good night, my darling."

Osyth stood on the landing. The day had been strange and, despite the pleasant evening, there was a restlessness in her heart. Kieran's words came back to her: "You are not safe here, and when you realise you reside among liars, thieves and lunatics, the door to my house will be open and waiting for you."

Liars. The word had stung her when Kieran had flung it at her but now it pulsed with meaning. Her grandfather's explanation was plausible and yet… Was he lying?

Osyth made her decision. Turning away from her bedroom door, she crept down the stairs and across the marble-tiled hallway, her slippered feet whispering on the diamond pattern as she crept down the corridor towards the parlour where she could hear the rumble of male voices. Beside this was a cupboard used to store household items. As a child, Kieran had discovered it was the perfect place to spy on the adults. The thin partition wall offered very little in the way of soundproofing and it was the ideal place to discover secrets. He would sit in the gloom for hours, writing notes, adding times, dates, names and details as he eavesdropped on a myriad of conversations.

When they were young, Osyth and Angharad had thought it hilarious. They would giggle over the stories he had overheard, feeling they were seeing into the privileged and distant world of adulthood. Now, Osyth wondered what else Kieran had learned while crouched in the cupboard that he had not shared with them.

Osyth opened the cupboard door and felt her way into the gloom, finding a coat which she could fold up and sit on. She

cleared a broom and old umbrella from the wall and, pressing her ear to the cold, cream-coloured lining paper, she listened hard. Her grandfather and uncles were speaking, their deep voices low but if she concentrated, she could strain her ears enough to hear their conversation.

"...but Pa," Solomon said, "Frederick is smitten with Osyth, you only have to mention her name and the young fellow blushes to the roots of his hair. If she asks him to investigate further, he will..."

"Would she ask?" asked Daniel.

Noah gave a short laugh. "Of course she would," he said and there was a clink as he topped up their glasses from the decanter. "Wouldn't you? She's been brought up to be imaginative and curious. You can't pretend to be shocked when all she's doing is behaving in a way we've always encouraged. In all seriousness though, Pa, what are we going to do? I don't like lying to her but do we have an alternative?"

"We've always known that the day might come when we have to tell her what really happened," added Solomon. "She's growing up. There's a chance she may well discover a version of the truth."

"You mean from Kieran," said Noah, his tone derisive.

"Yes, from Kieran. You may have always struggled with him but there is no point denying he and Osyth are friends. His behaviour has become worrying of late and she may well believe his garbled version of events."

"What do you think he knows, Sol?" asked Daniel.

"I'm not sure he knows much," replied Solomon, "but what he doesn't know, he may make up, which could be more detrimental."

There was a silence as the men considered this.

"Are you suggesting we should tell her?" said Noah.

"Yes," replied Solomon.

"All of it?" Noah was aghast.

"No," replied Daniel. "Not at first, but I think Sol is correct. We can't trust Kieran not to try and woo her away from us by telling Osyth his twisted version of events."

"But if we tell her, she'll know we've lied to her since she was a child," said Noah.

"Is it lying when you conceal a truth in order to protect someone?" questioned Daniel.

"What will you say? Will you explain the reason why you and mother sent her away? Osyth idolises her memory, wouldn't it be cruel to tell her what happened?"

"Perhaps at first, but we could tell her…" Daniel paused. "We could tell her that her mother is alive but has been seriously ill."

In the cupboard Osyth stifled her gasp.

"And then what?" snapped Noah. "We tell her why you banished Eudora, why you pay her feckless husband a lump sum every month? We undo all the good work you've done. She's a dreamer, which I know is partly my fault. She'll probably run off the moment she knows Eudora is in Switzerland."

"Would you prefer her to hear Kieran's version of the story? His will paint us all as villains."

"Perhaps we are, Pa," said Noah, wearily, "perhaps we are."

A little while later Osyth heard the three men leave. She remained in the darkness, her heart pounding.

CHAPTER TWO

"You did the right thing coming to us, my dear," said Angharad, pouring tea and passing a cup to Osyth. "Kieran has told me his suspicions about your mother and, while I find it hard to believe your grandparents would deliberately lie to you, there is something very strange about the situation."

They were eating breakfast at the townhouse Kieran had inherited from his parents on his twenty-first birthday. Osyth took the cup, her hand trembling as she placed it gently on the white cloth. "There must be an explanation," she sighed, "but I'm not sure what to believe any more."

After listening to the revelations of her grandfather and uncles, Osyth had crept back to her room and huddled on her bed, replaying the conversation in an endless loop in her mind. They had said her mother was alive and living in Switzerland with her father. The word that had stuck, rotating before her eyes like an accusation, however, was 'banished'.

We tell her why you banished Eudora. This was in complete opposition to what she had been told all her life, that her father had died in a shipwreck and her mother from a broken heart. She had believed she was an orphan when in reality, her parents lived abroad. *Banished.* Shuddering, she looked up and saw Angharad watching her with concern in her eyes.

After a sleepless night, Osyth had padded down the corridor, confused and angry, ready to confront her grandmother only to discover a flurry of people around the bed. Daniel, white-faced, sat beside Penny, holding her limp hand. Solomon was beside him, his face pale, a worried frown creasing his brow. When he had seen her hovering in the doorway, he had hurried

to her side. "Nain was taken ill in the night," he had whispered, leading her away from the doctor and nurse who were injecting Penny with a long syringe. "She will need special treatment in a hospital."

"But she will recover?"

"Yes," Solomon had replied. He had given her the loving and reassuring smile she had known and trusted since childhood, but Osyth was no longer sure if she could trust his words. She had stepped forward to help prepare her grandmother for the journey but had been shooed away as though she were a troublesome child. Furious at once again being dismissed, she had slipped from the room and made a decision. She had packed a bag, written a note and left through the back garden. Now, three days later, she was regretting her actions as her concerns about her grandmother's health haunted her constantly.

The door opened and Kieran entered. Osyth gave him a weak smile. Living in such close proximity to her cousin and her friend with their change of status as a married couple had caused her to question the happiness of their union. The change in Angharad whenever Kieran was in her vicinity made Osyth uncomfortable. Her friend's usual relaxed, calm nature changed to nervousness and unease, emotions which were heightened further if Kieran addressed her directly. As Angharad poured Kieran's tea, her hands shook, rattling the teacup, but Kieran smiled at her and Osyth watched Angharad's drawn face relax slightly.

"My two favourite girls," he said. "What a delight it is to have you both at my table. We three are together again and what adventures we will have now we are away from the poison of Cliffside." Osyth frowned but felt it was unwise to spoil Kieran's upbeat mood, which had been unpredictable

since she had arrived. "I must attend my classes today, but I will be home for tea," he continued. "Do you have any plans, my dears?"

Although he included them both in the enquiry, it was to Osyth he addressed the question, but she deferred to Angharad. *After all*, thought Osyth, *it's her house. She's Mrs Stone.*

"If the weather remains fine, we thought a visit to Kew Gardens would be an interesting diversion," said Angharad, her voice timid. "My plans for the garden are almost complete but they have a new exhibition which might be helpful."

"A marvellous idea," replied Kieran, then added in a light tone, "Jeakes will accompany you."

Jeakes was the steward of the household. To call him a butler was to raise him to a rank to which he could only aspire.

"Oh Kieran, we'll be fine on our own," said Osyth, who did not like Jeakes, finding him unpleasant and threatening in the way he entered rooms unexpectedly and stared too long and too hard in a way she felt was intrusive and impertinent. "Jeakes is far too busy to have to worry about following us around." Across the table she heard Angharad gasp, but Osyth ignored the frantic look her friend threw at her, and continued, "You're very thoughtful to think of us needing a chaperone but we are quite able to explore on our own."

"My dear Osyth, I wouldn't hear of it," Kieran replied and Osyth noticed a strange tick over his eye. It twitched as he spoke, causing him to rub his temple in short, sharp flicks. "While you are under my roof, your safety is my responsibility, and it is a charge I take with great seriousness. Jeakes will accompany you."

His tone was flat and there was a strange finality to it. Kieran picked up the copy of *The Times* that Jeakes had laid by his

plate and disappeared behind its wide pages, bringing the conversation to an abrupt halt.

Osyth stared down at her half-eaten piece of toast. Ever since her arrival, her usually robust appetite seemed to have deserted her and she wondered if she was sickening for something. A listlessness which she could not seem to overcome dragged at her throughout the day. *Either that*, she thought, *or I'm being poisoned by the unappetising offerings from Kieran's kitchen.* A bracing walk around the botanical gardens was the perfect antidote, but if Jeakes was trailing behind them, the pleasure of the outing would be considerably dampened.

The palm house was crowded and, to Osyth's relief, the sour-faced Jeakes announced he would wait for them outside.

"Too hot for me," he scowled and wandered off to a bench where he produced a pipe and was soon enveloped in a cloud of acrid smoke.

Angharad tucked her arm in Osyth's and drew her into the tropical heat of the extraordinary wrought-iron-and-glass structure. "This is the only place he won't follow me," whispered Angharad as they made their way through the throng. "It's why I suggested we come here. He and Kieran think I'm planning a garden for the house in Richmond but I come here to think."

A bench at the heart of the palm house was vacated by its incumbents and Angharad hurried forward to claim it, pulling Osyth in her wake.

"Tell me the truth, Annie," said Osyth when they were seated. "Is being married to Kieran what's making you unhappy?"

"Is it so obvious?" Angharad whispered, horrified. "Every day I try to hide it…"

"We're friends, we've known each other all our lives."

Angharad fretted at the lace of her gloves, then turned brimming eyes to Osyth. "I'm with child," she whispered.

This was the last thing Osyth had expected her friend to confess but she did not understand why it seemed to be such a cause for distress. In their family babies were a cause for celebration and excitement. "Angharad, that's wonderful news," she said, smiling.

"Is it?" Angharad whispered and her pallor was so shocking Osyth wondered if her friend was about to pass out. "Kieran was furious."

"Why?"

"He said I was foolish and should have been more careful. He is not in a financial position to start a family."

Even though Osyth was upset with her grandparents for their seeming subterfuge about her mother, she felt sure that once Penny had recovered and they were able to resolve the matter, they would be able to help and support Kieran and Angharad, which she told her friend.

"Oh Osyth, things are not as easy as you think."

"Tell me then."

Angharad hesitated, then to Osyth's relief, she began to unburden herself.

"When he was wooing me, Kieran was sweet and kind and charming," she began in a low voice, "he dazzled me. However, since we've been married, he has become cold. At first, when he came to my bed, he was tender but then he became brusquer, and now…" Her voice tailed away for a moment, then she took a deep breath and continued. "It is almost as though I am not there. He arrives, does as he wishes,

then leaves without a word. When I told him about the child the evening before you arrived, he said I was lying and it was an excuse for me to abstain from providing his conjugal rights."

"What?"

"As you know, Kieran has always suffered from these strange fits of melancholy and he has a cruel streak, but it was never aimed at either of us, his friends. To be on the receiving end of his anger, his darkness, is shocking. It's made me realise why Noah watched Kieran so closely. His moods are unnerving. Last night, I woke up to find Kieran sitting in the chair opposite my bed, watching me sleep. When he saw he had woken me, he came to sit on the bed and I hoped he would be gentle but he told me to think myself lucky that he had not turned me out."

"He didn't say that!" Osyth gasped, outraged at her cousin's behaviour. "You're his wife and you're carrying his child."

Tears welled in Angharad's eyes. "According to Kieran, he has the power to annul our marriage at any time, should he choose to take another wife."

"He's lying," Osyth said. "You married legally and he must face up to his responsibilities. Annie, you mustn't worry. As Kieran's wife, you're one of the family. Nain and Taid will help you if you are in need of assistance."

Osyth did not reveal to Angharad that Kieran had asked for her own hand in marriage. She felt it would be unkind and now she felt relief that his offer had been so vehemently rejected by Taid. But she wondered if it might be within her power to help her friends unravel the problem in their marriage. As Angharad had said, they had grown up together. Kieran could be strange but Osyth was normally able to win him around and make him smile. "Would you like me to speak to him?" she asked.

"No, it would make matters worse," Angharad replied. "He would be angry with me for discussing it with you…"

"Osyth!"

The two women looked up and Osyth stared in surprise. Frederick Meyrick was hurrying towards her.

"Did you arrange to meet him?" asked Angharad, her voice fraught with anxiety.

"No," replied Osyth, honestly. "I made no plans to meet anyone."

"Osyth, Mrs Stone," said Frederick, arriving in front of them looking flustered and excited. "What a marvellous coincidence. It's my day off and I was meeting my aunt and uncle for ices. When I saw you through the heat, I thought you were a mirage!"

"No, Frederick, we're real," Osyth said, squeezing Angharad's hand in reassurance. A man and woman approached, both well-dressed in an elegant, understated manner.

"Uncle Charlie, Aunt Jane, here is a wonderful surprise, my dear friend, Miss Osyth Attwater, from Cliffside in Milford Haven and her cousin, Mrs Kieran Stone. My uncle and aunt, Sir Charlton Bush Meyrick and his wife, Lady Jane Bohemia Meyrick."

The flurry of introductions hid Angharad's frantic gestures that they should leave, her eyes darting towards the bench where Jeakes could be seen as a smudgy figure in the distance.

"Alas," said Osyth, "we were about to leave. Kieran's steward is waiting outside to escort us safely back to Richmond."

There were general noises of disappointment, but propriety dictated they should at least walk to the entrance with Frederick and his relatives. To Osyth's relief, Sir Charlton and

Lady Jane swept Angharad off between them, allowing Osyth a moment alone with Frederick.

"Must you really return home so soon?" he asked.

"Kieran's house is not home," she said. "It is a place of misery and if I wasn't so concerned about Angharad, my plans would be to return with you to Windsor this instant."

"Are things really so bad?"

"They are not well," she replied. "Is there word of my grandmother? I have had no response to my letters and I am concerned this means the worst."

"But we have all replied," he said, surprised. "Your grandmother is recovering well but your grandfather and uncles have all written entreating you to come home. Xenia is determined to visit you to persuade you to return. They all wish to resolve whatever it is you think you know about your parents."

Osyth felt a swooping confusion, as though she had missed the bottom step in a flight of stairs. "Kieran has said there has been no post," she said.

Frederick's face puckered with concern. "Would you like me to accompany you back to Richmond, then home to Windsor? We could ask Mrs Stone to accompany us," he said. "I feel it would be the least I could do as it strikes me that the letter I sent you was the beginning of your woes."

"No, this is not your fault," she said. "Thank you for your kind offer but I shall return with Angharad and try to ascertain why Kieran is keeping my post from me. Don't worry, all will be well. Kieran can be a little strange but he always sees reason in the end."

Frederick looked unconvinced but Osyth was confident that she alone would be able to break through the carapace Kieran had constructed around himself.

"Osyth, we must leave," Angharad called from the entrance to the palm house.

"When may I see you again?" asked Frederick, catching her arm, holding her closely to him. "I miss you, Osyth."

"There are many things that I do not understand," she replied. "My grandparents, my aunt, my uncles, they have all conspired to lie to me. I don't trust their actions and at the moment, I intend to stay where I am in Richmond in order to help my friends. Write to me, Freddie, then you will know I'm safe and we'll arrange a meeting." She hesitated, then mumbled, "I miss you, too."

With a small, bobbed curtsey, she hurried away and said a polite goodbye to Frederick's aunt and uncle, before departing with Angharad to where Jeakes was waiting, his expression as bleak as a gargoyle's.

CHAPTER THREE

It was five days since the trip to Kew Gardens and Osyth sat in the sunny morning room writing to Frederick. Upon returning home, Angharad had retired to bed and Osyth had sought out Kieran, demanding to know why she had not received her letters. Kieran had been appalled, calling Jeakes to him, remonstrating with the man and insisting the matter be dealt with immediately. A short while later, Jeakes had appeared with a silver tray on which were a number of letters addressed to Osyth, muttering about an oversight.

A strange malady had overtaken her that evening causing extravagant and violent dreams that left her weak and unsteady the following morning. Kieran had insisted she remain in bed and had sent his own home-made tinctures to treat her. Osyth had found their bitter smell off-putting and when she had been left alone, she had poured them away in a nearby aspidistra. When Kieran had asked whether she was taking her medicine, she had assured him she was and would soon be fully recovered.

She had awoken feeling her usual energetic self. It was the first moment since her unexpected malady that she had found herself alone, and it was a relief. Kieran and Angharad were out visiting one of Kieran's professors at the university in London. Osyth hoped that her friends would have an enjoyable day together. *Perhaps they will recapture their former affection*, she thought. *It was always between them but is now noticeably absent.*

The room where she sat had once belonged to Georgina. As with the rest of the house it had been decorated in a simple,

elegant style. Since taking over the property, Kieran had removed all images of the extended family, leaving only the portraits of his parents and one small photographic image of Katherine. In the dining room, he had hung a vast portrait of his mother, a recent commission and one which Osyth felt did not do justice to the dainty woman in the images she had seen of Georgina. In this portrait, she appeared stern and unforgiving.

Osyth finally felt able to write to her family. The letters had informed her that Penny was recovering well and would be returning home to convalesce. The doctors believed she had a problem with her heart and advised rest and peace. She had hoped to be reassured with the truth about her parents but to her fury, they had all stuck to the same lies as before, and this had angered her beyond belief.

She had made a decision. It was time to prove to her family that she was no longer the fey child who dwelled in a land of make-believe and fairies. While her imagination remained vivid and her ambition continued to aspire towards the written word, it did not mean she was unable to cope with the growing complexities of adult life. Her morning had been spent composing a letter, which she had copied to each of them, stating that, while she knew she should not have eavesdropped on the conversation between Taid, Noah and Solomon, she was glad she had because they had revealed the fact that her mother was not dead but had been banished to Switzerland.

If the replies to her letters disappointed her and none of the family was willing to help, Osyth was determined to discover her mother for herself. She was a woman of some means and her plan was to travel with Angharad to Switzerland in search of her parents.

In the few moments when they were alone, not being watched by Kieran's motley collection of dubious staff, Osyth had whispered her intentions to Angharad. Hope had flared in Angharad's eyes and she agreed to accompany Osyth. They would tell no one, particularly Kieran, whose behaviour continued to alarm Osyth.

Finishing the letters, Osyth considered placing them on the silver tray in the hallway for the staff to post but it was a rare warm April day and the bright blue sky was an invitation too tempting to resist. The Thames flowed majestically through Richmond, and Osyth was overwhelmed by a need to be by water.

Kieran's house was positioned in one of the winding roads leading away from Richmond Green. The shops were a short walk away and, once her business was done, she would make her way back via the footpath along the river. Strolling across the green, Osyth watched as the residents of the town went about their business, feeling for the first time that she was one of them. No longer the youngest child, protected and pampered, she was now a young lady of means. A young lady with a secret plan, she reminded herself. A secret plan that she was as yet unsure how to put into action.

The business of travel was not alien to her — the family were steeped in the boating community — but it had always been her grandfather and uncles who travelled. On the few occasions she had accompanied her grandparents on their boats, they were the pleasure cruises on the Thames. Holidays had usually taken the form of visiting family friends or renting houses in other parts of the countryside near either Windsor or Milford Haven.

Osyth had never been abroad but she was aware that the large sea-going liners often docked near their boatyard in Neyland. *If I am to reach Switzerland, I will need to get to the Continent*, she thought. *Perhaps there is a train from London which would take me to the coast, but when I get there, what shall I do?*

Suddenly, it came to her. She would visit Blaise and Katherine. They were in Paris. Excitement coursed through her as she realised the first stage of her journey was possible. Even if her family were distressed at her plans to go in search of her mother, they would never complain about her visiting her uncle and her new aunt. Blaise would help her and, if he would not do it willingly, she was certain Katherine would pave the way for success in her venture.

They might even know where my mother lives, she thought. *Although Freddie might be able to help me there.*

Then she paused in her considerations. Asking Frederick to discover the truth about the payments had been more than enough. She did not want him to lose his job and if he continued to investigate on her behalf, she felt sure her grandfather would gently but firmly suggest he find other employment. *No*, she thought, *I can't ask him.*

Entering the busy Post Office, Osyth held the letters in her hand, ready to send them to her family, wanting to hurt them as much as she felt they had disregarded her feelings, when she saw Jeakes. He was leaning low over the counter discussing something with the postmistress. A rosy-cheeked woman in her forties, the woman's smile had flattened out into a frown and it was clear whatever Jeakes was saying was unpalatable. Not wishing to be seen by him, Osyth stepped out of the Post Office, planning to return later, and decided instead to visit the station where she might be able to discover more about travelling to Paris.

As she entered the bustling concourse, her breath caught in her throat. "Freddie?" she exclaimed.

Frederick looked up, astonishment flashing across his handsome face. "Osyth?" he replied, laughing. "You must be a magical being. It seems that whenever I think about you, there you are in front of me."

"I might say the same," she replied, flustered but delighted. "Why are you in Richmond?"

"It's my afternoon off and I decided to surprise you," he said, but the laughter in his voice was now fading away. "My sincere apologies if what I am about to say is an intrusion but after our unexpected meeting in Kew Gardens, you said things which gave me cause for concern."

"Concern?"

"You and Mrs Stone seemed nervous, which is unlike you."

"Oh Freddie, we're fine. My family are wary of Kieran for many reasons." Osyth paused, deciding this was not the time to tell him about her cousin's bizarre proposal of marriage. "The mishap with the letters has been resolved and, look, I have responses here. As you can see, I am quite well, despite the fact Kieran's cook is appalling."

"Perhaps tea would be advisable then, with plenty of cakes?"

Osyth beamed in response, all thoughts of travel plans wiped from her mind.

CHAPTER FOUR

Blindly he reached out, his fingers closing around the coolness of the pen's shaft. He had abandoned it the night before when darkness had fugged his brain, drawing him to sleep. As his mind scrabbled in the space between sleep and wakefulness, he scribbled the scraps of ideas into his small leather-bound book: thoughts, dreams, stories told, captured for him to explore when his mind allowed him to think of things other than her. Words streamed effortlessly across the page, isolated nouns, mystical thoughts, pairs and trios waiting to find the companions of their sentences, eager to reveal the secret hidden within their sinuous forms...

Mrs Jeakes knocked on Osyth's door to help her dress for dinner and Osyth quickly shut her journal, where she had been attempting to capture the image of Frederick as a poet. The return of her friends had been silent, and the time had passed more quickly than she had realised. As the silent woman tidied her hair and helped her to dress a surge of her usual *joie de vivre* pulsed through Osyth as she anticipated telling Angharad about her afternoon with Frederick. The delectable opportunity to relive every line of their conversation, to dissect it and cogitate the possibility of every nuance, glance, hint and meaning.

She rushed into the dining room as the vibrant echoes of the dinner gong faded into the grey silence, hoping she would find Angharad already seated but Kieran was alone, his face stony.

"Where's Annie?" she asked, waiting while Jeakes pulled out her chair, then arranged her napkin across her knees before indicating for his assistant, Pullet, to serve the watery soup, which reminded Osyth of cabbage water.

"My wife will be away for a few days, staying with friends," Kieran replied, dipping his spoon into the tepid grey liquid.

"How strange," said Osyth, taking a cautious mouthful, "she didn't mention it."

"The decision was sudden," he replied. "As you know, my wife is with child and it is causing her some discomfort. The friends with whom she is lodging are specialists in this matter. He is a well-known doctor and, rather surprisingly, his wife is also educated to a high medical level."

"Poor Annie, she seemed quite well this morning."

"To the trained eye, it's clear my wife is a very sick woman."

Osyth lowered her eyes, concentrating as best she could on the watery soup, upset that Angharad had been suffering. After a few mouthfuls, she placed her spoon to one side, unable to stomach any more, reaching instead for her wine. If Kieran's cook was substandard, the accompanying wine was the opposite. Osyth wondered if the many bottles of fine vintage wines were part of Kieran's inheritance and had been bought by his father. The extravagance and depth of their flavours were at odds with the remainder of the house, offering Osyth a taste of the comfort and luxury which had been her grandparents' past existence.

Kieran, too, picked at his soup. It seemed he was descending into one of his more tiresome moods and Osyth was eager to get away from him. During their childhood, there had been occasions when he would sulk for a week at a time. No one ever knew why and he would confide in no one. On rare occasions, Katherine could persuade him from his melancholia but the set line of his mouth this evening informed Osyth that this would be a tantrum starting, and she was not in the mood to pander to him.

Her afternoon with Frederick had been full of sunshine and joy. They had discussed books, art, plays and, to Osyth's delight, mythology. It appeared he was as interested as she was in things mystical, many of which he included in his poems. The other topic which had fascinated them both were the many newspaper reports of the seemingly magical mediums who were claiming to speak to ghosts. Neither could quite understand how they were able to create such illusions and both hoped there were people who could contact the dead.

With Kieran in such a dour mood and with no Angharad with whom to share her excitement and relive her unexpected afternoon, Osyth's intention was to return to her room and continue updating her journal. She smothered a secret smile at the thought of describing her growing feelings for Frederick.

The soup was cleared away and an inedible lamb chop with greens was placed before her, followed by a heavy Sussex Pond Pudding which did not cascade with the joyous mix of butter, caramel and lemon that she remembered from Angharad's mother's cooking. This was grey and damp, like an old bath towel.

Osyth nodded and pushed her food around her plate as Kieran talked, his monologue moving from a tirade about the stupidity of his fellow trainee medics to a poisonous diatribe about Blaise and his art.

Finishing as much as she was able of the pudding, Osyth placed her fork and spoon together, raised her napkin to her lips, then turned to Kieran. "Would you excuse me, Kieran?" she asked. "I am rather tired and intend to have an early night."

He did not reply. Osyth stifled her sigh of irritation and stood up, but she had taken only a few steps towards the door

when he spoke, his voice so low she struggled to hear his words.

"You saw him today," he hissed.

"I beg your pardon?"

"The man, Frederick Meyrick, who works with them. Your vile family. Did they send him to spy on you?"

Anger flared in Osyth's heart. "How do you know I saw Freddie?"

"Freddie?" His voice was heavy with sarcasm. "*Freddie?*" To Osyth's astonishment, Kieran rose to his feet and paced towards her, grasping her wrist with such force she let out a yelp and tried to free herself, before he began shaking her. "How dare you be so familiar with another man?"

"Kieran, what's wrong with you?" she spat, rage replacing surprise as she wrenched her arm free, her eyes flashing with fury. "Were you having me followed?"

"Jeakes saw you."

"Well good for Jeakes," she snarled. "Yes, I saw Freddie. He had planned to call here but by pure serendipity, we met each other at the station."

"Why were you at the station?"

"Not that it's any of your business but I wanted a train timetable to London. Annie and I planned to go to an exhibition at the Natural History Museum."

It was a lie but she was so angry with Kieran, she felt no qualms about throwing him off her scent. Too used to his outbursts to be anything but irritated, she reached for the door handle but to her amazement, it opened before she could touch it and Jeakes stood glowering on the threshold.

"Excuse me," she said, trying to imitate her grandmother at her most imperious, but Jeakes did not move. She felt Kieran's hands on her waist, pulling her back into the dining room and

forcing her back into her chair. "What do you think you're doing?" she shouted, kicking him away, her legs tangling in her skirts.

Kieran and Jeakes exchanged looks over her head.

"It's as we feared, she has been infected by my wife's malady," sighed Kieran. "Osyth has been drawn into her vicious web. It is a family trait — both her grandmother and mother run with insanity."

"It's very sad, sir," said Jeakes in a low voice. "Shall we lock her in her bedroom for her own safety? As we did the mistress?"

"Very thoughtful, Jeakes," replied Kieran. "She should not give us too much trouble. The sleeping draught I put in her wine will begin to take effect soon."

"You did what…" gasped Osyth, but he was right. Her eyes were heavy and her limbs were losing sensation. Her legs felt as though they would not support her and her head lolled. "Kieran," she gasped as the edges of her vision began to blur, "what have you done?"

PART SEVEN: PEMBROKESHIRE, 2019

CHAPTER ONE

Amelia stared at the page, horrified, then sense caught up with her fear. If Osyth had written this journal, she must have survived her bizarre ordeal. *Although*, thought Amelia, unfurling herself from the sofa and walking over to the tall, narrow windows and gazing down at the edge of the wood, *if she had been deliberately drugged, what sort of state had she been in, and how did she survive?*

Remembering the earlier entries when Osyth had watched Kieran and Angharad appear from the shadows of the woods from these windows, Amelia shuddered. The childhood friendship of the three companions was dissolving and this saddened her. Her own friends were as important to her as her family had been. Poor Osyth's idyllic childhood was fast dissolving and Amelia was concerned about where the story was leading.

Throughout her research into the Attwater and Stone families, Amelia had resisted beginning her own family tree. Irrational though she knew it to be, she could not bring herself to write down the dates of her daughter's short life, followed by those of her parents. Writing them together would somehow seem even more final than their funerals. It was something she had discussed with Melissa during one of their sessions.

"When I set out on this trail, it felt as though it was an adventure Mum and I had embarked upon together," Amelia had explained. "Our last hurrah but, if I'm to do it properly, there has to come a point where I discover whether I'm connected to the people in the photographs or whether they

were simply images Mum found in the house, left by a previous owner."

"Why are you finding this aspect of the search so difficult?" Melissa had asked in her clipped manner.

"Family trees have always struck me as being associated with dead people and the dusty past, not the living," Amelia had replied. "Names and dates from ancestors who we will never meet, whose lives will always remain elusive, yet my tree will begin by placing the three people I loved most in the world in those dusty tomes and it's not something that feels appropriate. Molly should be here, but she isn't, and to catalogue her on a family tree feels heart-breaking."

They had discussed it further and had considered whether using only the names might be helpful, leaving the dates off until Amelia felt ready to see them written on the screen. Amelia had been pleased with this solution and now, sitting at the table in her room, listening to the wind chime, she looked down at the photographs of Molly and her parents that she had placed beside her, wondering whether she could face it at last.

"Are we ready for this, gang?" she asked. "Mum, let's hope you knew what you were doing when you sent me on this quest."

The genealogy website displayed the family tree icon and Amelia tapped on it, writing her own name and birthday, followed by Molly's name. As she typed in her parents' names, she decided that today she would focus on her mother's side, certain that if there were any connections to the Attwaters or Stones, it would be there, but the moment she entered her father's name, name suggestions began flashing across the screen, asking her if she wanted to add people.

Startled as to who else might be researching her father's ancestry, she opened a few of the suggestions and relaxed

when she saw they had been made by her father's cousin, Nina, who lived in Australia. She accepted every hint linked to Nina's family tree and twenty minutes later, a sizeable side of her father's family was complete.

Taking a break and making herself a cup of tea, Amelia stared out at St Brides Bay. It was a grey day with a breeze ruffling the waves. The revelations of the past few days continued to reverberate around her mind. After she and Edward had discovered the long-hidden grave, they had returned to Cliffside and spent the rest of the evening trying every permutation of Eudora's name and possible date of death to find a link to a death certificate but there was nothing. In frustration, they had given up and it was not until Edward had let Amelia through the adjoining door and she was back in her room, she realised they had not, as planned, visited the veranda and the wind chime.

The next day, Edward had sought her out and handed her a padded envelope. "I spoke to Caitlin," he said, "and told her what we discovered. I also told her about your copy of Osyth's journal and she insisted I give you this."

"What is it?"

"She thinks this is a journal that was also written by Osyth but said it never really made much sense."

To Amelia's delight, this book had followed on from her own, but her joy soon turned to horror as she realised the lengths to which Kieran had gone in order to try and trap Osyth into marriage. What had shocked her most was the revelation that in 1884, when the diary had been written, Osyth had discovered that Eudora was alive and living in Switzerland with Osyth's father, Egan O'Reilly, and the couple had been supported financially by Daniel and Penny.

What happened? Amelia wondered as she returned to her research.

Since the unexpected discovery of Eudora's gravestone, which seemed to have unnerved Edward, the easy camaraderie that had sprung up between them had vanished and Edward had retreated into a more formal manner. Caitlin was home and he had taken a few days off to look after her so she had hardly seen him.

Pushing thoughts of Edward aside, Amelia returned to her family tree. Typing in her mother's full name, followed by those of her maternal grandparents, she waited to see if any suggestions appeared but there was nothing. Good old-fashioned research would be required and, with her notebook beside her, she began the journey back through her own past.

An hour later, she had just finished updating her great-grandparents, Rose and Edward Tunley, when the internal telephone rang.

"There's a package for you at the desk," said Kerry when Amelia answered. "I'm popping out for half an hour, so I'll leave it on the side."

"On my way."

A package, Amelia thought, *I haven't ordered anything*, but then she remembered the death certificates. Eager to see what these documents might reveal, she ran down the stairs two at a time. While they now knew about the tragic demise of Georgina, the death of her husband, Matthew, remained unchartered territory. Walking along the corridor, she was deep in thought when she heard a female voice saying her name. Pausing, she stepped back into the alcove in the corridor.

"Why have you got an invitation for Amelia?" came Melissa Forte's nasal tones. It was clear she was irritated.

"Ed asked," replied a man's voice that Amelia did not recognise. It was deep with a neutral accent, hinting towards a public-school education.

"What?" Melissa's tone was incredulous.

"Is she his new girlfriend? He wouldn't elaborate, you know what he's like," the man's voice was affectionate.

"She's a guest at Cliffside. I'm giving her grief therapy," replied Melissa. "You must have been mistaken. I can't imagine why he would want to invite her."

Amelia bristled with fury as she thought back over her sessions with Melissa. There had often been an edge of impatience in the woman's tone but Amelia had passed it off as professionalism. She wondered now if she had missed the signs of the dislike Melissa had felt towards her.

Feeling she had overheard enough, Amelia was about to march forward to break up the conversation when she felt a hand on her arm and she realised Edward was standing behind her, having emerged from the study. He drew her into the shadows and put his finger to his lips.

"Not sure you should be telling me…" began the man, his cheerful tone now uncomfortable as Melissa interrupted.

"I don't trust her," she snapped. "Turning up here, playing Little Miss Innocent, clutching a photograph of the house but claiming she knows nothing about the family. Something about her doesn't add up. I think she's after Ed and his money, maybe she's even going to try and claim the house. Even her story is too much…"

"I'll leave these here and perhaps you could distribute them," interjected the man, his voice dismissive.

"I'm not the postwoman," Melissa snapped but before she could turn to leave, Edward loomed around Amelia and blocked her path.

"Hello Edward," Melissa said, smiling to cover her irritation. "Hi Amelia…"

"Dr Forte, would you step into my office, please," Edward said, his voice calm but cold.

"Of course, but why are you being so formal?" laughed Melissa, although Amelia detected her hint of panic.

"We heard every word of your conversation," he replied. "Stu, can you take Amelia down to the bar? This won't take long. I'll be with you as soon as possible."

Amelia watched as Edward led the way into the back offices followed by a narrow-eyed and defensive Melissa. The man at reception smiled. He was tall with golden-brown hair, light hazel eyes, high cheekbones and a wide, generous smile. "Stuart Mackensie," he said, holding out his hand.

"Dr Amelia Prentice," she replied. "There's a package waiting for me at reception. I'd like to fetch it."

"Of course." He stepped aside as she picked up the manila envelope Kerry had left. "Edward asked me to take you to the bar," Stuart continued. "Shall we?"

Eager to return to her room to continue her research, Amelia hesitated, then her curiosity as to how this strange episode would end overtook her and she nodded, following Stuart down the corridor to the stone steps that led down to the honesty bar.

It was the most unusual room at Cliffside and had begun life as a natural cave hollowed into the bedrock of the cliff on which the house was built. A storage area had been created by joining up a fissure in the rock from the floor above and opening up the original cave. A set of stairs had been carved into the stone and it had been used to keep things cool before there were such modern conveniences as refrigerators. Over time, it had evolved into a unique space and was now a bar,

with old-fashioned doors opening on to a wide rock terrace giving stunning views through two free-standing stacks to the sea. The jutting veranda above created a sheltered area and it was here that Stuart steered her, returning a few moments later with two cups of coffee.

"Sorry about all that," he said, sitting opposite her. "Melissa's an odd one, and I think she might have worn thin even Edward's lengthy patience this time."

"What do you mean?" asked Amelia, then realised her indiscretion. "Sorry, you don't have to answer."

Stuart grinned. "Ed split up with his ex a little while ago and Melissa thought she would be next in line."

"Oh!" said Amelia, astounded by the woman's arrogance.

"Yep," laughed Stuart. "She's been here for about six months and she has been doing her utmost to seduce poor old Ed."

"And has he succumbed?" asked Amelia, thinking of Melissa's obvious attractiveness. The idea of the two them together made her feel slightly queasy.

"Of course not!" laughed Stuart, sipping his coffee. "She's not his type at all, far too brash. Not only that, she's on a final warning."

"Really?" Amelia knew she should not be indulging in such a salacious conversation but this unexpected side to Melissa was a revelation.

Stuart leaned towards her and whispered, "She slept with one of her clients a few months ago. Ed should have dismissed her but she sobbed and pleaded. He was in a bit of a bad way because of the break-up, so he caved in and agreed to give her one more chance. I think hearing her insult you and discuss your treatment in a public place is going to give him all the ammunition he needs to fire her."

Amelia gulped her coffee, unsure how to respond. Footsteps drew their attention to Edward as he marched into the bar.

"Aimes, I'm so sorry," he said, dropping into the seat beside her and taking her hand. Stuart disappeared to fetch more coffee. "Melissa had no right to say any of those things."

"Edward, really, it's fine," she said.

"No, it isn't," he responded. "I've suspended her, pending an enquiry. This isn't her first indiscretion, although knowing Stu, he's probably filled you in."

"Of course I have," replied Stuart, showing no remorse as he returned with more coffee. "With all your medical oaths, you wouldn't have been able to tell her, so it seemed my duty. Anyway, Ed, you should have sacked her ages ago."

"It's not quite that simple," Edward said, "but, she's suspended, effective immediately."

"Right," said Stuart, draining his cup. "I'd better get back. It's chaos at the heritage centre now we've actually raised the wreck."

"How's it looking?" asked Edward.

"A mess but Olaf's optimism is buoying everyone up. He's convinced we can salvage most of it. I'm not so sure." Stuart gave a shrug and then turned to Amelia. "Good to meet you — hopefully see you at the preview. Don't worry about seeing me out, Ed, I know the way." And with a flurry, he was gone.

"You'll have to excuse Stu," said Edward. "He likes to portray himself as an international man of mystery."

Amelia laughed. "He's very —" she searched for the word — "self-assured," she finally managed.

"Life has always come easily to Stuart," said Edward. "Loving family, a string of gorgeous women always on call, more money than he could ever spend in a lifetime, not to

mention a glamorous job. He spends a lot of his time in New York."

"Lucky him," Amelia murmured, finishing her coffee.

"Yes. I hope you don't mind that I included you in the invitation."

Amelia stared at him. "It's very kind of you," she said, "but what's it for?"

"The heritage centre that will be opening in a few weeks," he said. "It belongs to the sisters who own Marquess House, a private research centre in St Ishmaels, not far from here. It's the museum that has been purpose-built to house the wreck. It has all sorts of things for the local area, too, including a learning centre, an art gallery, and will link up with the archives. Stuart was telling me that last summer they were able to raise the mermaid figurehead from the ship — he's hoping it will be ready for display by the time they open. We've been invited to the preview because Caitlin and I have lent them some paintings. There's a whole gallery dedicated to the history of the area with a vast map showing an historical timeline. There are castles all around this coast but there are plenty of other important buildings too and they asked if they could feature Cliffside as part of the opening exhibit."

"That's so exciting!" exclaimed Amelia. "Why me though?"

"Well," said Edward, looking slightly nervous, "first, because I thought you'd enjoy it, and second, you're no doubt related to the family from this house somehow, so it felt appropriate."

"Thank you, Edward," said Amelia, reaching over to squeeze his hand. "You have no idea how much I appreciate your thoughtfulness."

Their eyes locked and Amelia felt her heart thumping. Forcing herself to look away, she reached for the manila

envelope and held it up. "This has arrived. I think it's the death certificates."

Edward grinned. "More family secrets," he said. "It'll be interesting to see what they say about Georgina. I doubt they would have put suicide if it was an unclear verdict."

With trepidatious fingers, Amelia ripped open the envelope. Both certificates were folded in half. Picking up the first, she opened it, spreading it out on the table.

"It's Georgina's," she said, aware of Edward leaning closer as he pulled out his glasses to study the cause of death. His shoulder brushed against her as he followed Amelia's finger tracing across the boxes, deciphering the ornate, old-fashioned handwriting.

"Myocarditis," read Edward, "which is a form of heart failure."

"No mention of laudanum. Now for Matthew. Perhaps you should be the one to make the big reveal?" she said, handing him the document.

"Thank you," he murmured. As he read, Amelia watched a raft of emotions chase themselves across his face: surprise, shock and revulsion. He placed the certificate on top of Georgina's. "*Wounds caused by person or persons unknown,*" he read aloud.

"No," gasped Amelia in horror. "Does this mean he was murdered?"

Edward's eyes were bleak. "I think it does, Aimes," he said.

CHAPTER TWO

The morning was silver with weightless sea mist. Amelia pulled her fleece around herself more tightly. Despite the weather, she could not bear to be inside a moment longer. She had woken from a restless sleep, full of terrifying nightmares and with the wind chime jangling tunes that jarred her nerves, she escaped to the calm of the woods. As she entered the dense air of the trees, an unexpected sense of relief flooded through her.

The breeze rustled the trees, causing water to shower over her. The brief jolt of iciness was a reminder of the present, rather than the strange, drifting, other-worldliness she had felt since waking from her tormented dreams. Distressing, brutal snatches of her nightmares hung on her shoulders like a hobgoblin: the running footsteps of a woman with terrible, eldritch laughter and piercing screams; the terrifying spectre of Matthew Stone, standing before her as he had been in his photograph, but with water streaming from him, flooding over Amelia's feet, engulfing her until she had woken up fighting with her sheets.

She and Edward had discussed his potential murder at length the previous day and Amelia assumed that was the cause of her strange dreams. Making her way along the path towards the stone circle, she inhaled the damp smell of the wood, throwing off the stench of rotten seaweed that had accompanied her night terrors. The mustiness in the air reminded her of the walks she had taken with her father when she had been a child. Her mittened hand in his, their delighted voices reverberating through the dappled glades as he told her stories. Singing

songs, laughing as they shared precious time in the endless chaos of life.

You would have loved it here, Dad, she thought.

The stone circle loomed through the mist; the granite edges of the monoliths blurred by the ethereal air. Walking from sentinel to sentinel, Amelia wondered again about the Attwater and Stone families. This spot had been a favourite of the teenage Kieran. Amelia stood in the silence, wondering about the strange young man. To be shy in a house of noisy extroverts would have challenged the most balanced of minds but to a boy whose mother had died from an overdose — intentional or not — and a father who was murdered, the sanctity within this space would have been a true place of retreat from the hubbub of Cliffside.

Pushing the branches back from the edge of the circle, the mist caught between the summer leaves seemed to shimmer with iridescent wings. Amelia breathed in the mingled scents of the wet earth and the sharpness of the salt in the air as the images left over from her dreams lingered at the edges of her mind. Each step through this uncanny landscape seemed to drag her further from the sanctity of the modern Cliffside and back to the world of secrets during its Victorian incarnation. As she walked, she felt she had been joined by the black and white spectral forms of the family from the photographs — their footsteps shadowing hers, their voices on the periphery of hearing, their lies creeping around her like a web.

Halfway around the circle was a gaping space where one of the stones had crumbled and fallen. Standing in the maw left behind, Amelia's eyes were drawn to the fog-smudged stone marking Eudora's grave. Someone, probably Edward, had cleared the remaining ivy away. Walking over to it, she bent down, outlining the inscription with her fingers.

"What happened to you?" she whispered. She started as a twig snapped and spun around, expecting to see Edward or one of the dogs, but there was no one. "Must've been an animal," she told herself, trying to ignore her racing heart.

Then as if drawn by a force stronger than her own will, she walked to the centre of the circle, to the large stone where Edward laid his wreath of white roses every year, and sat down. Crossing her legs, she rested her hands on her knees and shut her eyes, breathing in, calming her jangling nerves, clearing her mind as she had been taught in her relaxation and meditation sessions, she allowed herself to drift.

Listening to the gentle sounds of the leaves rustling in the soft breeze, the water running in tiny rivulets around the stone circle and the distant clamour of the ocean, it was a few moments before she heard it — the soft tread of footsteps and a voice calling her name. Tears streamed down her face as the persistent whisper on the breeze murmured words she could not understand, then she heard Molly's gentle laughter.

"Molly?" she gasped and, in the space between breaths, where the magic dwells, she saw her, smiling, laughing, whole and healthy, blowing her a kiss. A lightness entered her heart and Amelia felt the final layer of guilt and grief lift, the sludge-brown residue of all the emotions she had not been able to face finally seemed to float away, leaving her with a sense of calm and peace that she had not experienced for years.

It was not long before her tranquillity was shattered as Lara leapt onto her lap, barking in excitement. Startled, Amelia opened her eyes, gathering the squirming dog in her arms while she looked around for whoever had whispered to her, but she was alone and there were no footprints in the soft ground.

I must have fallen asleep, she thought, but the lightness in her heart remained.

Edward appeared with Nero ambling by his side. "Aimes!" he exclaimed. "I didn't expect to see you up this early." He paused, scrutinising her pale, sleep-starved face. "Are you OK?"

"A restless night," she admitted, disentangling herself from Lara who was still demanding her attention. "Bad dreams."

"What sort of dreams?" he asked, concern in his voice.

"Are you planning to analyse them?" she responded, trying to lighten the sudden tension that seemed to have sprung up between them.

"No," he said, bending to stroke Nero's ear. "I had strange dreams too, about Matthew…"

"Matthew?" Her voice came out as a startled whisper.

"Yes, and a woman…"

"Running away, screaming?" she finished.

His dark eyes came up to meet hers and he nodded. A shiver ran down her spine and she felt goosebumps prickle her arms.

"Did we have the same dream?" he asked.

"In my dream, Matthew was dripping water, reaching out to me," she said, shivering at the thought of his greying, bloated, fish-nibbled hands.

"Oh God, mine too," replied Edward. "And the woman — I couldn't see her face, she was in a flowing white nightdress, running through the dark house, either laughing or screaming, I couldn't make out which one."

Amelia's reaction was involuntary — her legs began to tremble with such ferocity she did not think they would hold her up, and she stretched her hands towards the nearest stone, using it to support herself. The atmosphere in the wood felt denser than usual, as though the mist truly had risen for Tylwyth Teg, and for a moment she choked, unable to force enough air into her lungs.

Edward's arms closed around her, holding her up. "I've got you, Aimes. Breathe," he said, his voice calm, measured. "Follow my lead. Deep breath in and hold…"

His words blurred and lights danced before her eyes, then as quickly as the malaise had overcome her, it cleared and she could feel her breathing returning to normal. Edward's arms felt safe, his warmth and strength bringing her back to life. To her surprise, the two dogs were twin pressures against her legs, offering their own comfort.

"Sorry," she muttered, moving in Edward's arms to encourage him to release her but he stared down into her eyes, checking her vital signs before relinquishing his grip.

"Don't apologise," he said. "You're recovering from a huge amount of trauma; these things could happen for some months to come. For someone who's dealt with all that you have, your progress is remarkable."

Amelia managed a wan smile. Needing to put some distance between herself and Edward, she wandered over to the headstone. The slate glittered in the wet morning light, shimmering with hidden lights. "Do you think it was her?"

"What do you mean?"

"In our dreams?"

Edward shrugged. "It's possible. We've spent a great deal of time discussing the Attwaters and Stones. Yesterday's discovery about Matthew's murder obviously played on both our minds, it's no wonder we both had strange dreams."

"I have to know," said Amelia. "I need the rest of the story."

"Perhaps Osyth's diary will reveal more," he said.

"Or local newspapers from then. If there was a suspicion of foul play, it would have been reported."

They stared at each other, then Edward said in an apologetic tone. "If you're feeling better now, I'll leave you in peace. Sorry Lara disturbed your meditation."

"No, I'm finished," she said, no longer able to stand the strange swirling mist, craving the open skies and broad horizons of St Brides Bay. "We can walk back together. I'm hungry."

They wandered through the haze, which was beginning to thin as the sun rose, burning it away.

"Do you think you'll be staying much longer?" asked Edward.

"Why do you ask?" Amelia tried to keep her voice level, but she felt a wave of panic. She felt safe here and was not ready to leave. "Do you need the room?"

"No, of course not," he replied, "the suite is yours for as long as you want it. We only opened it this spring. You're the first person to use it and I've asked Kerry to block it out of the online booking so no one else can book it."

Amelia felt a small spurt of happiness. "Really?"

"Yes," he said, then in a nervous tone he added, "I like having you here. It feels right."

Amelia was not sure which of them blushed the deeper shade of pink.

Amelia discussed her confusion over Edward's treatment of her with Benji and Louise later that evening. When Louise joined the video call she placed her hand on her slightly swollen stomach before putting her finger on her lips. "Two weeks until the scan," she whispered and Amelia felt her heart contract with love for her friend, hoping that this time, finally, Louise and Richie would have success.

"Edward definitely fancies you," Benji said when Amelia described Edward's behaviour towards her.

"But what if we're related?" Amelia asked.

"You'd be very distant cousins," replied Louise, "so it wouldn't matter. Anyway, what do you feel about him?"

Amelia sighed. It was so long since she had given a romantic relationship any thought that the idea of becoming close to someone was an alien concept. "He's quite challenging," she admitted, "but I do like him. On the downside, he recently finished a long-term relationship, and I don't want to be a rebound."

"Wise words," said Benji. "Who ended it?"

"He said it was mutual and all very calm and relaxed," she replied. "Although, I'm not sure I believe him. Remember how stroppy he was when I arrived? Apparently, she'd taken a few of his family items and he was really annoyed."

"Sounds as though she ended it then," said Louise.

"Do you think he wants her back?" asked Amelia and she was surprised at the pain this idea had caused her. Edward might not always be easy company but she was becoming used to his manner and had realised at heart, behind the shyness which often presented as aloofness, he was a gentle soul. His happiness was becoming as important to her as her own.

"No, but he might not be ready to move on," said Benji. "Don't be disheartened though, Aimes, the fact he basically invited you to stay for as long as you like is a very good sign."

CHAPTER THREE

When Amelia, Edward and Caitlin reached the heritage centre, there were already cars spilling out of the car park and they were ushered to the VIP parking.

"Posh," said Edward, and Caitlin, who was in the front passenger seat, laughed. Amelia, wearing a hastily bought new outfit, sat in the back.

Caitlin had greeted Amelia completely differently from the last time they had met. "My dear," she had said, holding out her hands to Amelia and beaming, "it's a pleasure to meet you properly at last."

"It's wonderful to meet you, too," Amelia had replied, startled as Caitlin had pulled her into an all-encompassing hug. Caitlin must not remember their previous encounter when she had been so ill.

Throughout the journey, Caitlin had chatted, questioning Amelia about her family, her life and her home in Windsor. "Maybank sounds wonderful," she said when Amelia had finished describing it. "I would love to see it and travel on our boats again."

While Edward locked the car and put out his arm for Caitlin, Amelia wandered away and stood by the impressive glass front doors, where the sign read: *The Mary Fitzroy Heritage Museum.* Taking a glass of champagne as she entered the heritage centre, she gazed around with interest. In the atrium was a portrait of a woman in her mid-forties, underneath which was a plaque reading: *Mary Fitzroy, painted in 1975*. It went on to explain that her granddaughters, Perdita and Piper Woodville-Rivers, had inherited her estate and this museum was their tribute to her.

The building had once been an old farmhouse with a series of barns and outbuildings but the entire complex had been sympathetically converted and where possible, the original buildings had been saved and restored. The additional galleries and chambers were modern glass and steel built in curves like the hull of the ship they would one day house. A café bar stretched along one side with an art gallery and gift shop, while in the main chambers were exhibits from the local area, including Cliffside.

A vast ship's figurehead in the shape of a mermaid dominated the central gallery. It rested in a Perspex wave, supported by a cat's cradle of cables from above. People milled around and there was a friendly, festive atmosphere. Amelia waved to Kerry and David who were chatting to a petite blonde woman on the other side of the room.

"What do you think?" asked Edward, gesturing around the extraordinary space.

"It's stunning," replied Amelia.

"There's going to be a tour later. David's mum, Jenny Procter, works for Marquess House, the research centre who own this, and she'll be walking us through the exhibitions. The mermaid was from the wreck they raised a few weeks ago but it was very delicate, so that was a separate salvage operation last year."

"Who are the people with Stuart?" she asked, glancing over as Edward waved a greeting.

"Perdita and Piper, who inherited the estate a few years ago from their grandmother." He indicated the dark-haired woman Amelia had seen at the beach. Next to her was the other woman from the boat. Her features were identical to her sister but she had fiery red hair and green eyes. "Kit is Stuart's younger brother." He pointed to the man beside Stuart with

dark hair. "And those are their parents, Alistair and Susan Mackensie."

Amelia followed Edward through the crowd to where Caitlin had joined another woman at a small table.

"Hi Pamela," Edward said, bending to kiss the woman's cheek. "I didn't know you were going to be here."

"And miss the preview of the museum?" Pamela laughed. "This was the perfect excuse to come and stay for a few weeks."

"Lady Pamela Johnson, this is Amelia Prentice, she's staying at Cliffside for the summer while we try to untangle our family trees."

"What do you mean 'untangle your family trees'?" asked Pamela, curiously.

"Amelia owns a set of photographs that match the Victorian images we have of Cliffside and some of its previous owners," said Caitlin.

"How intriguing," exclaimed Pamela. "We should call Perdita, she's adept at untangling genealogical mysteries. I'll see if I can grab her." Before Amelia could stop her, she was making her way through the crowd.

"Edward, could you fetch some more drinks, please?" requested Caitlin, draining her champagne flute and placing her hand on Amelia's arm. "I want to speak to Amelia."

"Of course," he said and disappeared into the crowd.

"My dear," said Caitlin, turning to face Amelia, her blue eyes full of concern, "I must apologise for the dreadful things I said to you. I can't remember the incident but Edward has told me what happened."

"There's no need, really," replied Amelia. "It's forgotten. I'm relieved you're well again."

"Edward said you were kind," she said, her voice wistful. "It's what he needs after that last baggage. Oh, that one thought she was something special but she wasn't good enough for him. In my opinion, she fancied herself living at Cliffside but the house always knows and it soon saw her off."

Amelia was unsure how to respond to this statement, so she simply smiled.

"Silly woman, she couldn't even hear the wind chime." Caitlin paused, her eyes fixed on Amelia.

"How could she not have heard the wind chime?" Amelia asked. "It's the background music to the days at Cliffside."

"Exactly," said Caitlin, who was beaming at her as though she was the most wonderful thing she had ever seen. "I knew you would come, my dear. I had lost you but I knew you were out there somewhere. You see, we all come home in the end. The wind chime calls us and our hearts respond."

"I'd love to see the wind chime," said Amelia.

"Perhaps you'd like to visit my rooms and we could go through the family tree together. I've drawn mine back to Penny and Daniel…"

"You're related to Penny and Daniel?" Amelia asked.

"Oh yes, my dear, they were my great-great-great-grandparents."

Amelia stared at Caitlin in astonishment. "Did you meet Osyth?"

"Many times."

"What was she like?" asked Amelia, unsure why this revelation made her feel tearful.

"A true free spirit," sighed Caitlin.

"Did she ever fulfil her ambition to be a published writer?" Amelia's online search for works by either Osyth or Freddie had given no positive results.

"I believe her uncle, Solomon, who had a publishing side to his magazine business, put out several books by Osyth. And by Freddie, too."

Amelia's pulse leapt with excitement. "Do you have copies of their books?" she asked but Caitlin, who was watching Edward as he chatted to Stuart and a glamorous blonde woman, did not seem to hear her question.

"Before he comes back," Caitlin whispered, her voice urgent, "I must ask you to help me, it is very important."

"If I can help, I will," Amelia replied, pushing her own curiosity aside in order to placate Caitlin, who was staring at Edward with rising nervousness.

"Between us, we must help Edward to hear the wind chime. He has closed his heart to it but now you are here, we can save him from the same fate as Kieran."

"What…?" Amelia began but before she could finish her sentence, Edward arrived at her side and handed her a drink.

"They're starting the tour," he said, smiling at Amelia and helping Caitlin to her feet.

Following them to the mermaid figurehead where people were gathering, Amelia wondered what on earth Caitlin had meant. How could Edward not hear the joyful tunes of the wind chime? Wondering if perhaps Caitlin was sliding into another infection, hence her confusion, she watched the older woman carefully as they were led around the museum.

The tour began with the history of the figurehead and a series of other items from Marquess House, including a small golden reliquary and an ornate Book of Hours before moving into the side galleries.

"This is us," said Edward as they entered one of the side galleries.

A vast map took up the entire wall. Amelia was impressed with the level of detail. It was a work of art. The clever design drew the eye along the timeline, with each important event or place written in short sections to interest and intrigue the reader enough to want to continue the story with the next instalment. Paintings of houses, castles and the oil refineries were all layered together to show how things had changed. From the arrival of the Vikings at Hubberston, to Mill Bay where Henry VII had landed before marching to defeat Richard III at the Battle of Bosworth, to the connections with Admiral Horatio Nelson and Emma Hamilton, to the site of the first oil refinery in the 1970s.

As each exhibit was explained by Jenny and two of her assistants, the family was thanked. When Jenny beckoned the crowd forward saying the Cliffside exhibit was next, Amelia felt a rush of excitement, as eager as the rest of the crowd to see what Edward and Caitlin had loaned.

"These usually hang in the hallway on our side of the house," Edward whispered, "but Caitlin had them cleaned as soon as Jenny approached her about this exhibition. Sorry I haven't mentioned it before but I wanted to surprise you."

Rounding the corner, Amelia gasped. "Edward, they're stunning!"

"Painted by local Victorian artist, Blaise Attwater, this collection has been loaned by Edward Stone and Caitlin Bathurst of Cliffside," began Jenny, beaming over at them. A small flurry of applause followed as it had for all the exhibitors, then Jenny turned to the paintings and as she described each one, lights swept across the delicate faces, warming them, highlighting the beauty of Blaise's work. "This is Penelope and Daniel Attwater, known for owning the Attwater Boatyard in Neyland and for many philanthropic works throughout the

local area, including sponsoring a village school. Beside them are Penelope's twin brother, Matthew Stone and his wife Georgina."

On this smaller oil painting, the couple wore wedding clothes and were smiling. Amelia felt a wave of delight to see the joy captured by their nephew. *They were happy*, she thought. *Their ends might have been tragic but at the beginning, they had a loving marriage.*

"This is one of the most well-known of Blaise Attwater's paintings and we're lucky to have the original. Known usually as *The Girl in the Fairy Ring*, we have it on good authority that the original title was *Princess Osyth of the Fairy Rings* and was named for the artist's niece."

Amelia stared in astonishment. It was the image she had grown up with, which Molly had gazed at throughout her illness. The tiny sketch which had captivated them both was manifested into a vast canvas bursting with light, colour and energy. Staggered that she had never thought to search the internet for the artist before, she stared at the magical image. The child in the flowing white dress danced at the centre of improbable fairy mushrooms while mythical figures swirled around her, watched over by a floating wind chime.

"It's Osyth," murmured Edward.

"With the wind chime," finished Amelia.

Staring back at her through time was the girl about whom she had been reading. The young woman who had captured her heart was finally facing her in glorious colour. Osyth's red hair seemed to crackle with life and her dark green eyes glowed. The wind chime hovering above her shoulder was like a guardian angel but all Amelia could think was how Osyth's smile was exactly the same as Molly's.

CHAPTER FOUR

Her visit to the heritage centre had galvanised Amelia and over the next few days a plan had formed in her mind. Her first task, she decided, was to research Blaise Attwater, before discovering all she could about the murder of Matthew Stone. After this, she would find the answers she had been avoiding and discover whether her genealogy search would reveal her to be related to the Attwaters and Stones. Blaise's painting, *Princess Osyth of the Fairy Rings*, was too similar to the sketch at Maybank for the two to be unconnected and this was surely another clue to suggest her veins ran with the blood of the family whose voices had once rung through the corridors of the house.

Knowing Edward was busy all day, she gathered her research before heading out into the sunshine and the National Library of Wales in Aberystwyth, seventy miles from Cliffside. Pushing aside the twinge of guilt at not telling him her plans or inviting him along, she spent the journey justifying her decision to herself. "Caitlin has researched their family tree," she said aloud as she followed the twisting coast road. "This is my quest, mine and Mum's."

The library was vast, and Amelia spent some time wandering around, trying not to feel daunted by the task ahead. Her brief foray into research at the Pembrokeshire Archives where she and Edward had discovered what they needed quickly and easily had given her false confidence in her ability and she felt thoroughly out of her depth. Following the librarian's directions to the Art section, her enthusiasm returned when to

her delight she discovered a book on the St Ives Artists — a group of creatives who had settled in the Cornish town.

A brief internet search had suggested Blaise's work was often listed with this group and as she turned the pages reading the names of Walter Sickert, John Noble Barlow, Elizabeth Forbes, Edward Simmons and Marianne Stokes, she found Blaise Attwater. Feeling pride of ownership in him, Amelia read the brief biography.

While not as well remembered as many of his contemporaries, Blaise Attwater's work is considered a strong example of the St Ives School and is much sought after. A catalogue published in 1899 suggested a body of work exceeding 100 pieces, including sketches, oil on canvas, watercolours and portraiture. Attwater's work rarely comes to sale.

Amelia's biggest shock came when she learned how he signed his work, not with a name but a cipher created from his initials: Blaise George Attwater — BGA — because she recognised it from at least three paintings hanging in her own house.

Amelia's resolve to discover more about Matthew Stone's death, as well as her own link to the family, if, indeed, she was connected, rose in her like a steely force. Although Edward had told her that Caitlin had amassed a great deal of family history, after their odd conversation of the previous evening, Amelia was unsure how much of it she would trust without corroborating it for herself.

Placing Osyth's journals on one side of her and the folder of family documents on the other, she opened her notebook and took a deep breath, preparing to set out on what she hoped would be the final stage of the journey. The librarian had given her some advice on how to search the newspaper index and

settling herself in front of the enormous leather-bound books of newspapers, she began turning the pages of the old copies of *The Pembrokeshire Herald*, looking for information on Matthew Stone's death.

On the day the death certificates had arrived, Edward had shown her a short cutting that Caitlin had acquired years earlier. It was very faded and difficult to read but they had managed to decipher it. "I remember helping Caitlin stick this in her notebook a few years ago but it didn't mean anything to me then," Edward admitted as he showed her the short piece. *"The man's body washed ashore at Newgale is believed to be Matthew Isaac Stone,"* Edward had read aloud, *"who went missing when out for his usual evening walk three days ago. He appeared to have been attacked and robbed, a cut in his neck was thought to have been the cause of death. The coroner has recorded an open verdict."*

"Coroner," Amelia had mused. "I wonder if there are still records. They don't always preserve them."

"But for a potential murder, if it was solved there will be court records too."

Bringing her full attention to the newspapers, Amelia quickly developed a way to assess the pages of close type, looking for useful words in headlines that might lead to something about Matthew, but as his surname, Stone, was a word used in common parlance, she often found herself partway through a feature about a quarry or road project before realising her error.

Each entry she found was fascinating, though. There were comments about local intrigue, deaths, marriages. The arrival of Isambard Kingdom Brunel's massive steamship and final engineering endeavour, the SS *Great Eastern*, made its first appearance as a passenger liner off the coast of Neyland on 26 August 1860. Other ships followed and Amelia finally

understood why the Attwaters had believed there was potential for transatlantic trade from the port of Milford Haven and why it had been worth investing in the boatyards in the area.

Her focus returned to Matthew Stone. Locating the short snippet Edward had shown her, she made a note of the date before searching the newspapers prior to his disappearance to see if it had been reported. She found an advertisement offering a £100 reward for information concerning Matthew's whereabouts.

Mr Matthew Stone, of Cliffside, Milford Haven, has not been seen since leaving his home for a night-time walk two nights hence. His family are extremely concerned and if anyone has further information pertaining to this disappearance, please contact this newspaper.

There was a sketch of Matthew, which Amelia felt did not do him justice but made him look brooding and severe. In his photograph, she had been drawn to the softness of his eyes and the small smile on his lips, both a direct contrast to the fierce expression of his wife, Georgina. Moving forward a few days, a larger headline shouted the discovery of Matthew's body: *Body Found, Believed to Be Local Businessman.*

As Amelia read it, she realised the snippet Caitlin owned was the final part of this news item but the full piece offered more information. It stated Matthew had been discovered by two fishermen off the beach at Newgale, not far from Cliffside. There was also a comment from Daniel.

The brother-in-law of the deceased, Mr Daniel Attwater, proprietor of Attwater and Stone Boatyard, Neyland, told this reporter: 'We are very sad and trust the local constabulary will be able to discover who perpetrated this shocking attack on a man who was respected by all'.

Then, two weeks later, there was a leader piece concerning the potential murder. From what Amelia could gather, the police had not been able to find any witnesses and it was generally believed that Matthew had stumbled across a nefarious group of smugglers, who having murdered him to keep him silent, had thrown his body into the sea, before disappearing into the darkness.

The police have diligently investigated the death of Mr Stone, whose family has also employed a private investigator in an attempt to uncover the true nature of the crime. However, even employing the full gamut of modern scientific research, it seems this is an unsolvable crime.

"Frustrating," Amelia muttered but the suggestion made by the newspaper seemed a possible option. The Welsh coast, like the Cornish, was notorious for smuggling and some of those involved in the crime were vicious criminals.

Turning to the monitor beside her, she spent an hour searching through the Aberystwyth newspaper catalogue and The British Newspaper Archive at the British Library. The same reports flashed up, followed by one additional note. It was a link to a short piece published three months later.

A potential witness to the death of Mr M I Stone gave a statement to the Haverfordwest police. Mr Pugh, a sailor who has been away at sea since the murder, reports having seen three men in a battered dinghy throwing what looked like a heavy sack into the sea not far from Newgale beach. He admits it was dark and he would recognise neither the men, nor the boat, but felt it was important to allow the police the opportunity to investigate. However, a statement today says in the case of Mr Stone, no further action will be taken.

Amelia gazed at the paltry number of entries; it did not seem much for the loss of a man's life. Returning to her laptop, she searched The National Archives, the Old Bailey Records, the coroners' courts, the local coroners' archive and found nothing more to add to the tragic tale of Matthew Stone.

Poor Penny, she thought. *Her brother was taken from her in the most brutal manner. It must have been a terrible shock.*

Typing up her notes, a new theory began to form in Amelia's mind. She and Edward had discovered that Eudora had been banished from the family not long after Matthew's death. Amelia wondered if Penny's fragile mental state had played a part in her decision to send her daughter away. Had Eudora somehow been made a scapegoat? But, she reasoned with herself, if that was the case, why had Penny and Daniel kept Osyth and adopted her under their name? The discovery of Matthew's death seemed to create more questions than it solved.

Pushing aside the sad news about Matthew's demise, she turned her attention to her final task: her own connection to the strange, twisting tale of this vast and complicated family. For the next few hours, she would find her way back to Osyth, Eudora and Penny. It would not be difficult. The dates she needed fell largely in the years when the census was operating, so a huge amount of information would be to hand.

Returning to her notes, and her great-grandparents, Rose and Edward Tunley, she logged in to the genealogy website and updated the final few things she had discovered, including her great-grandmother's maiden name, Rose Beasley.

Deciding it would be easier to follow Rose's paternal line, she guessed at a possible age for Rose's father, keyed it into the search and began scrolling through the list of documents. There were numerous Beasleys who could be Rose's father, so

Amelia narrowed the search, trying first Pembrokeshire where she drew a blank, then Windsor. Immediately, the place-name Clewer popped up and she gave a small exhalation of excitement but that quickly evaporated when she discovered there were a raft of Beasleys, several of whom had daughters called Rose, and she had no idea which was her Rose Beasley.

"This is madness," Amelia muttered in frustration, abandoning the census lists and scrolling through the marriage lists, when suddenly, a name caught her eye. "Meyrick," she exclaimed, clicking on a link and opening a wedding listing. "Richard Beasley and Marina Meyrick."

Excitement coursed through her. This was a huge step forward, as one of her census print-outs listed a Richard and Marina Beasley with a daughter called Rose, and the dates fitted. Feeling her hands tremble, she began searching for Marina Meyrick.

"Marina Meyrick," she muttered. "According to this you were married in 1910 and you were twenty-two years of age, so your date of birth was 1888."

Was Marina related to either Osyth or Frederick? If she was, then the dates suggested she could have been their daughter. It was time to enter Osyth's name into this strange mix. For so long Amelia had resisted finding the final piece of the puzzle but she could ignore the whispers of Osyth's voice no longer. From the journals she knew the date and location of her birth so she typed them in and an array of potential documents were listed, which Amelia hoped would lead to Marina Meyrick and, therefore, back to herself.

"Marriage," muttered Amelia. "Who did you marry?"

She thanked Eudora for giving her daughter such an unusual name because as she narrowed the search to the marriage records, there was Osyth, at the top of the list. A smile of

certainty played across her face as she clicked on the link but, as she read the details, her eyes widened. The name beside Osyth's was not Frederick Meyrick, it was Oran Walters.

"Who the hell is Oran Walters?" Amelia exclaimed, earning her a reproving look from several people nearby.

Searching frantically, wondering if she had made a mistake, she tried to calm her startled mind. Admittedly, she had not finished Osyth's journal but this new name felt like an unfamiliar note in a much-loved tune. What had happened to Freddie, the young man who seemed to have captured her heart?

"No," muttered Amelia, scrolling down the page, "she married Freddie. I want Osyth and Freddie to have had their happy ending. I want them to be Marina's parents."

She turned back to the family tree she had begun to draw, tracing her finger along the lines, first to Noah, then Eudora, Blaise, Solomon and Thomasina, then the line from Penelope Charlotte Attwater *née* Stone, through her eldest daughter, Eudora, to Osyth, where the tree stopped. Reaching for her own modern section, she stared at the name Marina Meyrick, then at the new information she had discovered: Osyth Walters.

Clicking on the image attached to the written information, she found copies of the marriage certificates. Enlarging it, she took a screenshot and printed it out. Osyth, age 18, was named as was her father Egan O'Reilly, whose occupation was listed as 'Sailor'.

"All fine," she muttered, "but what about Oran Walters?"

Her first shock was Oran's age: 42. He was registered as a widower. Oran's father was listed as the musician Chiumbo Walters (deceased) and Oran's occupation was 'Ringmaster'. Putting the name 'Chiumbo' into a search engine, Amelia

stared in astonishment. Its origins were Kenyan. Oran's mother, Manon Lafayette, was French and listed as a 'Dancer'.

Amelia stared at the irrefutable proof of the marriage but was unable to understand how Osyth could have married a man of Kenyan descent who was twenty-four years her senior and was a ringmaster, she presumed, in a circus. How was this possible? A dreadful thought raced through Amelia's mind — had Kieran sold Osyth into some ungodly union as a punishment when she refused his advances?

Then another devastating thought reached her — if Osyth married a man called Oran Walters, then she had no possible connection to Marina Meyrick and that meant no blood link to Amelia. Amelia felt a cold shudder as her certainty about her sense of belonging to Cliffside shifted. Was she just a cuckoo, trying to fit into a family to whom she had no claim? Devastated by this thought, Amelia gathered her research and left the library on shaking legs.

On returning from Aberystwyth, Amelia hurried to her room, trying to make sense of her unexpected discovery. As she stared down at St Brides Bay, the wind chime dancing in the breeze, an overwhelming desire to see it engulfed her. She was aware that Edward and Caitlin were out. They had been invited to drinks at Marquess House, which Edward had asked her to attend, but Amelia had been too engrossed in her research.

Amelia hurried down to reception and Kerry beamed at her.

"Anything I can help with?" she asked.

"Yes," replied Amelia. "If Edward was here I'd ask him, but may I go out on the veranda and see the view? Perhaps if you came and I promised not to throw myself over the edge, the insurance company would never need to know?"

Kerry laughed. "Come on," she said. "I trust you not to invalidate our insurance."

Fizzing with excitement, Amelia tried to control herself from skipping in delight as she followed Kerry through the summer drawing room to the locked door leading to the veranda. Seeing the ancient retainer would take the sting away from the shock of discovering Osyth had not married Freddie.

"It's all yours," said Kerry, stepping back to let her pass. "I'll wait here."

"Thank you, Kerry, thank you so much."

Almost stumbling in her haste, Amelia stepped through the door, her shoes clipping on the wooden planks. Her eyes travelled across the intricately carved edging of the hard rail and she breathed in the softening air, the sky showing hints of blue and sunset pink as she trailed her fingers along the wood, following its lead around the house, looking for a carved heart which she knew was there though she had never seen it before.

She reached the furthest corner of the veranda and looked back. For the first time the chimes were silent and she stared around her in confusion. From the photographs, the wind chime had always hung in this corner, offering the most spectacular views. It was wider here and this was where the family would congregate.

Where was it?

Panic rose in her chest as she retraced her steps, trying not to show her fear. Kerry was waiting, leaning on the rail, watching the ebb and flow of the tide. She turned and smiled but Amelia saw the smile freeze on her face.

"Amelia, what's happened?" asked Kerry, taking her arm and trying to lead her back inside, but Amelia held her ground.

"The wind chime," Amelia said, forcing herself to keep her voice calm despite the panic climbing in her chest. "Where is it?"

Confusion clouded Kerry's face. "What wind chime?"

"The one I've been hearing since I arrived," Amelia said, fear racing through her.

"We've never had a wind chime," replied Kerry.

Amelia was about to deny her mistake, to demand its whereabouts when she faltered. If there was no wind chime on the veranda, what had she been hearing? Was it a symptom of her grief? Floundering, she fought to salvage the situation, forcing a smile to her face. "It must have been the gulls," she murmured. "Yes, my mistake."

Amelia spent the evening packing and the following morning, she loaded her car as dawn crept over the horizon, before leaving a note for Edward at reception and driving into the bright summer morning. She was desperate to return home to Maybank, to familiarity and a place where she could understand what was happening to her. In the note she had explained she had borrowed the second journal and would return it as soon as she had finished transcribing it, which she hoped they did not mind and understood.

Now, standing in her kitchen several hours later, she observed her house with new eyes. Maybank looked different. It was nothing to do with the pile of mail, stacked and waiting on the hall table, or the horse chestnut tree in the garden that was now covered in leaves. She had changed, the history of the house was part of a story to which she was unsure whether she had a claim. Yet, if there was no connection, why did she have the photographs? Why did she own the cottages that had once belonged to Osyth?

This had once been home to Penny and Daniel Attwater. How had it come into the possession of her family? Had the Attwaters sold it? Had her family bought the house and that was the connection? Not blood; coincidence? But there were too many other links: the cottages, the photographs, the physical similarity between Osyth and Molly, and even Amelia's own vibrant hair, which she had inherited from her mother.

Outside, a wind chime sang, and Amelia's heart clenched in fear. Was she going insane? Everywhere she went there seemed to be a wind chime. Then she remembered Osyth's journal. Throughout it Osyth had claimed to hear the song of her beloved chimes in her heart. Noah had told her he felt the same. Were they delusional? Caitlin had mentioned the wind chime too, and she had lamented the fact that Edward could not hear it. Was hearing the chimes part of the family malady?

Amelia mentally shook herself. From what she had discovered, she did not seem to be connected to the family by blood, so why would she suffer from the same fantasy?

Letting herself out into the back garden, she listened as the chimes jangled again. Peering over her neighbour's fence, knowing they would be at work, her heart leapt in relief as she saw a wind chime attached to a low-hanging tree branch. "Not insane," she muttered to herself, before retreating inside, but that did not explain the endless tunes of the wind chime she had heard at Cliffside. "I have to know," she said aloud. "Whatever is happening, I am going to find out the truth."

Sitting in her favourite armchair, she pulled Osyth's journal from her bag and opened it to the marked page, hoping it might help her understand the strange events unfolding around her.

PART EIGHT: LONDON, 1884

CHAPTER ONE

The wind chime woke Osyth from a deep, cloying sleep. Silver chimes and coral shells singing in the breeze beckoned her back from her frightening and disjointed dreams.

"Nain?" she murmured as a soft, cool cloth was placed on her burning forehead. "I'm sorry for being angry, for leaving you…"

"Don't speak, Osyth, they're listening."

"Annie?" she murmured, unsure whether her friend was real or another dream-spectre. "Who's listening?"

Osyth's eyes fluttered open and as the haze cleared, she stifled a scream of horror. Around her were grey walls on which guttering gas lamps cast eerie shadows. Her bed was chipped grey metal with sheets that might once have been white but were now threadbare, mottled and of an uncertain colour somewhere between light brown and grey.

The air was freezing cold, causing her breath to form in clouds as she spoke. Beside her bed sat Angharad, her face stark white, her dark hair pulled back from her face and covered with a white cap. She wore a thin striped dress and in her hand was the cloth which she had been using to mop Osyth's brow. Her hazel eyes were wide with terror as though she was trying to tell Osyth something without words.

"They're always listening…" Angharad began but her words faded to nothing.

The last thing Osyth remembered was being helped to her bedroom by Mrs Jeakes. Hands bearing down upon her, peeling away the layers of her dress, sliding soft linen over her head as she drifted away from the light, fighting the enveloping

blackness, shouting at Kieran to stop whatever it was he was doing and set her free. In the distant corners of her heart, she had heard the wind chime stir, it's lilting tunes connecting her to Cliffside, to home, to the family she loved, but she had been powerless to resist the dragging waves of darkness. Voices had whispered all around her, distant, lost, her name drifting forward, then away, her mind filled with the familiar song of the waves, lulling her, hypnotising her, calling her below, far, far below to the hallowed halls of Tylwyth Teg.

"Nain," she had whispered, struggling to free herself from her grey slumber. "Taid."

"I am here, my dear," had come the cold voice of her cousin.

"Kieran, what are you doing to me?"

In the distance there had been noises, rustling, shadows, a woman, the silver prick of the needle in her arm and once more she was dragged under, slipping ever lower into the subterranean depths. Light and dark, grey to black, she had no control where her mind wandered, but gripped in her heart were the sound of the wind chime and his face. Her twin points of salvation, of hope. His eyes dancing with laughter, welcoming, safe, full of love.

"Love," she murmured. "Freddie…"

"Increase the dose."

The words had shimmered, iridescent, fluttering like birds' wings, Kieran's voice like claws scratching her face.

"When she wakes, she will be certain to capitulate."

She was unable to hold a thought as sketchy images drifted past. Her family from the house on the cliff — Penny, Daniel, Katherine, Noah, Solomon, Xenia, Blaise — calling her name, hands outstretched but too far away to pull her to safety, their love offered like a sacrifice for her return. The insistent notes of the wind chime reminded her of home as the gleaming

white figure of the Lilu fairy swirled around her, dressing her in sparkling night, leading her deeper into the magical, shadowy world.

This beauteous creature, her touch like ice on Osyth's hand, whispered tales from Osyth's nightmares, her darkest thoughts, wrapping themselves web-like around her. Lilu was the fairy who crouched on the edge of rationality, the provocateur of restless nights, the dancing light who ensnared her prey in their darkest compulsions, the feverish fixations of sensuality, woven together with the glittering thread of their own healing, the gatekeeper to the furthest palaces of Tylwyth Teg.

"Osyth, my dear, can you hear my voice?"

"Kieran?"

"You are safe, my sweet girl." His words had hovered in front of his thin pale lips as his angular face came into view. That was her last recollection, her bedroom in Richmond. "There is a question you must answer and when you have said the words, this will be over." He had swept his hand to encompass the room with its quaking walls and silent, uniformed figures whose faces seemed to be covered.

"Where is Nain?" she had whimpered.

"I am all you need and when you have agreed to be my wife, this will end."

"No, you're married to Angharad," she remembered gasping. "I love Freddie."

Kieran's hand had slipped from hers and once more the sting of the needle overwhelmed her senses, sending her back to the darkness of Tylwyth Teg.

"Freddie," she gasped, clawing the air and there was a shout of fury from above, following by a stinging slap across her face.

"Take her," a bored voice found her through the haze of shimmering figures. "A few weeks incarcerated with my wife might do them both some good. We shall see who survives."

There was another prick in her arm, pain had shot through her and she had gasped, her voice disappearing into the black cloud.

"Where are we?" Osyth asked now, looking at Angharad.

"Kieran has placed us both in an asylum," Angharad whispered, crouching beside Osyth's bed. "I have been here three weeks and a few days ago, you were brought in. Osyth, I was so scared, I thought you were dead. You were so pale and lifeless. Kieran has been drugging you with laudanum. It's his own blend and is very high in opium."

"Opium?"

"Yes," whispered Angharad. "It was after Kieran and I were married that I discovered the reason behind his mood swings. He's been taking opium for years. One night he told me he stole some from Solomon's bedroom when he was younger."

"Uncle Solomon smokes opium?"

Osyth's whirring mind could not keep up with Angharad's stream of words, each one seemed to be taking on a life of its own, winding themselves around her friend as though they were magical beings. Fairies made from words, each letter a leering, giggling creature of the night. *That must be the opium*, she thought, trying to contain the blurred edges of her mind.

"Yes, and Kieran's been taking it ever since."

There was a click behind them as the door was unlocked and a woman entered. Her clothes, in contrast to Angharad's ill-fitting gown and the thin nightdress Osyth realised she was wearing, were warm and well-made. Her dough-like face was set in a stern expression. Glaring at Angharad, she took

Osyth's wrist and held it for a few moments, checking her pulse.

"You," she said to Angharad, "get into bed. All this girl needs is sleep. When she wakes in the morning, she will be recovered. Unless, of course, Dr Stone has been mistaken in his doses again. It would not be the first time. Let's hope this girl doesn't crave it like the last one."

With these strange and ominous words, the woman snatched the cloth and bowl from Angharad, marched from the room and slammed the heavy door, locking it behind her. Osyth noticed there was a narrow window set in the metal, where those outside would be able to spy on them. The woman's footsteps faded away and Osyth fell back against the mean pillow which offered no softness, only lumps.

Angharad crept across to her own narrow bed, slid her dress from her shoulders and draped it over the chair, pulling on a nightdress identical to the one Osyth was wearing before climbing beneath the thin blankets.

Kieran took opium. Perhaps that explained the change in his appearance, the increasing paleness of his skin, the violet shadows under his eyes? But, Uncle Solomon, he was calm, serene, loving. It made no sense.

"But why are we in an asylum?" Osyth persisted, staring at their grim surroundings.

"I don't know," Angharad whispered back, "but I'm scared."

"Don't worry, Annie," Osyth replied. "My family will find us. They once rescued my grandmother and my great-aunt. They will come, I know it."

That was the truth Osyth held on to. Her faith in her grandparents, her uncles, her aunt, and Frederick was the talisman that helped her to rise from her cold bed every

morning, it was the strength that forced her to drag herself through each torturous day in this strange twilight world in which she had awoken and from which, at present, there seemed to be no escape.

Each morning, they ate breakfast with the other inmates, a thin gruel with hard, dry bread, slopped into their bowls as they shuffled to the long, scratched tables. Lunch was the same, while the evening meal was a thin, greasy soup of indeterminate taste with the occasional stringy piece of fatty meat or wizened vegetable. Neither of them could understand why Kieran had incarcerated them here or what his intentions were for their release. Angharad's belly began to swell but they never mentioned her condition. Their comfort was the fact they had a room to themselves and were spared the fear of the long open wards where other patients slept. The screams at night haunted Osyth. She wondered what manner of evil was taking place in the name of medical science.

When Osyth was deemed well enough, she and Angharad were sent to work in the laundry, scrubbing sheets and clothes from the wards, trying to ignore the blood. The work was hard and exhausting, leaving them dripping with sweat as they fell into their cold beds each night. The laundry area was situated in the basement of the vast asylum, its brown walls dripping with an endless flow of murky water and reached by a series of dark, narrow corridors and steep stone staircases which seemed to transport them to the bowels of the earth.

Each morning as they scurried towards the sticky grey clouds of condensation, they were thankful they were together and could protect each other as they tried to stay away from the more frightening patients within the hospital. With the passing days, Osyth began to understand that any form of treatment usually came in the form of brutality and restraint, and, despite

her fear of the screams and disturbing ramblings, she felt a deep desire to try and help the other inmates.

"I was at Hanwell Asylum when I was young to be treated for melancholia," whispered a woman a few weeks after they arrived. "They were kind there. They helped us and made us well. We were treated like real people. When I first came here, the warders were gentler but since that man came, Dr George Savage, things have become dark."

"What do you mean?" Angharad asked, her voice quavering.

"Restraints, confinement, drugs; these things were supposed to have been stopped but he enjoys torturing us."

Osyth had seen some of the methods used, the contraptions made from metal and ropes attached to chairs and beds to hold people prisoner, the foul-tasting medications they were forced to swallow, the cruelty, the physical punishments and, on occasions, people vanished. They were told by the warders these people had been released to their family in order to resume their previous lives but rumours were the currency of the asylum and the lurid tales told among the inmates suggested otherwise.

"Sally was sold," murmured another woman, who upon their arrival had introduced herself as Dolly, tipping soiled sheets into the steaming water.

"Sold?" gasped Osyth.

"They're used by medical students for experiments," whispered another woman who had once been at Hanwell but could no longer remember her name.

"Some are sold to brothels," giggled Dolly, who when Osyth had first seen her had been frail but pretty, but now her light brown hair was shaved off and her front teeth were missing.

"But what do their families say?" Osyth whispered.

"Nothing," replied Dolly. "They don't know. They're told we've died."

Osyth and Angharad exchanged a terrified look.

Dolly's eye rested on Angharad's slight bump. "You need to be careful," she hissed. "They'll take your baby, then they'll mutilate you, down there." She pointed to Angharad's skirt.

"Why?"

"Stop us enjoying 'ow's your father." Dolly giggled again. "The men think all our problems is about doing it but it don't stop them, does it? They done it to me after they caught me wiv Terry."

Osyth watched in amazement as she lifted her skirts, showing terrible scars.

"One night, they'll come for you," hissed No-Name. "You're young and sweet but you won't be for long, not now you're 'ere."

Turning back to the laundry, Osyth tried to stop her hands from trembling. There were stories of the inmates taking comfort from one another, acts which were deemed indecent and punished brutally, but the warders turned away when it was one of their own who selected a patient to satisfy their carnal needs. It had never occurred to her that they could be forced into such a terrible situation.

"The man who brought you in, Dr Stone, who is he?" asked Dolly, as they hauled out the wet sheets.

"My husband," admitted Angharad.

"My cousin," added Osyth.

"You're not the first women he's placed here but..." Dolly hesitated, her expression one of revulsion.

"Please tell us," implored Osyth.

"None of the others survived," Dolly whispered. "They was drugged and they never woke up."

Osyth and Angharad exchanged horrified glances.

"It's his experiments with his own medication, isn't it?" said Angharad, as she and Osyth wheeled the vast basket full of wet sheets to the wringing room.

"It must be, but could Kieran really have been responsible for their deaths?" said Osyth. "Could he really be a murderer?"

A few days later, Osyth and Angharad were hustled into Mrs Freeman's office. The woman who had entered their room on Osyth's first night sat behind a large desk, a triangular wooden sign announcing her as 'Senior Warden for Women'. Her eyes remained fixed on the enormous ledger she was writing while Osyth was beckoned into a chair by one of the younger female warders and Angharad was left standing. A moment later, Dr Savage, the chief physician, strode into the office. A tall man with a thick, luxuriant beard, he was crisply dressed and exuded an air of authority. His cold grey eyes offered no hint of comfort. Taking a seat beside Mrs Freeman, Osyth winced as she felt his gimlet gaze rove over her with slow deliberation. It felt uncomfortable to be so intensely scrutinised by a man.

"Girls," said Mrs Freeman, giving them a look of loathing before throwing Dr Savage a smile of sickening sweetness, "you are very lucky young ladies to have such a fine benefactor. Are they not, Dr Savage?" She patted a letter which was folded on the desk in front of her.

"Indeed," he replied, his voice deep as his eyes moved to examine Angharad, who stood trembling beside Osyth.

"Benefactor?" asked Osyth, her voice barely above a whisper, unsure whether this was a good or a bad thing.

"Yes, my dear. Dr Stone —" as Mrs Freeman said Kieran's name, a fond smile radiated across her face, as though he were a favourite son and any glimmers of hope that had arisen in

Osyth were instantly dashed — "desires that you be kept apart from the rest of the patients and come to no harm. However, you are both very sick and until such time as you realise you are deluding yourselves, he believes this is the safest place for you to reside."

"Mrs Stone," Dr Savage addressed Osyth, who knew confusion must have registered on her face, an emotion she tried to quash, "your husband has told us that you are of the belief that you and he are not married."

"We're not," Osyth snapped as Angharad gasped.

Mrs Freeman and Dr Savage exchanged sad shakes of their heads.

"While your maid, Angharad Williams, believes she is married to Dr Stone and she is carrying his child," Dr Savage continued.

This time, Osyth did not reply.

"The situation is most interesting," said Dr Savage. "However, until Dr Stone has finished using his own methods of persuasion and treatment, he has requested we do not enter into the full programme of remedies here."

Osyth felt fear rise in her. Kieran held their lives in the balance. He could control them, punish them, possibly even use his strange and dangerous drug concoctions on them with impunity. He was claiming to these people in authority that she was his wife, and it was clear they thought he was a qualified doctor when Osyth knew he had barely begun his training. It was a situation she could never have imagined. Despite everything, his mood swings, his strange fits and outbursts, she had never doubted his friendship and love for both her and Angharad. Now though, she realised he was the one who was ill, but as a man, he would be believed, while she and Angharad were at his mercy, labelled insane.

"We have been told to leave you without treatment for the next few weeks," continued Dr Savage. "You will continue to work in the laundry and when Dr Stone returns to assess you, we shall consider your future."

Very carefully, Osyth moved her foot under her skirt, hoping neither Mrs Freeman nor Dr Savage would notice, touching Angharad's shoe with her own, warning her not to speak. Her friend shuffled slightly but did not offer any acknowledgement of Osyth's warning. An idea had sprung to Osyth's mind. "Dr Savage," she said, "where is my husband?"

Mrs Freeman raised her eyebrows in fury at being slighted. "He's your husband now, is he?" she laughed, scorn in her voice, trying to regain control. "I thought he was married to Miss Williams?"

Osyth did not reply, merely glaring at the woman until the silence became prolonged and Dr Savage, with a smirk at Mrs Freeman, replied, "He's abroad, researching cures for you both. We don't expect him for another fortnight."

"May I write to him?"

Mrs Freeman and Dr Savage consulted for a few moments.

"You may but we will, of course, check the correspondence in order to ensure there is nothing dangerous or upsetting in your words," said Dr Savage.

Osyth nodded as though the transaction had been carried out to her satisfaction and stood, determined to try and take back some power from these people.

"Return them to their room," snapped Mrs Freeman. "We will send paper and pencil to you later today, Mrs Stone."

Resisting the urge to shudder, Osyth took Angharad by the hand and they hurried away.

"What are you doing?" asked Angharad when they were locked back in their room.

"There are two things," Osyth whispered, her eyes bright with excitement. "First, I shall write to Kieran, agreeing to his madness, in the hope that he will release us from this awful place…"

"Osyth, no…" moaned Angharad.

"Yes. If I pretend to be Kieran's wife, it may ensure our release." Angharad stared at her aghast. "But," Osyth continued, her eyes sparkling for the first time in weeks, "I shall use some of the paper to write a note to my family, asking for their help. Dolly has told us she can get word out to friends, letters unseen by our gaolers. I will ask them to come for us, whether it's here or at Kieran's house. Once we are free of this place, my family will stop Kieran and protect us."

"Do you think they will protect me too?" asked Angharad.

"Of course, Uncle Noah was very concerned after your marriage. He always viewed Kieran with suspicion when the others thought there was a good heart beating under his aloofness."

Angharad's face hardened. "We were all wrong," she said, her voice cold. "He has no heart at all."

CHAPTER TWO

"Get up!"

The sky outside the narrow windows was dark as Osyth struggled from sleep a few days later. Ever since Kieran had drugged her, the dreams she had endured were strange and vivid, lingering in her mind for hours after she had woken. Cruel fingers pinched her arms before cold air engulfed her as her sheets were pulled away.

"Wake up!"

Osyth screamed as a hand grasped her ankle, dragging her from the rickety bed and pulling her into a heap on the floor before rough hands stripped away her nightgown and threw icy water over her. From the other side of the room, she heard a yell as Angharad was tipped onto the floor beside her.

"What are you doing?" shouted Osyth, raising her hands to ward off the blows from the burly female warders who loomed towards her.

"Don't hit her," came Mrs Freeman's voice from the shadows. "The gentlemen won't pay for damaged goods."

"Gentlemen?" Fully awake, the word cut through Osyth, scalding her like ice on flesh. "No," she gasped, trying to stand to fight the women off but as she stared around, noticing Mrs Freeman and three female warders, she realised her strength would not be enough and, even if she and Angharad escaped the room, how would they flee the asylum with its bars and locks, its warders and its punishments?

"Thought you'd be clever, did you, Mrs Stone?" sneered Mrs Freeman, walking around Osyth, who was trying to cover herself with her hands. "Tried to humiliate me in front of Dr

Savage, did you? Pretty little lunatic, you're about to get what you deserve. So is your whore of a maid." Striding towards the doors, she commanded: "You have twenty minutes to make them clean and respectable. Remember, there must be no marks on them, though there will probably be plenty when they return. *If* they do, of course." With a harsh laugh, she stalked from the room, leaving the door open so the male warders patrolling the corridors were able to glance inside.

Tears sprang into Osyth's eyes. "What's happening?" she asked one of the warders.

"A little side-line we have going," the warder replied with a dark laugh.

"I don't understand…"

"Mrs Freeman has a sister who has house for young ladies," the warder said, her eyes sparkling with malice. "It's surprising how often the gentlemen ask for a sweet little lunatic to entertain them."

"No," gasped Osyth, as the meaning behind the woman's words hit her. "No, no, no!" She began struggling but another warder arrived and gripped her arms to her sides, as her first tormenter forced a white lawn nightgown over her head.

"Don't worry about shoes," came Mrs Freeman's voice from the door as Osyth and Angharad were propelled towards her. "They won't be needing those nightgowns for much longer either."

Osyth struggled, fighting against the burly female warder but she could not break free. Beside her, Angharad was limp, her eyes wide and glassy, stumbling as she was dragged along. The warder's fingers dug into Osyth's flesh and she felt her feet falter as Mrs Freeman trilled, "Hurry now, the gentlemen are waiting and they're eager to claim their wares."

Osyth was terrified. Mrs Freeman was speaking about them as though they were goods to be bought and sold. Despite the promises the woman had made to Kieran about their safety, it seemed Mrs Freeman had her own agenda, making as much money from abusing her position as possible. *This must be where the other women have vanished to*, thought Osyth, and fear rose like bile in her throat.

"We know Miss Williams is more than happy to accommodate men," laughed Mrs Freeman, "and, as a married woman, Mrs Stone, you are no innocent."

"But I'm not Mrs Stone," Osyth gasped. "My cousin married Angharad."

"It seems we will have to take a firmer line with you upon your return," Mrs Freeman said and her smile widened. "Until then, my dear, married or not, you are not my responsibility."

They had arrived at a suite of rooms set away from the rest of the asylum. The floor was carpeted with fine rugs and the doors were more like those of an ordinary drawing room than the brutal metal deterrents in the rest of the building. A male and female warder stood outside two rooms.

"Her, in there," snapped Mrs Freeman, nodding to Angharad, who was seized by the two warders and marched, kicking and struggling, into the nearest room. "You're in here," smirked Mrs Freeman and Osyth found herself being bodily lifted through the door. "Make sure you do everything you're told. These men have paid good money to be entertained by a lunatic."

"No," shrieked Osyth. "NO!" She fought against the male warder who had grasped her but he threw her through the door as though she weighed no more than a child. The door slammed shut and was locked. Osyth began hammering on it, begging for release but outside, all she could hear was laughter.

"No, please, no," she sobbed, her face pressed hard against the door.

Her eyes closed as two hands slid around her waist and a male voice said: "Don't struggle, my dear, it'll be far easier if you do as you're asked."

Tears spilled down Osyth's cheeks as her hair was smoothed back from her face and she began to twist and turn, struggling to escape. "No," she whimpered, "don't hurt me."

"It's all right, Osyth, you're safe, it's me," said a familiar voice, "we're here to take you away."

Away. The word penetrated her panic. *Take you away.* Her fear began to calm. Opening her eyes, she turned within the circle of his hands and looking down at her, his face fraught with worry, was Frederick. Reaching up, she touched his cheek, ensuring he was real and not another of the strange spectres caused by the residue of Kieran's drugs.

"We must hurry," he said, "we're going to pretend we're taking you somewhere more private." He wiped away her tears with his thumb. "We heard about this terrible arrangement through one of Solomon's journalist friends," he whispered as he fastened a thick cloak around her. "The police have been turning a blind eye but it seems the chief warders here regularly allowed those who can pay to…" He paused, hesitating as though what he was saying might shock her but Osyth had understood his meaning and was equally as terrified.

"Did you pay to be able to…?"

"Yes, there was an auction taking place for you," he said, causing Osyth to shudder. "Your uncle outbid everyone and insisted on a signed receipt from Mrs Freeman and Dr Savage. He intends to publish it in order to stop this happening here or anywhere else."

"Angharad?" she gasped.

"Safe. She's with Solomon and his friend, Drake. Come, Osyth," he whispered, hammering on the door. The relief at seeing him made her legs shake and to her surprise, tears continued to run down her cheeks. "Pretend to struggle, we have to make this look realistic."

Outside they heard Solomon's relaxed laughter and when Frederick knocked, the door was unlocked. With a mumbled apology, he grabbed her wrist, dragging Osyth from the room, smiling at Solomon and Drake who were holding up a trembling Angharad between them.

"They'll be back by sunrise, what's left of them," Solomon leered, causing the two burly warders to laugh.

Moments later they had been bundled into a waiting carriage where to both Osyth and Angharad's relief, Xenia and Noah were waiting. Xenia's face was white with terror as she enveloped both girls in a maternal hug. Noah seemed ready to explode with fear and fury.

"Go!" Noah shouted to the driver almost before they were all inside, then he turned to Osyth and Angharad. "Oh my darling girls," he whispered, taking their hands as Xenia pulled them tightly to her. "We are so sorry that you have been through such an ordeal."

As though sensing the urgency, the horses whinnied, their hooves sliding on the grimy cobbles in the asylum yard. Osyth felt sure they would be stopped but the heavy grey gates were thrown open and the carriage raced through. Leaning into the familiar scent of her aunt's White Rose perfume, Osyth felt tears of relief slide down her face. Her uncles spoke in low, urgent voices and Noah consulted his pocket watch.

"We must hurry," she heard Noah mutter. "We have until morning but no longer."

Osyth's heart contracted with fear. "You're not taking us back?" she whispered.

"What?" exclaimed Noah.

"You said we have until morning."

"Of course we're not taking you back," he said, his tone more tense than she had ever heard, "but, my darling girl, we've stolen you from a notorious asylum. When you don't return tomorrow, questions will be asked. From what we've discovered, Kieran has paid a great deal of money to have the two of you incarcerated there, although for what purpose we have yet to ascertain. We need to hide you and Angharad somewhere safe and beyond the law while we find Kieran and resolve this matter. This is why there is very little time."

"Where are we going?"

"There is a train at 4am from Liverpool Street which will take you to the coast and from there you will travel to France," said Xenia. "Drake's friends will escort you to the town where Blaise and Katherine have taken a house for a few months. Once you are there, Blaise will explain everything, I promise."

Osyth stared at Xenia in bewilderment. She had thought that this midnight flight to freedom from the asylum meant the worst was over but it seemed the lurking danger represented by Kieran and his obsessions continued to hang over their heads like a curse.

The next few hours were a blur. The carriage took them to Solomon's flat, where Osyth was plunged into the waiting bath of hot steaming water. Xenia helped her to scrub away the filth and stench of the asylum. Osyth felt her sense of self returning as the water soaked away the lingering tang of fear from the asylum. When Xenia turned to help Angharad, she paled at the sight of her bump.

"The baby is Kieran's," Osyth assured Xenia, "they're married and he was determined to have his way with her but he was furious when Angharad told him about the child."

"He's insane," shuddered Xenia. "He was always close to the edge but if what we've discovered about his opium habit is true, this may have pushed beyond the realms of help."

"Where is he?" asked Angharad who had not spoken since they had left the asylum. Her voice was low, bitter.

"Abroad somewhere, we don't know where exactly," replied Xenia. "Sol thinks he might be trying to find a new place to buy opium. We've hired a private detective to locate him."

"I hope someone slits his throat," said Angharad before lowering her head below the steaming water.

Osyth and Xenia exchanged horrified looks. Xenia hovered beside the bath but a moment later, Angharad bobbed up, sluicing the water away from her hair and eyes.

"Thank you for rescuing me," she said to Xenia, as she climbed out of the water a few minutes later into the waiting bath sheet. After this, Angharad remained silent and pliant, allowing herself to be led by Osyth and her family.

"And my mother?" whispered Osyth to Xenia, after Angharad had settled in a chair staring at the fire. With long, firm strokes, she combed her hair, staring at Xenia's reflection in the mirror, determined to discover the truth. Her aunt inhaled deeply, as though trying to gather her strength before responding.

"When we received your letters telling us you had overheard Father and your uncles discussing Eudora, we realised we had made a terrible mistake in not telling you the truth," admitted Xenia, "but, please believe me, we did it to protect you, not isolate you. The mistakes we made were never intended to hurt you. We love you, Osyth, and we love Eudora, too."

"You admit it then, my mother is alive?"

Biting her lip as though the confession caused her great pain, Xenia nodded.

"And my father?"

"Yes, he is also alive, but there is much to explain and there is not the time this evening. Blaise will tell you everything, I promise."

Emotions rushed through Osyth with such force she could not distinguish one from another. Fury at having been lied to, curiosity as to why, and, despite everything, the overriding trust and love she felt for her family, knowing that they would never hurt her.

"Do Nain and Taid know of your plans?"

"Taid and William helped us secure your freedom this evening but Nain doesn't know the details. She's been very ill, my darling, and the worry of trying to find you has laid her low. We've sent word to her and Mary at Cliffside that you and Angharad are safe but they understand you won't be able to return home yet."

"Is Nain recovering? Truly?"

"She is and knowing you're safe will give her even greater strength."

Osyth looked into Xenia's green eyes and knew Xenia was telling the truth.

"You must dress, my darling," said Xenia. "These should fit you." Xenia handed her and Angharad men's trousers and shirts.

"Those will be the best disguise," said Drake when the two girls entered the sumptuous living room. "No one will be looking for three young men."

"Three?" Osyth queried.

"I'm accompanying you," said Frederick, who was dressed in the rough trousers and cap of a dock worker. Osyth felt her heart beat with excitement and relief.

"We must leave," said Noah, consulting his watch. Solomon put a calming hand on his brother's arm and they exchanged a glance.

"There's time, Noah," Solomon said. "The plan is a good one. Drake's friends are trustworthy, they will keep Osyth safe, as they protected him when he was in need."

With a sigh, Noah nodded his agreement but Osyth thought her uncle looked older, more haggard than she had ever seen him. Running across the room, she threw her arms around him.

"Don't fret, Uncle Noah," she said. "The fairies will protect us."

Tears sprang into Noah's eyes as he looked down at her. "You have the sweetest soul, my darling," he said. "Even after all you have endured, your heart remains pure."

Clambering back into the carriage, they set off into the night. The streets were empty but as a precaution, Solomon suggested they keep the curtains closed.

"Let's not draw any more attention to ourselves than is necessary," he murmured, his hand on Drake's knee.

The cacophony on the platform that greeted them sent Angharad backing into the safety of Solomon's arms.

"My friends," said Drake proudly, spreading his arms wide to encompass the shouting, laughing, tumbling troupe of performers with their piles of trunks.

"It's a circus!" exclaimed Osyth, gazing around at the colour and chaos in wonder.

There was a shout from the crowd and two men of similar height and build to Drake hurried over, embracing him, one of

them running his eyes over Solomon before slapping Drake on the back and laughing appreciatively.

A moment later a tall man with skin darker than Osyth could have imagined noticed them. He shouted in rapid French to another man, equally as tall but his build was slenderer, his skin honey-toned, like burnished gold in the guttering lamplight. Scowling, they prowled towards the group of strangers and Osyth felt herself being pushed behind Noah, Solomon and Frederick. When the men saw Drake, their expressions lightened, as understanding replaced their intimidating gazes.

"My name is Oran Walters, and this is my brother, Caius," said the thicker set of the two, shaking hands with Noah, Solomon and Frederick before bowing to Xenia, Osyth and Angharad. "Drake has explained the situation. I will deliver your nieces safely to your brother," he assured them. "A circus is a good place to wear a disguise and lose yourself."

Oran clapped his hands and two women hurried forward, taking Osyth and Angharad by the hands, preparing to lead them towards the waiting train.

"No, wait," said Osyth, turning to her aunt and uncles. "Thank you," she said, hugging each in turn. "I knew you would come for me, for us."

"We will always come for you, Osyth," said Noah, squeezing her tightly. "Stay safe, my darling, until we meet again."

Frederick ushered Osyth and Angharad forward, helping them on to the overflowing train before stepping on himself. Osyth's last glimpse of her family was of them waving her goodbye, then she was absorbed into the chaos on board.

CHAPTER THREE

Two weeks had passed since Osyth and Angharad had been smuggled from the asylum. Now, as they rattled across France, Osyth's shock was diminishing. Her nightmares were less frequent and she finally acknowledged a gentle wave of happiness. It was a relief after months of trauma.

The circus train was winding its way down the country, stopping at a variety of towns, setting up the brilliant red big top and beckoning the townspeople into the world of sparkle and glamour. At first, Osyth had been terrified of the heated conversations in the variety of languages that burst through the walls and windows of the snaking carriages, the bustle and the histrionics of the performers as tempers frayed and egos soared, but as she recovered, what had begun as a wall of dreadful black noise had reformed into a backdrop of colour and light, reminding her of the friendly chaos of her family when they were all in residence at Cliffside.

Everyone seemed to know Drake and his patronage ensured they were trustworthy. Osyth and Angharad had spent the first part of the journey on the stormy crossing to Calais hugging each other tightly, both too scared to speak. It was only when they had embarked on a train occupied solely by the circus that Osyth had begun to feel safe.

"Here you are." The door to her compartment opened and Frederick arrived carrying a tray with three steaming bowls of fragrant stew, another of fluffy couscous, apricots and slices of crumbly cheese. "Caius sent the apricots for you, Angharad," he added.

Caius was Oran's younger brother and the two ran the circus with fairness and respect for their players.

"We have no wild animals," Oran had stated during the journey to the coast. "Only horses and a few goats, all of whom have the best accommodation. On occasions we rescue mighty beasts from other circuses and send them to our eldest brother, Ezra, who has huge vistas of land in Africa. The animals are nursed back to health and put into the wild to live in peace. No man can hold his head high if he tries to pretend he is the master over a magnificent beast. We are lower than them in every sense and these great creatures must be treated with deference."

Africa, wild beasts, thought Osyth. *That is a world of which I never dreamed.*

Frederick sat beside Osyth, passing her the steaming food. She inhaled the rich spices, wondering if she would ever be used to the delight of real food after her weeks of gruel. Angharad was stretched out opposite them on the banquette where she slept. When they were alone, Osyth and Frederick had whispered conversations about Angharad, both concerned for her health. Ever since they had departed the asylum, she had been in a frozen state, behaving like an automaton, unable to make decisions for herself, even needing help to wash and dress.

"She's in shock," one of the other women, Lela, had said in her broad London accent when she had seen Angharad. "Poor little love, give her time, she'll recover."

"Thank you," Angharad murmured as Osyth passed her portion of stew.

Osyth dipped her spoon into her dinner, eating small morsels with great care. Her instinct was to cram in as much food as possible, to stave away the intense hunger wrought by the

asylum, but Lela had admonished her, explaining that after a few months of gruel, her body would need to adjust to the rich, flavoursome food cooked by Caius.

"I must hurry," said Frederick, mixing couscous into his stew and eating with speed. "There is much to prepare. Lille has proved a town in love with the circus, we've been playing to packed houses every night."

There was an excitement in his voice and Osyth smiled. Frederick had been her constant companion since their escape and the two were gently finding their way towards an agreement. His smile made her heart flutter and when he took her hand, her skin tingled. Seeing his enthusiasm, she found herself laughing too, something she had been unsure she would ever do again.

"Are you helping tonight?" she asked, selecting an apricot and biting into the sweet flesh.

"Yes, I'll be with Anil and Joe moving the scenery and making sure all the props are in the right place," he replied. "It's important everything backstage runs smoothly, then the magic of the circus can captivate its audience. They've asked me if I'd like to train to take over Drake's old role."

"You're a circus ruffian!" Osyth laughed.

"Watch the show with me tonight," he said. "You haven't experienced its full magic yet."

Osyth wrinkled her nose, her way of expressing her reluctance, not through snobbery but from fear of all she had experienced.

"You can stand with me in the wings and if you don't like it, I'll bring you back to your carriage."

"What about Angharad?" she whispered, aware her friend became agitated when left alone for too long.

"I'll be fine, Osyth," Angharad said, her food abandoned, half-finished. "Perhaps Caius would consent to sit with me. We are friends."

Osyth and Frederick exchanged a surprised look. While Oran reigned supreme as ringmaster, Caius was the chef who kept everyone fed. He never strayed into the spangled arena of the big top.

"Shall we ask him?" queried Frederick and Angharad gave a quiet affirmation.

Taking Osyth's hand, Frederick led her into the corridor of the train. The circus was pitched near the sidings and the entire circus lived on the train. Some towns offered showgrounds further from the stations and then the company would load up wagons with their equipment, costumes and extra tents, forming a miniature village around the big top.

Pausing to allow Pipette and Lela to pass with armfuls of costumes, Frederick leaned out of the window, breathing in the spicy air. "Don't you love all this?" he said, his eyes brimming with eagerness. "Whoever knew this would be such an exhilarating way to live. To be among creative people who want nothing more than to be free to express themselves, to live in the way they choose rather than the way society dictates."

"What do you mean?" asked Osyth in surprise, her interest piqued even if she did not fully understand his words.

"Lela and Grimes share a carriage but they're not married," he said, lowering his voice as though this might make it less shocking for Osyth to hear. "She has a husband who was a drunk and would beat her. When she and Grimes fell in love, her husband threatened to murder them both. They stowed away with the circus several years ago and when they told Oran their tale, he took them in."

"Really?" Osyth was agog.

"Yes, Lela was a dancer but now she's on the trapeze with Jeanne, while Grimes was a groom at a big house. It's why he looks after the horses and rides them during the show." He paused. "I'm sorry, Osyth, have I upset you?"

"No, I'm not shocked," she said, considering his words. This was an adventure and, while their path to the circus had been a terrifying ordeal, on this train of acrobats, singers, dancers and magicians she was discovering a whole new world. It was thrilling, exhilarating and her fear was beginning to ebb away in its light. "Oran is a good man, isn't he?"

"It does seem that way," replied Frederick. "Drake told me Oran and Caius saved his life, as well those of Anil and Joe. This circus seems to gather up waifs and protect them."

Caius had agreed to sit with Angharad and an hour later, Osyth allowed Frederick to take her hand and lead her into the darkened wings at the back of the big top.

"Stand here," said Oran, looming behind her. "You'll be able to see everything, my little runaway." He beamed, before striding away, shouting instructions to his glittering performers.

Frederick raced to and fro, handing out props, shifting scenery, holding the reins of the horses while Grimes sprang on to their backs. Osyth watched, unsure at first, but as the lights danced and the crowd was drawn into the spectacle, she felt any final remnants of fear dissolving. Gasping with the audience she watched Lela and Jeanne fly through the air on the trapeze, before Grimes and his assistant, Theodore, flashed through an astonishing series of stunts on the backs of the gleaming horses.

Pipette was next, singing in a beautiful soprano, while other performers spun in wheels and on strips of silk hanging from the ceiling, defying gravity. When Osyth had first met the tiny woman, she had mistaken her for a child. However, once Pipette's tirade of furious and insulting French had subsided as Osyth, with tears in her eyes had apologised, the woman had smiled, shrugged in true Parisian style and forgiven her with a grin of glittering white teeth. She had since taken it upon herself to look after Osyth.

Frederick's hands slid around her waist, drawing her against him as the notes of Pipette's song floated to an end and Oran strode into the spotlight to announce Anil and Joe with their fire-eating, fire juggling and sword swallowing.

"You know what's happened, don't you?" whispered Osyth, staring out into the glittering arena.

"What?"

"We've stumbled into Tylwyth Teg."

"Osyth, you're right," grinned Frederick. "We're in our own magical land."

They beamed at each other and Osyth felt herself tingling from head to toe as though fairy magic sparkled through her soul.

"Will you accept Anil and Joe's offer to work with them in their act?" she asked, watching as the two young men threw flaming torches to each other with ease.

Frederick cleared his throat before responding and when he did, his voice was higher than usual, "Osyth, may I ask your opinion?"

"Of course."

"Rather than work with Anil and Joe, I was considering asking Oran if I could perform in my own act."

"Would you read your poems?"

"Yes," he replied, his eyes cast downwards and his cheeks pink.

"Freddie, that's a wonderful idea," she said, enthusiasm bubbling through her words.

"I thought perhaps Lela could dance or act them out while I read," he said, his cheeks flaming red.

"Annie and I used to dance and tumble on the beach," Osyth said, "perhaps I could help you, rather than Lela. After all, she's busy with the trapeze. We could work out a routine to your poems and show it to Oran."

"Would you really help me?" asked Frederick.

Osyth nodded. "Yes," she replied, a sense of her old joy and verve for life winding its way through her blood. "Oh Freddie, yes, let's create an act for Oran as a thank you for saving us. What tales we shall have to tell when we reach my mother."

Spurred on by the idea of creating their own act to perform, Osyth and Frederick spent many days closeted in her and Angharad's carriage, he working on his poem, she bending and stretching, watching the dancers and trapeze artists. It had surprised them both when Angharad had asked to join their endeavour.

"From now on," Angharad said, "I plan to do all the things Kieran would dislike and he never approved of our tumbling displays. He thought they were unladylike but he put up with them because everyone else enjoyed them."

"I didn't realise," said Osyth. "My eyes must have been permanently shut while I was a child or my head really was in fairy land. It seems the world was going on around me without my knowledge."

"You were only a child…" began Frederick, but Osyth shook her head.

"A child who was so spoiled, self-absorbed and dreamy that I was gullible to lies told by my family," she said. "My naivety was such that the cousin who I thought was my friend and found my ways charming, in reality found me ridiculous." Anger bubbled inside her as her life spread before her and she re-evaluated all she had thought was important.

"You're being very hard on yourself," said Angharad, her voice gentle. "You weren't spoiled, you were loved and protected by a family who wanted to keep you safe. Don't let Kieran's madness poison your memories."

Osyth bit back the tears that were once again threatening to spill out, not from sadness or self-pity but from anger and frustration. "If my family loved me so much, why did they banish my mother and tell me she was dead?"

Angharad shrugged. "That is why we're going to see Blaise and Katherine. They'll tell us the truth and then we can decide what to do next."

"What do you mean?"

Angharad glanced at Frederick who was watching Osyth.

"Blaise and Katherine are staying in a house not far from La Chaux-de-Fonds which is a town renowned for its watch-making," Frederick said. "Blaise wanted to learn about it for his art. Their house is in France but the town where Blaise is spending a great deal of time is in Switzerland…"

A smile spread over Osyth's face as she finally understood the plan. "Do Nain and Taid know?" she asked.

"How do you think we knew where your parents lived?" said Frederick.

When Osyth, Frederick and Angharad tentatively asked if they might show Oran their act, Osyth could tell from Oran's expression that he was preparing to let them down lightly, but as Frederick's words stole around the ringmaster, while she and Angharad cartwheeled and span as though they were circus-born, an appreciative crowd gathered and when they finished, applause resounded around the big top.

"I think we have a new act!" roared Oran in delight, his dark eyes glittering as Osyth threw herself into his arms. "I believe, with some work, this could be a finale piece. Caius and I have been searching for something new, challenging, exciting, and if we work together, this will cause a stir among the polite folk who come to be outraged by our wild antics."

CHAPTER FOUR

Grimes smoothed out the cheap piece 'wanted' poster, which showed a blurred image of Osyth, only recognisable because her name was written below. Osyth slid her hand into Frederick's, biting her lip nervously as Grimes said in his Cockney drawl, "We need to be careful, Oran."

"And this was given to you by one of the men who have been at the show every night this week?" Oran asked, scowling.

"Yes," Grimes confirmed, then added, "Your friend, Philippe, from the local gendarmerie has said there is a well-connected man asking questions about the circus."

Oran did not reply, but turned away, stalking back to his carriage and shutting the door.

"Will he throw us off the train?" asked Osyth, alarmed. The circus was beginning to feel like home and the thought of being made to leave was heart-breaking.

"Of course not," said Lela. "He's deciding what to do next. Oran will never allow anyone on this train to be in danger. Don't fret, Osyth, he'll think of something."

Angharad flitted into the corridor where the discussion had taken place. "Is it Kieran?" she asked.

"No," replied Frederick, "but it's clear these men are working on his behalf. They've been questioning people in the nearby town, showing them this sketch, which is supposed to be Osyth, saying she's his wife and she's been kidnapped." Frederick pointed to the representation on the leaflet.

"Osyth?" whispered Angharad, gazing at the picture. "Not me?"

Osyth reached out to take her friend's hand. "You're his wife, Annie, I'm sure he —"

"Don't say, 'he loves me'," Angharad snapped. "He never loved me. You were the focus of his obsession, always. I was a means to draw you to him, I see it now." Her voice was low and cold.

Osyth shifted uncomfortably. "Do you hate me for it, Annie?" she whispered.

"What?" asked Angharad, appalled. "No, of course not. Osyth, you're my dearest friend. It's Kieran I hate for using us both so cruelly. My fear's for you, not me. In his mind, I no longer exist. It's you we must protect and before you ask, my overriding emotion at his abandonment of me and our child is relief. We're better off without him."

"Will it be safe for you to perform tonight?" asked Frederick, turning to Osyth.

"I must," she exclaimed, "we've been working so hard, and this is your night, Freddie. The poem, the story, it's yours."

"Oran will decide," said Anil who stood behind Angharad. "The big top is his domain. His word is law."

The door to Oran's carriage opened, and he beckoned Osyth, Frederick and Angharad inside. Caius leaned against the wall, his face inscrutable. Oran pointed to the chaise opposite his own vast armchair and they sat, staring at him, knowing he held their fate in the balance.

"Do you really think this man, your cousin —" he looked at Osyth who confirmed the question in his tone with a nod, then to Angharad — "and your husband would bother to track you all the way across France?"

"Kieran is determined," said Angharad, her face paling. "When he thinks he's correct, he will pursue his ends without mercy."

Osyth shifted as Oran considered her response.

"Yet, he claims you are his wife, Osyth?" queried Oran. "You must be honest with me, to whom is this man married?"

"To me," said Angharad, "and the child I'm carrying is his, but he has always been obsessed with Osyth. He told me on our wedding night that he married me because her grandfather refused permission for him to wed her." Angharad turned her sad face to Osyth's. "Did you know?" she asked.

"Yes, Uncle Noah told me after Kieran had persuaded you to elope," Osyth admitted.

"But now," continued Frederick, "he's telling people that Osyth is his wife, while Angharad is her maid. He has suggested their refusal to admit this proves they are insane, but he is the madman. His mind is devious to the extreme."

"Dangerous, too," said Caius from the shadows. "This does change things."

"In what way?" asked Frederick.

"We're in France, so it isn't so easy to access your legal system. If this man comes here with police, things could be difficult. You are eighteen, Osyth, you need permission from your parent or guardian to be here. He could swoop down and take you —"

"But he's married to Annie," Osyth protested.

"You need to be protected —" began Oran again but he was interrupted by Frederick who had been listening intently but spoke in a sudden rush, his cheeks glowing.

"Osyth, this is a little unorthodox, but if you marry me, you will be safe from Kieran."

Although, this was not the form of proposal Osyth would have imagined, her heart burst with excitement.

"How old are you, Frederick?" boomed Oran.

"I am twenty."

"No good," Oran sighed. "You are underage here. A marriage between the two of you would be annulled in an instant. She needs to marry a French citizen of full age, then she has the full weight of French law to protect her."

"But I want to marry Freddie," exclaimed Osyth.

"And I want to marry you," he said.

"This is about safety, not romance," cut in Caius. "If there are men sniffing around asking questions about you, it is important this crazy man, your cousin, has no way of claiming you and dragging you away under the pretext of your own protection."

"And Angharad?" Osyth asked.

"I will protect her," came Caius's swift reply and Osyth watched as they exchanged a knowing smile.

"You're in the most danger, Osyth, your name is on the leaflet. It's you he's hunting," said Frederick.

Their words made Osyth shudder.

"My life has been about travelling," Oran sighed. "I have witnessed many things and fought many battles, not all of them my own. Men like your cousin —" he shook his head in disgust — "are not to be reasoned with. They are to be stopped before they can do damage. Once you are safe, we can deal with him, but you must be put beyond his reach." He stared around at them and Osyth watched, cautious, her heart still beating with excitement at the thought of Frederick's proposal. "I will marry you," he announced and Osyth yelped in astonishment. "My father was from Kenya but our mother,

Manon, was French. It's why we tour here so often, we are French citizens and, since my wife, Anna-Maria, died —"

"No," exclaimed Frederick, rising to his feet.

"It will be in name only," said Oran, "and when you are safely home, it shall be annulled. There will be no more to it than a legal protection for our little runaway."

Osyth felt cold fear run through her. While she understood Oran's reasoning, would this be the solution, or would she be in even deeper trouble? The strained silence grew between them.

"Do you trust me?" asked Oran into the growing unease.

"Yes…" began Osyth.

"Then do we have an accord?"

"No!" exclaimed Frederick again.

"Don't you understand?" Oran turned to Frederick. "If he brings the gendarmes here, they will arrest you all and it will be impossible for me to stop him taking Osyth away. He could take her anywhere and we might never find her. If she is my wife, she is a French citizen, the law protects her."

"And what would you want from me? As your wife?" asked Osyth.

"Nothing," replied Oran. "You are young enough to be my daughter!"

"You must think about this before you give us your response," said Caius, "but trust us, we have your safety at heart." He glanced at Angharad again.

"Continue to prepare for tonight's show and discuss this suggestion," said Oran. "Do not be afraid, my little runaways, this is to save you and ensure you may marry happily one day. When you do, we will hope to be there to add our joy to your own."

Osyth realised they were dismissed and, grabbing Frederick's hand, she dragged him from the carriage, leading the way to her own. Angharad followed, her eyes determined and full of fury.

As they slammed the door shut, Osyth turned to her friends. "What shall we do?"

"Kieran is mad," said Angharad, "but he's believable to those who don't know better. He could persuade the French authorities you're his wife and have you removed. He uses his pretend status as a doctor to trap us at every turn."

"You think I should marry Oran?" Angharad's expression was her reply. In desperation, Osyth turned to Frederick. "And you?"

Frederick stared down at his feet, then taking Osyth's hand, he said, "The idea is repellent because I want to marry you, to protect you, but he is right. We're both under twenty-one — even if we eloped, the authorities could still annul the marriage."

"But if Kieran discovers I'm married to Oran, he will claim it's bigamy."

"You're not married, Osyth," said Angharad, "it doesn't matter what he claims. If you and Oran did wed, you would be safe in his protection."

Osyth let out a sob. "And us?" she said, turning again to Frederick.

"When this is finished and we are home, then we shall marry at the chapel behind Cliffside," he assured her, "and we will live happily ever after, as all your fairy tales have always promised."

With tears in her eyes, Osyth knew she had no choice. Once again, her cousin was controlling her life, forcing her into circumstances against her wishes. Then the notes of the wind chime floated into her heart and she felt the love of her family around her. If the wind chime was offering solace, then this path was the one she should take. Flinging open the carriage door and storming down the corridor to Oran's compartment to tell him she would accept his offer, Osyth prayed the wind chime would protect them all from Kieran's madness.

CHAPTER FIVE

The procession of colourful wagons transporting the circus from the train to their next venue wound its way into the vast open space on the outskirts of La Chaux-de-Fonds. A horse and trap containing two people waited, and, riding between Oran and Frederick, Osyth peered at the couple in the carriage.

"It's Uncle Blaise," she exclaimed, standing up and waving with such enthusiasm that she knocked Frederick's shoulder, forcing him to grab her legs to steady himself as he lurched forward.

"It is sad that this is where you will leave us," said Oran as he drove towards Blaise and Katherine. "Your uncle and aunt sent me a telegram stating they would be waiting at the showground but part of me hoped they would not arrive. These last weeks with you, my little runaway trio, have been exceptional. You sprinkle your fairy magic around my big top and draw a larger crowd."

Osyth stared up into Oran's face in surprise. Two weeks earlier, their strange wedding ceremony had taken place in the local town hall. Oran and Caius had organised the necessary path through the labyrinthine paperwork, while Frederick strode off in a furious temper, refusing to witness the event. Officially, she was now Mrs Oran Walters, but moments after the ceremony, her new husband had kissed the back of her hand, saying, "You don't have to wear the wedding ring but keep it near you. If the circus is searched by men representing your insane cousin, you must replace it and play the part of my willing wife."

With these words, he had led the small party of witnesses back to the big top and Osyth was left with Angharad, relief flooding her as she realised Oran was an honest man. Her biggest fear had been that when their union was official, he would insist she behave like a wife in all manners but his interest in her remained avuncular. Oran had also promised to explain their union to her uncle in order to continue her protection until such time as she returned to England, when he assured her that he would begin annulment proceedings.

"I ask one last favour," Oran said, as the carriage slowed, "would you join us for the shows in La Chaux-de-Fonds. Would your uncle and aunt approve?"

Osyth grinned, "My uncle will probably want to join us," she said. "Or, at the very least, to paint us. He's a well-known artist."

Oran beamed in appreciation, stopping beside Blaise and Katherine, who were already reaching up to draw Osyth and Frederick into their waiting arms.

"Where's Angharad?" asked Katherine, her red hair fierce in the morning sun.

"With Caius," replied Osyth, pointing to a wagon further down the processions.

As she spoke, Angharad appeared from the covered rear section. Katherine gasped when she saw her. "She's with child…" Katherine groped for Blaise's hand. "Why did no one say?"

When Angharad saw Katherine, who was legally her sister-in-law, she paused, her hazel eyes narrowing. Osyth and Frederick exchanged an awkward look but before anyone could comment further, Katherine was striding towards Angharad. The two young women, who had grown up together, stood silently contemplating the changes in their lives and the

circumstances which had been created by Kieran. Osyth made to move towards them but both Frederick and Blaise reached out to stop her.

"Oh Annie," they heard Katherine sob, then she wrapped her arms around Angharad, who stood, stiff for a moment before hugging Katherine in return. "I am so sorry for all the things my brother has done," whispered Katherine, "but you're safe with us. We will never let him hurt you again. You're my sister now and we shall protect you."

Angharad stared at Katherine, then a tiny nod of her head seemed to commit to this promise and she gave a shadow of a smile. Osyth gripped Frederick's hand in relief and they walked to join the two women who were staring at each other in sorrow and forgiveness.

Osyth's assessment of Blaise and his response to the vibrancy of the circus was correct. Rolling up his sleeves, he was soon firm friends with Oran, even after the ringmaster had explained about the sudden marriage. After questioning Osyth, Blaise turned to Oran and shook his hand. "You will always be welcome in our family," he said, and the two men had surprised Osyth by embracing.

"Your aunt and uncle are going to watch from back here," called Caius to Osyth, a few evenings later. "He wants to sketch your final performance." Then his voice dropped and he whispered, "The men are here again. After the show, you and Freddie must leave immediately with your aunt and uncle."

"What about Angharad?"

"We are leaving now; Lela will take her part in the finale."

Angharad appeared through the flap at the rear of the big top. Her hair was captured in a bun and for the first time in months, she was dressed in a neat dark blue dress, her circus

clothes abandoned. Caius was in a smart suit, his face clean shaven and a hat under one arm. Osyth realised there was a travelling trunk waiting to be loaded on to the small pony and trap.

"Where are you going?" she whispered, catching her friend's hand and squeezing it.

"Caius knows France well; he's taking us to his cousin in Lyon. I will write when it's safe."

Osyth hugged Angharad, tears welling in her eyes at the thought of parting from her. In the past months, they had shared so much, experiences no one else would ever understand. "When will we see each other again?" she asked.

"One day," said Angharad. "Know that I will always be grateful to you and your family for saving me. Take care, Osyth."

Then they were gone, leaving Osyth alone in the dark while the crowd roared in the big top beyond the curtain.

"Time to get ready, *ma chérie*," said Pipette, bustling up to her. "You must be suitably attired to shock our delightful audience." When Osyth did not respond, Pipette squeezed her hand and said, "Make this the best performance you've ever given. Do it for Annie, do it for yourself, and do it to show everyone you are a woman of great talent, compassion and power. Send our audience home with a sprinkling of your fairy magic in their hearts."

As Oran finished his introduction and left the big top, the circus was plunged into darkness. Scurrying like mice, the performers took their places. Osyth, aware Blaise and Katherine were watching, hoped they would understand why she and Frederick had created this story. A tale of women, men, control, despair and salvation. Clambering on to the raised circle in the centre of the sawdust strewn floor, she

could make out the shapes around her and the rest of the troupe as they created the tortured positions of the first tableau, either lunatics begging for help, gurning in despair, weeping from fear; or their keepers, brutal, faceless and sadistic.

"Ready," Osyth whispered to Lela, who was arranging pretend chains around her legs. Lela gave the signal to Grimes, and to the discordant rattle of assorted metal chimes, a single light picked out Osyth. She stood in her ripped dress, her wrists manacled, her eyes downcast, causing a woman in the crowd to scream. A dirge began to play and Osyth raised her head with painful slowness. Her eyes were shut but she had brilliant blue eyes painted on her lids to make them look as though they were open, and she presented a horrifying figure. There was an uncomfortable rustling from the audience.

Taking a deep breath, thinking of Annie, of her grandmother, her great-aunt Georgina, No-Name, Dolly, Lela and all the other women she had encountered on her adventure who had suffered at the hands of the harsh uncaring world and, knowing this would be the last performance with the circus who had gone to extraordinary lengths to keep her safe, Osyth allowed her heart to lead her as the music changed and her performance began.

Widening her smile until it was broad enough to be unnerving, she opened her eyes, gazing around in the uncomfortable silence, before rotating slowly on the spot. When she had completed a full circle, she bent forward from the waist, oozing her way to the ground like a snake before raising her bare feet and walking them over her head, grinning maniacally throughout. A woman in the crowd screamed and was hushed, before Osyth unfurled her body, rattling her chains as Frederick's voice filled the big top.

"The perfect child with the dimpled smile.
Nobody thought it would end this way.
Happy and gentle, full of hope,
Until the day he stole her away.
The Lunatics' Ball; The Lunatics' Ball,
Dancing until we slip and fall."

As he spoke, Lela and Pipette, one dressed in angelic white, the other devil red, moved around Osyth like elfin devas removing her manacles, placing them at her feet. With great care, they removed the top layer of her costume to reveal a simple white gown underneath.

As Frederick spoke the final line, the lights flashed up for a moment, giving the briefest glimpse of the macabre ensemble of dancers surrounding Osyth as they reached towards her, then jerked back into their positions, whispering the two lines of the refrain. There was a gasp of horror from the audience before the lights were doused and a red spotlight picked out Oran. His ringmaster's outfit replaced with that of a dandy, he stalked across the big top, the lights picking up shadows of the assembled frozen figures of the troupe. He began creeping around Osyth, who pretended not to notice him.

Frederick, dressed in the same drab colours as the others, now appeared like a Greek chorus, twisting between Osyth and Oran, as they enacted an innocent courtship.

"The lure of his charm, the flash of his eyes,
She did not see the demon's snare.
Hand in hand, they ran away, dancing to the tune of love.
Except for her, it would lead to despair.
The Lunatics' Ball; The Lunatics' Ball,
Spinning in circles, forgotten by all."

In the shadows, the audience rustled uncomfortably, while the troupe moved to new positions. Once again, as the stanza

ended, the lights flashed up and they hissed the refrain. Osyth and Oran remained frozen in a tableau of innocent love, while the others rotated, whispering; their mannerisms exaggerated, their faces ranging from blank to contorted with insanity.

When the lights dropped, Frederick was alone in a spotlight, his tone sombre as he recited the next verse.

"The ring on her finger, her money in his grasp,
He locked her away. Fed with fear, she began to cry.
Opium trickled, drop by drop, into her innocence.
Then he locked her away and left her to die.
The Lunatics' Ball; The Lunatics' Ball,
Dizzy we spin, desperate we crawl."

Throughout this, Osyth and Oran continued to act out their tortured romance. First, Oran pulled a ring from his finger, making a great show of kneeling down and placing it on Osyth's. She beamed and patted his cheek, while the audience oohed. Then from within Osyth's bodice, Oran drew out pretend money and his charming smile changed to one of cruelty as Osyth began to back away from him. He held a small bottle aloft and there was another agonised gasp from the audience. Osyth tried to run away but he caught her, replacing the manacles and linking arms with Lela and Pipette, who had arrived dressed in gaudy finery. As Osyth began to scream and beg, Jeanne and Joe, dressed as gaolers, grabbed her arms and pulled her back.

This time, the audience gasped as one and a man was heard to shout, "No, someone save her!"

With a twirl, Frederick spun into the spotlight beside Osyth, winking as he began to stalk around her. He paused as he spoke, accentuating the lines.

"Poor little lost girl. All alone. Chains on her ankles,
Hands broken and bound. Nobody left to hear her call.

But every Monday night, as the toffs paid to watch,
The lost girl, the dead girl is allowed to dance at The Lunatics' Ball.
The Lunatics' Ball, The Lunatics' Ball,
Dancing forever at The Lunatics' Ball."

As he shouted the final line, he ripped the dress from Osyth to reveal her final, glittering costume. She pulled the scarf from her head to show off her magnificent hair and as the orchestra struck up a wild tune, the lights blazed, revealing the frozen forms of the other lunatics. Frederick took Osyth in his arms and with a manic laugh, they began to waltz. As Osyth and Frederick passed each pair of lunatics, they pulled the drab costumes from them, revealing the glitter and sparkle of their costumes, and each couple swirled after them, until the whole big top was a blur of colour and noise.

Osyth threw back her head and laughed, safe in Frederick's arms, the beat of the music pulsing through her. The thud of the feet around her was like a heartbeat, leading her deeper and further into the shimmering, sparkling mirage of the circus — the lunatics' ball, the entrance to Tylwyth Teg, the land of fairies with their duplicitous natures and their quicksilver moods.

Frederick's breath was on her neck as he pulled her close before they twisted together and he lifted her high, her arms outstretched as they spun and spun at the centre of the dancers. The feeling of him, this close to her, this unexpected sense of belonging, and knowing they had outwitted Kieran and that she and Annie were safe and, soon, she would meet her mother, caused Osyth to throw her head back and laugh with sheer joy.

CHAPTER SIX

Leaving the circus in a rush of fear and adrenalin, Osyth and Frederick travelled with Blaise and Katherine to the house they had rented in Interlaken, the closest town to her parents' home.

"Water always soothed Eudora," Blaise explained, "so my parents tried to find somewhere near the lakes as Switzerland has no coastline. Unfortunately, Eudora's home doesn't have a view of the water but she's close enough to be taken there for visits."

That evening, Osyth and Frederick exchanged uneasy glances across the dining room table. To be dressed in clothing from their old world, in the time before the circus, to be eating a formal dinner, felt strange. Where once this was expected, the past few months had shown them both a new way to live.

"We have had responses to the telegrams I sent the family to ensure them of your safety," said Blaise as the final course of fruit and cheese was served. "My father sends you his love and promises Nain is recovering, her health boosted even further to hear you are now with us."

"How about your family, Frederick?" asked Katherine. "Are they concerned about your absence?"

"No, I wrote to them from Paris, explaining I had been allowed some time to travel abroad to expand my knowledge of the business. They would not have understood or condoned what we had done. I was concerned they would report us to the police or, at the very least, to Kieran."

There was a silence as Kieran's name hovered in the air like a bad spirit they had conjured. Osyth sipped from her wine glass,

trying to push her cousin from her mind, focusing instead on the question that had been burning in her heart for weeks. "My mother," she said into the thickening silence, her voice tinged with nerves. "Aunt Xenia promised you would tell me the truth. She assured me Nain and Taid had asked you to be the one to explain." Osyth stared at Blaise as he swirled the brandy in his glass, as though steeling himself to the weight of this task.

"Yes, my darling, I have agreed to tell you the tale and it seems proper and correct as we face this unexpected maelstrom. Let us depart this table, settle on the chairs on the balcony and together, we will explore the past."

Blaise rose, offering his arm to Osyth. Frederick had followed suit with Katherine and the four walked on to the wide balcony overlooking the beautifully tended garden with its splashing fountains offering soothing background music.

"It's not quite our veranda overlooking the ocean," sighed Blaise as they sat, expectant, "but this was the best I could manage."

Osyth heard the sadness in his voice and for a moment, the impulse to stop him ran through her, to remain in the blissful ignorance of her childhood, to hide forever behind her grandparents but, even as these thoughts scurried through her mind, she dismissed them. The enormity of all she had experienced in the past months had changed her forever, drawing her into adulthood and all its difficult confusions. This final chapter in her story was necessary if she hoped to understand.

She sought Frederick's hand. He squeezed hers reassuringly and, drawing comfort from his strength, she turned her attention to Blaise. He smiled at her as he took the storyteller's seat, while she sat with her catcher of dreams about to receive

the answer to the question that had been in heart since childhood: *Why did my mother leave me?*

Blaise began to speak: "The child, a daughter, did not ask to be born. Cradled in the arms of her young mother, her eyes, the deep green of polished emerald, were wise, belonging to an older soul, a life already lived. Observing her mother, Eudora, the second born child of Penny and Daniel, as she danced in the niveous haze of the autumn moon, the child chose survival.

"A creature of the night, roaming the beach, the rocks, the woods caressed by starlight, Eudora was loved and loveable, with her sunshine smile and her rainbow laughter. Rarely contained, she danced and sang through her childhood, her smile entrancing those who crossed her path. It was with her teenage years, the shadows began to gather at her shoulders, beckoning to the spectral form of death who dogged her footsteps, changing her smile from joy to cruelty in the space of a breath, thrilling her as she chose to destroy the golden warmth of love.

"Married on an impulse when she had been transported across to Ireland on a ship with her father, the baby was a surprise to all, including Eudora and her husband, Egan. He was a man blinded by the beauty and strangeness of his young bride, obsessed with her laughter, entranced by her changing moods. Eudora said the baby came from Tylwyth Teg, a beautiful fairy child, full of promise, love and starlight. Egan believed her every word.

"The house on the cliff surrounded Eudora and her daughter, Osyth, with love. Her husband was welcomed into the family but the darkness in Eudora's soul was leaking into her heart and it was not long before her dance of love turned to one of despair. The child, silent, wary of the gathering cloud,

reached for her grandmother instead of her mother, who watched with angry eyes.

"One storm-soaked night, when Osyth slept in her crib, a tiny movement in the darkness woke her from her star-strewn dreams. She looked up and saw the glowing blue eyes of her mother staring through the gloom. Her skin, pale, dusted with moonlight, was waxy in its perfection. The mane of red hair circled her, curling and bending into the night, crackling with a manic energy, begging to be gone, to be swallowed up by the adventure of the howling wind and the lashing rain.

"Eudora stared down at her child. The daughter who had barely cried, who had viewed the world through solemn eyes, questioning all and withholding her love until she was sure the family was really hers. The child stared back and for a moment Eudora faltered, reaching forward, her hand hovering above the silent infant, tracing her finger through the soft downy curls already clustering across the baby's head, down the silken cheek to the perfect rosebud mouth. Eudora's hand quivered, then she snatched it back. Her breathing was heavy as though her heart had stopped, air gasped in from the depths of the night filled her lungs. Her eyes glazed over with her selfish intention and once more she reached forward, ready to end the story before it had begun.

"Osyth, the silent child, stared into her mother's eyes, and for a brief moment their souls locked and the child felt the ancient pull of survival. Her mind clouded over, her mouth opened and she screamed, shattering the peace of the house. Eudora, the soft down pillow held above her daughter, stared down at the squalling creature. The shadows whispered in her ears, 'Do it, do it, then you will be free…' She took one final glance at her daughter and brought her hands down, the child squirming under the softest whisper of death…"

"My mother tried to kill me?" Osyth's voice was a hoarse whisper.

Blaise seemed to have aged in the telling of the tale, his skin was the colour of parchment in the candlelight. "We couldn't tell anyone the truth. If we had, Eudora would have been locked away, possibly hanged. Mother and Father arranged for Eudora to be taken to a special clinic abroad where she could be treated."

"And my father?"

"He was sent away with her," said Katherine, taking over from Blaise who was too consumed with misery to continue. "Your mother recovered enough to eventually be released to a private house, one bought by your grandparents, under the care of special nurses. Your father remains there too, and your grandparents support them financially. Your grandparents believed it was better that you grew up without the horror of this story hanging over you like a curse. I believe they planned to tell you soon, but Penny's illness caused them to delay their plans."

Osyth was frozen, her heart counting its beats. Of all the stories she had imagined about her parents, this was never the tale she had told herself.

"Do you still wish to see your mother, Osyth?" Blaise's voice crept towards her through the night.

"Yes," she whispered. "I must. I need to see, to know." Her green eyes locked with Blaise's blue and with great sorrow, he nodded. In her heart, Osyth heard the wind chime rattle a lament.

CHAPTER SEVEN

Looking up at the house, Osyth drew in a deep breath, trying to calm her pounding heart. It was bigger, cleaner, older than the one in her dreams. Painted shutters protected the front windows from the glare of the fierce midday sun. Drawn tightly shut they gave the impression of a slumbering home, one put to rest, left to its own devices. Only the pots of brilliant red flowers standing guard, freshly watered, indicated the house was inhabited.

The silence crowded in upon Osyth, oppressive in its desolation. She bit her lip, trying to stem the torrent of words, the screaming horror her new reality was forcing her to assimilate. Blaise and Katherine stood behind Osyth and Frederick. Raising her hand, Osyth lifted the heavy lion's head knocker and let it fall, the clang of its summons resonating. The circle had closed around her and she was in the hands of the fae.

The echoing of her knock faded to blistering silence. It had never occurred to Osyth that there would be no one here to greet her. She hesitated, wondering whether to knock again but then she heard the soft padding of footsteps as they made their way towards her. Osyth held her breath, her ears full of the wind chime as it screamed in her mind, begging her to flee while there was time.

The polished wood of the door swung backwards, revealing the shadowy hallway, cool and dark in comparison with the glare of the midday sun. Osyth felt the power of the fairy realm on her shoulders as her green eyes locked with a matching pair. For the first time in her memory, she was looking at her father.

They stared, neither able to move as their instinct introduced them. Then he was crying and opening his arms to her. She was powerless to resist. This was her father and, despite everything, she wanted to feel his arms around her.

"But how?" Egan gasped, his voice deep, rasping.

Blaise stepped forward, his hand outstretched. "Things have changed," he said, his voice firm. "Osyth has been told the truth. We have brought her here to discuss the past, as well as the future."

Egan seemed to shy away from the authority in Blaise's voice. Osyth narrowed her eyes, glancing from her father to her uncle. One a stranger, one she had known all her life, but she felt a confusing confliction of where her loyalty should lie.

"There are things we must discuss," continued Blaise, entering the house and beckoning for the others to follow. "I wish to see my sister."

Egan paled at these words, shutting the door with quiet deference as though trying not to wake a bad spirit. His every move appeared muted and Osyth found it hard to believe her mother had fallen in love with such a timid man. A woman appeared in the doorway and Osyth's breath caught in her throat until she noticed the nurse's uniform.

"This is Brigitte," said Egan, his eyes locking with those of the woman. "She attends to your mother when she is indisposed. I have visitors," he added to the woman unnecessarily, "my brother-in-law and," he paused as though unable to say the word, "my daughter, Osyth. We shall take tea in the garden. Would you please ask Hilde to send it out?"

Brigitte nodded, her eyes watching with unease as the group followed Egan through the silent house.

They sat in the shady garden, facing each other. Soft-scented bougainvillaea draped its petals and leaves around them,

protecting them from the glittering sun. Two women, one elderly, one younger arranged tea before disappearing, whispering to each other in German. Both shot inquisitive glances towards Osyth, but neither would catch her eye.

Katherine stepped into the breach, making small talk, pouring tea, passing the delicate pastries around while Osyth watched the man who was her father. There was a tremor in his hands, a downcast, exhausted air. His skin was lined with deep marks which scored his face like a map of pain. It was as he drew a black leather flask from his pocket and added a sizeable dash of a brown spirit to his drink, she realised the cause of his disintegration. *Had he sought refuge in alcohol because of her mother?*

"How is Penny?" she heard her father ask.

"Recovering," replied Blaise.

"And your father?"

"He is with her. Noah is running the boatyard. It's likely he will take over from father next year."

"Your eldest brother has always been good to me," Egan said, his tone obsequious.

"As have my parents."

"And who is this young man?" asked Egan, as the conversation lulled and he turned to Frederick, who had remained silent and stern-faced at Osyth's side.

"Frederick Meyrick," he said, extending his hand.

Egan shook it. "Yes, but who are you in connection with my daughter?"

The words fell strangely on Osyth's ears. "He is my friend, my soulmate," she replied, her voice challenging him, showing he had no claim on her, her life or her decisions.

"Your soulmate?" he smirked, leaning back and sipping his laced tea. "Did you know about this?" He directed the question towards Blaise and Katherine.

Osyth felt a sudden shiver and exchanged a bemused glance with Katherine.

"What are you talking about, Egan?" asked Blaise, not bothering to conceal his irritation.

"My daughter arrives with a young man in tow whom she claims is her soulmate," he repeated, relishing the words. "Does her husband know?"

The sun seemed to darken as all four exchanged a horrified look.

"Her husband?" queried Blaise.

"Yes, the young man who visited me a few days ago, distraught, looking for his missing bride."

Osyth reached for Frederick's hand but both he and Blaise were on their feet glowering at Egan. "What?" Osyth was also on her feet, her blood running cold. "Kieran is here?"

"He'll be back soon. He's gone to town, to ask about the circus."

Ice seemed to cascade through Osyth's heart.

Blaise was pulling Katherine to her feet. "You fool," he snarled at Egan, "Osyth is not married to that man. He is Katherine's brother and he has lost his mind thanks to opium."

"A family affair," said Egan. "Did Solomon give him the hash?"

In all her years at Cliffside, Osyth had never seen Blaise lose his temper but now he seemed to be emitting a violent energy as he reached towards her father. Frederick, too, was struggling to control his fury.

"No!" Osyth exclaimed, stepping between them. "We must leave before Kieran returns." She shivered in the sunshine

before fixing her father with a desperate gaze. "Where is my mother?"

"Yes, Egan, where is my sister?" Blaise's voice echoed her own.

Egan cringed, his green eyes dulling as tears sprang into them. "You must understand, it was not my fault, she is devious in her ways. She waits in the shadows, pouncing when she knows I am weakened by my own ill health…"

"What have you done to Eudora?" Blaise's lips were white with fury.

"Nothing," responded Egan, "she has gone. One night, she stole away…"

"Gone?" gasped Katherine. "When? Why didn't you tell anyone?"

"A few weeks ago," he murmured.

"He didn't want to lose his money," snapped Blaise. "With no Eudora here, there would be no reason for my parents to support this scoundrel."

"Where is she?" gasped Katherine.

Egan recovered himself and took another swig from his flask. "There was a note," he murmured.

Frederick moved before anyone could stop him, picking up Egan with his newfound strength and pinning him against the wall. "Tell us," he said and Egan's face paled in fear. "Where is Osyth's mother? Where has she gone?"

Rising his head, Egan met Frederick's eyes. "Home. My wife has gone home. You should have heard her, prowling the house, muttering to her shadows, 'I want my baby back'. It was pathetic."

Fury rose in Osyth at her father's words but before she could act Blaise and Katherine were hurrying her away. Egan's drunken shouts followed them towards the door. They were

eager to be gone before Kieran returned, but as Blaise wrenched open the door, Osyth hesitated.

"Kieran is capable of bad things," she whispered to Katherine. "Do you think he'll hurt my father if he discovers we were here?"

Katherine hovered beside Osyth, unsure whether to leave.

"Hurry," Frederick implored Osyth, taking her hand.

"But, my father," she said. "Kieran might hurt him."

Blaise turned a furious face to them. "We are leaving," he shouted, gripping Osyth by the arm. "My priorities are you and your mother. Your father chose his path, he is a grown man."

"Uncle Blaise, please," Osyth yelped, but he refused, dragging her out of the house and into their waiting carriage.

"Egan has taken more from this family than I can even bear to acknowledge, he must face his own mistakes this time." Osyth stared at him, white-faced, holding tight to Katherine's hand and, after a brief hesitation, Blaise relented. "Frederick, run back and see if you can persuade the idiot to accompany us."

When Frederick returned alone a few minutes later, Osyth admitted defeat. Her father, the man who had given her life, was a stranger. Her conscience was clear, she had tried to persuade him away from Kieran's malice and mania, but it was Egan's choice to remain in the house.

"If Eudora left some weeks ago, she could be anywhere," Blaise muttered as the carriage raced away from the tainted house. "We must telegram the others immediately to warn them. If Eudora arrives at Cliffside, we must be ready."

"Is my mother dangerous?" asked Osyth.

"No, my darling, but she is ill," replied Blaise, "and she must be protected."

314

PART NINE: WINDSOR, 2019

CHAPTER ONE

"A secret at home is like rocks under the tide and they had more secrets than the sea has tides," murmured Amelia as she pushed herself away from the dining room table where she had spread her research. These were secrets indeed.

Running her fingers over the pages of faded writing, she felt a thrill of excitement at these new discoveries. Osyth, Freddie and Angharad had taken refuge with a circus and Osyth had married a man twice her age in order to protect herself from Kieran. Amelia's mind was spinning at these unexpected twists. She wandered about, nervous, unsure, drawing to a halt in front of one the paintings she had discovered was by Blaise Attwater. It was an abstract image of vibrant red spirals, flecked with silver and white iridescent lights, shimmering creatures with wings and chains dancing through the twisting brushstrokes.

Staring at it, the images which had always been beyond her understanding began to shift as she realised this was a circus, the inside of a big top, captured perhaps when Osyth was performing her exhilarating dance about the asylum. Feeling the ridges and textures of the oil paints, Amelia examined the painting in intense detail, as though trying to climb inside the magical world. Circuses were not an entertainment she had ever liked, finding the clowns unnerving and the sad animals heart-breaking but the world created by Oran and Caius seemed unlike any circus she had even experienced. It had been a land of secrets, where those who had fallen off the grid could live in peace and find solace.

As she stepped back, taking in the painting as a whole, she gasped. She was baffled as to how she had never noticed it before. The many spirals were linked and drew the eye to a shadowy shape at the centre. It was a man, dark-skinned and emanating a golden glow, pulsing with power. Amelia stared, an unexpected lump in her throat: had this image been inspired by the ringmaster, Oran? The man who saved souls and had married the runaway Osyth in order to keep her safe?

Returning to the dining room table, Amelia flicked through the remaining pages in Osyth's journal, wondering what had happened next. Amelia did not doubt Oran's integrity and felt sure he would have made an annulment easy for Osyth's family to procure, but had Osyth and Freddie married? The lack of any further journals made her feel bereft.

Another thought wound its way around her mind — Eudora. No longer safely at the house in Switzerland, the wayward and, Amelia realised, extremely unwell woman, had fled into the night, determined to return to Cliffside to claim her baby. A baby who was now eighteen years old. The image of the grave in the wood, positioned beside the ancient stone circle floated before Amelia's eyes: *Eudora, loved and loveable, our changeling princess who went home to the fae. 1849–1884.*

Flicking back to the date written at the top of Osyth's final entry in the journal, Amelia's curiosity notched up another level — *August 1884.* Even with the slowest journey, Osyth, Freddie, Blaise and Katherine would have returned by September 1884, in time for Osyth's nineteenth birthday and, at some point, Eudora must have followed the call of the wind chime and gone home to Cliffside, to die.

Since her return to Windsor, Amelia had set about uncovering the family tree with a new determination but, despite her best efforts, gaps remained, and she did not

understand why. Frustrated, she had begun to delve into other resources around her, accepting a dinner invitation with Julian and Lily Lovegrove in order to question them on their local historical knowledge. After their three sons had scattered to their bedrooms, Amelia had told Julian and Lily all she had discovered.

Julian repeated the information that as far as he was aware the house had been handed to Amelia via several generations of mothers bequeathing it to their daughters. Lily had mentioned that the boats on the river had been sold in the 1930s to a family who she believed still owned them.

Amelia had contacted the historical society but they had only a few details of the boats, so instead she decided to take up residence in the local library, trying to research the boatyard, eager to know what had happened to the thriving business. Bob from the boats, whose surname she discovered was Chester, proved helpful. His sister, Anna, had traced the family tree and discovered they were descended from Solomon's middle daughter, Sarah, who had married into the Jacobs family.

"But," said Anna, when Amelia met her and Bob for a drink, "my knowledge is patchy because there aren't many records. A lot of what I know was written down by my mum and gran."

"Does this mean we're related?" Bob asked.

"We're distant cousins," Amelia replied.

"So, your little girl, Molly, she was family?"

To Amelia's astonishment, tears welled in Bob's eyes.

"Always had a soft spot for your daughter," he said. "Blood, you see, we recognise each other, even if we don't know why."

The following day, Amelia wandered to the cemetery to see her family and she found a vast wreath on Molly's grave, addressed to, "Our lost cousin, Molly," and signed from Bob

318

and the extensive Chester family. As Amelia stared down at the flowers, she felt as though her mother was smiling down at her.

"You did know what you were doing, didn't you, Mum?" she said.

Despite the new information Amelia had gleaned, the lack of online records continued to hamper her. From Edward, after one brief, terse phone call, there had been silence and Amelia, unsure whether he was angry, busy or indifferent, and feeling this was one layer of emotion too many at present, had worked hard to convince herself it did not matter and she was not upset by this cessation in communications. Instead, she furtively checked her phone every half an hour, pretending not to be disappointed when there was no message.

"I'm thinking of hiring a professional genealogist," she told Benji a few days later as they sprawled on the sofa at Maybank while Amelia continued scrolling through the census on her laptop. "Why is it that there are thousands of records but none seem to feature this huge family?"

Benji shared Amelia's bafflement. "Perhaps they moved and you're looking in the wrong place?"

"But they didn't move, they lived here."

"Would it help if I suggested you give it up?" asked Benji.

"Nope," Amelia replied. "New records are being added all the time, there might be something I missed the first time around."

Benji rolled his eyes. The doorbell rang and he leapt to his feet, delighted to have a reason to leave Amelia to her scrolling. "Are you expecting anyone?" he asked.

"No," she replied.

"Even if it's only the postman I might get more sense out of him than I'm getting from you," he said, marching towards the door.

Amelia grinned; she knew him too well to even begin to think he was irritated. He was the one who had suggested the new search this morning, although she was certain he was hoping he might be able to persuade her to turn her stories into a TV documentary. Ever since she had told him about the escape from the asylum and Osyth, Freddie and Angharad's sojourn with the circus he had been pushing her to finish the tale.

Benji's voice had dropped and Amelia could not hear who he was speaking to but there seemed to be more than one voice.

"Who is it?" she asked, putting her laptop aside and standing up but before she could reach the hallway, Edward was standing in the doorway to the living room, Caitlin leaning on his arm, her eyes moving restlessly around the room, as though she were trying to memorise it.

"I'll put the kettle on," trilled Benji, heading off to the kitchen, his eyes wide with questions.

"Edward!" Amelia exclaimed as he glowered at her, his dark eyes pinning her to the spot. "Where are the dogs?" she asked, unable to think of anything more coherent.

"With David and Kerry," he replied.

They stared at each other. She had forgotten his imposing height and build. When he was on the beach or striding around Cliffside, the backdrop of the rugged cliffs and the violent seas suited him but here, he seemed to overwhelm the space, a wild creature captured in a cage.

"They'll have a lovely time," beamed Caitlin. "Kerry spoils them rotten. Oh Amelia, this place is beautiful, far bigger than I'd imagined, and the stained glass in the door, is it original?"

"Yes, as far as I know," Amelia replied, ushering Caitlin into the living room. Caitlin began examining the family photographs on the mantelpiece. Edward continued to block the doorway.

"Why are you here?" Amelia whispered to him.

"Caitlin wanted to speak to you," came his abrupt reply. "I said I'd drive her here."

There was such coldness in his voice, Amelia felt as though she had been slapped and she took a step backwards. Benji arrived with the tray and Amelia used this as an excuse to get away from Edward. Ensuring her back was to him, she left Benji to offer him a seat. Caitlin settled herself into Joan's golden wing-backed armchair, looking thoroughly at home.

"My dear, don't be angry with Eddie," said Caitlin. "It's my fault. I should have told you the family story while you were at Cliffside. It was only when you fled, I realised what a silly old woman I'd been."

"You aren't a silly old woman," said Amelia, handing her a teacup.

"I have been," sighed Caitlin, then she glanced at Edward. "He's sulking," she whispered, as though he might not be able to hear.

Amused, Benji leaned forward and whispered back, "Why?"

Caitlin turned to him with a smile and said in a stage whisper, "Because I told him off on the way here. He needs to apologise to Amelia and he refuses."

"We are both in the room," snapped Edward but Amelia was fighting not to laugh.

"How about I start," Amelia said. "Edward, I apologise for fleeing at dawn, it was a cowardly thing to do. I also apologise for removing the journal without your permission, it is your property and wasn't mine to appropriate."

Edward looked at her with narrowed eyes before replying, "Thank you for the apology about the journal, although I never doubted you'd return it. Yes, it was cowardly of you to flee," he continued, before adding, "I'm sorry too, that whatever it was about, you couldn't speak to me."

"The problem was mine," admitted Amelia. "It was something I needed to work out."

"And have you?"

"Not yet…"

"Which is where I might be able to help," interrupted Caitlin. She placed her teacup on the table beside her and turned her blue eyes to Amelia. "It's time I was honest with you, my dear."

"About what?"

"Who I am and who you are."

A chill ran down Amelia's spine. "What do you mean?" she asked.

Caitlin took a deep breath. "Osyth and Freddie were my great-grandparents."

"What?" gasped Amelia. "On thank goodness, they did get married. Oran Walters must have annulled the marriage as he promised."

Amelia explained all she had learned from the journal Caitlin had loaned her. Taking Caitlin by the arm, she led her to the dining room where Blaise's abstract painting hung and pointed to the image at the centre. "I think this might be Oran," she said.

Caitlin and Edward gazed at the shimmering picture.

"Their marriage must have been annulled," said Caitlin, when they had returned to the living room, "because I'm descended from Osyth's younger daughter, Alice, while I

believe you are descended from her elder daughter, Marina. Their surname was Meyrick, not Walters."

"How do you know this?"

"My mother, Aurelia, told me some of it but I also have a great deal of paperwork to do with the family — marriage, birth and death certificates, deeds, letters…"

"But I can't find anything online," interrupted Amelia. "There are gaps everywhere."

"It's because the family was Jewish," said Caitlin, "and many of the records from synagogues are missing from these new ancestor websites."

"Jewish?" exclaimed Amelia. "How? We're not Jewish. I was baptised at the church up the road which is Church of England."

"There's no clear reason why the family's faith changed," admitted Caitlin. "There are no written records that I've found to explain it but it's the reason you haven't been able to trace the last part of your family tree."

Amelia stared at Caitlin, excited by this unexpected discovery.

"The turn of the century was a time of huge social change," said Benji. "Attitudes towards religion changed enormously and there was a movement towards the advancement of Liberal Judaism, perhaps that was when they changed faiths, many families did around then."

Amelia stared at him in surprise.

"We've been working on a documentary," he explained. "There was far less anti-Semitism towards the end of Queen Victoria's reign than was assumed. Perhaps, if as you said, the family wasn't driven by religion, it slipped away over subsequent generations."

Caitlin had hung on Benji's every word. "Fascinating," she said. "My mother always spoke about our Jewish ancestry but she was vague on the whys and wherefores."

"What about your grandmother?" asked Benji and Amelia could tell he was thoroughly enjoying himself, almost framing shots in his mind as he spoke to Caitlin. "Did she ever discuss family issues?"

"My grandmother, Alice, was a difficult woman," Caitlin sighed. "Depression haunted her throughout her life."

Amelia and Edward exchanged a glance.

"It was due to her illness that the family fractured," Caitlin continued. "When they were in their twenties, she argued with her sister, Marina. My grandmother refused to explain what had happened, probably nothing important in the greater scheme of life, but she refused to speak to her sister again. Eventually, my mother, Aurelia, lost touch with her cousins, Rose and Joseph. The two families grew apart and the extended family scattered to the winds."

"How awful," exclaimed Amelia.

"It was," agreed Caitlin. "You're descended from Rose, Marina's daughter. Her brother, Joseph, never married, but she married Edward Tunley, who was your great-grandfather."

"I found them online," said Amelia.

"The inheritance had been passed to Osyth when her grandparents died and then Cliffside was passed on to Alice, while Maybank was given to Marina," finished Caitlin.

"What about the rest of the family?" asked Benji. "Those were the two biggest assets, why did they both go to Osyth?"

"Her grandparents wanted to ensure she was financially secure because Freddie had no fortune of his own," said Caitlin. "Noah inherited the boatyard and, I believe from the paperwork, bought out Katherine who inherited her father's

and brother's interests. Solomon had his magazine and publishing company; Blaise had his art and Xenia was married to very wealthy businessman. The needs of their granddaughter seemed to have taken precedent over the other family members."

As the consequences of Caitlin's words began to permeate Amelia's brain, realisation began to dawn. "So, you're my cousin?"

"Second cousin once removed or maybe twice removed," said Caitlin. "Something like that, but we are related, my dear. You are one of the family and that is why you were drawn home to Cliffside. Your mother must have left the photographs so you would be able to discover you aren't alone in the world."

A lump formed in Amelia's throat. Edward had been silent throughout this exchange but as she looked up, his eyes burned into hers.

"Are *we* cousins?" she asked.

"Distantly," he replied. "I think."

"Those DNA tests you made us all take should prove it beyond all doubt," beamed Caitlin. "Welcome home, Amelia." Rising from the chair, she opened her arms wide and Amelia stood, walking into the older woman's embrace. Tears were in both their eyes.

"What DNA tests?" asked Benji.

"When Edward and I first began comparing notes, the three of us did a DNA test on one of the ancestry websites. I'd forgotten all about it," admitted Amelia.

"I had an email a few days ago saying my results were available," said Edward.

"Oh, let's look," said Benji jumping up and rushing over to grab Amelia's laptop.

Amelia flicked through the results, checking Caitlin's markers which showed a blood link but when Edward pulled his up, something was awry. Amelia, Benji and Edward stared in silence.

"How is that possible?" Edward asked. "There are no connections at all." His voice sounded hollow, confused.

"Let's check again," said Amelia, running her eye down the results, but there was nothing. No blood link to either her or Caitlin.

"There must be a mistake. Edward is descended from Kieran and Angharad's son, Henry," said Caitlin. All eyes turned towards her and she smiled. "Very sadly, Angharad died giving birth but Katherine and Blaise adopted Henry as they were unable to have children of their own."

"What happened to Kieran?" asked Benji.

"I am unsure," Caitlin replied. "He was rarely mentioned while I was growing up." She turned to Amelia. "The wind chime drew you home. We all come back in the end."

"But there is no wind chime at Cliffside," Amelia exclaimed, unable to help herself. "Kerry let me see the veranda and there's nothing there. Does it hang somewhere else? A place I didn't discover?"

Edward, who had been scrolling through the DNA results, let out a sigh. "The sound of the wind chime is a hallucination brought about by grief," he said. "It's a common reaction to traumatic loss. As for you, Auntie, I think you hear it because you have tinnitus and you interpret it as the wind chime."

Caitlin made an impatient noise, while Amelia stared at him, curious as to this logical explanation of the noise that had been haunting her. Yet, she found it difficult to believe there could be such a mundane dismissal of the magical tunes which had made her feel connected to Cliffside and Osyth Attwater.

"Edward, that is nonsense," replied Caitlin, "we hear the wind chime because it's in our blood. As for your DNA test, I think we should repeat it, there is obviously a mistake."

Edward did not respond and a heavy silence settled over the room.

"Where are you staying?" asked Amelia, trying to emulate the hospitality her mother used to exude with ease.

"We're going to book into a hotel," replied Edward.

"No, stay here," said Amelia, not wanting either of them to leave but feeling especially wretched at the idea of him disappearing. "I have plenty of room and you'd like that, wouldn't you, Caitlin?"

"It would be delightful," Caitlin enthused, then threw a look at Edward of huge smugness. "I told you Amelia would invite us to stay."

CHAPTER TWO

After a brief rest, Caitlin insisted on a tour of Windsor. Having ascertained Caitlin would be well looked after, Edward excused himself, saying he had an appointment he could not avoid and he drove off with barely a goodbye to Amelia.

Upon returning to Maybank, Amelia settled Caitlin in the largest bedroom, thinking she would enjoy the views of the garden. Half an hour later, Edward returned and after a brief hello, he hurried upstairs to see his aunt. Irritated at his dismissiveness and under the guise of giving Caitlin more towels, Amelia wandered after him, standing on the landing outside Caitlin's door, which was ajar, and listening.

"She apologised," said Edward, his voice sounding lighter and happier than it had been throughout their visit so far.

"Did you make it up with Ella?" asked Caitlin.

"Enough," he responded. "It was worth it; we can move forward now and hopefully put this episode behind us."

"When will you tell Amelia?"

"As soon as I can…"

Amelia felt sick. She heard Edward's footsteps coming towards the door and she rushed into her own bedroom, not wanting to be caught eavesdropping. Sagging on to the bed, her heart pounding, she felt numbness spreading through her. Had she read the situation incorrectly? In her mind, she and Edward had been moving towards — what? A relationship? Was her radar so off that she had mistaken his friendship for something it had never been? From what she had overheard, it seemed Edward's plan was to win back his former girlfriend.

"You fool," she whispered to her reflection. "It was all in your imagination. Focus on Caitlin and nothing else."

A takeaway provided by Louise and Richie led to a lively evening with Benji bringing Patrick's old cine camera and various DVDs of the family downstairs for a film show, including footage of Amelia as a child and Molly. By the end, Caitlin had agreed to Benji's request to be interviewed for his documentary on Jewish heritage.

"What?" Benji exclaimed when Amelia cornered him in the kitchen. "All I did was mention in passing how interesting a documentary would be and Caitlin leapt at the chance. You know what I say, Aimes, everyone wants to be on television."

Throughout the evening, Amelia was aware of Edward watching her. Once Louise and Richie had arrived, his natural manners had chased away his sullen expression but when he tried to speak to her alone, she avoided him, hiding behind her duties as hostess. When her friends left, Edward helped Caitlin up to her bedroom, and Amelia relished the silence and the chance to allow her despair an outlet. She took solace in the mundane actions of methodically loading the dishwasher, allowing her mind to unwind from the unexpected day and her overnight guests. Flicking on the kettle, she made a cup of tea and carried the mug into the dining room where she had placed the photographs in rows.

"Hello." Edward stood in the doorway, his hands behind his back.

"Hello," she replied.

"Do you mind if I join you?"

Amelia forced a smile, wondering if he was about to impart his happy news. "Not at all."

He pulled out the chair beside her and stared at the images, then to her surprise, tears welled up in his eyes. "Aimes, I'm so sorry," he said, placing his hand over hers. "Whatever happened, I wish you'd come to me. I thought we were friends. Was it because of Melissa?"

"We *are* friends," Amelia replied. "The Melissa thing did unnerve me a bit. I was shocked at her lack of professionalism."

"Her appointment was a mistake from the beginning. A friend asked if I would give her a chance and I agreed." There was something odd in his tone as he said the word 'friend'.

"Who asked you?"

"Ella."

"Your girlfriend?" Amelia tried and failed to hide the astonishment in her voice.

Edward looked at her curiously. "*Ex*-girlfriend, and, as I said, it was a mistake. Ella and Melissa had been at university together. Unfortunately, a week after Melissa arrived, Ella accused us of having an affair and stormed out. Melissa seemed to take this as being given carte blanche to pursue me. It was embarrassing."

Sickened at the thought, Amelia managed to croak, "What did she do?"

"Really crass stuff like knocking on my door at night wearing a see-through nightdress."

Amelia had taken a mouthful of tea and inhaled, choking as she tried not to laugh. "Seriously, do people do that in real life?"

"Apparently so," he replied. "It was such a relief to see you that day at the raising of the wreck — she was driving me insane with all her constant touching of my arm and calling me 'babe'. You were like a lifebelt in a storm."

"Happy to help," she murmured.

"When you fled from Cliffside, I wondered if it was because of her behaviour, that you felt betrayed?"

"No, it wasn't Melissa," Amelia said. "When I look back, I realise my behaviour was foolish. During my visit to the library in Aberystwyth, I discovered that Osyth married Oran Walters. We know why now but it made me feel foolish, trying to attach myself to the Attwaters, when really I had no claim on them at all."

A look of relief passed over Edward's face. "Thank goodness," he said. "The thought of you not being at Cliffside was like winter arriving in July. A horrible, cold shock." He handed her a brown paper package. "I must also apologise for abandoning you without a proper explanation earlier, but it was important." Amelia stared at the package between them. "When you arrived at Cliffside, do you remember that I accused you of stealing the photograph from our private collection?"

"It's something I'm unlikely to forget," she murmured. "You were very intimidating."

He hung his head. "Ella had taken some family items and I was furious. Today, I visited her to reclaim our possessions. Caitlin and I have decided that we'd like you to have these, our gift to you." He indicated the package, his eyes expectant.

With trembling hands, Amelia unwrapped the paper and gasped in astonishment. A number of slim hardback books lay inside. The top was entitled *The Wind Chime* by Osyth Meyrick, and underneath were *The Lunatics' Ball* and *Circus Nights*.

"I believe they were a trilogy based on her adventures," he said as she turned them over in wonder. The remaining four books were volumes of poetry by Frederick Meyrick: *On Love*, *On Life*, *On Escape* and *On Joy*.

"Oh Edward, these are stunning, but I can't take them," she whispered.

"You can, they're a present for you." His voice was so gentle, so full of love that Amelia felt angry tears well in her eyes.

"What about you and Ella?" she asked, unable to keep quiet any longer.

"What about us?" he replied.

"I heard you say to Caitlin that you'd made it up. I came upstairs with towels and…"

To her surprise, Edward laughed. "Serve you right for eavesdropping," he said. "Yes, Ella and I have made things up. We're adults, we've decided to stop sniping at each other, but we haven't got back together."

"Really?"

"Really," he said. "I'm no longer interested in Ella and feel nothing for her but vague friendship. I would never hurt you, Aimes. You've become important to me, to us, even the dogs have been insisting we come and fetch you. Cliffside feels wrong without you."

Amelia could not speak for the lump in her throat. "Thank you, you've all become important to me," she managed. "Especially you, but it's a long time since I've thought about anything other than illness, death and grief."

He put his hand over hers. "Small steps?" he asked.

"Tiny," she replied and he smiled in acquiescence.

After a moment, she nodded towards the photographs. "Did you know?"

"About Caitlin being descended from Osyth?"

"Yes."

"Not until she insisted on coming to Clewer. After you left, she had another strange turn or we'd have been here sooner. I promised to bring her to see you when she was well enough to

travel, it was the thing that sustained her." He paused, running his fingers through his hair. "I don't want to add to your woes but Caitlin doesn't have long to live. She's in the final stages of acute kidney failure. She's had Type 1 diabetes since she was in her early thirties and it's taken its toll."

The familiar wave of despair rolled through Amelia as she faced another loss. Even though she had known Caitlin for such a short period, to discover they were related and to know she would once again be losing a family member reignited her grief. She grasped on to the positivity of having discovered Caitlin before it was too late, and put aside her own fears and pain to reach for Edward and offer her strength to him.

"I'm so sorry," she said, squeezing his hand. "You must be devastated."

"We've known for a while; the diagnosis was confirmed at the beginning of the year. It was what made her more determined to finish her family story. When you arrived with the photographs, she felt sure you'd been sent by Osyth so I wouldn't be alone after she was gone."

"How long does she have?"

"A few months at most."

At last Amelia understood the erratic moods from which Edward seemed to suffer. He was dealing with grief, too. While she was in recovery from her trauma and learning to rebuild her life, he was living on a knife-edge, waiting for the dark tunnel which would take Caitlin from him.

"Stay a few days," she said. "We can take Caitlin around Windsor, go on the boats, let her experience Maybank. This house is as much part of her history as it is mine."

"Thank you," he said, leaning over and resting his head on her shoulder in a gesture of release Amelia had not expected.

Stroking his hair, she leaned back towards him, their hair and hands tangled. "She'd love it."

"And you?"

"I would too." He wiped away a tear with the back of his hand. Looking at the photographs, his eyes lingered on the image of Osyth. "Did you ever discover what happened to Eudora?" he asked and she shook her head.

"The journal only has a few pages left and they're about Osyth's return to Cliffside. Perhaps we should stop and leave Eudora and Kieran in peace."

Edward considered this for a moment, then he picked up the photograph of the house, the image where Amelia's quest had begun, and gazed at Kieran's furious face. "No," he said. "We've come this far, let's tie up all the loose ends. It can be our present to Caitlin."

"But I've searched and searched," said Amelia, "there's no information anywhere."

"What about here?" Edward was pointing at the window where the child stood, glaring down.

"What do you mean?"

"He's either standing in a room or on a staircase," he replied. "The tower on that side of the house has always been blocked up. I'd assumed it was a false piece of architecture — a tower with no rooms, placed there to balance out the overall dimensions of the house — but what if it wasn't? What if it was a room and it was deliberately boarded up?"

"Would you be prepared to devastate your house?"

"For Caitlin, yes, I'd do it."

Amelia stared from the picture and back to Edward, excitement building in her. A grin unfurled across her face and she turned to him with shining eyes. "I'm in," she said.

CHAPTER THREE

Over the next few days, Amelia took huge pleasure in showing Caitlin her world. The familiar streets where she had grown up, the cottages which she now knew had once belonged to their shared ancestors, and they took endless trips on the boats. When Amelia explained to Caitlin that Bob and Anna were descended from Solomon's daughter, Sarah, she had asked to meet them. A long discussion had ensued to try and trace any other cousins or family members and the women had exchanged phone numbers. Having grown up thinking she was alone in the world, Amelia was having difficulty adjusting to the possibility that she might have any number of cousins waiting in the wings. The idea was as unnerving as it was exhilarating.

Her friends insisted on visiting the evening before Amelia planned to return to Cliffside.

"When will you be home?" asked Louise. "Will you be here for the birth?"

"Yes, no matter what," Amelia promised, "but now I've found her, I want to spend as much time as possible with Caitlin. Edward will need my support too."

"And you'll need his," Louise replied. "Look after each other as well as Caitlin. Before you go Aimes, I need to give you this." She handed Amelia a gift bag.

"It isn't my birthday for a few weeks," Amelia said.

"Your mum gave me this before she died and asked me to give it to you when the moment was right. I'd planned to keep if for your birthday but this seems more appropriate."

"Oh Lou," was all Amelia managed as the two friends hugged.

Later that night, alone in her bedroom Amelia opened the final gift from her mother and again the strangeness of her quest wrapped itself around her. Beautifully wrapped was a bottle of Floris White Rose perfume, with a handwritten note from Joan.

My darling, I gave you your first bottle of this scent when you were 16 years old. It felt right to reintroduce you to what was once your favourite fragrance. All my love, Mum xxx

Amelia stared at the bottle in wonder. Her mother was correct, this had been her signature scent for years but then new fashionable brands had captured her and she had forgotten this delicate, feminine fragrance. Spraying it on her wrists, she breathed it in, transported back to her teenage years, to her early twenties, then a wave of emotion overwhelmed her and an image of Osyth shimmered in her mind. What else was she going to discover about this vast family of which she was a member? Where would this quest take her next?

With Maybank locked up, Amelia led the way on the road back to Pembrokeshire. When she pulled into the car park and saw the imposing, turret-strewn house her heart leapt. Maybank might be her house but Cliffside felt like her home. The dancing tune of the wind chime that immediately engulfed her was a comfort and, despite what Edward said, she did not believe it was a hallucination of her grief. As Caitlin had said, it was in their blood.

Upon returning to her tower room, it had surprised her how homely it felt, more so than her old bedroom at Maybank.

Drifting off to sleep with the sound of the waves and the gentle wind chime, she had fallen asleep with a contented smile on her face.

"Are you sure about this?" she asked the following day as she and Edward surveyed the turret where Kieran had glared at the world through troubled eyes.

"Yes," Edward said. "Caitlin and I discussed it on the journey home and she was very excited at the prospect there might be a hidden room up here."

"How is she this morning?"

"Tired. She's decided to stay in bed. Nero and Lara are keeping her company. Her doctor will be here later."

Neither of them said what they were both thinking, that Caitlin had seemed vague again when they had arrived back at Cliffside.

"Benji wants to make a documentary about our family," Amelia said and when Edward pulled a face expressing his distaste at the idea, she continued, "Caitlin has already agreed to take part in Benji's film about Jewish ancestry, why don't we allow her to be the star of a programme of her own?"

"Would she be well enough?"

"We'd only agree if her health could cope," Amelia assured him. "Benji would make it as simple as possible."

"If you think Caitlin might like to do the documentary, then let's ask her. It can be her decision. If she agrees, my cooperation will be wholehearted. Now, let's get started."

"Are you sure this isn't a load-bearing wall?" Amelia asked, gazing at the ceiling, concern in her voice as they laid out the dustsheet.

"No, Geraint, an architect friend, checked it a few years ago when a small crack appeared. He explained it looked as though

someone had blocked up a doorway which means we should be able to get through it easily."

Amelia's apprehensive stare made him grin again.

"Stand back," he commanded.

Amelia backed away a few steps and watched as Edward ran his fingers across the plaster, his dark hair swept back and his even darker eyes intent on his task. The sun had given his skin a burnished glow which made him look as though he had Mediterranean blood.

If I met him on holiday in Greece, I'd think he was local, she thought.

He turned and smiled, a glint in his eye which made her stomach flip. "Geraint was right, I can feel the edges of a door frame."

Working with caution, they began to pick away at the ancient plaster, their progress slow but dogged until with a final shove from them both, the wall collapsed in a shower of dust and plaster. As the cloud cleared, it revealed the continuation of the corridor, which led to a staircase identical to the one in Amelia's tower.

"Wow," said Edward.

Amelia clicked on her torch. "Come on."

Creeping down the cobweb-strewn corridor, Amelia felt as though they had gone back in time. Gas lamps were positioned at various intervals along the walls and a strip of thick, red carpet that emitted clouds of dust at each footstep wound its way towards the staircase. At the foot of the stairs, she shone the beam of her torch up into the cold air.

"Do you think the stairs are safe?" asked Edward, his dark eyes wary in the yellow light.

"Only one way to find out," she replied and, with a hint of trepidation, stood on the first stair. It creaked but felt firm.

"I should go up first," said Edward.

"Why? I'm lighter. If the stairs are damaged, it would be better not to place them under undue stress."

"True, but it's my house, so the risk is mine."

Amelia rolled her eyes. "Seriously?"

Edward gave a rueful smile, then taking hold of the banister, he shook it hard. Nothing moved.

"After that scientific test, can we go up now?" asked Amelia.

"Yes," he said, "but I'm going first…"

"OK, because it's your house."

Stepping aside, she allowed him to pass. With each step she felt they were creeping towards the heart of things. As Osyth had lost herself in the world of fairy tales, traversing the winding lanes of her magical adventures, they were lost in the story Osyth had created. Swallowing her unexpected rush of nerves at this thought, Amelia followed Edward into the shadows; tensed for the possibility of the staircase collapsing underneath them.

"There's a door," called Edward. "Oh! It's bloody locked."

Reaching into her pocket, Amelia extracted a key and passed it to him.

"Where did you get this?" he asked in confusion.

"When I first got here I was examining the bookcases and I found a book of fairy tales by George MacDonald, a Victorian writer. Next to it were hardback copies of his most famous works, *The Princess and The Goblin* and its sequel, *The Princess and Curdie*. My mum used to read them to me and I read them to Molly. Osyth mentions them in her journal, too. When I opened the second one, this was hidden among the pages. A section had been cut out and the key slotted inside, so the book remained flush when it was closed. The name written in the frontispiece was 'Osyth Attwater' and, this morning, I

picked up the key on my way to meet you. It was as though it called to me, as though we might need it. And, I reasoned, if we didn't then I'd replace it and no harm done."

Placing the key in Edward's outstretched palm, she could see he was unnerved. When the key slotted neatly into the lock and turned, his face paled.

"Edward," she said, grabbing his arm to stop him opening the door, "remember, there might not be anything inside other than abandoned furniture or even an empty room."

"I know," he replied, "but whether we're able to find the answers to finish the story for Caitlin or whether we find several hundred years of cobwebs, it's time this tower was reunited with the rest of the house." Taking her hand, he continued, "Let's do this together."

Amelia smiled. Edward opened the door and they peered inside.

"Oh!" exclaimed Amelia as the beams of their torches flashed around the room.

The dimensions were the same as her tower on the opposite corner of the house but whereas her suite was bright and full of modern conveniences after years of life and renovations, this bedroom was a perfect Victorian time capsule. It was as though the owner had simply walked away, locking the door, never to return. The neatness was marred only by two paintings, wrapped in oilcloth which leaned against the wall and a leather trunk which stood beside it. Wooden boards blocked the windows, giving the room a shadowy, other-worldly feel.

On one side was a four-poster bed, its blue curtains thick with dust, the horsehair mattress and flat-looking pillows covered with a dark blue counterpane. A washstand with a china jug and bowl stood beside it, while on the bedside table

was a gas lamp and a copy of Charles Darwin's *On the Origin of Species*, with a bookmark positioned halfway. The walls were covered with specimen cases containing the skeletal remains of small mammals — bats, mice, voles — and a variety of butterflies, moths and insects.

A writing desk stood to one side and Edward began searching through the pile of notebooks. He flipped through the most dog-eared, shining his torch on to the neat, utilitarian letters. When he looked up, his face was pale. "This was Kieran's room," he said. "This paperwork is all his and this notebook contains his recipes for the tinctures and drugs he brewed. If he used such strong doses of opium, it was no wonder he was addicted and lost his mind."

Amelia felt revulsion as she imagined the teenage Kieran alone in his bedroom creating the bizarre collection of dead creatures adorning the walls, his heart beating with fury at the family below. Edward held the notebook out to her and she shuddered when she read the balance of his homemade medications. "It's amazing Osyth survived without developing an addiction herself," she said, turning the pages with care.

"And Angharad, if he'd been drugging her too."

Handing the book to Edward, Amelia approached the paintings and the trunk. "Do you mind?" she asked, bending down.

"Go ahead," he murmured, his torch searching the room, lighting it a section at a time.

Placing her own torch on the smooth top of the leather travelling trunk, she lifted away the oilcloth and gasped. The blue eyes, high cheekbones and tumbling red curls were familiar. The plaque at the bottom read *Eudora Attwater, 1865*, confirming what Amelia had known in her heart. This was Osyth's mother, the woman who had torn her family apart

with her terrible mental afflictions. Amelia had long since suspected Eudora's symptoms were schizophrenia and she knew the treatment of this debilitating illness would have been misunderstood in the Victorian era.

"It's Eudora," she said, as she flooded the portrait with light: the loved and loveable Eudora, the woman who was buried in the stone circle but whose death was missing from official records. "Osyth describes the portrait in her journal. This was painted when her mother was sixteen. It must have been around the time Osyth was born."

Edward joined her and they stared across time at the young woman, her life before her, or so she thought, yet within a year of this portrait being painted, her illness had wrenched her from her family. Sadness welled up in Amelia as she stared into the familiar blue eyes. They were identical to those of her mother, Joan.

"We should take it down and show it to Caitlin," said Edward. "Who's in the second one?"

This was smaller, a black-framed oval, and when Edward turned it around for them to see, they both gasped. A young man gazed at them, his dark eyes solemn, his high cheekbones sharp in his pale face. His mouth was generous and had he smiled, his face would have been handsome but there was a pinched quality to his expression, an anger.

"Kieran," said Edward. The plaque on the bottom said 1883.

They stared at the young man who, like his cousin, Eudora, would wreak such torment on his family. Standing the portrait to one side, Edward opened the leather trunk and together they sifted through the contents. Amelia lifted out a tissue-wrapped dress, carefully folded but marred by age. With great care, she laid it on the bed and smoothed back the fabric

wondering if she could smell a hint of White Rose perfume or whether it was her own.

"This is the dress Osyth describes in her journal," she said. "Her first proper evening gown. I wonder if it could be restored…"

"You might want to see this, too," Edward interrupted. He was still leaning over the trunk.

"What?"

"Another journal, a pile of letters and this…" He held up a wooden box. Joining Amelia beside the bed, he slid back the lid.

"The wind chime," gasped Amelia. "Do you think this is the one Osyth wrote about?" With great care, she lifted it from the padded box where it had been hidden for over a century. The enamelled sun glowed again as she wiped away the dust, but the chimes were tarnished and the shells cracked and dirty. The strings holding it together were knotted and broken, but in her heart, the chimes sang and Amelia felt a smile lighting up her face. "It is hers; this is the one."

"Let's take it all downstairs to show Caitlin," Edward said, replacing it in the box and closing the lid. He picked up the portraits, while Amelia draped the dress over her arm, before gathering together the leather-bound journal and the letters.

Following him into the corridor, she said, "Perhaps we will finally discover what happened."

PART TEN: PEMBROKESHIRE, 1884

CHAPTER ONE

The return journey to Pembrokeshire was shorter and more desperate than Osyth's escape through the night with Angharad and Frederick. When they returned to Blaise and Katherine's rented house in Interlaken, he took charge, showing an efficiency Osyth had never imagined her usually equable uncle to possess. Telegrams were sent and tickets bought. Hours later, the four of them were heading across the border into France and on a train to transport them home. As they sped across the Continent, the depth of Kieran's madness in his pursuit of Osyth presented itself when her travel documents were scrutinised with great diligence by the guard on the train.

"Is there a problem?" Blaise asked.

An uneasy silence descended.

"My apologies, sir," the guard said, taking the badly drawn sketch of Osyth from his pocket, staring at her with great intent. "We are searching for a young woman who has been kidnapped. Her husband, a respected doctor from London, believes she is in France. This young lady —"

"— is my niece," Blaise interrupted. "Mrs Walters. She travels under my and my wife's protection, as we accompany her to the bedside of her ailing grandmother."

To Osyth's surprise Blaise produced her marriage certificate and a letter from Oran giving permission for his young wife to travel with her family. Backing down, the guard left their carriage with a flurry of apologies but it was not until they arrived in Dover that Osyth felt truly safe.

After their arrival back at Cliffside, the family gathered together. Noah and his wife Hannah had arrived with information, which Noah declared would resolve their problems. Penny continued to struggle with her illness and Osyth retired to her grandmother's bedroom to look after her.

Guilt seeped through Osyth as she sat by Penny's bedside, and she wondered, for the hundredth time, how she could not have known intuitively of the severity of Penny's illness. She berated herself for her selfish flight, for the pain she had inflicted with her childish behaviour. Penny had cared for her, cherished her, protected her, but she had chosen to reject this love in favour of Kieran's twisted lies. A movement from the bed caught her attention.

"Hello, my dear," sighed Penny, her voice approaching its usual strength and bell-like clarity. "Is there any news?"

"Uncle Noah is with Taid," Osyth replied, "but there has been no word yet about my mother or Kieran." Even saying his name caused her anguish.

"Taid will find them both," Penny reassured Osyth. "We found you and Angharad. We shall not fail Eudora or Kieran."

Osyth reached for Penny's hand. "Uncle Noah said I was to fetch him when you were awake and feeling well enough to hear his news. He says he has discovered information that will keep me safe from Kieran."

Penny's face brightened. "Clever Noah," she said, pride in her eldest child apparent in her tone. "Help me to tidy myself, Osyth, then run down to fetch them."

Half an hour later, with Penny comfortably reclining on a mound of silken pillows, her exquisite robe draped around her and with hot tea supplied by Mary, Osyth ran down the stairs to fetch the others. The rumble of male voices from the study caused her to pause. She heard her uncle's voice.

"Should we inform Mother?" asked Noah. "It would be better if she was prepared for the possibility."

"Come in, Osyth," called Daniel, who had glimpsed her reflection in the mirror above the fireplace. "How is Nain?"

"Awake; demanding Uncle Noah and his news, as am I."

The air was thick with pipe and cigar smoke. Despite Daniel's smile, there was a tension in the room.

"Has something happened?" Osyth asked.

"Not since yesterday," replied Noah.

Seated beside one another on a loveseat were Xenia and William. Upon seeing Osyth, her aunt's face broke into a smile. "Shall we adjourn to Mother's bedroom?" said Xenia, who was already standing, her question more of a command.

Solomon held out his arm and Osyth took it, smiling. Ever since the revelation of his desire for opium, Osyth had envisaged her uncle as a debauched fiend, but confronted with him for the first time since he had rescued her from the asylum, he looked the same as always: blond hair flopping into blue eyes, and a sense of relief washed over her. He remained her loving uncle, the man who had rescued her.

Drake stubbed out his cigarette and followed, his expression as serious as that of the other men. When Solomon and Drake had arrived together a few days earlier, Osyth had been surprised, questioning the whereabouts of Solomon's wife.

"Marianne is in the country with her parents," he had replied. "The children have colds. Drake decided to keep me company instead."

Gathering in her grandmother's room, Osyth felt honoured to be included in the adult conversation. As everyone found chairs, making themselves comfortable, Penny beckoned Osyth and Xenia to join her on the bed. The murmuring ceased and Penny turned to Noah.

"What have you discovered, my dear?" she asked. "Keep nothing from us, we must all work from knowledge if we are to contain this situation."

There was a steel edge to her grandmother's voice that Osyth had never heard before.

Noah cleared his throat. "As you are all aware, since Osyth, Frederick and Angharad went to France, we have been investigating Kieran," he began and Osyth reached for her grandmother's hand. She had known this but to hear her uncle expressing it so formally was unsettling. "My apologies to the ladies present —" he took them all in with a sweeping glance — "what I am about to divulge is shocking."

"Perhaps the ladies should leave…" began William, but Xenia silenced her well-meaning husband with an icy glare.

"The day after we removed Osyth and Angharad from the asylum," continued Noah, "Solomon spoke to a friend within the police force and showed him the signed receipt we had from Mrs Freeman. He suggested the police might like to investigate as he intended to print the receipt with an accompanying piece about this scandal. It seems Mrs Freeman was not the only person in such a position of power selling her patients to brothels."

Osyth felt sick at Noah's words. During her first days travelling with the circus, she had been haunted by the terror of what might have happened had her uncles not outbid the other men to whom she and Angharad been offered by the chief warder.

"When she was arrested, Mrs Freeman decided to cooperate with the detective in charge and gave him Kieran's address. She explained that as a doctor, she had believed his work to be legitimate — which we know to be nonsense — however, she said Kieran claimed the women he delivered to the asylum had

come to him for help and he had done his best but none of them ever woke from the medication he had administered. Mrs Freeman believed this was because the young women had been ill, but we think Kieran had been using them to experiment with his own remedies and, thanks to Solomon's contacts, we have a witness."

"Was Kieran keeping women at the house in Richmond?" asked Xenia in revulsion.

"No, he had rooms in Southwark, near St Thomas' Hospital. There have been rumours for a while about women vanishing a few miles away in Whitechapel and we can't help but think Kieran may have been involved. Osyth, do you remember the Chapmans at Sir Francis Tress Barry's house, not far from Maybank? John Chapman was the coachman and he had a wife, Annie…"

"They had a daughter, she was Anne Georgina, but they called her Georgie," interrupted Osyth.

"Is this relevant?" asked Daniel.

"Perhaps," said Noah. "Earlier this year, Annie and John separated and she moved back to London, which is when she approached Solomon with her story."

"What sort of story?" asked Penny. "Poor Annie fought a battle with drunkenness. It was very sad to see her struggle. Even with the support of her family, she couldn't seem to win her fight. Sadly, that makes her tales highly unreliable."

"Which was why Sol asked a friend to look into it before he believed what Annie had told him but we should never have doubted her because every word was true. Annie had heard a tale about a young woman named Honora who had been living in Whitechapel working as a seamstress, when two well-dressed young men approached her. Fearing they thought she was a prostitute, she hurried away but the men followed. One

grabbed her and the other injected her, rendering her unconscious…"

"Two?" interrupted Osyth and Noah nodded.

"Two," he repeated. "We suspect Kieran was working with another medical student or doctor, but, unfortunately, we haven't been able to identify the other man. The following day, when Honora awoke, she was in a clean bed, locked in a room, alone. Through the window, she could see the river and recognised one of the wharves as being near Southwark. Honora smashed the window and escaped, taking refuge with her uncle who was a blacksmith living not far away in Roupell Street."

"Brave girl," murmured Hannah, and Katherine, who was standing near Blaise, nodded, her face stark white.

"Honora's uncle was furious and reported her kidnap to the police," Noah continued. "The girl even gave a description of the two men. Annie heard about this and when the descriptions reached her, she thought one of them sounded like Kieran. This was the reason she approached Sol; she knew they were cousins. Annie wanted to tip him off in case there was a scandal."

"Why would she care?" asked Blaise.

"When I spoke to Annie," said Solomon, "she said Mother had always been decent to her and she wanted to repay the favour."

There was a pause as everyone considered the source of the story.

"Noah, are you suggesting Kieran has been procuring young women in order to inject them with drugs?" asked Penny, eventually.

"When Angharad and I were at Richmond," said Osyth, "Kieran told us he wished to explore the pharmaceutical side

of medicine and boasted about creating his own tinctures and remedies."

"In order to test the strength of his medications, he would need someone to test them on," said Noah. "We think he was going to slum areas and luring women back to his rooms in Southwark for this purpose."

"He's insane," murmured Solomon, then all eyes turned to Katherine as she stifled a sob.

"I'm so sorry," she whispered. "He's my brother…" then her voice trailed off. Hannah rose and, taking Katherine's arm, led her from the room.

Silence greeted Katherine's troubled exit and Blaise turned to Noah. "Is there more?" he asked.

"I'm sorry, yes," said Noah. "None of us hold Katherine responsible for her brother's behaviour."

Blaise inhaled furiously, his anger directed towards his brother-in-law and all the distress Kieran had caused.

Noah waited while his brother composed himself, then continued, "The police have agreed to arrest and question Kieran as soon as he can be found. Not only for the assault of Honora Rogers but in connection with the disappearance of four other women, all of whom died at the asylum."

"Where is he?" asked Osyth, fury and fear rushing through her at the thought of her childhood companion, the man she had trusted and who had betrayed her, being free to continue to perpetuate his terrifying experiments.

"Kieran left your father's house the day you paid your visit," Noah replied. "It seems he followed the circus, never visiting himself but sending in the two men whom I believe you witnessed taking notes. When he had ascertained you were no longer in their midst, he set out across France, perhaps having guessed you were with Blaise and Katherine and were travelling

home. He somehow managed to secure help from some senior politicians and powerful men to search for you…"

"Angharad and I were surprised to discover that Kieran had made friends with many of the senior lecturers during his medical studies," interrupted Osyth, "and, using these connections, begun to ingratiate himself into even more splendid company."

"But how?" asked William. "The young man is insane."

"He's plausible," replied Solomon. "Kieran believes his own lies and creations, therefore when he speaks, it's with genuine conviction which makes him believable in conversation. However, his true objective is what he desires. If he must charm other people to reach his own ends, then he is capable of great feats of flattery and manipulation. Add to this his good looks and his tale of being a tragic orphan, then I imagine he could attract the attention and help of powerful men, especially if you throw in a supposed runaway wife."

Osyth shifted, sickened by this discussion. "But where is he?" she persisted.

"He was last seen in Paris, where we believe he was the guest of Jean-Martin Charcot, the neurologist," said Daniel. "Charcot specialises in the treatment of hysteria with hypnosis. From what we have been able to ascertain, Kieran has managed to secure a place at his neurology clinic in the hospital Pitié-Salpêtrière."

"However," continued Noah, looking at Osyth, "your mother remains our greatest concern. As you are aware, my darling, we've hired an investigator, Mr Smith, to try and find her. A message from him this morning suggests your mother has been sighted. If his source is correct, then she has been travelling with a man named Robert Cockaigne. We have yet to ascertain who he is and how they are connected."

"Cockaigne?" murmured Osyth in confusion. "Cockaigne is a mediaeval myth."

"What do you mean?" asked Blaise.

"In tales, Cockaigne is a land of plenty; there is extreme luxury, no discomfort or unhappiness. It's a mirage, a magical place but it isn't real."

Silence greeted her words.

"Perhaps Robert Cockaigne is not this man's name," said Blaise.

William gave an uncomfortable cough before saying, "This is speculation and until we know otherwise, we must continue to search for him under that name."

"The last sighting of Eudora was in Cardiff," Noah continued, "where, on this occasion, she appeared to be travelling alone. Mr Smith's associate engaged her in conversation and she explained she was on her way to see her daughter, a baby, from whom she had been separated due to a family squabble."

"Baby? I'm nearly nineteen years old."

"It may have been a turn of phrase," Noah replied, "but we must all be aware that it is possible Eudora could arrive here at any time. Until we can assess her health, we must all be alert to the fact that she is often unable to control herself. We must be ever vigilant. Kieran is another matter entirely. We have alerted the British police and we must pray he remains in Paris until they can arrest him."

CHAPTER TWO

Night gathered Cliffside into her arms, rocking it to sleep, gently dousing the inhabitants with the first hint of autumn starlight. The moon bathed the house in her silvery glow, softening the hard edges of furniture with her ethereal strength. Liquid mercury merging, changing with the clouds as they scudded across the surface of the black sky, travelling further in time with each gust of wind, leaving no trace, life discarded with no thought to the shadows of night, whispering away the past with the turning of each tide.

Osyth sat on her window-seat, alert to every creak and groan from the walls of the house, her journal balanced on her lap as she wrote, her eyes lingering on the photograph of herself and Frederick in their circus clothes. Since his return to his family at Bangeston Hall, in Loveston, twenty miles away, there had been silence from Frederick and she feared she might never hear from him again. On good days, she felt sure he would return, but there were days of doubt, where she would replay their adventures and wonder whether his feelings towards her had changed.

A stone tapped at her window making Osyth jump. There was another ting and this time there was a light. A lantern like a will-o'-the-wisp guttered, followed by a whistle, a long low note followed by a series of sharper calls. Opening the window to hear better, she leaned out, intrigued. It was the opening bar of their song from The Lunatics' Ball.

"Freddie?" she called in a low voice.

"Osyth," he whispered in return.

"What are you doing?"

"Will you let me in?" he entreated. "There is news and it cannot wait until morning."

Moments later, as she eased open the front door, Frederick stood there, his dark hair glistening with sea mist and moonbeams.

"Oh, my darling, Osyth," he whispered as he stepped into the hallway, drawing her into an embrace. "Have you been furious with me for not writing? I will explain everything but first, we must wake your grandfather and your uncles. It is imperative we speak immediately."

The tweed of his jacket was rough against her cheek as she leaned into him, revelling in his touch, his smell, the nearness of him.

"Please, Osyth," he said as he released her, "your grandfather."

Ushering him into the study where the embers of the fire glowed, Osyth gathered her nightgown in her hand and ran up the winding stairs. A glimmer of light showed under Noah's door, giving her the boldness to knock.

"Freddie is here," she said when Noah flung it open. "He says he must speak to Taid and the family urgently."

"I'll fetch them," Noah assured her and she fled back downstairs to Frederick who was warming himself by the fire. A wave of shyness washed over her as he turned to smile at her, holding out his hands.

"Where have you been?" she whispered as, once again, he pulled her into an embrace.

Before he could reply, Daniel entered followed by the rest of the family. Upon seeing them, Osyth leapt away from Frederick, expecting a reprimand but none came. Instead, Frederick moved aside to allow Penny and Xenia to take their seats by the fire. Frederick paused and, from the discomfort on

355

his face, Osyth knew he had not expected to be faced with the entire family. Moving closer, she took his hand and smiled, offering her strength and support. Frederick responded with a gentle squeeze of his fingers, then taking a deep breath, he spoke. "Kieran is nearby."

His words destroyed any hint of sleepiness among the family. An electricity flowed through the air as looks were exchanged and knuckles whitened over clenched fists. Osyth felt a shiver of fear trickle down her spine.

"How can you be sure?" Noah's response was harsh and in the flickering shadows of the firelight his face was cadaverous.

Frederick ran his fingers through his hair. "When I returned home," he said, his voice low, edged with apprehension, "I told my family the extent of my adventures. When they understood the gravity of Kieran's behaviour and all we were forced to endure, they were concerned and my uncle, the baronet, decided to search for Kieran himself."

"Why?" asked Xenia.

"He felt Kieran should be held accountable for his actions."

"He was last seen in Paris at the Pitié-Salpêtrière Hospital —" began Daniel.

"No, he wasn't," interrupted Frederick. "He was offered a place there to study but he never arrived. It appears that instead he encountered Eudora after she fled her home. I suspect the family likeness must have drawn him to her. Our investigator has been very thorough and discovered that Kieran, under the name of either Dr Stone or Dr Viner, his mother's maiden name, began to see the signs of Eudora's illness and he stepped in to help."

"To help?" exclaimed Solomon, his tone derisive. "Kieran has never helped anyone unless there was something in it for him. What happened, Frederick?"

Frederick loosened his grip on Osyth's hand and slipped his arm around her waist, pulling her close. Osyth noticed Daniel and William exchange a surprised look but she did not care how much she shocked them — being in Frederick's arms made her feel safe.

Frederick continued to speak. "It appears he had access to opium and he used it to mix his own laudanum. Under its influence, Eudora told Kieran the full story of his father's death."

Osyth stared in confusion at Frederick as Blaise groaned.

"We are undone," Blaise said, sinking onto the chaise. Katherine leaned into his side, her eyes downcast as tension filled the room.

"Our man has suggested that Kieran is intent on disgracing you all while he battles for what he sees as justice for his father," said Frederick.

"What does Kieran propose?" asked Noah, his mouth set in a tight line.

"To inform the police of Eudora's version of events, to implicate you all in Matthew Stone's murder — Angharad, too, unless you agree to annulling his marriage to her and to him marrying Osyth instead."

A stunned silence greeted this pronouncement. All colour had drained from Frederick's face. Osyth stared around the room, not understanding.

"Madness, sir!" bellowed William, recovering first. "Eudora has spun him a story and he has believed every last lie..."

"No, William," interrupted Daniel. "Eudora must have been lucid when she spoke to Kieran. He must have worked hard to gain her trust once he realised who she was, but she would have had no recollection of him."

"Nain, Taid, what's going on?" asked Osyth as panic began to build in her chest. "I thought Matthew was murdered by smugglers…"

Katherine let out a sob as Osyth looked from Penny to Daniel and felt genuine fear. It was Penny who broke the silence.

"Osyth, we have more to tell you about your mother," she said in a calm voice. "While you were with Blaise, he told you some of the tale but there is more."

Around her, Osyth was aware of the family reaching out for each other. Blaise wrapped Katherine in an encompassing embrace, Xenia stood within the circle of her husband's arms. Noah and Hannah held hands, her eyes shut as though in prayer, his focused on his niece. Even Drake had slid his arm around Solomon's waist. Beside her, Frederick gripped her to him. Her grandparents stared at each other, the look passing between them one of understanding, love and acknowledgement that the time had come to reveal the final secret.

"Blaise explained to you that in one of her fits of frenzy, your mother tried to smother you while you were a baby," continued Penny, as the words hit Osyth anew with their violence. "However, he didn't tell you what happened next."

Penny paused and Osyth felt as though the air had been sucked from the room. She wanted to hear her grandmother's next words but at the same time she dreaded the darkness she felt was about to engulf them.

"Matthew had heard Eudora stir and had followed her. When he realised what she was doing, he leapt forward to save you and…" Penny's voice faltered, so Daniel stepped in to save his beloved the task of reliving one of the worst nights of her life.

"Your mother had a small silver knife which she carried everywhere with her," said Daniel. "When Matthew pulled Eudora away from you, she spun around and cut his throat. It wasn't deep but she caught an artery and we could not stop the blood."

"My darling brother died in my arms," whispered Penny, "and to protect your mother from either the asylum or the hangman's noose, we —" she pointed to her husband, Noah and Blaise — "tried to hide Matthew's body. We wrapped him in cloth and tied weights to it, giving him a sailor's funeral but the ropes must have worked lose because, three days later, his body washed up at Newgale."

Osyth gasped in horror.

"It was my fault," continued Penny in her voice low. "It was my idea to give Matthew a burial at sea. He had never been interested in religion. His heart was that of a sailor and I knew he would be happier under the waves than buried in the earth."

"And Kieran wishes to blackmail you with this information?" said Osyth. "He wishes to force me into marriage to save you all from arrest?"

The word came out as a question and Daniel nodded.

"Father, we must confess," sighed Noah. "It is the only way to end this insanity."

"No," exclaimed Osyth, terrified her family would all be hanged for concealing the crime. "No, you can't."

"If we confess, then Kieran holds no power over us," explained Blaise.

"Where is Kieran now? Do you know?" asked Daniel.

"Somewhere close. He was travelling with Eudora under the name of —"

"Mr Robert Cockaigne?" supplied Osyth as everything fell into place.

Frederick nodded.

Glancing at the clock, Blaise spoke into the silence. "It's midnight, too late to call the constable. I shall ride for him at daybreak. The truth should have been told; Matthew deserved better."

From her seat by the fireside, Penny gave a sob.

"Let us have a few hours' sleep," suggested Daniel, "then we will face this threat together at first light. Frederick, your room is ready for you, should you care to stay. It is a cold night and a long way to Bangeston Hall."

Dousing the lights and fire, Osyth clutched Frederick's hand as the family moved along the corridors, returning to their rooms, preparing for battle. Waiting until they were out of sight, Osyth led a bewildered Frederick to her bedroom.

"What are you doing?" he asked, startled, as she closed the door and indicated for him to take the chair by the fire.

"There is something I must show you," she whispered. "Taid received it by the evening post."

Opening her jewellery box, she lifted out the top layer, then removed the folded document her grandfather had given her earlier in the day, handing it to Frederick. His fingers trembled as he opened it but as he read, a smile broke across his tired face.

"Your marriage has been annulled," he said.

"Yes," she whispered, too afraid to say more.

"Oran Walters was a brave man to offer you such protection," said Frederick, reaching to take her hand. "We must be grateful to him."

"Thank you for understanding, for helping to protect me, and I'm sorry if this has altered the way you feel. My love for you remains unchanged." Osyth felt the heat rising in her cheeks.

"Oran has behaved like a gentleman," Frederick said. "His bravery and clever thinking saved you from Kieran."

Osyth did not respond. Frederick slid his arms around her, pulling her close and buried his face in her neck. "I'm so sorry," he whispered. "My behaviour was that of a petulant child. Can you ever forgive me?"

"Forgive you?" said Osyth, in surprise. "Of course. Can you forgive me?"

"There is nothing to forgive," he replied. "We were under an enchantment in the magic of the circus, our own Tylwyth Teg."

"And now we have passed through the door in the stone circle and we are back home," she replied.

"Home," he echoed. "Where your fairy marriage has been annulled and now, if you will have me, we can be married?"

Osyth gasped as his words wound their way around her mind, leaving their glimmering imprint of joy. "Do you mean it?"

"Yes," he said, dropping to one knee. "Will you marry me, Miss Attwater?"

"I will," she replied, tears and smiles wreathing her face. "Oh yes, Freddie, I will."

As his arms encircled her, Osyth felt the safety of his embrace and wondered if it would be enough to save her again from Kieran's dark wrath.

CHAPTER THREE

"Your grandfather, uncles and Frederick are in the study," said Penny as Osyth arrived in the summer drawing room the following morning. "Sergeant Evans is with them."

Sick fear clutched at Osyth's heart as she wondered how the day would play out. Beside her, Penny's fingers trembled but a look of such determination blazed on her face that Osyth felt compelled to follow her example. Xenia and Hannah sat near the window, sewing delicate flowers on to a pale yellow shawl, their expressions calm but Osyth noticed neither had steady hands.

"Perhaps you could help me sort through my shell collection," Penny continued, beckoning Osyth to the table where she sat with Katherine. "While I was in bed recovering, I thought it might be pleasant to refresh our beautiful wind chime. We thought we might string some new shells as a thank you present to our guardian angel."

A large jar had been half-emptied on the table and Osyth realised it was the many shells she had collected for her grandmother over the years. *My days of innocence*, she thought, *before the madness in the family blood claimed us.*

Silence fell in the room. In the distance there was the boom and swoosh of the tide as it raced across the beach, the jeering cry of the gulls and the rustle of the trees in the wood, but no one spoke. The darkness of secrets enveloped every corner of the house as they waited.

"What do you think will happen?" Despite her best efforts, Osyth's voice cracked as she spoke, not being able to bear the hush.

"Your grandfather and uncles are good, kind people," Penny replied. "We must pray the law of your beloved fae rules here today ensuring the good are rewarded and the wicked are punished."

Katherine reached over to squeeze Osyth's hand. "We're strong together," she said. "Kieran may have tried to rip us apart but he will never succeed. He is ill, though, you must remember that."

"What about his plan to blackmail me into marriage?" asked Osyth.

"Those were the ramblings of an unwell mind," sighed Penny. "Your grandfather and uncles will resolve the matter, but whatever happens, you will be protected."

"Not at the expense of the lives of everyone I love…"

"Hush Osyth," came Xenia's voice. "You're not thinking clearly. No one can force you into marriage, least of all a man who will be likely arrested for murder when the police find him."

Hannah rose. "I shall arrange refreshments," she said. "We must focus on our belief that with the help of Sergeant Evans, this matter will be resolved."

At midday, footsteps in the corridor heralded the return of the men. All pretence at sewing and shell-sorting were abandoned as the women stood as one, looking to their partners, who in turn, faced Daniel.

"Sergeant Evans listened to our version of events," he said, sitting beside Penny and taking her hand, "before explaining it was far too late to prove who might have attacked Matthew and how he felt it was unlikely a girl as light as Eudora could hurt a grown man."

"Did you tell him about us taking Matthew out to sea?" asked Penny, trembling.

"When we told him, he didn't even take any notes," said Noah, lacing his fingers into Hannah's. "By the time we had all given a full confession, he was ready to dismiss the entire episode as one which we must have misunderstood. He refused to believe we were involved."

"He was more concerned about the possibility of Eudora being lost somewhere," added Solomon.

"And Kieran?" Penny asked.

"He concluded that was a matter for the police in Richmond where Kieran now resides, but he has suggested it would be wise to contact him if Kieran were to arrive. He was more interested in protecting my business reputation within the community and in sending his officers to search for Eudora."

A stunned silence followed this pronouncement.

"What do we do now?" asked Osyth.

"We wait," said Penny. "They will come home, both of them. We all return to Cliffside in the end."

When they came, it was from Osyth's dream. A chill, like ocean water streaming through her veins, woke Osyth from the swirling music of the circus and the urgent call of the wind chime. They were standing at the foot of her bed; moonlight frosting their hair, glazing their faces with an unearthly shimmer as they stared down at her, their arms linked. Her mother glared from hooded eyes and her cousin sneered, his

face a mask of glittering anger. An involuntary scream rose in Osyth's throat but the flash of silver in her mother's hand and the memory of what had happened to Matthew caused her to swallow the cry for help.

In a mingling of blue and green, their eyes locked, as mother and daughter faced each other for the first since Osyth had been a few weeks old. Their matching red hair sparked around them, igniting the softly scented air in the room, drowning the sound of the delicate warning tunes of the wind chime.

"Mother," whispered Osyth, pushing herself into a sitting position.

Eudora's intense gaze was curious and Osyth realised her mother did not recognise her. As the moonlight illuminated her features, Osyth gave a cry of shock. Time and illness had destroyed the fae-like beauty she had seen in her mother's portrait. The laughing young woman in the canvas bore no resemblance to the creature looming in her bedroom. Osyth gulped back her mingled feelings of despair and revulsion as the tale of the Gwrach-y-Rhibyn, the witch of death from Welsh myth, flooded her mind. This terrifying creature with her red eyes, green-tinged skin and dark leathery wings, who gathered the souls of the dead, was manifest within Eudora's shattered soul.

Eudora's blue eyes bulged in her skeletal face, their rims tinged with red; her pale skin was lacklustre and waxy, while deep lines fanned out from her eyes, a map of hatred and misery, the story of a life lived in despair. Her lips were narrow, drawn together, all laughter long since lost and as she gazed at Osyth, her distorted features contorted her face into a haunting death mask. The silence between them grew as they stared deep into each other's souls looking for the answers to questions they were too afraid to ask.

"What are you doing here?" Osyth eventually managed to whisper as Kieran and Eudora stared at her.

"Your mother wished to see you," said Kieran, his voice calm as though this were a pleasant afternoon visit.

"It's the middle of the night," Osyth hissed.

Eudora untied her bonnet, placing it on Osyth's dressing table, while Kieran made himself comfortable in the low armchair beside the fire.

"You have caused me a great deal of concern," said Kieran, his trembling hands drawing a flask from his coat pocket. "However, your mother has given her blessing to our nuptials. Perhaps you would care to dress and we can depart with haste. There is no time to lose."

"You're insane," murmured Osyth, her bedclothes pulled up to her chin as she watched them.

"I will help you," said Eudora, padding towards the bed and peering at Osyth with quizzical eyes. "When you are dressed, you will take me to my baby."

From his position by the fireplace, Kieran gave a low, unpleasant laugh. "Your mother does not believe you are the baby she left behind," he said. "She is, of course, insane. Let's hope her blood does not run in your veins. At least your father was easily controlled. You will, I anticipate, follow his example rather than this wilful creature."

Osyth stared from one to the other, her eyes wide with horror. Kieran drank from his flask, his eyes glowing with satisfaction with each swallow, before sliding it back into his pocket.

"You will prepare to leave," he instructed. "I would like to catch the morning train to London. Your mother will assist." With his final word, a stillness enveloped him and Osyth wondered if he was asleep or perhaps in a drug-induced trance.

"Sweet child," murmured Eudora, reaching claw-like fingers towards Osyth. "You have pretty hair." With fluttering, jerky movements, she stroked Osyth's abundant red curls, singing in a flat tone: "Pretty hair," as she wound her fingers deeper in her daughter's curls.

"Stop, Mother, please," whispered Osyth as the singing became more persistent and Eudora's fingers tangled themselves cruelly into her abundant tresses, drawing their faces closer, closer, with each twist.

"Pretty hair, pretty hair…"

Osyth could feel her mother's breath on her cheek. The strange, sweet smell of the alcohol Kieran had mixed with the opium to create his powerful laudanum made her gag. The memory of being forcibly dosed with the same mixture flooded her and, sick with fear, she squirmed, trying to unravel her mother's sharp fingers from her scalp.

"Pretty hair, pretty hair…" murmured Eudora. "Where is the wind chime?"

"What?"

"It sings to me; I shall see it when my baby is in my arms." Releasing Osyth, Eudora began to pad about the room, whispering and giggling to herself, lost in her own world.

For a moment Osyth watched her, then a realisation rose through her terror. Kieran was motionless, his eyes half-open, his breathing shallow and Osyth remembered her days in a drugged stupor in the bedroom at Richmond. On one occasion she had been lucid and Kieran had been sitting, trance-like, looking at her without seeing but, when she had tried to stand, her legs had given way and it had brought him from his reverie, leaving her once more at the mercy of his potions.

However, if he was in this semi-conscious state, with her strength regained and her head clear, she would be able to

overpower him. Flinging the covers from her legs, she padded on silent feet to where her mother was staring out of the window, singing a halting tune to the glowing full moon.

"Let me take you to the baby," she whispered to Eudora. "She is asleep in another room but she will be pleased to see you. The wind chime is above her cradle."

A furtive expression flashed across Eudora's face and she whispered into Osyth's ear, "He will not let me." Eudora's eyes darted towards Kieran. If Osyth had not known better, he could have been mistaken for a corpse. "He is wicked."

"I know," replied Osyth, "but together, we are clever enough to trick him."

Eudora considered this for a moment before giving a throaty cackle. "Yes," she hissed, "he is a fool, we shall escape. I am always cleverer than the shadows, I always escape." Glee flashed into her eyes and she encircled Osyth's fingers with a grip of iron, causing Osyth to cry out in pain.

"Be quiet," Eudora admonished, a small silver knife flashing in her hand. "We mustn't wake him; I must take my baby and flee."

"The baby is this way," Osyth whispered. "If we are quiet, we can creep past him."

Osyth's bare feet made no sound as she encouraged her mother through the darkened room, past Kieran's fixed figure, to the corridor, where moonlight shadows draped themselves across familiar furniture and well-worn carpets to create a monochrome world offering suspicion and danger.

"Not far," whispered Osyth.

"Have I been here before?" Eudora murmured, her voice childlike, her fingers dragging along the walls.

"You have," said Osyth. "This is where your baby lives."

"My baby…?" Eudora stopped, her body tense.

Swallowing her panic, Osyth saw a momentary flicker of confusion as Eudora gave her an intense stare.

"You have stolen my baby," Eudora snarled. "Thief!"

As Eudora lunged towards her, the knife clasped in her hand, Osyth gathered her flowing white nightgown in her hand and screamed, wrenching her arm from her mother's and running towards the nearest door.

"Help!" Her high-pitched shriek caused doors to crash open and voices to shout in response. Her grandparents' room was the nearest and Daniel was the first to reach her, as he raced into the corridor. Eudora gave an eldritch shriek at the unexpected pandemonium.

"My mother!" spluttered Osyth. "Kieran, in my room."

Penny's arms surrounded her, pulling her into the safety of their bedroom, followed seconds later by Daniel, half leading, half dragging Eudora, who writhed and struggled. Noah and Blaise arrived next with a groggy Kieran supported between them. Osyth took refuge on her grandparents' bed, watching as the family gathered, complete for the first time in years. Solomon, Xenia, Drake and William encouraged Eudora into a chair beside the bed, forming a circle around her.

"Osyth is a magnet, drawing you all back to Cliffside," said Noah from the doorway where he blocked the exit.

Osyth had long been aware of the animosity raised by Kieran's behaviour but the pure white anger radiating from Noah shocked her. Noah's eyes were hard chips of emerald ice, pinning Kieran to the spot. The battle they had spent so long avoiding had begun. Families are like armies, they grow, they gain power and then from within the ranks come the traitors. Kieran, the instigator of violence, betrayal and despair,

stood poised, unsupported and desperate, while Noah, his brothers ranged around him, glared down at his nephew.

"You are not head of this family," sneered Kieran.

"Stop it, Kieran," said Katherine, her clear voice cutting through the heavy air. Her red hair caught the glinting light of the candles as she walked across the room to face her brother.

"Traitor!" Kieran exploded, his hand raised to strike Katherine but Blaise, who was a footstep behind his wife, caught Kieran's wrist.

"There will be no violence, Kieran, not in my house," came Daniel's voice. "Your actions have caused enough pain."

"My actions?" Kieran struggled against Blaise's grip. "My actions? What about your filthy secrets? How much damage have *they* caused?"

"How dare you…?" began William but Kieran spoke over him, cutting his words short.

"Your insane daughter slit my father's throat!" Kieran screamed. "But what can you expect from the daughter of a lunatic?" He spat at Penny, before pointing to Eudora who lay slumped in the chair, her eyes wide, her face a series of ticks and twitches, unaware of anything. "That she-devil murdered my father and you, Daniel Attwater, with your villainous sons with their blackened and depraved souls disposed of my beloved father in those wicked waves. You suggest I am mad but you are the ones who are insane. Yet, I am prepared to offer Osyth a home and a place in society, to save her from this lunatics' paradise, to rehabilitate her in the eyes of important men. It is likely she, too, will suffer the family mania but this is treatable as she will be forever at my mercy…"

Blaise had released Kieran, who through his speech had turned away from them all and no longer seemed to be addressing anyone, his words becoming a nonsensical gibber as he circled the room, swigging from his flask, unable to keep still. All eyes followed his movements. With each deep draft he took from his flask, Kieran seemed to fade, the drug creeping around his mind, subduing him until his speech slurred, his eyes rolling, on the point of collapse.

"Kieran, take my hand." Penny had risen from her position beside Osyth, her voice cutting through the stream of her nephew's incessant, rambling chatter. With gentle hands, she captured him in her arms, calming him, forcing the son of her beloved twin to look into her eyes. "Do you know what you have done?" she asked. A blank expression came into Kieran's eyes. "Do you know where you are?"

There was no response. Instead, Kieran's arms dropped to his sides and he sagged in Penny's arms. Blaise and Katherine rushed forward, taking his weight. None of them had realised the depth of his illness, the endless passages he had walked in his mind, creating his world of pain and unrealistic expectations, unaware of any feelings other than his own. Throughout his childhood, Osyth had seen her grandmother watch and hope that underneath his strange outbursts, Kieran was a good man but as he stared at Penny, the aunt who had loved him through his hatred and loathing, Osyth realised the Kieran from her childhood was lost.

Clattering footsteps drew all eyes except Kieran's and Eudora's as Frederick skittered into the room.

"Sergeant Evans is on his way," he gasped.

Katherine, calm but with a look of infinite sadness in her eyes, took her brother's hand. Kieran looked down at her but showed no recognition of his younger sister. "We must go, Kieran," she said.

"To see my mother and father?"

"Yes, my dear, perhaps you will see Mother and Father."

Blaise and Katherine led the opium-doped Kieran, docile and confused, from the room.

"Where will they take him?" Osyth whispered to Xenia.

"The police station, then perhaps the asylum," she replied, her voice cold. "We may yet have to take your mother there, too."

Osyth watched as her childhood friend walked from her life, realising, finally, that no matter how hard her grandparents had tried, they had never been able to save Kieran from his own demons.

Later that day, on the veranda, Osyth confessed her fears to Frederick. "Katherine has had word from the asylum about Kieran," she said, watching as Frederick scraped at a soft piece of wood, gently scoring a heart into the rail.

"What did they say?"

"His doses of opium have been so strong, they have altered his mind. He no longer recognises Katherine."

"Oh Osyth, that is awful. He's such a young man."

"The doctor doesn't think it's entirely due to the opium. He suggests Kieran has other health issues. When he asked Katherine about the family history, she told him about their mother's melancholia and accidental death, as well as my mother's…" Osyth hesitated over the word, "…problems. The doctor has suggested Kieran will never stand trial for his crimes because he is no longer coherent." Her voice faded

away. "I'm scared, Freddie," she admitted. "If this has happened to Kieran, could the same thing happen to me?"

Frederick slipped his arm around her waist. "There are many paths to travel in life, my love," he said. "We are young but look at all we have experienced. Your mother has always been different — from everything your uncles and your grandfather have told me, she carried this with her from childhood. Look to the rest of your family, Osyth, they are kind, sensible people. Your mother's illness is a terrible curse for her, but it doesn't mean you will suffer the same fate."

CHAPTER FOUR

"Aunt Xenia, it's my turn to watch Mother," whispered Osyth.

It had been a week since Eudora and Kieran's unexpected arrival. After Katherine and Blaise had delivered him into the custody of Sergeant Evans, it had been decided Kieran would be safest in an asylum. Daniel had accompanied his son, daughter-in-law and nephew to a private establishment with kinder treatment than the grey prison in which Kieran had incarcerated Osyth and Angharad.

Penny had persuaded the family that, for the present, she would care for Eudora. After her own experience in an institution, Osyth understood her grandmother's desire came from the need to protect the daughter she felt she had abandoned and let down. However, when the nurse arrived and suggested keeping Eudora in a state of drugged incomprehension, Osyth was unsure whether this was the best way to treat her mother.

"Thank you, my dear," whispered Xenia. "She is asleep. Nurse Wilson will return later. Your mother's medicine is on the table. If she wakes, try to encourage her to take some more. She refused to swallow it all earlier." There was no pity in Xenia's eyes as she stared at her elder sister. "She's been restless this afternoon. I think the wind chime's disturbing her, rather than offering comfort but Mother insists." Xenia shook her head, not wishing to undermine her mother's wishes but glancing at the wind chime above her sister's bed with concern. Osyth felt Xenia's arms around her before her aunt melted away into the shadows.

Placing another log on the fire, Osyth approached the bed. Eudora lay, pale-faced, her red hair spread across the pillow, a princess in a fairy tale, sleeping until help arrived, but Osyth knew there would be no true love's kiss, no happy-ever-after to release her mother from the madness in her mind. Tears welled in Osyth's eyes as she stared down at the emaciated figure. Loved and loveable, she may have been, but death hovered near her shoulder and Osyth's heart broke to see the shadow her mother's illness had made of the once young and vital woman.

Osyth took her mother's hand and began to sing. Her voice recalling a time of innocence for them both.

"Fairy maiden, draw near to me,
Take me far below the sea,
Water maiden, wild and free,
With the fairies of the deep…

"Fairy maiden, full of glee,
I'll tell my secrets for you to keep…
Water maiden, promise me,
You'll keep them safe in the deep blue sea."

Eudora's eyes sprang open and she stared at Osyth.

"Mother?" Osyth whispered in a surprised voice.

"Osyth?"

Recognition glimmered in Eudora's eyes and when she opened her arms to her daughter, Osyth leaned forward into her mother's embrace.

"Osyth," Eudora murmured again as they rocked together. Saltwater tears slid from Osyth's eyes into her mother's red hair, a perfect replica of her own. "Save me from this hell, Osyth," Eudora whispered, her words drenched in misery and loss. "Set me free, my darling."

Osyth hesitated. Her instructions had been clear, whenever her mother began to awaken, she was to be subdued with laudanum but as Eudora's eyes swam with tears, Osyth questioned the method of control. Remembering her own days of hell swimming through the murky world created by Kieran's drugs, she stared into her mother's momentarily lucid eyes.

"Help me," Eudora implored, reaching for her daughter's hand. Osyth hesitated beside the table where her mother's medication waited. "Osyth, please…"

Savouring her name on her mother's lips, Osyth paused again, staring at the wrecked face, unsure how to help, then, her decision made, she replaced the bottle on the table and reached for her mother's hand. But then she saw a fog slip over Eudora's eyes. The moment of clarity had passed and her fingers were suddenly vice-like around Osyth's hand.

"Where is my baby?" hissed Eudora in her cracked voice. "I came home for my baby."

"I'm no longer a baby," said Osyth, wanting to make her mother understand, yet not wishing to scare her. "Your baby has grown up. I am your daughter."

Osyth felt the fingers grip her hair, holding her head rigid. Eudora's breath was ragged and Osyth felt an icy torrent chilling her heart and freezing her soul. Above them the wind chime sang, the sound jerking Eudora's gaze upwards. Osyth stumbled as her mother threw her aside, distracted by the tunes. Her fingers lacing in the delicate string of the coral shells, Eudora swayed on the bed, a tuneless song flowing from her lips as she stroked the wind chime, searching each strand of shells.

"Where is it?" she howled, when she came to the space. "Where is my shell?"

"You took it," whispered Osyth.

"You stole it!" Eudora shrieked, turning with such force that her fingers wrenched the wind chime from the ceiling. The old strings split apart, sending coral shells sailing in an arc across the room, while the silver chimes clashed together, their melody destroyed as with a final rainbow of sound, the wind chime crumpled to the floor. Eudora stared down at the wreckage, before letting out an unearthly wail. "It was you," she howled. "You killed my baby. All I wanted was to love her but you wouldn't let me." Her voice rose to a frightening scream. Her hair wild around her head, flying in all directions, her blue eyes full of fever and anger. "Murderer!" she cried, leaping from the bed and grasping Osyth, shaking her. "Murderer!"

Osyth tried to defend herself as Eudora's torment grew louder and louder, her mother's fists slamming into her again and again, a whirling, manic creature from the depths of the darkest corners of Tylwyth Teg. Venom and despair flew from her, as Osyth screamed, fighting back, calling her family. As her hands reached out she was flung backwards by the crazed strength of Eudora's madness.

"Where is my baby?" Eudora shrieked and the silver of the blade flashed in her hand as she lunged towards her daughter.

Osyth darted aside, grappling through the air for her mother's arm, trying to dislodge the knife.

Eudora slipped on the fallen shells, skittering aside, her breath fast and panicked as she glowered at her daughter. Osyth sprang backwards, her tumbling skills giving her the balance and agility to escape the wildness of her mother's mind. The shock of the movement startled Eudora, causing her to shriek in anger as she turned on her daughter: the baby she had already tried to kill once. Eudora ran at Osyth, knocking her to the floor before fleeing from the bedroom.

Osyth shouted for help as she ran through the house after her mother, her hair spreading behind her, blood red in the moonlight. Eudora fled from the house and Osyth followed her across the veranda and through the gate leading to the cliffs. Eudora's feet found the path her mother, Penny, had taken all those years ago when her own mother, Eleanor, had died.

Eudora ran, terrified of the sounds of people chasing her, her blue eyes wild, rolling in her head as she screamed incoherently for her child, while Osyth begged her to stop.

"Mother, no!" Osyth screamed over the roar of the autumn tide as it lashed menacingly against the cliffs.

Waves reached out, their spiky fingers beckoning Eudora forward, calling her name, promising the green lands of Tylwyth Teg. Behind her, Osyth, leading the family in a roaring, desperate procession, called her mother back to Cliffside, while above them the ghostly echoes of the wind chime added its tunes to the maelstrom.

All around was noise, water rushing, pounding waves, mingling with the sound of Osyth's beating heart and her mother's manic laughter. Osyth saw her, poised on the rocks, allowing the elements to lash her with their fury. Osyth finally understood that this was what her mother had been searching for — the release of unquestioning oblivion, the unconditional acceptance which had never been hers, the promise of holding her baby in a land where she was free.

The sky was split in two as lightning showed Eudora, her arms wide, welcoming the waves as they spread before her like a vast carpet of carefully woven dreams.

Down the cliff path raced the family, their voices mingling, led by Osyth, screaming for Eudora to return, tears flying as

she tried to reason with her mother. "Mother, no!" pleaded Osyth as her words were ripped away by the wind.

The storm whipped Eudora's hair as she stood, unaware of the pain and fear swirling around her family. Eudora smiled, her sweetest widest smile. It was the reminder of her childhood innocence, of all the love from her family. It was the joy of the love shared with Egan before the fear and the shadows claimed her mind. It was the sweetness of her daughter, the baby Osyth.

Her smile suffused her in joy and in the certainty of peace. Her blue eyes were wide open as she turned away from her sobbing family, no longer needing their love, no longer aware of their voices. The wind howled around her, the rain lashed, darkening her hair. The Gwragedd Annwn sang, offering her the world she craved, the end of her misery. Her smile widened and she abandoned herself to the green lands of the fairy realm, plunging under the waves to be welcomed back into the arms of her beloved fae and their magical kingdom on the edges of her mind.

PART ELEVEN: PEMBROKESHIRE, 2019

CHAPTER ONE

"Oh, my word. How dreadful for the family," gasped Caitlin as Amelia stopped reading Osyth's journal. They were in the living room, Caitlin in her favourite armchair, the dogs on their sofa, while Amelia and Edward sat on the other vast couch.

"Not to mention Eudora," said Edward.

"Do you think so?" Caitlin asked. "For Eudora, it was probably the one moment where she had complete control."

"What do you mean?" asked Amelia.

"After a lifetime of being drugged and forced to submit to the will of others, her death was under her control," said Caitlin. "If she'd stayed, what would have happened? More years of misery, half out of her mind because of her illness, semi-comatose due to the sedatives she was forced to take."

"You condone her suicide?" Edward sounded horrified.

"Of course I don't condone suicide," said Caitlin, "but I doubt Eudora saw it that way — to her it was escape. When you're faced with the end, knowing your heartbeats are numbered, death becomes less frightening. It's a new adventure, perhaps the greatest of all, and Eudora had carried death on her shoulder since she was a teenager. For me, this seems a fitting end for a troubled woman in a time when mental illness was not understood in the way it is today."

Amelia could sympathise with Caitlin's sentiments — she had watched her own daughter live with the looming spectre of death throughout her short life and by the end, Molly had chatted about her death as though it were something as commonplace as going to the shops. The feeling of release and the knowledge her suffering would end was what had given

Molly her brave, sunny disposition. The pain was for those left behind who had to live without her.

"It's devastatingly sad," agreed Amelia, "but there's a bit more. Osyth explains that her uncles and Freddie formed a rescue party, tying themselves together in a long line, before Noah ventured into the surf."

"Were they trying to save her?" asked Caitlin.

Amelia closed the journal, placing it on the long low coffee table in front of the sofa. "By the time they found her, she was dead. The women of the family laid her out in time-honoured tradition and her father, brothers and Freddie dug the grave beside the stone circle…"

"The mythical entrance to Tylwyth Teg," interrupted Caitlin.

"Exactly," said Amelia, smiling at Caitlin. "They obviously decided never to register her suicide, which was why we were never able to find her death certificate in the records." She took a deep gulp of wine, feeling its warmth creep down to her heart, offering her a moment of release.

Edward took his own glass and sipped, his face thoughtful. "Perhaps they felt it was their way of showing how much they loved her," he mused.

"Penny would have done anything for her family and by sending Eudora away, she thought she was helping her but with hindsight, perhaps she felt she had failed her and should have kept her near," Amelia added.

Caitlin sighed. "We are all wise after the event," she said. "Penny had experienced horror at the asylum and she didn't want her daughter to suffer the same way. The family was probably also desperate to cover up the fact she murdered Matthew."

Amelia had found this discovery one of the most uncomfortable. "Eddie, how do you feel about the fact that my ancestor murdered yours, in this house?"

Amelia and Caitlin exchanged a nervous glance. Edward sipped his glass of wine, looking from one woman to the other.

"The most upsetting part is the idea that such a violent crime took place in a house where usually love was the prevailing emotion," he said, "but, a house as old as this is going to have experienced no ends of deaths. As for your ancestor murdering mine, there's no reason for me to feel strange about it, these people died many years ago and we were never part of their lives. However, on a medical level, it's fascinating that two members of the same family suffered such severe mental health conditions."

"Eudora was a very sick woman," said Amelia. "It's sad how misunderstood her condition would have been at the end of the nineteenth century. As for Kieran, was he born with his disorder or did the circumstances of his youth create the environment for his mental illness? We'll probably never know. His addiction, which he had obviously been hiding for years, would have contributed to his issues."

"It occurred to me that while he was at Cliffside, under the watchful eye of his family, he may have been like any teenager stealing alcohol or cigarettes, so his intake was minimal. I suspect it was Solomon who was his main source of opium..." Edward said.

"What? You think Solomon was his dealer?" asked Caitlin, aghast.

"No, I think Kieran stole it from Solomon whenever he visited, possibly building up a small stash but when Kieran came of age and received his inheritance, he had the money to enable him to increase his intake. It's possible his habit went

from the occasional puff of opium to a daily dosage that was far stronger than anything he'd experienced in the past."

"You might be right," Amelia agreed. "His strange behaviour could have been down to crippling shyness and the mental discomfort of being brought up in a family that was his but, at the same time, was one step removed. Not to mention his awkwardness with an aunt whom he irrationally blamed for his parents' deaths. When he was free, like many youngsters who come into a lot of money, he overdid things with terrible results."

The fire crackled against the autumn wind as it whipped around the house. Edward had deliberately wound down the clinic for a few months, wanting to be free to tend to Caitlin as her condition worsened. There was one remaining guest who would be leaving in the morning, then it would be only the family. Although none of them spoke about it, Caitlin's life was being measured in months and with each trip to her consultant, they knew this could easily shorten to weeks if things worsened. Amelia remained in her tower room but Edward assured her that once the final guest had departed he would unlock the adjoining door so the house could function as one again.

"How are you getting on with the letters?" Caitlin asked.

Amelia sipped her wine. She had completed one set of letters earlier that day and their contents had been unexpected. She wondered how many more shocks Caitlin and Edward could withstand.

"What?" Edward asked, his eyes narrowing in a shrewd expression. "Have you found some other shocking secret? If it's about Solomon and Drake, I'm aware they were lovers."

Caitlin beamed. "Of course they were," she said. "If we hadn't guessed, the drawing you found would have confirmed it."

Edward grinned. The papers in the bottom of the trunk had been an odd mixture of letters, bills, receipts and sketches. Amelia had suggested they divide up the spoils to see what they might reveal. Edward had scooped out half, taking what he claimed were the bits connected to the house, leaving Amelia the letters and the journal. A sketch of a naked man, reclining on a chaise, had dropped out of Edward's pile and they had both examined it in surprise.

On the back were the words, "*To My Sweet Sol, Ever yours, Drake*". Amelia had searched online for lesser-known Victorian artists and had discovered a collection by a man named Amir Drake Daher, of Arab descent who enjoyed modest success in the 1890s. One of the paintings accredited to him was entitled *King Solomon is Mine*. The sketch was a forerunner of the finished nude of an exquisitely handsome man, with blond hair and blue eyes, reclining naked among luxurious cushions and throws while fountains played and peacocks strutted.

"It's Angharad and the baby," said Amelia, aware Edward was waiting for her to share her discovery. "Kieran's baby, your ancestor Henry."

"What happened?"

"Caitlin was right that Angharad died in childbirth but that wasn't the whole story. Her letters are to Osyth and they're a record of what happened to her while she was in the circus."

"And…?"

"She married Oran's brother, Caius," said Amelia.

"Really? But wouldn't that make her a bigamist?"

"Yes, I suppose it would. Perhaps she didn't feel she was married any more, especially when Osyth told her about Kieran's breakdown. The baby was born while they were touring in Russia and it was over a year before Oran and Caius arrived unannounced at Cliffside with the baby. Angharad had asked them to take her son home to her parents, Mary and Owain Williams."

"So, that was how the baby came home, I'd wondered," said Edward, intrigued. "But why was he brought up by Katherine and Blaise?"

"Mary and Owain were elderly and it seems, while they played a part in their grandson's life, as Katherine was the child's aunt, she seemed a more appropriate person to raise him. She and Blaise were unable to have children, so they adopted Henry with the blessing of Mary and Owain, as well as of Penny and Daniel. Henry came home and apparently adored Katherine and Blaise, referring to them as his parents."

"What a complicated family we have," sighed Caitlin.

"There's something else, too," said Amelia and she felt her skin crawl at what she was about to reveal.

"More?" asked Caitlin.

"This is really a rock under the tide," Amelia said. "When we opened up the tower, there was a letter left by Osyth — do you remember? It must have fallen off the desk. In it, she explained why they had boarded up the rooms. It was only yesterday I realised the significance of the date and I wondered whether Osyth and Katherine had their suspicions too. Perhaps this was what finally made them lock everything away. Listen, I'll read you the opening lines:

"*March 1891, To Whomever Finds This Letter. From: Osyth Meyrick*

"Today, we shall board up Kieran's tower. Katherine and I have decided it is the correct action to take and we have assembled the remaining evidence of the joint misdemeanours of both my beloved mother and Katherine's wayward brother. To keep these items safe, we also leave our broken but still beloved wind chime. On his last trip to India, Solomon bought home a new wind chime and it is with this guardian that we shall begin to look forward and will continue to mark the turning tides and the passing seasons."

"I don't understand," said Edward, who had exchanged a quizzical glance with Caitlin.

"It was the year 1891 which triggered my memory," Amelia explained. "I wanted to check my facts first but I wonder if this is connected to something larger and Osyth was scared."

"What do you mean, my dear?" asked Caitlin.

"When Noah was telling the family about Kieran's whereabouts after Osyth, Freddie and Angharad had escaped he mentioned an Annie Chapman who lived in Clewer, with her husband, John, the coachman at St Leonard's Hill House."

"Yes," said Edward, topping up their wine glasses while Caitlin sipped her sparkling water.

"Do you know the identity of Annie Chapman?" asked Amelia.

"No, should we?" said Edward.

"Not necessarily. I suppose she's familiar to me because of her connections to Clewer. Although she wasn't born in Windsor, she was seen as a local girl, which is probably why I recognised her name."

"Well?" prompted Caitlin.

"Annie Chapman was one of the canonical five women murdered by Jack the Ripper," said Amelia.

"What?" Edward's response was like a whip-crack.

"Are you suggesting Kieran was Jack the Ripper?" gasped Caitlin.

"No," said Amelia, "but I wonder if he was connected. You see, during the period from 31 August 1888 to 9 November 1888, there were the five murders that have always been accredited to Jack the Ripper, including Annie Chapman. Sadly, these deaths were only a portion of the horror that took place in Whitechapel. There were eleven unsolved murders in all, including the five, taking place from 3 April 1888 until 13 February 1891. Whether they were the work of one serial killer or multiple murderers has never been proven. We know Kieran was in an asylum by then and he died there in March 1891, so it wasn't him, but, if you remember, *two* men abducted Honora, the woman who managed to escape from Kieran's rooms in Southwark. The other man was never identified."

A chill silence enveloped them.

"How very eerie," said Caitlin.

"Perhaps Osyth and Katherine thought so too and decided to lock everything away. Out of sight, out of mind. The family had already covered up a murder and managed to escape punishment, perhaps Osyth felt this was tempting fate." Amelia glanced at Edward, who was white with shock.

"I may not have been upset by your ancestor murdering mine but it is shocking to think my ancestor might have known, or worse, inspired the serial killer who mutilated so many women."

"It's only a theory," said Amelia, trying to take away the thought of the abominable connection.

"The coincidences are compelling though," he said.

Again they sank into silence, then Caitlin struggled to her feet.

"I'm exhausted," she said. "This family really does have a story to tell, which is why, Amelia, I've decided to say yes to doing the documentary. I've thought about it and count me in."

Amelia smiled, rising to help Caitlin to her room.

"And you, Eddie?" Caitlin asked.

He hesitated for a moment, then gave a reluctant nod. "Fine by me," he said. "Especially if it's what you want, Auntie."

"Yes, my darling, it is," Caitlin said and Amelia led her to the bedroom.

As Amelia helped Caitlin prepare for bed, she hoped there would be no more chilling secrets about the Attwaters and Stones to reveal.

CHAPTER TWO

Amelia had never been directly involved with Benji's work before but watching him throw himself into the documentary about her family history made her realise the extent of his creative talent. Six weeks after Caitlin and Edward had agreed to her suggestion, a whirlwind seemed to have taken place around them and, despite the many long phone calls with Benji or one of his irrepressible team, Amelia was glad of the distraction it created. Caitlin had been the first to be interviewed, but once she had finished her three days with Benji, answering his questions and proving a natural in front of the camera, her condition had begun to deteriorate.

"The finale of this documentary is the reunion," Benji explained to them one evening. He and Doug had travelled to Cliffside for a week for Benji and a small camera crew to film Caitlin.

"What reunion?" Edward asked throwing a suspicious glance at Amelia who shrugged, as bemused by this comment as Edward.

"The one I'm organising," Benji announced with a grin. "There will be as many members of your extended family as we can persuade to come here for a big party. Obviously, if that's OK with you and Caitlin."

When Caitlin had nodded, her eyes sparkling with enthusiasm, Edward and Amelia had realised she had known about this all along.

"Do your worst!" Edward laughed.

The party was now only days away, and Amelia stared around in bemusement as Benji and his team moved into Cliffside. A commission had been found swiftly due to various favours Benji was owed and with money secured, he had thrown everything at the project: hiring genealogists, art historians to track down Blaise and Drake's paintings, social historians, archivists, DNA experts and picture restorers. Amelia had taken him to The Mary Fitzroy Heritage Centre and shown him their map of the local area, which he photographed and then contacted the team at Marquess House to request their help in creating something similar for the Attwater and Stone families. The response had been positive and enthusiastic and today they would finally take delivery of the vast family tree, with its story told across the many panels that had been created by the artists at the Marquess House studios.

The other surprise was the number of family members Benji's team had discovered and persuaded to attend the grand finale.

"We don't want them wandering all over Cliffside and ruining the surprise," said Benji, "so we've booked as many rooms at local hotels, cottages and guest houses as were available."

Amelia and Edward exchanged a nervous look.

"He's found people?" Edward confirmed after Benji had left.

"Yes, and he won't tell me who or how they're connected to us," Amelia replied. "He wants us all to be in the dark so he can film our reactions when we meet for the first time in a few days."

Edward looked aghast. "Why did we agree to this circus?" he asked.

Amelia grinned. "It doesn't matter how we feel," she reminded him. "Caitlin is having a ball and she's more important than either of us."

"You're right. Without this, I really think we'd have lost her by now."

"Then it's worth all the embarrassment and potential awkwardness," Amelia replied.

The wind chime had been expertly restored by one of the artists staying nearby at Marquess House and later that evening, during the party, it would return to its proper home and be hung in pride of place on the veranda as it had been when Penny's mother, Eleanor, had first received it as gift over a hundred years earlier. Of its replacement, mentioned in Osyth's letter, Amelia had never found a trace, assuming it must have been discarded at some point over the years. To be replacing the original felt as though she were giving a gift to her ancestors, a thank you for guiding her home.

Eudora's portrait, which stood on an easel in Caitlin's bedroom where she could see it whenever she was awake, would be added to the many others Amelia, Louise and an art historian from Benji's production team had gathered. Louise and Richie were staying with Amelia, Edward and Caitlin at Cliffside, along with Benji and Doug. This merging of Amelia's two worlds had seemed strange at first but as they approached the party and reunion, Amelia found the overlap between her old life and her new was seamless, with everyone getting along, as though they had known each other all their lives. It was a strange sensation and there were occasions when an irrational wave of guilt would overwhelm her as she thought about Molly and how much she would have loved Cliffside and how her mother and Caitlin would have been firm friends.

The biggest sadness, however, was Caitlin's deterioration. Amelia knew it would not be long until she and Edward were faced with another goodbye. She and Edward had insisted Caitlin rest before the excitement of the party and Amelia was watching over her as the house was being transformed around them by Benji and his enthusiastic team.

Moving quietly around the bed, Amelia checked Caitlin's morphine and was about to tiptoe from the room when Caitlin stirred.

"Amelia," she said, her voice resonating with joy. "It's always a delight to wake up and know you've been watching over me, as Osyth watched over Penny."

Caitlin had begun to speak about her ancestors as though they were more real than the people around her and Amelia wondered if this was another part of coming to terms with death. *Perhaps those whose blood run in our veins begin to emerge from the shadows*, she thought, *ready to collect us as we prepare for the next part of the journey.*

"Where's Edward?" asked Caitlin, as Amelia helped her to sit up and passed her a glass of water to sip.

"Walking the dogs on the beach," she replied.

Amelia knew Edward was waiting for her to be ready to move their relationship from friendship to something deeper and she knew it would not be long before she felt able to return his feelings, but, at the moment, her focus was on Caitlin. In a strange way, the sadness as they waited for death to claim her was more familiar and comforting to Amelia than the idea of beginning a relationship, which felt at the same time both wonderful and terrifying.

"Good, because I'd like to talk to you," Caitlin said, reaching over to her bedside table and removing a brown A4 envelope, which she passed to Amelia. "Open it, please, so I may explain."

Bemused, Amelia slit it open and pulled out a solicitor's letter stating that Caitlin had left her half of Cliffside to Amelia. Delight, then horror, raced through her. "No…" she began but Caitlin held up her hand to silence her, her manner imperious.

"You may not refuse the request of a dying woman," Caitlin said.

"Don't pull the guilt card," Amelia retorted, then wished she could take the words back. It was the response she would have thrown at her mother, with whom she had bickered and sparred all her life, even though they loved each other deeply, not a woman she had known for barely five months. Caitlin, however, was delighted by her response.

"At last, the fire of the Attwaters!" she exclaimed. "By leaving you my half of the house, I am continuing family tradition. If you choose to give or sell it to Edward, that is your decision. However, you are the true recipient, as you are descended from Osyth…"

"But I have Maybank and the cottages, which is more than enough," Amelia interrupted.

"Now you have Cliffside, too," said Caitlin, her tone final.

"What about Edward?"

"He also has Cliffside."

"It was his inheritance," Amelia protested.

"Not really," said Caitlin. "My will remained unfinished. I was waiting, you see, to give it to the heir who heard the wind chime, as I have heard it all my life. If you had not arrived, then Edward would have inherited my half too, but this house

is in your blood, my dear. You heard it's call and you responded. It is rightfully yours."

"There are hundreds of other potential heirs and they'll be here this afternoon," spluttered Amelia. "What about the descendants of Noah, Solomon or Xenia?"

"They didn't reply to the call. We found them and brought them home; you found your way through blood and the wind chime."

"This is ludicrous."

"Perhaps, but whether you agree or not, my half of the house will be yours. As I said, after I'm gone, you may do with it as you please. I hope, though, that one day the two halves will become one family."

Amelia blushed.

Three hours later, Amelia hovered outside the summer drawing room. Caitlin leaned heavily on Edward's arm, while Louise, Richie and Doug lingered behind Amelia, all three intrigued to see what magic Benji had created. From behind the closed door, they could hear him issuing instructions to his camera crew, discussing things with the director and then, he called, "Edward, could you and Caitlin come in first, please, so we can film your reactions."

An assistant opened the door and with a smile from Caitlin and a grimace from Edward, they disappeared into the summer drawing room. The door firmly closed behind them.

Louise stifled a giggle. "Benj is loving every minute of this," she said. "Are you excited, Aimes?"

"Yes, and nervous," she admitted. "I wish Mum, Dad and Molly were here, they would have loved this. It's also thanks to Mum that I even found my way to Cliffside."

"You'd have found your way here eventually," said Richie, taking Louise's hand. "Like we all found each other all those years ago. The right people appear at the right time and Edward is the right person."

"Aimes, your turn," called Benji before Amelia could respond. "Can the rest of you wait outside for a minute? I want to film Amelia on her own."

Taking her hands, Benji instructed Amelia to close her eyes, then he led her into the summer drawing room. It was a magnificent space, running the entire length of the house with windows framing the beauty of St Brides Bay and the roaring Celtic Sea. The veranda ran along part of it and Amelia could hear the gentle tunes of the wind chime as she waited, trusting Benji implicitly as he guided her forward. When Cliffside was in normal use, two sets of intricately carved folding doors divided the space into three rooms but she was aware Benji had opened them wide to enable enough space for his grand finale.

"Mind the cable, lovey," he said, "over to your left. There, perfect. I'm going to count to three, then open your eyes. Try not to swear, we're filming you."

Amelia grinned. Nervousness and wonder ran through her as she listened to the countdown, then as commanded, she opened her eyes and gasped in astonishment. The room had been transformed. The vast family tree took pride of place against the wall facing the windows.

Radiating from this imposing and beautifully decorated artwork were vast images of the Victorian photographs that had begun her journey to Cliffside so many months before. These were the pictures she and her friends had discovered in the attic after her mother's funeral but as she stared at them, she realised there were more than the images owned by herself and Edward. Other family members must have contributed, people she was yet to meet but who were related to her by their mingled Attwater and Stone blood.

Walking towards the vast family tree, she realised it was bigger than the brief one she and Edward had drawn for Benji when they had agreed to his making the documentary. She traced her finger towards Noah and Hannah. Their four offspring were named and from these fanned more names, the same for Solomon and Xenia. When she saw Molly's name, tears threatened in her eyes, but she blinked them back; this was a happy day and it was for Caitlin.

Paintings hung around the walls or stood on easels. Her own, which she now knew to be by Blaise Attwater, was there next to the stunning picture of *The Princess of the Fairy Rings*, belonging to Edward and Caitlin, and there were more. There was a portrait of a woman who had to be Xenia, her golden hair gleaming and her upturned nose and green eyes exuding pixie-like mischief across the centuries. Beside her was a double portrait of Xenia and a man who Amelia guessed must be her husband, William Pettifer. Noah shot sultry looks from another portrait and Amelia remembered when she and Louise had been examining them and Noah had been declaimed as "hot", from this image she would conclude he was more than hot, he was gorgeous.

Turning again, she choked back laughter as she encountered the beauty of Solomon Attwater, sprawled naked on the chaise as painted by his lover, Drake. Beside it was another, obviously painted by his brother Blaise and supposed to be a pair with the portrait of Xenia. Solomon, too, exuded mischief and laughter, his eyes blue to Xenia's green, but beyond this, their faces were striking in their similarity. There was even a self-portrait of Blaise, as well as a lovingly painted full-length portrait of Katherine. Amelia was relieved to see Kieran hung beside his sister. Even in paint he appeared distant and scared. In the centre, presiding over the family, were the double portraits of Penny and Daniel, and Matthew and Georgina, smiling over their children.

Knowing her own troubled ancestor, Eudora, would be next, Amelia pivoted again, to see Edward and Caitlin waiting beside the image of the red-haired teenager who would face such strife and cause such pain. A glass cabinet displaying Osyth and Freddie's books was under the portrait but Caitlin was beaming, watching Amelia, waiting for her reaction as her eyes swept to another painting. Beside Eudora was a portrait of Osyth and Freddie. The two stood, hands entwined, in the room where the painting now hung again, their smiles radiant as they faced the world and from the swell of Osyth's dress, impending parenthood.

"Where did you get it?" Amelia gasped, almost stumbling in her haste to reach the image.

"Louise found it on an auction website in Holland where we discovered a few of Blaise's other paintings, too," said Edward. "We bought it for you as a surprise."

When the tears welled up this time, Amelia did not try to be brave or wipe them away, she allowed them to flow. She was overwhelmed with the love of the welcome she had received from Cliffside and from Edward and Caitlin, family she had never known existed but who had welcomed her home.

"Thank you," she choked, hugging first Caitlin, then Edward. "Thank you. It's like looking at Molly."

Amelia felt as though Edward might break her ribs, such was the strength of his hug in response.

"And now," said Benji, looking at his watch and surreptitiously wiping away a tear of his own, "Caitlin, you should take your seat, and Aimes, Edward, I need you by the door to start welcoming your new family because they're arriving in droves and they're very excited to meet you."

CHAPTER THREE

The next few hours passed in a whirl of laughter, champagne and chatter as the descendants of the Attwater and Stone families began to mingle. Exchanging histories, family stories, snapping selfies, admiring Cliffside, Amelia noticed more than one person drawn towards the sound of the wind chime on the veranda as though an unconscious connection had been made. Benji's director, Jamie, had arranged the room so the different members of the family could congregate under the portraits of their ancestors and Amelia watched as groups formed, merged and scattered as each member of the family greeted new cousins.

To Amelia's amazement, the other surprise her friends had created was a written history of the Attwaters and Stones. Having emailed the transcripts of the diary and her notes to Benji, Amelia had not given them any more thought, but Louise, who had taken early maternity leave in order to prepare for the twins she was having, had been bored and had offered to write the history for Amelia. The production company had then paid for copies to be printed for all the members of the family who were attending the finale.

"It's what I do, isn't it?" Louise laughed when Amelia hugged her, gibbering her thanks. "I lecture in history and I write about it!"

"But there's more than the information I gave you," Amelia said.

"I've been very busy interviewing your new family," Louise beamed. "Let's go and meet some more of them."

Several hours later, Amelia found Edward and whispered in his ear, "We need to talk," then when he looked startled, she added, "in a good way."

Taking his hand, she led him out on to the veranda where the sun was setting over St Brides Bay.

"What do you want to talk about?" asked Edward with a certain amount of trepidation, his fingers running over the heart carved by Freddie.

Amelia reached up and kissed him. He hesitated for a moment, then his arms encircled her and he responded with a passion which she had never expected.

"Are you sure?" he said, when he let her go.

"Yes," she replied, gazing up into his dark eyes. "I think I knew from the beginning, from the moment you questioned me in the car park — even though you were quite rude and annoying —" he made a noise of protestation — "that you had won me over."

"Really? It isn't the house? Or the champagne?"

She laughed, then said, "No, I did question myself thoroughly as to whether it was you or the house I was in love with and, while the house does give good hugs, and I love it dearly, my feelings for you are rather different and far more intense. In fact, it's taken me a while to recognise it but, Edward Stone, I'm in love with you."

Edward was staring out to sea and he did not immediately respond. Not long ago, Amelia would have felt panicked by this silence but she knew him better now, understanding his cautious nature, as well as his intense loyalty to those he loved.

The sun was dipping low in the sky, its fiery rim nudging the watery horizon, dispersing its rays into the waiting waves. Her breath caught in her throat as he turned to look into her eyes,

the blackness of his meeting the blue of her own, then he bent his head and she lifted hers as their lips met again.

"I've wanted to do that for so long," he sighed as they parted. "I'm in love with you, too."

A cough from the doorway caused them to break apart. Benji was in the doorway.

"Caitlin owes me a fiver," he said, grinning.

"What?" spluttered Amelia.

"We had a bet you two wouldn't be able to hold out much longer," Benji said, then his tone changed, "Guys, sorry to interrupt but I need you both, our last guests have arrived," and for the first time, Amelia sensed a nervousness in his tone.

"Who else is there?" she asked. "We've accounted for nearly everyone on the family tree."

"This is a surprise for you, Edward," said Benji.

"For me?"

Benji turned, disappearing back into the mêlée. Exchanging a bemused glance, Amelia and Edward followed. Stepping into the corridor, Benji turned to face them both. "I thought we should meet these guests out here first," he said, "because this is something my genealogists discovered and I wanted to warn you before we filmed it, in case you don't want it included."

"What's happened?" asked Amelia, fear coursing through her.

"It's about you, Edward," said Benji. "We tested your DNA again and, it transpires, the first set of results were correct."

"What?" gasped Amelia.

Benji swallowed, as though bracing himself.

Amelia felt a rising panic. "What did you discover?" she asked.

"When we examined it further, there were many hits to Edward's DNA," said Benji, "but they weren't connected to you or Caitlin or any of various hundreds of offspring from the Attwaters. There was Welsh DNA, linking Edward to the extensive Williams clans in Pembrokeshire, as well as links to Kenyan families."

Benji's words dropped into Amelia's mind like pebbles in a pond, the significance of their meaning rippling across her consciousness.

"Kenyan," she whispered. "Caius, you're descended from Caius. Angharad must have lost Kieran's child either while she was in the asylum or when they were travelling with the circus."

"And that was why she married Caius," said Edward, "when they realised the baby must have been his, not Kieran's."

"But why did she send the baby home to Cliffside, why didn't he stay with his father?"

"Aimes, they were circus people," said Edward, his eyes shining, "imagine how tough their life must have been. Osyth's tale is a romanticised version but it would have been brutal. Perhaps Angharad requested Henry be sent to her parents, and I'd guess that Oran and Caius felt the child would be more happily accepted if the family thought he was Kieran's. Although, it does explain why I tan so easily."

"Oh Eddie, how can you joke about it?" Amelia was still in shock.

"What else is there to be done?" he asked. "I may not be part of the Attwaters by blood, but my great-great-great-grandfather was adopted by Katherine and Blaise, and he was family. If anything, after what we've discovered about Kieran, I'm relieved not to have a blood link to him. It changes nothing, Aimes, except for the fact that I have potentially hundreds of

new cousins to discover." He kissed her on the forehead and turned back to Benji, who grinned.

"Cousins who are arriving in your car park as we speak."

A moment later, a tall man walked through the door and beamed at Edward. The most startling thing about him was his facial similarity to Edward. The two men gazed at each other, then walked forward and embraced.

"Cousin," said the man. "My name is Caius Walters, named for my father, my grandfather, my great-grandfather and many strong, brave men before them."

"And I am Edward Stone. Welcome home."

Amelia hurried forward as more people arrived, welcoming them to Cliffside, to the wind chime and to the family in the house on the cliff, understanding the final secret at last.

EPILOGUE

One Year Later

Caitlin died peacefully in her sleep three days after the party. Amelia and Edward held her hands while Nero and Lara lay quiet and solemn on their giant cushions beside the bed of their beloved mistress. Her requests had been simple, a quiet funeral, then cremation. Today, Amelia and Edward would fulfil Caitlin's final wish.

Pausing as she felt her baby kick, Amelia hovered her hairbrush above her flowing red hair.

"Everything all right?" Edward's concerned voice came from the other side of the room where he was sitting on the bed beside Nero and Lara, the urn containing Caitlin's ashes cradled in his lap.

"We're fine, stop panicking," Amelia replied, pulling on her hiking boots. "Ready?" she asked, and held out her hand to her husband, the flashing sun glinting on her gold band as sunset approached and the sky lowered, beckoning the mystery of twilight.

Gazing down at the urn in his hands, Edward braced himself, then rose, taking Amelia's hand. His own gold band was lustrous against the vermillion red of Caitlin's final resting place. Together they walked through the study into the main part of the house where the rest of the family waited. At the front were Louise and Richie with their twin sons; Benji and Doug; and David and Kerry. More familiar faces stood behind them, including Stuart Mackensie and the extended Attwater and Stone families, as well as the Walters family, an unexpected but delightful addition to the extensive clan from Cliffside.

Edward and Amelia took their places at the front and, after managing to stutter a few words of thanks, Edward led the way to the woods and the winding path to the stone circle. It had surprised Amelia when Caitlin had requested her ashes be scattered here rather than in her beloved ocean, but she had insisted.

"It feels right," Caitlin had whispered, squeezing Amelia's hand. "I don't want Eudora to be alone any longer."

Unbeknown to Edward, Amelia and her friends had transformed the clearing earlier in the day, placing jars containing flickering candles along the path and around the old monument. Twinkling fairy lights were strung through the branches of the trees, while wreaths of white roses glowed.

"Thank you, Aimes," Edward whispered, and she felt the familiar warmth of his hand on hers, the touch of which felt like home. "Caitlin would have loved it."

As the group of celebrants arranged themselves around the circle, Amelia and Edward walked towards the large flat stone in the centre, the entrance to Tylwyth Teg. Breathing in the damp air, the scent of the roses and the brine of the sea, the air seemed to thicken and shimmer around Amelia and the song of the wind chime filled her heart. She knew they were there, all of them, Penny, Eudora, Osyth, Molly, Joan and now Caitlin, shadows, memories, women who loved and were loved.

Edward read the short eulogy he had written and when he had finished, Amelia took a deep breath and recited:

"Fairy maiden, draw near to me,
Take me far below the sea,
Water maiden, wild and free,
With the fairies of the deep…

"*Fairy maiden, full of glee,*
I'll tell my secrets for you to keep...
Water maiden, promise me,
You'll keep them safe in the deep blue sea."
And the words from Osyth's journal came back to her:

Every summer we wait for the wind chime to indicate the change, we wait for the soft tinkling of the coral shells to lose their harmonious song and crash together discordantly. The signal, the end of another long, lazy summer, a return to reality, to the cold winter days when our family will once more scatter itself around the world, exploring our way through our lives, living our hopes, chasing our dreams, waiting, watching for the first hint of summer when we will find ourselves drawn inexorably back to Cliffside. Every summer we part on smiles, hugs, promises of love which will last forever, none of us ever speak the words we fear, we simply wait, noticing if there are any changes in ourselves, in each other, protecting those we love from the fae-blood running thick and dangerous like a changeling spell through our veins. As the wind chime indicates another summer's end, we drink a toast, a promise to return as soon as the air turns soft and golden to the house on the cliff, the keeper of our secrets and the never-ending ocean covering our lies.

Only now, Amelia thought, as she and Edward held hands with tears in their eyes and allowed the final remains of Caitlin to rise with the wind, *there are no more lies, no more secrets and no more fear, only the song of the wind chime to draw us home to Cliffside and its love.*

As they turned to leave, above the rustling of the trees, Amelia heard the words, "Thank you," whispered on the air and gathering Edward to her, she led him home to the house on the cliff.

A NOTE TO THE READER

Dear Reader,

Thank you for taking the time to read *The Wind Chime*. I hope you enjoyed joining Amelia as she discovered her long lost family.

This is fiction but I have included historical detail, as well as my own family history. Before embarking on this version of *The Wind Chime*, I did a huge amount of research into the treatment of mental health during the Victorian period, as well as attitudes to women, much of which I have filtered into the story. The most useful books were Catharine Arnold, *Bedlam: London and its Mad* (London, 2008); Elaine Showalter, *The Female Malady: Women, Madness and English Culture, 1830–1980* (United States and Canada, 1985); Joan Perkin, *Victorian Women* (London, 1993); Maggy Parsons and Alice Miles, *Every Girl's Duty: The Diary of a Victorian Debutante* (London, 1992); Hallie Rubenhold, *The Five* (London, 2019).

The Lunatics' Ball was a genuine phenomenon which took place at Bethlem Hospital, London (aka Bedlam). It was viewed as a treat for the inmates and one great advocate was Charles Dickens. The references to the changing treatments are taken from real case histories, as is the reference to Hanwell Asylum and Dr George Savage.

Throughout, Osyth refers to fairies, mythology and folklore. These are from local legends and you can read more at: Brian Froud, *Good Fairies, Bad Fairies* (New York, 1998); Peter Stevenson, *Welsh Folk Tales* (Gloucestershire, 2017); Christine Willison, *Pembrokeshire Folk Tales* (Gloucestershire, 2013); Jill Young, *Pembrokeshire Standing Stones* (Llanrwst, 2015).

Thank you to everyone at the West Wales Maritime Heritage Society and the Pembroke Dock Museum, where I bought the invaluable: David James, *Hancock's Shipbuilding Company in Pembroke Dock, The Ships and the Men who Built Them* (Pembroke and Monkton Local History Society).

Thank you, too, to Taya Snow at Floris London who advised me on a suitable perfume for a young woman during the Victorian era.

The storm, referred to by Amelia and Edward while they are at the archives, happened in 1866, thank you to the Pembrokeshire Dive website for the information.

Annie Chapman was one of the victims of Jack the Ripper and did have connections to Clewer and St Leonard's Hill House.

Nero and Lara were my greyhounds, sadly now both deceased. This is my small tribute to them.

Obviously, this is a slightly alternative world to our own and there is no Covid-19, which was prevalent when I wrote this in the 2020 lockdown.

However, for me, this book is about family. So, if you would like to read another, much shorter story, settle down and come with me to the real world of strangeness that is this novel. Everything that follows is true.

One November morning in 1996, I awoke from the strangest dream with the words, which are now the *Prologue* and *Epilogue* of this work, running through my head. Firing up my Mac Classic, I began to write and three hours later, the Attwater family, the house on the cliff, the boats they built and the story of Eudora's illness was on the page. Osyth set out on her quest, while Frederick chased her heart. Kieran brooded from the corner, watching as Katherine and Blaise fell in love and the rest of the family went about their lives. These people and

their boat business had appeared from nowhere but I liked them and they felt real.

A few years later, I wrote a complete version of this outline but, despite sending it out, it was never accepted anywhere, and in my heart, I knew it was because it wasn't quite right. It languished in a drawer but the family never left me.

Fast forward several more years and, thanks to my maternal uncle, I began researching our family tree. My mother produced a family Bible, which rather stunned me, as I hadn't known we owned one. Inside was a brief family tree. Using this, I was able to search the census records and discovered my first family secret: my great-great-grandparents, Charles Beasley and Laura Jacobs of Clewer, Windsor were stepbrother and stepsister before they married. Laura was four months pregnant when they finally made it up the aisle. This was a revelation and, this year, their real relationship was transferred to Penny and Daniel, who always felt like free spirits. I felt Laura and Charles would have liked them.

This was followed by the discovery that Laura's family, the Jacobs, owned boats and were descended from boat builders. Further research revealed the boats still exist and operate on the River Thames in Windsor, although my family no longer has a connection with them. This was another detail unknown to me when those words tumbled from my mind that November morning.

However, the oddest thing was my discovery of an ancestor named Eudora. I had chosen the name because she was a Greek sea goddess and it meant 'good gift', which seemed appropriate for the character. It's an uncommon name, so to discover it in my family who had built and owned boats seemed odd. There were fewer documents online back then and, at that time, the real Eudora remained a mystery.

Returning to *The Wind Chime* in 2020, I decided to use the family details from my own ancestors for the Attwaters. My family's home in Clewer, Windsor was called Maybank and we once owned a row of cottages known as Beasley Cottages. Even the solicitor, Lovegrove and Durant, was real as a letter from them exists in the family archive.

Then, I made another very unusual discovery.

While doing my research, it seemed appropriate to look again for Eudora and with a greater number of records online, I discovered more about her. Eudora moved from Clewer to Aberystwyth, where she married Thomas Cimatti. It was with real sadness, I discovered she had lived into my lifetime, yet we never met. Then I discovered her death certificate and it was November 1996, which was the month this story and her name arrived in my mind. Read into it what you will but I do wonder if the real Eudora found me and inspired a magical story of boats and fairies and family.

Thank you to everyone who has helped me with *The Wind Chime*, particularly Amy, Caoimhe, Richard, Natalie, Matilda and Helen at Sapere Books and Sara Keane, my lovely agent. It has been a huge and thoroughly enjoyable task. Once again, any mistakes throughout the text are mine. Please forgive me.

If you have enjoyed the novel and would like to leave a review on **Amazon** or **Goodreads**, I would be so grateful as reviews are very important to authors. I love hearing from readers, so if you would like to contact me, you can through **Twitter**. You can also follow my blog on my website.

Thanks again for reading *The Wind Chime*.

Alexandra Walsh

www.alexandrawalsh.com

Sapere Books is an exciting new publisher of brilliant fiction and popular history.

To find out more about our latest releases and our monthly bargain books visit our website: **saperebooks.com**

Made in the USA
Columbia, SC
27 April 2023

A Note on the Author

William G. McLoughlin, Jr., graduated from Princeton University and received his doctorate in American civilization from Harvard University. After three years as Assistant Dean of the Graduate School of Arts and Sciences at Harvard, he spent a year as a Fulbright scholar gathering material on the revivals of Moody and Sankey in Britain. Since 1955 he has taught at Brown University, where he is now Associate Professor of History and Chairman of the American Civilization Program. Dr. McLoughlin is the author of two previous books, *Modern Revivalism—Charles Grandison Finney to Billy Graham* and *Billy Sunday Was His Real Name.*